A HISTORY OF THE
AMERICAN DENTAL ASSOCIATION

A History of the

American Dental Association

A Century of Health Service

BY ROBERT W. McCLUGGAGE, Ph.D.

Department of History, Loyola University, Chicago

American Dental Association · Chicago

1959

THE CELEBRATION of a centennial should not be an unanticipated event except for the most casual of persons and associations. The American Dental Association properly anticipated the 100th anniversary of its founding which is being celebrated during 1959. Not the least item in the elaborate program which marks the centennial year is the publication of this history of the Association. In 1952, the editor of the Association was requested by the Board of Trustees to assume responsibility for the preparation and publication of the history. In the intervening years, many problems were encountered and, as it is hoped this volume will attest, solved.

The first major problem arose out of the wish not to present the history of the Association as a series of dates, marshalled in unrelieved chronology and illustrated by faded photographs of bearded men, most looking bafflingly alike. The second was not to make the history compare to the record of a single neutron racing through a vacuum to produce only its own identifiable track on a photographic plate scarred by the cross-hatching of many unknown particles.

Both of these problems were solved, happily as it turned out, by asking a distinguished scholar to write the history of the Association and to write it against the social background of the times in which it achieved its ten decades of existence and growth. The Association, by means of a grant to the Department of History of Loyola University, Chicago, prevailed upon Robert W. McCluggage, Ph.D., to undertake this task, and the enormous success of this solution will be evident to those who read and enjoy this book. It will be evident not only to members of the health professions interested in dentistry's growth as a responsible and professional unit of society, but to all of those who are concerned with the development of an essential resource of the nation to enrich the lives of its people. It will be evident, also, to many in other countries because dentistry first assumed professional status in the United States and thus established patterns of education and practice which today are still found worthy of emulation.

Dr. McCluggage has synthesized his account of events since the Association's founding from available records—not always adequate—which picture the personalities, crises, failures and achievements of the past one hundred years. He has integrated this story of dentistry with the story of the passing years so that men and events are seen in real perspective and not in the foreshortened view of our own day and of our own time. He has written not only the history of the American Dental Association but

5

a perceptive and vivid account of the growth of a major health profession and its contributions to ever increasing standards of health and life in this country. Although this history has a background of claims and charges, conflict and compromise, it is also forelighted by selflessness, vision, ideals, leadership and achievement which cannot help but add luster to the celebration of the centennial year.

The officers, Board of Trustees and members join with the editor in acknowledging the services of Dr. McCluggage to the Association and to the dental profession. This acknowledgment will be a long continuing one for, of necessity, all students of history of dentistry in the United States and of the Association will be compelled to have frequent and rewarding recourse to the history he has so skillfully documented and set forth.

In the many byways of preparing the history, Dr. McCluggage has traveled the lonely route through the original sources but, on occasion, he had the company of members of the profession and others who had made forays in the field. Foremost among these are two men who with the editor comprise the Association's Centennial History Committee: George B. Denton, Ph.D., research consultant in the Bureau of Library and Indexing Service and himself a distinguished historian of dental affairs, and Donald A. Washburn, D.D.S., director of the Bureau of Library and Indexing Service of the American Dental Association. The Centennial History Committee would be remiss if it did not join with Dr. McCluggage in acknowledging the advice and technical assistance received from Paul S. Lietz, Ph.D., chairman of the Department of History, Loyola University, Chicago, and an authority on the history of Latin America. In the reading, preparation and typing of the manuscript, the editor also had the assistance of many members of the Association's staff, particularly of the editorial office. Dr. McCluggage has gratefully acknowledged their assistance in his author's addendum on page 7, an acknowledgment in which the Centennial History Committee heartily joins.

The editor himself has been enormously intrigued with the problems of publishing the history of the Association. In its service, he has participated for more than thirty years in the events which are here recounted. He is grateful for the privilege of directing this project which puts the seal of history on the chapters of the first century and provides fresh pages for the chronicle of the second.

Lon W. Morrey, D.D.S.
Editor-in-Chief
American Dental Association

ACKNOWLEDGMENTS

IN PREPARING THIS HISTORY, I have received encouragement and assistance in many forms from a great number of kindly and generous people whose help has benefited the book in all of its aspects. These brief words of appreciation cannot fully express my gratitude. It would be impossible to list everyone to whom I am obligated, but the aid of the individuals listed below deserves particular recognition.

Many members of the dental profession helped me in the collection of material or contributed to my understanding of the subject, among them W. G. Adair, D.D.S., Milton B. Asbell, D.D.S., C. Willard Camalier, D.D.S., James R. Cameron, D.D.S., John Carr, D.D.S., Van B. Dalton, D.D.S., Harold L. Faggart, D.D.S., William N. Hodgkin, D.D.S., Earl G. Jones, D.D.S., Harry Lyons, D.D.S., the late Edward C. Mills, D.D.S., Bertram B. Otto, D.D.S., Archibald B. Patterson, D.D.S., Kenneth A. Reid, D.D.S., and Laszlo Schwartz, D.D.S. General Neal A. Harper, USA (DC), Ret., Mr. Richard H. Burkhart, and Dr. George B. Denton placed manuscript collections in their custody at my disposal. Their explanations illuminated many obscure references in the old correspondence.

In the course of the research I drew heavily on the resources and, I fear, the patience, of Miss Minnie Orfanos and Miss Adele Fisher of the Arthur D. Black Memorial Library of the Northwestern University Dental School and Mrs. Josephine P. Hunt of the American Dental Association Library. Several of my colleagues and friends, Charles B. Forcey, Edward Maher, Edward T. Gargan, John J. Reardon, and Paul S. Lietz, aided me with their suggestions and critical comments on the manuscript.

The American Dental Association has spared no expense and has exerted every effort to make this history not only a handsome memento of the Association's first century, but also a frank examination of the development of a professional guild and its relations with its constituency and with American society. Many members of the Association staff contributed information and special knowledge arising from their connection with the Association: Gerard J. Casey, D.D.S., Bernard J. Conway, LL.B., B. D. Moen, M.A., H. Trendley Dean, D.D.S., J. Roy Doty, Ph.D., Shailer Peterson, Ph.D., and Ben F. Miller, M.A. The entire editorial department of the Association shared in the production of the book, but I am under particular obligation to Miss Viola I. Nelson, Miss Geraldine Udell, and Mrs. Mayme O. Bound for tireless and painstaking preparation, editing, and verification of the copy and proof. Only one who has worked with her can fully appreciate the contributions of Mrs. Velma M. Child to the foregoing and to many other aspects of the book as well. In spite of the pressures of other duties, these ladies accepted cheerfully the multiplication of their labors necessitated by many changes in copy and proof.

Inevitably, my heaviest obligations are to the Association's committee on the project, headed by Lon W. Morrey, D.D.S. Donald A. Washburn, D.D.S., head of the Association's Bureau of Library and Indexing Service, has forwarded the project in innumerable ways—in the compiling of materials, in the locating of sources, and in steering me through the intricacies of the guides to research in the field. George B. Denton, Ph.D., research consultant in the Bureau of Library and Indexing Service, shared with me his vast knowledge of the history of dentistry and allied fields and subjected my findings to the stern scrutiny of his critical eye. His advice has spared me many errors.

The administration of Loyola University reduced my teaching duties while the volume was in preparation and furnished the secretarial assistance of Miss Rita C. Kucera, who typed much of the first version of the manuscript.

Mr. Richard H. Shryock, librarian of the American Philosophical Society, kindly made time in his busy schedule to write the Introduction. Mrs. Phyllis McLaren graciously agreed to undertake preparation of the Index on extremely short notice.

Finally, these acknowledgments would be incomplete without special notice of two men whose contributions to the book were virtually those of collaborators: Lon W. Morrey, D.D.S., editor of the American Dental Association and chairman of the committee on the history, and Paul S. Lietz, Ph.D., chairman of the Department of History of Loyola University and a member of the committee on the project. Dr. Morrey could hardly have given the book more careful attention if he had written it himself. My every request for advice, information, or assistance has received his prompt and wholehearted cooperation. Dr. Lietz has sought incessantly to lighten my labors in research and writing. He has helped in the collection and verification of materials. He has given me the benefit of his critical acumen. And, most of all, he has sustained me throughout with his sympathy, understanding, and friendship. It is safe to say that without the help of these two friends, this history could never have been written. I am eternally grateful to them. They deserve much credit for whatever merit the book possesses. For its shortcomings I am alone responsible.

ROBERT W. McCLUGGAGE

CONTENTS

FOREWORD 5

ACKNOWLEDGMENTS 7

LIST OF ILLUSTRATIONS 11

INTRODUCTION 13

PART ONE

THE HERITAGE OF THE

AMERICAN DENTAL ASSOCIATION 17

Chapter

  I   Beginnings 19

  II Early Professional Organization 35

  III Policies of the American Society 49

  IV The Amalgam War 67

  V The End of the American Society 89

  VI The American Dental Convention 103

  VII The American Dental Association 123

PART TWO

DEVELOPING CONCEPTS OF PROFESSIONAL

LEADERSHIP (1860–1912) 139

  VIII The Civil War Decade 141

  IX Problems of Dental Education 155

  X Professionalism in the Gilded Age 177

  XI Dentistry and Science 199

  XII A National Dental Society 215

  XIII Currents of Reform 231

  XIV Progressivism in the Association 245

  XV Reorganization Begun 267

  XVI Moving Forward 285

  XVII Reorganization Accomplished 319

PART THREE

PROFESSIONAL ORGANIZATION IN
CONTEMPORARY AMERICA 347

Chapter

XVIII   The Association and Its Members 349

XIX   The Association and the Profession   377

XX   The Association and the Public   405

REFERENCES   442

INDEX   508

ILLUSTRATIONS

Central Office of the Association, 1959 . . . . . *Frontispiece*

Founders of the American Dental Association 18

Baltimore College of Dental Surgery 47

The American Journal of Dental Science, Vol. I, No. 1 . . . 65

Minute Book of the American Society of Dental Surgeons . . 86

Early Leaders in Dental Organization, Education, and
    Publication 101

Jonathan Taft and J. H. McQuillen 117

Sites of the First Meetings of the American Dental Association . 122

Annual Session of the Association, Niagara Falls, 1864 . . . 140

Annual Session of the Association, Boston, 1866 153

Annual Session of the Association, Niagara Falls, 1886 . . . 175

Site of the Philadelphia Centennial Session, 1876 221

World's Columbian Dental Congress, Chicago, 1893 . . . 223

Site of the Old Point Comfort Session, 1897 241

Cleveland Square, 1911 244

Site of the Cleveland Session, 1911 244

Relief Fund Seals of the American Dental Association . . . 315

Prominent Figures in the Reorganization of the Association . 317

Central Offices of the American Dental Association . . . 346

Sites of American Dental Association Research Activities . . 348

Organization Chart of the American Dental Association, 1946 . 356

Organization Chart of the American Dental Association, 1959 . 357

Presiding Officers of the American Dental Association . . . 438

INTRODUCTION

THE PLACE OF DENTISTRY in American medical history has never been made entirely clear, since studies of medical developments usually overlook those associated with such related fields as dentistry, pharmacy, and veterinary medicine. In the latter three areas, professions evolved which were separated from that of physicians, and these guild distinctions seem to have given the cue for similarly separate, historical treatments. Quite naturally, moreover, major attention has been accorded the story of medicine in the usual sense. Hence, with the possible exception of pharmacy, even the history of the related fields as such has received inadequate attention.

Logically, dentistry is simply one of many present specialties in medical science and practice; and its original separation from medicine proper resulted from social and professional circumstances rather than from scientific considerations. This isolation of one specialty as a distinct guild is one of the most interesting phenomena in the professional history of medicine as a whole. In order to understand it, one needs to follow the evolution of dental practice, and particularly the development of what may be termed "organized dentistry" in the United States.

It is just this theme which is followed in the present work on "A History of the American Dental Association." Dr. McCluggage has provided the first thorough study of the evolution of organized dentistry in this country, based as it is on a systematic use of the great mass of dental literature as well as of more general sources.

The story is presented against the background of social trends in general and of medical developments in particular. But emphasis is quite properly placed on dentistry as such, and particularly on its professional record. Technical aspects are noted when these are essential to an understanding of the major theme, but there is no pretense at tracing the scientific aspects of dental surgery.

For most of us, the history of organized dentistry is new in itself, and the account of the early societies, colleges, and national bodies is most informative. So, also, is the analysis of the problems—both technical and professional—which these institutions encountered. But for anyone possessing some familiarity with medical history, the most intriguing aspect of the narrative is its bearing on the larger epic of American medicine as a whole.

Analogies and contrasts with the history of organized medicine appear in almost every section of the work. Both the medical and the dental guilds confronted many of the same issues, although these appeared—in many

13

cases—at different times in the development of the two groups. In a general way, the dental profession recapitulated in the 1830's and '40's the experience of the medical profession during the later decades of the eighteenth century. There were the same efforts, in both cases, to organize pioneer local and state societies, to found the first colleges, and to set up the original professional journals. And in both instances, there were transitional periods during which the leaders strove to reconcile, in training and licensing arrangements, the co-existence of practitioners holding degrees and of those without benefit of formal education.

There were also, inevitably, differences between the experience of one guild and that of the other. Although dentists were relatively late in attaining group identity, they anticipated physicians in organizing a general, national body and also a society of college faculties. Their first national agencies did not long survive, as did the American Medical Association; although the structure of both organized professions was thoroughly overhauled in the early twentieth century. In this connection, dentists learned much from the forms earlier adopted by the A.M.A.

Of especial interest, throughout portions of the study, are the relations between dentistry and general medicine. For a generation after 1830, the lines between the two were still not sharply drawn. Some early dentists held M. D.'s, and some medical schools gave a limited dental training. But the thesis is suggested that the dental guild emerged because medical schools usually failed to provide adequately for dentistry. If so, several explanations are possible.

Dentistry, in effect, was one of the first medical specialties, and the medical schools of the 1840's were not yet sympathetic with specialization in the modern sense. Nor had these schools forgotten the early associations of dentistry with itinerant tooth-pullers and quacks. Yet there was a wide, social need for well-trained, dental practicitioners. Ergo, those interested would form their own guild to meet this demand. Later, when the latter became well established, it naturally exhibited vested interests in its own, continued identity.

Dr. McCluggage makes clear the perennial debates among dentists over the relative significance of "mechanical" dentistry and of dental science. There is some analogy here to the discussions among physicians concerning the relative merits of practice and of research; though dentists were of course especially apt, because of the nature of their work, to be relegated to the level of skilled technicians.

Yet technical skill must have been a factor in enabling dentistry to become one of the first scientific fields in which Americans could claim preeminence. The author notes that French dental literature (like the medical) was still much sought after in the States as late as the 1840's; but it will be remembered that, less than a generation later, American dentists were already establishing a superior reputation in European centers. Curiously enough, the most dramatic achievement of American dentists—the demonstration of ether anesthesia—does not seem to have received much attention within organized dentistry.

It is hardly necessary to add, with regard to Dr. McCluggage's study as a whole, that the preparation of so thorough and comprehensive a work must have entailed considerable time and devotion. For all those who are interested in the background of the present dental profession, and likewise for those who would welcome a comparative perspective on the history of the medical profession, this work will prove rewarding.

RICHARD H. SHRYOCK

PART ONE

The Heritage of the
American Dental Association

ON AUGUST 3, 1859, twenty-six men representing the "various existing
Dental Associations" met at Niagara Falls, New York, "with a view
to forming a National Delegated Association." Today's American
Dental Association had its origins in that convention. Its history,
however, begins nearly a quarter of a century earlier. Between the
1830's and the momentous Niagara meeting, American dentists encountered many of the problems facing a profession in a democracy.
They devised tentative solutions on which the answers of the future
were to be based. The pioneers of professional dentistry founded its
basic institutions. They established a literature, an educational system, and a number of local societies. They made two attempts to
organize a national dental association. The American Dental Association inherited the experience of a generation, its errors and misconceptions as well as its enduring accomplishments.

J. H. McQuillen

Founders of the American Dental Association

Seventeen of the Association's twenty-six founders. Photographs of the following nine are unavailable: W. Calvert, S. L. Hamlin, H. McCullum, J. T. Toland, E. Taylor, D. W. Perkins, W. M. Wright, R. Vandervort, and J. G. Cameron

W. W. Allport

G. Barker

T. L. Buckingham

I. Forbes

P. G. C. Hunt

C. H. James

J. F. Johnston

G. W. Keely

H. J. McKellops

A. M. Moore

J. Richardson

H. A. Smith

J. L. Suesserott

J. Taft

J. Taylor

G. Watt

Chapter I   BEGINNINGS

IN THE BUSTLING DECADES following the War of 1812, American society greatly increased in numbers and complexity. From a population
of 9,638,453 in 1820, the country grew more than three millions in the
next decade and more than four millions in the 1830's, so that by
1840 the total stood at 17,069,453. Undoubtedly the most spectacular
feature of American history was the movement of population across
the continent. At the time of the adoption of the Federal Constitution, our country was a cluster of settlements principally confined
to the Atlantic slope. Expansion to the Pacific and the occupation
of most of the intervening area took scarcely more than a century.
Such a stupendous achievement cannot be ignored. American historians have given the story its just due. Preoccupation with the westward movement, however, has tended to obscure the fact that a
considerable proportion of American development has been urban
in character. Nor was the growth of cities confined to the period
following the Civil War where attention of historians to urban development has been concentrated. Indeed, one prominent American
economic historian has pointed out that between 1820 and 1860 American cities grew at a more rapid rate than ever before or since. While
the national population increase was 226 per cent, urban population
increased 797 per cent.[1]

The great valley west of the Allegheny Mountains underwent impressive development during this age. The proportion of the national population residing in that region almost doubled. Nor was this expansion confined to axe-swinging pioneers. The western cities commanded as much attention from the travelers of the day as did the newly tamed wilderness. "The wilderness has melted away and cities, towns and villages have risen as if by enchantment," one eloquent booster declared.[2]

The rate of population increase favored the western part of the country, because of the high proportion of the national population that was still living on the farms. The increase in eastern urban centers could not overbalance the declining rate of growth in eastern rural areas. Yet the urbanization in the east proceeded apace. New York quadrupled its population between 1820 and 1850. Boston and Philadelphia each more than trebled in size, while Baltimore's increase was of the order of two-and-a-half times.[3]

This remarkable growth in the number and size of population concentrations raised a host of new problems—and created a multitude of new opportunities as well. Conditions of urban life required more elaborate social and political institutions. The situation encouraged, if it did not demand, specialization. The pioneer jack-of-all-trades gave way to the city-dwelling expert who confined his attentions and abilities to a single line of endeavor. Comparable statistics of occupations spanning appreciable periods are difficult to obtain. To note, however, that in 1820 only 28 per cent of the gainfully employed were engaged in non-agricultural pursuits, while the figure for 1860 is 41 per cent, is to gain at least a crude measure of the American response to these new conditions.[4]

Dentistry benefited by the rise of the cities. One recorder estimated that the number of American dentists nearly doubled in the two years following 1836. In 1835, the *New York Mirror* commented, "We have often been struck with admiration at the vast increase in the number of dentists practicing in this city within the last few years; we can remember, and that not very long ago, when there were but six or eight, and at present, we are informed that the list is swelled to eighty." Toward the end of the decade, Solyman Brown, one of the leading, and one of the most vocal, practitioners of the time, noted with dismay, "There are now almost a hundred individ-

uals calling themselves Dentists, in the city of New-York alone."
Among the cities beyond the mountains, Cincinnati may be taken as
a typical example. In 1841, Cincinnati, with a population of 46,000,
had a law school, a medical school, and a theological seminary among
its educational institutions. It was also a thriving publishing center.
The city, which boasted but two dentists in 1827, had ten times that
number hardly more than a decade later.[5]

Unfortunately, the increasing number of specialists did not always
result in an improved quality of services rendered. Access to most
pursuits was unrestricted. "The calling of dentist seems to be considered open ground," complained one observer, "into which any
fellow who has impudence, some steadiness of hand, and a case of
instruments, thinks himself free to take up a position." "Nothing was
more common than for the young man to leave the plough or workshop, as he was prompted either by indolence, bodily infirmity or
caprice, and, after spending a few months, or more frequently weeks,
with some neighboring dentist, pass, without examination, diploma
or license, to all the privileges of a regular member of the profession,"
one dentist recalled in 1848. Of course due allowance must be made
for exaggeration in these outraged cries of legitimate practitioners.
But they were not alone in their observations. The editor of the *New
York Mirror* complained, "Any person who can possess himself of a
key and a few scrapers is at liberty to do what seems good to him
with the ivories of all who have courage enough to intrust themselves
to his hands."[6]

In the interest of dentist and layman alike, there arose a demand
for the elimination of unqualified workers from the dental field. "This
is a crying evil acting with a two-fold prejudice—affecting the profession, by the disgrace which this wretched bungling sometimes
attaches to it, and periling [*sic*] the lives of those who are simple
enough to be imposed upon by their pretensions," an anxious dentist
exclaimed. "It is high time that the public and the profession should
unite in devising means for the suppression of such impostures."
"Most other professions are protected either by statute or organized
associations, from the encroachments of incompetence and imposture," Solyman Brown argued. "Ours is guarded by no civil enact-
ments and in consequence, the members should supply the defect
either by their individual or collective efforts."[7]

Nor was the dental profession confronted solely with the problems arising from a rapid increase in its numbers. Against the invasion of poorly qualified, but reasonably orthodox practitioners, the established leadership of dentistry could hold its own. But, in 1834, there appeared in New York City, two elegant and enterprising individuals of French extraction, the Messrs. Crawcour, who made serious inroads on even the best practices through a combination of vigorous and eloquent advertising and a radically different, and infinitely more comfortable, treatment for dental caries.

The accepted technique of the day required laboriously removing the decay by hand instruments and then filling the cavity with gold foil, a tedious and often painful procedure. The ingenious Crawcours proclaimed that they could obviate the discomfort of the orthodox treatment by filling the cavities with "Royal Mineral Succedaneum," apparently a not-too-scrupulously prepared amalgam of silver and mercury. Reportedly they did away with cavity preparation entirely.

The Crawcours' methods ran counter to the best dental thought of the day in a number of ways. The first related to the filling material on which they relied. Primarily, the objections to the use of amalgam derived from the fact that it contained mercury. Many physicians of the time used calomel, mercurous chloride, as a sort of universal remedy. The abuse and misuse of calomel was then under heavy attack from the better-informed quarters of the medical profession because of the evil effects of mercury poisoning on the system. The proper mode of compounding the amalgam was not then understood. A careless preparation of the mixture, with too much mercury, it was then thought, not only retarded the setting of the amalgam, but might easily result in the introduction of free mercury into the mouth and thence into the system—with deleterious results. On the other hand, the behavior of the amalgam as it hardened was not fully understood. Amalgam fillings made by some formulas tended to expand, others to shrink. In the latter case, a filling might fall out. This phenomenon was more than an inconvenience to the patient because it permitted a recurrence of decay. The supposed evils of the Crawcours' practice arose not alone from the presence of mercury in their filling material. Failure to prepare the cavity properly also had harmful effects. Filling over the decay created only the illusion of treatment—and frequently precluded salvaging the tooth. There was valid reason for the legitimate dentist to oppose the Crawcours in the interest of the welfare of their patients.

The Crawcours proclaimed the attractiveness of their treatment which consisted of "a few moments' reclining in a luxurious easy-chair" undergoing "the gentle insinuation" of the amalgam. The contrast which this type of treatment made to the orthodox treatment with its accompanying discomfort attracted many unsuspecting patients to the Crawcours' dental parlors and provided ethical dentists with economic, in addition to humanitarian, grounds for opposing the charlatans.

As the clientele of the best established and most respected practitioners in New York City turned toward the Crawcours, the leaders of the profession determined to take defensive action. They organized the Society of Surgeon Dentists of the City and State of New York to "promote the respectability of the profession, by putting down, if possible, all imposition and unprincipled quackery, by which the public and the profession at large are made to suffer."[8]

Relatively little is known of the history of this earliest of dental societies. Four addresses delivered at its first anniversary meeting were summarized and published in the *U.S. Medical and Surgical Journal.* These furnish some indication of the excellent quality and varied interests of the membership. According to the by-laws, the Society planned monthly meetings, which were to feature lectures and discussion. The example of the New York City group seems to have fostered the establishment of an auxiliary association in the western part of the state. Before many years, the pioneer Society of Surgeon Dentists, a purely local organization motivated by a local and transitory problem, fell into decrepitude and finally disappeared with the founding of the American Society of Dental Surgeons.[9]

Whether as a result of the organized dental opposition or not, the Crawcour menace soon passed. But the influence of the charlatans lingered. They had introduced a filling material that even the poorest operator apparently could manipulate. "I am pained to hear," wrote Solyman Brown in 1839, "that this execrable material [amalgam] is still used by some unprincipled men in this country." The connection of amalgam with the operations of the Crawcours suggested the identification of users of the substance as quacks, a fallacy that was to breed trouble for the profession.

Of course, quackery was not confined to the unscrupulous use of "Royal Mineral Succedaneum." The early dental press reported an interesting variety of frauds involving, among many, mesmerism, fabulous dentifrices, and the treatment of ailing teeth by "steam dentistry," using smoke, vapor, or even true steam.[10] Thus in the 1830's, conscientious dentists confronted the twin problems of incompetence and quackery.

By the end of the decade, the answer of the profession was beginning to emerge. The institutions developed in the ensuing years were substantially the same as those upon which the profession relies today. The response of the dentists to their problems was three-fold: foundation of a professional literature to disseminate correct principles and expose error, establishment of special schools for dental education, and organization of professional guilds. The dental pioneers even considered legislation, which has come to play an important role in professional life today, but the times were unsympathetic to this approach, and the profession was too imperfectly developed to make statutory regulation feasible.

Of the elements of organized dentistry, the journal was the first to appear. It might be argued that a dental publication was a necessary first step. While all of the factors were important, and each ultimately depended upon the others for its success, the rallying of a movement for a dental association and the effectiveness of a society once it was formed, depended upon communication among the members of the guild. Provision had to be made for relating the correct principles of dental health and describing the essential qualifications of a good dentist to the public and for announcing new discoveries and proper procedures to the professionals. Shearjashub Spooner, an outstanding dentist and the author of one of the best of the contemporary dental books, gave, in 1838, his prescription for elevating the profession. Spooner urged that means be employed to inform the community sufficiently on the subject of dental surgery, to convince people of its utility when judiciously practiced, and to enable them to discriminate between a scientific dentist and a charlatan. The second phase of Spooner's program sought improvement of the quality of the dentistry practiced in the United States. To effect this end, Spooner proposed that the profession unite in establishing a semi-annual or quarterly periodical devoted to dental science and information.[11]

Before the establishment of the first specialized journal, dental articles appeared in the medical periodicals of the day. In some ways, this was a satisfactory mode of communication, but the inclusion of dental subjects among the medical tended to emphasize the medico-scientific, or theoretical, phases of dentistry at the expense of its practical and mechanical aspects. Furthermore, publications dedicated to medicine could hardly spare sufficient space for adequate coverage of developments in dental art and science.

Finally, the champions of dentistry felt that the status of their specialty required a journal. The Publishing Committee of *The American Journal of Dental Science* argued that "the publication of such a Journal, will have the effect of giving dignity and importance to the general subject of Practical Dentistry; and thus result in solid advantage to each and all of its professors, as well as to the community at large." [12]

The steps by which the establishment of a dental journal was accomplished are difficult to reconstruct. The matter appears to have been determined upon at a meeting held at the home of Solyman Brown in May, 1839. The principal difficulty apparently related to finances. This problem was temporarily solved by securing guarantors among the leading dentists of the time. These individuals subscribed for some twenty to forty copies each, enabling the publishers to make favorable terms with the printer. With this obstacle cleared, the promoters got the enterprise under way.[13]

In June, 1839, Eleazar Parmly, Elisha Baker, and Solyman Brown addressed "their Professional Brethren throughout the United States of America" with a specimen number inaugurating *The American Journal of Dental Science*. "There is no fraternity in the United States, of equal magnitude and importance, which has not some publication devoted to its interest," the prospectus began. This appeal to the dentists' professional pride was buttressed by a series of arguments addressed to self-interest. The journal would enable dentists to profit from the experience of the best practitioners. "There are many high-minded men of great knowledge and experience in our Art, who will gladly communicate the results of their observation, for the benefit of the younger members of the profession," the promoters declared. They reasoned that the publication of their subscription list would help to inform "that portion of the profession who are not stationary in their labours, to what points their exertions may be most profitably directed." The announcement continued, "The publication of the entire list of Practitioners in the United States will have a tendency to check the exuberant influx of half-educated aspirants, who imagine that the field of labour is but partially occupied, and thus expose themselves to ultimate disappointment." Not only would the publication discourage competition from the unqualified, it would expose the charlatans. "Such a work," the editors reasoned, "will have a tendency to expel from Dental Practice the quackery which disgraces it, just in proportion as it dissipates ignorance . . . from the community at large." Several additional arguments rang the changes on the themes already established. The prospectus concluded on a challenging note: "If the members of the Profession, few in number compared with the patrons of other periodicals, do not subscribe liberally to the work, there is little probability that it can be long sustained." [14]

The appeal apparently struck the right note, for the *Journal* continued publication, albeit somewhat irregularly at first. Correspondents emphatically endorsed the objective of the promoters. Enoch Noyes of Baltimore wrote so enthusiastically that the editors committed his letter to print. Noyes pointed out that many persons aspiring to perform dental services sought "to conceal their ignorance, to veil the art with as much mystery as possible." To inform the public and expose "the impositions daily practised by such persons, a periodical publication, devoted to the science of dentistry, is eminently calculated," Noyes asserted. Apparently 348 dentists agreed with Noyes, for that is the number reported by the editors in early 1841 as the first volume neared completion. That these individuals subscribed for a total of 767 volumes furnishes an index of their enthusiasm. One devoted supporter became a perpetual subscriber. [15]

Institutional support for the venture was not lacking. "The Dental Association of Western New York, (auxilliary [sic] to the Society of Surgeon Dentists of the City of New York)" recognized the *American*

Journal as tending to exalt the character and standing of the profession. Accordingly, the Association very practically resolved to exert its utmost endeavors to help the project by procuring subscriptions and by contributing to its pages. At its first session, the American Society of Dental Surgeons endorsed the purposes of the *Journal* and pledged its support. In spite of all these avowals, however, it took the proprietors more than two years to publish the twelve issues promised for Volume One.[16]

At the second annual meeting of the American Society of Dental Surgeons, in August, 1841, the Society determined to establish a periodical as the organ of its opinions on subjects of dental theory and practice, and for the purpose of advancing the interests of the science and the profession. On behalf of his associates, Chapin Harris tendered the *American Journal* for this role. The Society accepted the offer. With the support of the national organization of the profession, the *Journal's* relative permanence was assured. Soon other periodicals made their appearance. In 1844, *Stockton's Dental Intelligencer* began publication, to be followed, two years later, by the *New York Dental Recorder*. Eighteen forty-seven was a banner year for dental journalism. The Mississippi Valley Association of Surgeon Dentists launched a new publication, the *Dental Register of the West*, which was destined to flourish as a leading periodical through a long career. The same year witnessed the inauguration of the *Dental News Letter*, organ of the dental supply firm of Jones, White and Company, predecessor of the modern firm of S. S. White. The *News Letter* began as a small, sixteen-page quarterly, but soon expanded both its size and publishing schedule and became one of the major journals of the time. Thus, within eight years of the first publication, dental periodical literature was firmly established.[17]

The inauguration of a specialized literature was linked to the other elements of organized dentistry. The first volume of *The American Journal of Dental Science* itself records the initiation of all three movements between its covers. Thoughtful observers in the medical field recognized the connection between issuance of a journal and establishment of collegiate education in dentistry. *The Maryland Medical and Surgical Journal* praised the fledgling *American Journal of Dental Science* and used the occasion to summon the dentists "to an immediate effort . . . to establish schools of dental surgery." The medical publication explained that improvement in the training of both physicians and dentists would soon be appreciated and rewarded by the public. Specialized professional education, no less than public information, would help dentistry "escape the reproaches that have been but too frequently heaped upon it, and [enable it to] rise in respectability to a level with those of the most favored and useful," Chapin A. Harris, editor of the *American Journal*, argued. "We should furnish the necessary facilities for those who may design practicing the art, to qualify themselves properly for its duties."[18] Not long after, Harris became dean of the first dental college.

The pioneers of organized dentistry confronted a difficult situation in seeking to establish formal instruction in the dental art and science. The accepted method of training in dentistry, as it was for many years in medicine and the law, was a system of private tutoring. An accomplished practitioner took the aspirant into his office and taught the novice in return for services and, quite frequently, a considerable fee. Among many of the most successful dentists, students' fees represented a lucrative supplement to the income from their practice. This situation had a tendency to create a vested opposition to institutional dental training in the very group upon whose support a program of dental collegiate instruction would have to depend.[19]

Fortunately, there were two men in the very forefront of the profession, Horace H. Hayden and Eleazar Parmly, who had concluded that special schools for the education of dentists were a necessity. Horace H. Hayden was perhaps the dean of the dental profession in his day. Born in 1768, Hayden began to practice dentistry during the 1790's. He served a number of cities and towns in New York State, but by 1800 he had located in Baltimore. Hayden, like many of his outstanding contemporaries, pursued a variety of interests. He was an ardent amateur geologist and botanist. Possessed of some medical knowledge, Hayden published papers on ulcerated tonsils and on the various glandular systems. Bond says, in his obituary notice, that Hayden "entered with great zeal upon physiological researches, especially upon an investigation of the uses of the thyroid gland, which, though they did not result in any important discovery, displayed great acuteness of mind, and experimental abilities." He produced some of the earliest items in the bibliography of American dentistry. He helped found the Maryland Academy of Sciences and served as its president. Hayden's scientific activities tended to enhance the status of dentistry in the circles in which he moved.[20]

His social and cultural attainments redounded to the same effect. Baltimore, in those days of the early nineteenth century, was a lively cultural center. Here lived Francis Scott Key, Edward Coote Pinckney, one of the best of America's early native poets, Rembrandt Peale of the famous family of American artists, John H. B. Latrobe, son of the architect of the capitol in Washington, William Wirt, lawyer and biographer of Patrick Henry, Jared Sparks, noted historian, and many others. In 1816, seven men of literary interests established the Delphian Club, which became an important part of the gay Baltimore social life. One of the charter members of the new club was Horace H. Hayden.[21] By the late thirties, Hayden was nearing the end of his long career. His scientific and social attainments, as well as his accomplishments as a dentist, undoubtedly lent weight to his arguments for institutionalized dental education.

Eleazar Parmly performed for dentistry in New York much the same role that Hayden played in Baltimore. Parmly was a much younger man than Hayden, but he had been established in New York since 1821. Parmly enjoyed considerable financial, as well as professional, success. He moved in the better social circles of New York City. His social connections paved the way for a greater public appreciation of dentistry. Parmly was one of the founders of the Society of Surgeon Dentists of the City and State of New York. His election as president of that organization indicates the esteem of his colleagues.

A sought-after preceptor, Parmly was nonetheless an ardent supporter of the movement for collegiate dental training. His service to dental education only began with his backing of the movement that eventuated in the founding of the Baltimore College of Dental Surgery. Parmly later served as provost of the Baltimore College. He led the long fight to charter a dental college in New York. When the victory was won, Eleazar Parmly served as a professor and the first president of the New York College of Dentistry from 1860 to 1869. The Association of Colleges of Dentistry, organized in 1866, chose Parmly as its first president.[22]

The prestige of men like Parmly and Hayden was buttressed by the energy and persistence of others, notably Chapin A. Harris. Harris was much younger than Hayden and some eight years Parmly's junior. Harris received his early training, first in medicine, then in dentistry, from his brother, John Harris, in Ohio. Subsequently, Chapin moved east and won a license from the Maryland Medical and Chirurgical Faculty in 1833. He practiced as an itinerant in the area around Baltimore and in eastern Virginia. During this period, Harris began to contribute to the literature of his chosen profession with a series of papers in the medical journals. This writing was climaxed in 1839 by the publication of *The Dental Art: A Practical Treatise on Dental Surgery*. In this version, and some twelve subsequent editions through 1896, the book has been called the most popular and most widely distributed dental book of its time. Harris became one of the editors of *The American Journal of Dental Science,* a post he held through the first series of the magazine under the auspices of its private promoters and then under the American Society of Dental Surgeons. When the Society abandoned sponsorship, Harris took over the publication and managed it as a private venture through its second series. Harris used his vantage point in the editorial chair to advance the cause of collegiate dental education and to promote dental organization. He served as the perennial corresponding secretary of the first national dental association and dean of the first dental school.[23]

The united efforts of the leadership of the profession finally won a charter for a dental college from the Maryland legislature. The Baltimore College of Dental Surgery opened its doors in November, 1840.[24]

The new establishment was warmly welcomed. Chapin A. Harris announced in one of the introductory lectures that the project had been greeted "in a manner calculated, not only to inspire its friends with confidence, but also that promises perpetuity to it." He alluded to the cordiality of the medical profession toward the college, but modestly forebore to quote any of the "flattering notices" the institution had received in the scientific and newspaper press. A month after the opening of the first session, Harris wrote to Solyman Brown in New York, "There is now no question as to the future." The initial class was small, Harris admitted, "but perhaps as large as we had a right to expect." He based his confidence on the letters he had received from prospective students "who were unwilling to incur the expense of coming here until they should ascertain that the school was actually in operation." [25] The verdict of time would tell whether the support was merited and the confidence warranted.

"Wherever you go, the diploma you hold in your hands will be a passport to public consideration, and an abundant introduction to usefulness," Professor Thomas E. Bond, Jr., assured the students at the first commencement. Although the diploma may not have become an automatic assurance of success, a number of circumstances soon strikingly substantiated the value of institutional dental education. Toward the end of the decade, a southern practitioner reported that "wherever the graduates of the Baltimore College have gone out into the south, they have taken away the business of old practitioners. . . . People believe that a graduate from that college knows more than any one else." In a way, this testimony was corroborated by news of an impostor traveling through the middle south posing as a graduate of the Baltimore College.[26] The school soon received the endorsement of imitation. The Ohio College of Dental Surgery was founded in Cincinnati just five years after the pioneer school began operation. In 1852, another college opened its doors in Philadelphia. The medical fraternity acknowledged the success of the movement for formal dental education. "Dentistry is an essential branch of business in every community in this country," the *Boston Medical and Surgical Journal* announced. "We believe these colleges will ensure to the community good dentists." The editor of the *New York Dental Recorder* declared that "nothing would be more terrible in its consequences to our profession, than a blow at Dental Collegiate education." By the middle fifties, institutional dental education had so far proved itself that it justified favorable comparison with medicine and law.[27]

The successful inauguration of formal dental education did not completely dispose of the problems facing the profession at the onset of the forties. Chapin Harris remarked at the opening of the Baltimore College, "Filled as the ranks of the profession are, with individuals who have never learned the first rudiments, . . . it will doubtless require some time to effect the wished reformation, and [it] will only be accomplished [by fixing] a line of distinction between the competent and the incompetent." "It is necessary that there should be some test of qualification by bodies qualified and regularly appointed for the duty," an earnest dentist insisted after pondering the problem.[28]

Given agreement on this point, the question still remained: Shall the line of distinction be a matter of legislation or shall it be determined within the profession? Shearjashub Spooner had given his prescription in 1838. "The Dental profession should be protected by legislative enactment: every person before he be permitted to practice it, should serve a term of pupilage and pass an examination before a competent board of dentists." Eleazar Parmly agreed. "If the legislature will do nothing more than merely to regulate the conditions by which members shall be admitted to practice . . . it would serve, at least, to draw a line of distinction, which the public would understand, between the regular members of the profession, and the quacks who disgrace it." Chapin Harris also subscribed to this view. "Were the enlightened of the profession to unite in a measure of this kind, their petitions would be granted without a doubt," he thought, "for the community at large have experienced too much of the bad effects growing out of the ignorance of dental practitioners." [29]

On the other hand, some dentists feared that legislation might not be sufficient to achieve the purpose in view. One critic argued that it was impossible to fix a definite standard of qualification by law. He doubted that a bill could be drafted that would separate the qualified from the unqualified among those already in practice. The unqualified men, as well as the competent, then, would be charged with enforcement of the law. "And if this be the result, it is far better there be no law," the critic concluded. "A licensed quack, of all things else, is to be despised and dreaded." [30]

Limited experience tended to support this theoretical judgment. *The American Journal of Dental Science* printed a report on the operation of the Alabama statute of 1841, the first law regulating the practice of dentistry. It seemed that the legislation had failed to cure all the ills of incompetence and quackery. The dental profession continued to be invaded by poorly trained practitioners. The economic stringency following the Panic of 1837 received part of the blame for the influx of unqualified pretenders. But there were other causes alleged. The examining boards were composed of physicians—and they did not always take their duties seriously. The *Journal* editor concluded, "The insuperable objection to committing the interests of dental surgery, into the keeping of the general surgeon and the physician, is, that gentlemen who are only medically educated, as far as it regards dental surgery, are oftentimes as ignorant as the most unlearned." [31]

Furthermore, Chapin Harris's opinion was erroneous. The general sentiment of the country at that time opposed legislation governing access to any occupation or regulating the conduct of any economic pursuit. "A people accustomed to govern themselves, and boasting of their intelligence, are impatient of restraint," a legislator argued, in proposing repeal of New York's medical licensing restrictions. "They want no protection but freedom of inquiry and freedom of action." This was the age of Jacksonian Democracy. It witnessed, as one historian has expressed it, "The Rise of the Common Man." Dentistry's response showed a remarkable accord between the views of the profession and the sentiments of the community. "Let every person who has defective teeth have an opportunity of reading the opinions of the best operators in the land," a medical spokesman proposed at the beginning of the epoch. Many voices of professional dentistry endorsed the suggestion.[32] "In some of the governments of Europe, charlatanism is restrained by laws," a dentist explained, "But in a government like ours, where the people make and administer their own laws, a statute which does not harmonize with public sentiment will be repealed or not enforced." The era was characterized by boundless optimism and furious activity. Every man was considered capable of any task to which he set his hand. "It's a free country," Lemuel Shattuck, public health advocate, explained as he bemoaned the reluctance of the people to regulate access to the professions.[33]

Since legislative action was not in prospect, Solyman Brown urged the members of the dental profession to supply "the defect" by their "collective efforts." "The American character and the popular genius of all our institutions immediately direct us to lay hold of the great principle of voluntary association, . . . to effect any desirable good," Chapin Harris explained. "We have no wealthy and powerful privileged orders to command any given amelioration or improvement, and hence we combine the power of popular number and bring it to bear upon the objects we desire to accomplish." [34] "This national peculiarity," as Harris called it, is a feature of American life that has excited the comment of foreign observers throughout our history. Certainly it was exceedingly active at the time Harris invoked it on behalf of dentistry. Among the "numerous benevolent and scientific associations" to which Harris referred were the Association of American Geologists, established in 1840, the American Statistical Association, founded in 1838, and sundry philanthropic, humanitarian, abolitionist, and temperance organizations that took their rise in those turbulent years. By 1843, the American Association for the Advancement of Science could have been added to the list.[35] Eleazar Parmly, appealing to the authority of the venerated Hayden, proclaimed, "Every important and useful profession among men, requires organization, by which is denoted a system of mutual instruction, protection, support and encouragement." And so the leaders of dentistry decided upon the creation of a voluntary association "to run a clear line of discrimination between the man of competent attainment and the impudent empiric." [36] This was the final move in the establishment of organized dentistry.

The step was accomplished in the late summer of 1840. On the morning of August 18, fifteen leading dentists, mostly drawn from New York, met at the American Hotel in New York City. Horace H. Hayden initiated proceedings by nominating Elisha Baker to be chairman and Solyman Brown secretary. Chapin Harris proposed a resolution to the effect that a national dental society would advance the profession. A committee was appointed to draft a constitution and the convention adjourned to Brown's home at 17 Park Place. The next day, the meeting moved to the residence of Elisha Baker in Warren Street. On August 20, the itinerant founders labored in Park Place again, at the establishment of Messrs. E. G. Tucker and Joseph H. Foster. In the course of their three days' deliberations these earnest pioneers organized the American Society of Dental Surgeons.[37] The institutional foundations of dentistry in the United States were complete. The years that followed were to show whether the profession and the country were ready for such measures and how wisely the dentists of the day would use the new tools they had forged.

Chapter II   EARLY PROFESSIONAL ORGANIZATION

THE FOUNDERS of the American Society of Dental Surgeons showed
a clear appreciation of the obligations and functions of a national
dental organization. Their understanding of the needs of the profession was comprehensive and acute. The constitution adopted in the
home of Solyman Brown on August 18, 1840, set forth their appraisal
of the duties of a national association and of the requirements of the
profession. Other early actions gave additional precision to the
founders' conceptions. The pioneers of organized dentistry assumed
the whole range of professional responsibility. Their vision included
the problems of relations with the public, public information, professional education, the advancement of dental science and art, the
elimination of fraud and quackery, and the welfare of members beset
by personal misfortune. Article One of the constitution of 1840
stated the objectives of the Society in general terms:

The objects of this Society are to promote union and harmony among all
respectable and well informed Dental Surgeons; to advance the science by free
communication and interchange of sentiments, either written or verbal, between
members of the Society, both in this and other countries; in fine, to give character and respectability to the profession, by establishing a line of distinction
between the truly meritorious and skilful, and such as riot in the ill gotten
fruits of unblushing impudence and empiricism.

35

Additional articles spelled out these ideals of the founders in more detail. A series of sections defined the qualifications of membership, the processes of election, and the obligations of members. These measures aimed to make all legitimate and respectable dentists eligible for membership in the Society and, at the same time, to establish a definition of a dental surgeon that would exclude impostors and incompetents. For the basis upon which to make the distinction, the Society turned to an appraisal of the training rather than the performance of the candidate, perhaps because the latter allowed too much room for subjective judgment. The requirements of 1840 stipulated a minimum age of twenty-one years, "a good English education," and at least two full years' preceptorial study "with some practical dentist known as such to this Society." A second section of this article provided exceptional treatment for holders of the diploma of any dental college, regularly chartered in any of the United States. (There was at that time only one, the Baltimore College of Dental Surgery.) Candidates for membership from this last classification were exempted from examination "in relation to their qualifications to enter upon the practice of the profession." [1]

By defining the qualifications for membership in terms of training, the Society also evidenced its concern to raise the standards of dental education. The Society approved the establishment of the Baltimore College of Dental Surgery and asserted its determination to co-operate with the other friends of that institution in promoting its designs. Subsequent actions of the Society continued this interest in collegiate instruction. In 1846, when the revision of the constitution was under consideration, Chapin Harris, dean of one of the two schools in operation at the time, proposed to extend the favoritism shown dental college graduates. His proposal lost by a tie vote. But the amendment that was adopted recast the original article in such a way as to emphasize collegiate rather than preceptorial education. The constitution now required that the candidate "shall have studied and practiced for the full term of two years, in a regularly chartered Dental College in any of the United States, or with some respectable dental practitioner, known as such to this Society." [2]

The founders exhibited their concern for the scientific advancement of the profession. Each year, the founders decreed, five members were to "prepare Dissertations on some subjects connected with the profession." The same article also provided that the Society might from time to time designate certain members to prepare "Essays or any other Documents." The succeeding article authorized the Society to award premiums for dissertations on subjects specified by the Society at any annual meeting, "also, for important improvements in Mechanical Dentistry, and the manufacture of Incorruptible Teeth."

The ninth article of the constitution dealt with the fees expected from examinations of candidates and from members-elect. In addition, this article anticipated contributions of money, books, or other property. These resources, the constitution declared, might be either used or sold in aid of the Society's purposes. Another article made allowance for the expenditure of surplus funds "for the aid and relief of the widows and orphans of deceased members; or for the benefit of living members reduced to want, by sickness or other calamity." Another section controlled disbursements for other charitable or patriotic purposes. These grants of Society funds could be made only by action at an annual meeting. A final section of this article, however, authorized the president to "give pecuniary assistance to any member, or to the surviving family of any deceased member, out of any monies in the treasury deposited there by benevolent individuals." [3]

Insofar as the fundamental ordinances of the American Society of Dental Surgeons reflected the thinking of its founders, it is clear that they entertained a broad view of their responsibilities. To a twentieth century student of dental organization, the founders' interests, and many of their actions, must appear strikingly similar to those of the present. Yet the American Society of Dental Surgeons failed to endure. Much can be learned from an examination of the reasons for the failure of this boldly conceived pioneer effort at professional organization.

The first national dental society never achieved a truly national scope. Perhaps the sheer physical distances the country embraced were sufficient to prevent such an accomplishment. In terms of time, comfort, and convenience, the broad reaches of the nation were vaster still, for, in 1840, the day of the railroad was just dawning and the principal transport for most of the country remained the horse-drawn coach, the river steamer, or the canal boat. These modes of travel were neither speedy, reliable, nor safe. "It is not so easy a matter . . . to travel from St. Louis to New York, a distance of fifteen or eighteen hundred miles, to attend the annual meetings of the Society,—not to mention the small matter of expense," a western member informed his eastern friends in 1848. In typical straight-faced frontier style, the writer explained that the distance and expense were not the only considerations involved. "On one occasion we made the effort for the sole purpose of being present at its deliberations, and unfortunately for us, we remained long enough on a sand-bar in the Ohio river to deprive us of the pleasure of meeting with the Am. Soc. of Dent. Surgeons, so that . . . we were 'just soon enough to be too late,' the Society having adjourned several days previously." Other travelers had not been so fortunate in their river voyages. Of one hundred boats steaming out of St. Louis in 1841, twenty-three were lost. In September and October of 1842, eight boats sank between St. Louis and the mouth of the Ohio.[4]

Difficulties of travel not only inhibited the movement of the people but it also hampered the communication of intelligence. Editors of the dental press frequently complained of the tardiness and unreliability of the mails. This was a factor hampering the activities of the American Society as well. In 1854, the *Dental Register* reported a meeting of ten dentists who had gathered in Cincinnati expecting to attend the annual meeting of the American Society of Dental Surgeons. Notice of the postponement of the meeting had failed to reach them. The West Point meeting of 1853 was handicapped by a similar communication failure.[5]

In spite of the dangers and difficulties of travel, the Society insisted that its members attend its annual meeting at least once in three years. Each year the meeting was called for a different city, but always the convention site was on the eastern seaboard. Not until May, 1855, did the American Society at last convene in annual session west of the Allegheny Mountains.[6]

The preference of the Society for the coastal region might have aggravated a feeling that was for many years a persistent feature in all facets of American life. The rivalry between East and West, between the established settlements along the coast and the rude, unstable, furiously-growing empire beyond the mountains, was a divisive influence that found expression in many ways. The appearance of competitors in an area where conditions offered great opportunities and few obstacles in the way of achieving them disturbed the easterners. They tended to deprecate the crudities and backwardness of the frontier region. Westerners, on the other hand, were jealous of the prestige and control the greater age of eastern institutions gave them. The westerners' reaction varied. They emphasized their freedom from the unreasonable checks of established institutions. The frontiersmen gloried in the opportunities the new land offered. At the same time, they labored furiously to emulate the East and boasted of the rapidity with which they approached or surpassed eastern accomplishments. And they did not hesitate to remind the older section of its shortcomings. This often-fruitful competition between the old and the new regions of the country was reflected in the early development of the American dental profession.

Undoubtedly, the unstable conditions of the West served to impede the development of professionalism. At the outset, legitimate dentistry was confined to the larger urban centers beyond the mountains, Cincinnati, Louisville, and St. Louis. Vast expanses of the western states remained the domain of the itinerant dentist or the quack-of-all-trades. One of the pioneers of the profession in the West, James Taylor of Cincinnati, recalled, "In 1827, there were but two Dentists in this city, and in the State, not over half a dozen." He added, "This we believe is true if we were to call every pretender a Dental Surgeon." As late as 1850, an Illinois correspondent of the *American Journal* gave a harrowing description of the state of the profession in the West. "Dentists here, who deserve the name, are few and far between, and when of the right stamp in soul as well as professional skill, their visits are much like Angels," he wrote. "There is a class who can only live by travelling. These are not only ignorant of the first principles of the profession, but what is worse, unwilling to learn, and are unprincipled." Eastern journalists hailed the founding of the *Dental Register of the West.* "A periodical of this character . . . has long been needed in the West, where the want of skillful dentists is more felt than in the older states," an editor explained. The promoters of the *Register* urged physicians to subscribe in order to secure the rudiments of dental knowledge necessary to assess the qualifications and performance of the itinerants.[7]

As time passed, the number of dentists increased, but the quality of many of their operations was dubious. "Some have art without science, others science without art; some have neither, and all think themselves dentists," one westerner ruefully acknowledged. In the new society of the West, rigid lines could not yet be drawn between specialities. Westerners insisted on their right to try their hand at any opportunity that presented itself. The proud eastern professional who reported the story of an ex-barkeep, who left for the West "with a drove of horses," and six weeks later reported himself a dentist, did not paint too distorted a picture of much of western dentistry. "A very large majority then entering the profession were mere mechanics, and never looked upon the profession in any other light than that of a trade," James Taylor recalled in later years. Furthermore, the frontier tended to lack appreciation of the niceties of life. Westerners were notoriously in a hurry. They might not have been sure where they were going, but they were certain they could not pause for ordinary dental care. In an emergency, resort was had to the nearest volunteer "dentist." [8]

Yet the westerners could justly boast of the spectacular rise of professionalism in their region. From the nucleus of two dentists in Cincinnati in 1827, Taylor remembered an increase in the profession to some twenty individuals by 1841. "In the winter of that year we organized an Association for our own improvement," he boasted. In other ways, too, the transmontane dentists showed an appreciation of their professional obligations that often rivaled, if it did not surpass, that in the East. Cincinnati became as much a center of the profession as Baltimore, Philadelphia, or New York. Scarcely four years after the foundation of the American Society of Dental Surgeons in the East, the little society of which Taylor spoke expanded to become the Mississippi Valley Association of Dental Surgeons. Soon after came the founding of the Ohio College of Dental Surgery in Cincinnati, to be followed in 1847 by the inauguration of the *Dental Register of the West*.[9] This was no very great time lag behind the establishment of the trappings of professionalism along the seaboard.

The western dentists were by no means contented with the outward manifestations of professional organization. They undertook to war on "empirics," cut-rate dentists with cut-rate skills and materials, and advertisers with fancy endorsements and instruments. They denounced these and other forms of imposture and quackery as vigorously as any easterner. Furthermore, the westerners boasted of their freedom from the vexatious controversies and distracting fads that flourished east of the mountains. In 1844, the Mississippi Valley Association, following the lead of the American Society, declared its abhorrence of amalgam fillings. A member of the Mississippi Valley Association, recalling the action, said it was taken "probably from a desire on the part of every member present to separate ourselves so far as possible, in faith and practice, from a certain class of operators who made a free and reprehensible use of amalgam." [10] But the amalgam question never assumed the exaggerated proportions that so disrupted the East.

A note in the *Dental Register* epitomized the westerners' amusement at the easterners' amalgam obsession. The editor gleefully reproduced a flagrant dental card clipped from a New York paper. He apologized for his failure to discover the man's secret. "Unfortunately for the introduction of improved dentistry in the West," the editor explained with unconcealed relish, "a grave and very important question in relation to the use of Amalgam in fillings for the teeth so completely absorbed the attention of the Profession while there, that the other [great discovery] was entirely neglected." [11]

There was more than a little justice in the westerners' derogation of eastern assumptions of superiority, as a cursory reference to the newspaper press of the day readily reveals. For example, on the very day that the founding fathers of the profession convened in New York to organize the American Society of Dental Surgeons, two flamboyant dental advertisements appeared in the *Baltimore Sun*. In the summer of 1843, Baltimore was stimulated and edified by a spectacular controversy over the merits of mesmerism. Jokes about dentists were fairly common in the press of the time, and the incidents were not always given a western setting. [12]

Just as there was reason for the westerners to remind the easterners of their shortcomings, there was justification for the western complaints of unwarranted discrimination against their section. The abortive meeting of the American Society, scheduled for Cincinnati in the autumn of 1854, was deferred, in part, because of the press of business among the eastern practitioners. Some easterners were particularly offensive in their assumptions of virtue. Amos Westcott, for example, rejected the idea of controlling practice through statutory authority vested in local societies. "At least three-fourths of these societies would be composed of a majority of those having no claim to skill or science," he explained. At the time Westcott made this sweeping assertion, there were but two local associations in existence, the Virginia Society and the Mississippi Valley aggregation. The record of these two organizations gave no support for Westcott's assumption.[13]

In the long run, however, intersectional rivalry or ill-feeling cannot explain the demise of the American Society of Dental Surgeons. A careful student of this period has concluded that there was as yet no separate and distinctive western life. Most of the citizens in the interior had migrated to that section and had brought with them from the East their standards and ways of life.[14] This was especially true of the professional classes. Mutual expressions of regard were at least as abundant as exhibitions of rancor. On the eve of the first convention of the American Society west of the Alleghenies, the Mississippi Valley Association held a called meeting, the prominent object of which was to welcome the older society to the West. This mingling of the East and the West evoked an exchange of warm sentiments of high esteem. "The harmony and good feeling manifested by the two societies, and by members of the profession individually," the editor of the *Register* declared, "cannot fail to produce a happy and lasting effect on the welfare and prosperity of the profession."[15]

By 1853, at least, the East had acknowledged the full equality of the western branch of the profession. In that year, Chapin Harris printed in the *American Journal* a plea from Jacksonville, Illinois, for more well-trained dentists. "We thank our correspondent for the kind invitation, and the liberality of feeling which prompted . . . it; but as yet," Harris ruefully admitted, "we have none such . . . to spare." He announced Baltimore's intention to do everything possible to meet the need. Then, significantly, Harris enlisted the new college in Philadelphia and the Ohio College of Dental Surgery in the campaign. "No doubt our friends a little further east and north, as well as those of the Queen City, will aid us in our charitable desire to oblige him." [16]

In the words of Elisha Townsend, president of the American Society, the recognition of the high status of trans-Allegheny dentistry went even further. At the Cincinnati meeting of the American Society, in his address, Townsend admitted full equality for the westerners, and allowed that perhaps greater acknowledgement would soon be required. "The dentistry of the West has honorably earned fair recognition of its claims," he declared. "The Star of Science, like the Star of Empire, westward holds its way, and the centre of influence is rapidly traveling toward the centre of territory." It is not without significance that the movement for reform of the American Society of Dental Surgeons, which eventuated in its dissolution, got underway at the Cincinnati meeting.[17]

Equally with sectional feeling, the physical distances and difficulties of the country prevented the formation of a successful national organization. The disappointed group that met in Cincinnati only to find that the meeting of the American Society had been postponed adopted resolutions of reassurance to their eastern confreres. "Cincinnati is, and has been during the season, almost entirely free from cholera, probably more so than any of the larger Eastern cities," they argued. This was a shrewd hit. The increasing size of population concentrations had created public health problems that the nation was only beginning to master. Boston suffered a cholera epidemic in 1848, and the meeting of the American Society, called for Baltimore in 1849 was postponed until the following spring because of the general prevalence of cholera. The hazards of disease and epidemic were a constant factor in the urban life of the day, East and West.[18]

The disappointed Cincinnati dentists were also reassuring about transportation facilities. "As far as the necessity for using the Western Waters as a medium for reaching Cincinnati is concerned, we would assure our brethren that our country is well supplied with railroads, so that the use of the rivers may be dispensed with for that purpose." [19]

This proud statement records a truly remarkable fact. The United States during the period between the War of 1812 and the Civil War experienced a "transportation revolution," a series of new developments that had far-reaching influence on the course of events at that time and in later years as well. At the beginning of the forties, the only means of communication between the interior valley and the seaboard was a combination of rugged travel on horseback or by coach, and the hazardous and unreliable waterways. By mid-century, railroads were beginning to pierce the Appalachian mountain barrier at several different points, and the Ohio Valley was bound to the eastern centers with bands of iron. Even before this, the connections among the principal eastern cities had been forged. The revolution was by no means confined to the carriage of goods and passengers. Telegraphic communication between Washington and Baltimore was accomplished in 1844. Before many years virtually instantaneous communication linked the major centers of population. In 1845, 1847, and 1851, the postal service was reformed and first-class postage was reduced to three cents. Clearly, by mid-century, sectionalism, isolation, and physical distance were on the decline as factors inhibiting national unity of the dental profession.[20]

Perhaps, however, the country was not yet temperamentally ready to sustain a corps of specialists in dentistry. The prevailing sentiment of the people seemingly demanded freedom of access to all lines of endeavor for all who wished to take them up. For this reason, as the founders of the American Society had observed, legislative controls over entry to the profession were infeasible. The same prevailing equalitarian sentiment engendered antagonism toward the more formal disciplines as well as did anti-intellectualism. Another aspect of the national character also militated against assigning a monopoly of the treatment of any specific type of ailment to a single specialty. The country, then as now, delighted in sensational, radically novel, and easy, panaceas.[21]

The avidity with which the Americans embraced curative novelties inspired Thomas E. Bond, Jr., a learned and sober physician on the faculty of the Baltimore College, to undertake a full scale analysis of the phenomenon. "The success of quackery in our land is indeed one of those strange things that, at first sight, appear to baffle philosophy, and to present . . . the anomaly of a thing done in contrariety to apparently well-known circumstances that should have prevented it," Bond declared.

Professor Bond first compared and contrasted the attitudes of the African savage and one class of the civilized American when confronted with seemingly extraordinary happenings. For all their superficial differences, Bond concluded that they were remarkably alike. It was merely necessary to make a small distinction. "We require to be cheated into a belief in the wonderful," Bond explained, "while the African, having no faith in what is merely extraordinary, offers no resistance to the reception of the marvellous."

Next, the critic turned his attention to another class, "perhaps a small one, . . . who are absolutely amateurs of physic." His isolation and description of this species was a genuine scientific triumph. In botany or zoology, a similar feat might have won Bond the honor of having the new group named after him. On the basis of Bond's description, it is still possible to identify specimens of this ubiquitous breed. "They are neither driven to it by imaginary disease, nor by real suffering, but they seem to take it by way of amusement. I know some that regularly take all the new physic that comes out," he noted. "Thomsonianism and Homeopathy, have equal charms for them, and Dutch doctors, and Indian doctors, are blessed by their equal confidence."

The gullible and the "amateurs of physic" accounted for part of the success of quackery. Professor Bond attributed the major share of the blame to a fault of the "whole enlightened world," which the American exhibited to an eminent degree. "The whole energies of the people are directed to increase and develop talent, not to gain wisdom, to multiply the powers of action rather than to establish sound principles whereby to direct them," he charged.[22] The utilitarian bent of the American mind has been the subject of frequent comment. The age that Bond studied showed this feature to a preeminent degree.[23]

Bond's adverse appraisal, however, was one-sided. Sole attention to the negative aspects of this national characteristic obscures understanding of the dynamic milieu that was Young America and prejudices the adequate assessment of the remarkable attainments of the pre-Civil War era. "Thanks to the genius of American liberty

'Young America' is in the field—his watchword 'onward,' the counter-sign 'improvement,'" a contributor exulted in the *Dental Register*. Comments such as this more nearly represent the spirit of the age than the glum observations of Dr. Bond. The prominent dentist and organizer, J. H. McQuillen, writing at the close of the period, explained both the limitations of the epoch and its amazing accomplishments. "In a young country such as ours," he said in 1859, "seclusion of the highest energies and best intellects from the active world, and their exclusive devotion, in any numbers, to science, literature, and art, is impossible, on account of the demands made by the practical pursuits of life." [24]

A pragmatic concern with results certainly did preoccupy Americans during the years preceding the Civil War. The accomplishments of that age, nevertheless, were impressive. McQuillen went on to observe that the same vigor with which his countrymen had addressed themselves to the conquest of the wilderness had, in the preceding two decades, been directed also into fields previously neglected. "In this onward movement it is a source of felicitation that the dental profession has taken an active and prominent part," he continued. "Rousing its latent energies, and developing its resources, it . . . organized societies, established colleges and magazines, and sent representatives to Europe, that the *Old* World might enjoy the practical advantages of the *New*." [25]

"The *practical* advantages" were precisely the area of the achievements of Young America. American innovations of the day—the telegraph, the harvester, anesthesia, the sewing machine, and the rotary press, for example—were of the practical, rather than the theoretical order. [26] Such a bias underlay the contemporary advances in both medicine and dentistry. Abandoning an earlier preoccupation with systemic theories, medical practice in those days turned its attention to the clinical approach. A leading dentist of the time acutely described the new developments in medicine. "It is from the simple collection of facts, that the whole diagnosis of the medical profession is based," he noted. "But a short time ago, and it was not considered possible for the medical practitioner to distinguish pleurisy from pneumonia." Dental writers constantly urged their readers to adopt the same precept of careful observation of the facts prior to the enunciation of any theory. [27]

Progress in dentistry was likewise along utilitarian lines. The major dental discoveries of the time reflected this character. Reviewing the achievements under the aegis of the Mississippi Valley Association of Dental Surgeons in the two decades preceding the Civil War, a commentator in the *Dental Register* listed "cylinder or block fillings, continuous gum work, the swaged socket rim in plate work, the warm air blow-pipe, the best, and generally adopted method of using crystal gold, the most simple and convenient non-explosive spirit-lamp, the improved sherwood forceps," and so forth. A survey of the innovations wrought by all American dentists would have added a design for complete dentures that would remain in place without

Baltimore College of Dental Surgery

resort to springs, the dental use of vulcanized rubber, more durable and attractive denture teeth, and a mode of cavity preparation that permitted better retention of the filling.[28] The longer list, however, only serves to underscore the practical bias of dental advances during the pre-Civil War era.

The chaotic society of those decades encouraged a repudiation of traditional institutions, forms, and theories. Americans concentrated on solving immediate practical problems and scorned any relic of a former day that stood in the way of immediate practical solutions. This atmosphere of freedom made possible the specialization of dentistry. This factor was recognized as the reason for much of its spectacular progress. Indeed, Elisha Townsend, an outstanding dentist of the late forties and fifties, claimed for his profession priority in exploiting the virtues of specialization. "We may fairly claim something more than the faithful and successful husbandry of our own field of scientific truth; we have developed and demonstrated the method and system by which general medicine is yet to be improved," Townsend declared. "After our plan of individualizing one distinct branch of the remedial art, and making all the others justly subsidiary and subordinate to it, medicine will ere long be divided into surgery, therapeutics, and obstetrics, at least." [29]

At the same time, the heyday of Young America did not prevent the development of professional organization. Paradoxically, this age of individualism and libertarianism and antagonism to state intervention was a prolific period for the formation of societies seeking sundry objectives. "In all great movements, either in religion, politics, science, or benevolence, the American character and popular genius of all our institutions immediately direct us to lay hold of the great principle of voluntary association," Chapin Harris declaimed in 1843. Examples of enduring organizations may be found in all of the fields Harris mentioned. As a matter of fact, the revolution in transport and communications encouraged these movements by reducing the barriers to travel and the exchange of information.[30] Nor was it a problem peculiar to dentistry that dictated that the American Society of Dental Surgeons should die an early death. Several dental organizations founded during this epoch flourished long after the Civil War. The reasons for the demise of the American Society of Dental Surgeons must be sought in the internal history of the Society itself.

Chapter III   POLICIES OF THE AMERICAN SOCIETY

THE MEMBERS of the American Society strove to carry forward the program set down by the founders. The policies adopted by this pioneer association during its first years often displayed attitudes and aspirations remarkably like those of its twentieth-century successor. It might be argued that this characteristic was a fault in the fledgling organization, its views were too advanced for the primitive conditions of the time. By setting its standards too high, the American Society of Dental Surgeons not only sealed its own failure, but its rigorous demands may have alienated popular and professional support that might have aided the pioneer organizers in elevating the status of dentistry. At the same time, the Society presumed too much in setting itself up as the arbiter of the profession. Here its high standards created cleavages that hampered attainment of the Society's goals. Furthermore, some of the perennial problems of professionalism proved to be beyond the wisdom and the knowledge of the members of the Society. In this way, too, the grand aspirations of the first national dental association contributed to its ultimate failure.

The founders of organized dentistry assumed an active role in the field of education. Writing in 1839, before any of the institutions, save the *Journal,* had been launched, Solyman Brown warned, "Let no one be deceived into a belief, that, in a few weeks or months, he can become master of the art." In a later issue, Chapin Harris echoed the caveat. He also noted that many of the greatest contributors to dental advancement, Hudson, Gardette, Hayden, Greenwood, Parmly, Baker, Newton, Koecker, Harrington, Waite, and Cartwright, did not have medical diplomas. This, he explained, was not the point. "What I mean to say is," he concluded, "that no man is competent to practice dental surgery, without first being properly instructed in it." [1]

At the outset, as Harris's discourse indicated, it was necessary to accommodate a situation where the vast majority of practitioners, respectable or otherwise, had alike acquired their training in unregulated fashion. The American Society of Dental Surgeons sought to effect a change in this situation. It consistently favored the establishment of special schools for the education of dentists. In 1848, C. O. Cone delivered a "Report on Practical Dentistry" before the American Society. With considerable exaggeration, Cone claimed that "no young man would be received at scarcely any point of our country, as a dentist, who cannot produce his testimonials from some established dental institution." He acknowledged that sole credit for this development did not belong to the Society. "But the Society has been a powerful auxiliary to this end, by becoming the patron to the dental colleges; since it extended the demand for instruction by the necessities it imposed on members and candidates," Cone continued. "This is one of the peculiar provinces of the association, and its powers in this respect are ample, and should be most rigorously, faithfully and perseveringly executed." In 1849, when the alumni of the Baltimore College of Dental Surgery met to organize a society, Joseph H. Foster remarked upon the importance of collegiate training to a dentist opening a new practice. The trend toward respect for a college diploma represented, in Foster's eyes, "the gradual yet forcible reaction which is progressing in the popular mind." [2]

By the end of the forties, there were still only two "regularly chartered" dental schools in the country. While collegiate dental education had made a fine beginning, only a continuance of preceptorial training could permit the profession to expand at the rate required by the increasing demand for dental services. For this reason, the Society rejected Chapin Harris's move in 1845 to extend greater favoritism to the graduates of dental colleges. Even so, the preferential treatment accorded institutionally trained applicants for membership undoubtedly generated some antagonism toward the Society and its objectives. Perhaps the commitment of the American Society of Dental Surgeons to collegiate training for the profession was premature.

The education of the practicing dentist was a major objective of the Society's patronage of dental journalism. At the second annual meeting, the American Society decided to "establish a periodical as the organ of its opinions on subjects of dental theory and practice, and for the purpose of advancing the interests of the science and the profession." The upshot of this resolution was that the Society assumed control of *The American Journal of Dental Science*. Through the balance of the first series of the *Journal*, until 1850, the Society maintained the publication. Under the aegis of the Society, the *Journal* expanded to reproduce standard works of dental literature not otherwise available to the profession.[3]

The chief function of the *Journal* was the dissemination of scientific knowledge among the profession. Still, there was another facet of dental journalism that likewise attracted the support of the American Society of Dental Surgeons. Publicizing the true principles of dental practice served to eliminate quackery. In this aspect of dental journalism, the lay public had a direct interest. An early supporter of the *Dental Register of the West* urged the importance of dental periodicals in teaching the proper principles of dental health and argued that attention to this, the preventive, side of dentistry would certainly command the "hearty co-operation" of the public.[4]

The American Society of Dental Surgeons early turned to this aspect of its duties. "The people must be enlightened on the subject of their physical organization, and the best modes of avoiding disease," Solyman Brown wrote in 1840, as he announced the program of the American Society. He reported "a system of popular Essays . . . in progress of active preparation . . . intended to instruct, not so much the profession as the community at large." It appears that the mode of distributing these tracts was not settled at the first meeting of the Society. In the January, 1841, issue of the *Journal*, Solyman Brown announced that several of the tracts were then available "for private distribution . . . at the rate of two dollars per hundred previously to the meeting of the Society . . . when a tariff of charges will probably be established."[5]

In after years, complaints were heard that these tracts had been used for personal, rather than professional advantage. A sturdy supporter of this activity lamented "that this mode of disseminating correct information among the 'sovereign people' should have declined, . . . for whatever might result to individual benefit in this particular, must also redound to the good of the great whole." Although the program of popular tracts on dental health temporarily languished, the Society maintained its interest in preventive dentistry. At the second annual meeting, L. S. Parmly addressed the assembly on preventive measures. *The American Journal of Dental Science* editorially endorsed his scheme: "We hope, therefore, that more attention than has hitherto been bestowed, will be given to the prevention of disease in these organs, and that every dental surgeon will not only urge its importance upon his patients, and more especially upon the heads of families in which he practices, but will also supply them with the means recommended by Dr. Parmly, for its accomplishment." These two elements, public education and preventive dentistry, remained prominent features of the Society's policy.[6]

Through the next few years after Parmly's harangue in 1841, the Society's attention was diverted to other matters. In 1845, however, it reaffirmed its concern with public education. The spring meeting, at Baltimore in 1850, again reverted to the problem of public instruction in the principles of dental health. S. P. Hullihen, the noted oral surgeon, was appointed a committee of one to prepare an address for the public. His commission was confirmed at the meeting held at Saratoga Springs later that same year. At that time, too, the project inaugurated in 1845, "the dissemination of practical precepts on the teeth," was revived. A new committee was appointed with instructions to prepare the aphorisms and submit them to the publishing committee of the Society immediately. A considerable portion of the Philadelphia meeting of 1851 was devoted to revising and approving the labors of the Committee on Aphorisms. The Saratoga Springs meeting of 1850, "deeming the preservation of the health of the dental organism of the highest importance," publicly avowed its support of the system of hygiene recommended by L. S. Parmly.[7]

In the field of professional and public education, the American Society of Dental Surgeons showed an advanced understanding of the needs of the times, but it lacked the numbers and the resources to give much of an impact to its views in this department. In other areas of professional activity, the problems themselves proved baffling.

Article One of the constitution had proclaimed the Society's intention "to advance the science by free communication and interchange of sentiments." The membership constantly protested its devotion to this principle. Each year the Society commissioned an annual address and a series of dissertations on some subjects connected with the profession. The bias of the Society's interest lay in the direction of the discussion of practical subjects. C. O. Cone, in 1848, said that "the oral discussion of practical subjects . . . will be attended with most positive benefits to members of the Society." He explained, "It will present . . . information which would never find its way into the text books or literature of the profession." Although the distractions of Society affairs often turned the meetings away from these strictly technical concerns, the merit of the principle and the benefits of such exchanges can hardly be denied. Other societies, founded after the inception of the American Society, devoted themselves exclusively to this form of activity.[8]

The American Society of Dental Surgeons pioneered in an effort to develop statistical information on dental diseases, injuries, operations, and materials. C. O. Cone advanced the initial proposal at the New York meeting in 1846. Cone obtained the appointment of a committee to draw up a tabular sheet "to be used by its members to make an annual report to the Society of all previous failures, in either surgical or mechanical dentistry, that may come under their treatment, together with what, in their judgment, they considered the cause of such failures." Under Cone's urging, the Society declared the preparation and submission to be the duty of each member of the Society. At the next meeting, a plan of the sheet was submitted. It was referred back to the committee for revision and distribution. Again, in 1848, Cone presented the form on which the tabulation was to be kept. On this occasion, the Society directed him to have copies printed and to distribute them among the membership.[9]

After this auspicious beginning, the scheme seems to have collapsed. In the final years of the Society, the affair of the tabular sheets degenerated into an unhappy wrangle between the Society and Chapin A. Harris over the payment of the bill for printing the sheets.[10]

Cone's scheme, however, was not entirely without results. He envisioned the appointment of a committee "to condense such statistics, and publish the same with the doings of the Society." At the session of 1847, this proposition eventuated in the appointment of a Committee on Practical Dentistry. The duties of the Committee involved more than a mere compilation of the members' reports. They were also charged with the preparation of "an annual report to the Society of the improvements effected in this country in the management of disease coming within the scope of the dental practitioner, and the condition and progress of dental knowledge in America during the year of their service. . . . This is an important move on the part of the Society, and cannot be otherwise than productive of much good," the *Dental Intelligencer* observed.[11]

The prescience of the *Intelligencer* proved sound. In the first year, the policy produced C. O. Cone's "Report on Practical Dentistry," an excellent summary of the development and contemporary status of American dentistry. Not the least of the interesting features of Cone's report was his tentative analysis of the various phases of dental science and art. Cone suggested that the Society "appoint distinct committees . . . upon all the more important subjects connected with dental practice" to take advantage of the benefits of specialization. He proposed a committee on "dental and surgical instruments, as employed or relating to the practice of the dental surgeon." Another group, Cone thought, should attend to problems of "dental practice, relating to such operations as are demanded by the living dental organs." He allotted to another committee the domain of mechanical dentistry with instructions to note and suggest improvements. He recommended a committee to examine and report on the subject of dental physiology and pathology. The final group contemplated in

Cone's plan would survey the status of dental education.[12] This represents the earliest attempt to subdivide the field of dental science and art for the purpose of evaluating the contemporary situation.

In addition to advancing dental science in its own activities, the American Society of Dental Surgeons functioned as a patron of dental science. The original constitution and by-laws authorized the payment of premiums in recognition of substantial contributions to dentistry. The Society used these provisions to reward and encourage innovations. At the New York meeting of 1845, for example, Chapin Harris proposed "that Dr. Robert Arthur have his dues remitted, and that he be furnished with the Journal for the term of seven years from the time his membership commenced," in recognition of his services in translating a rare and valuable dental treatise from the French.[13]

The aftermath of the actions honoring another dentist at the same session revealed the difficulties into which the policy might lead. John Allen of Cincinnati "read an essay and exhibited an apparatus for restoring the shape of the face, lost from any cause." Allen's device was evidently impressive and successful, for the Society promptly accorded him high recognition. The meeting officially declared that Allen's invention should be regarded as important. The Society also awarded him a medal and five bound and subscribed volumes of the *Journal*. In the following year, Allen was further honored by elevation to a vice-presidency of the Society. In 1847, however, the picture changed. Grave charges were brought against Dr. Allen. A committee investigated the matter and submitted a report and recommendations. The committee found that "after having freely offered the benefits of his invention to every member of the Society, to be used gratuitously . . . without their knowledge he had secured a patent therefor . . . and saw fit . . . to make an attempt to exact . . . a certain percentage for the privilege of using it." The report concluded, "Your committee deem his conduct highly reprehensible." The members of the Society present at the meeting unanimously resolved, "That the censure of the Society be passed upon Dr. Allen, for having acted in a manner derogatory to his character as a professional gentleman, and attended with consequences highly detrimental to the Society of which he is a member." [14]

All of this action against Allen was taken in his absence. He sub-

sequently charged, "by this precedent, any member, through personal envy, or private pique, may be hurled unceremoniously from
his station, however exalted." No one had offered a defense of Allen's
actions at the 1847 meeting. "One side of the question only is heard,"
the aggrieved dentist complained.[15]

The Allen affair served to introduce the problem of patent rights,
a question that was to prove consistently troublesome over many
years. The same session that condemned John Allen adopted a long
resolution opposing patents and the retention of professional secrets.[16] The subsequent efforts of the Society to delineate a policy in
this matter called forth considerable ingenuity, but failed to produce
a satisfactory solution.

The Saratoga Springs meeting of 1848 encountered the problem
in a slightly different aspect. Asa Hill, one of the most respected
members of the Society, was a collaborator in developing a gutta
percha compound called "Hill's Stopping." During a discussion of
matters of practice, Hill rose to address the assembly. "But it appeared very soon that instead of wishing to enlighten his brethren
in regard to the compound, he only wished to bring to notice its
virtues," an observer reported. "He was asked whether he intended
to give to the society or to the world, his receipt." Hill felt himself
bound to his partner and hence was unable to do so. When this was
made evident to the meeting, the question was then raised, whether
it was proper for the Society, as such, to listen to his mere recommendations of his secret compound. The sentiment of the meeting
ran against this position, so Hill reserved his remarks until after the
adjournment of the session.

The Hill episode precipitated another consideration of the patent
question. According to the reports, "it was contended by several
members, that while they did not wish or intend to advocate either
secrets or patent rights, as connected with direct and actual practice
of dental surgery, they deemed the resolutions [provoked by the
Allen case] quite too general in their scope." In consequence of their
inability to agree upon satisfactory amendments to the policy, the
members decided to repeal the standing resolutions entirely. An unsympathetic observer noted that this action revealed inconsistency
on the part of the Society. The repeal amounted to "permitting a
course of conduct which the report of the proceedings indirectly

censures," the editor of the *Dental Recorder* commented. The Society
had refused to hear Hill's praise of his stopping, then, in the next
breath, it rescinded its opposition to patents and secret remedies.[17]

Around 1850, another patent controversy arose. This time the object in question was an improved forceps devised and patented by
S. P. Hullihen, probably the outstanding oral surgeon of his time.
Hullihen became involved in an infringement quarrel with a dentist
who patented an improvement on the basic instrument. A third party
added another improvement and gave it to the profession "in the
hopes thereby to save [his] professional friends the mortification of
using a patented instrument."[18]

The West Point meeting of 1853 reverted again to the problem
of how to reward individual innovations and still to prevent a retrogression to the conditions of secrecy and private nostrums that had
vexed the early days of the profession. Consideration of a revision of
the constitution and by-laws furnished the occasion of this debate.
J. D. White, who, through his position as an editor of the *Dental
News Letter,* was connected with a dental manufacturer, tried to
distinguish between devices like Allen's and products like Hill's.
White pointed out that, even if products such as teeth (or chemical
compounds like Hill's) were unprotected by patents, practicing dentists would still resort to the manufacturer's product because of the
superior facilities the manufacturer enjoyed. Such a distinction between the operative and mechanical variety of dental innovations
had been suggested earlier, by Eleazar Parmly among others. The
concepts involved still needed clarification and refinement. A definitive stand on the patent question could not yet be reached. The
conclusion of the debate brought almost unanimous endorsement of
an anti-patent article as strong as that of 1847. Its prohibition applied
to all the varieties of innovation about which the controversy had
raged. The new Article Thirteen of the by-laws read: "Any dentist
who shall procure a patent for a remedy or instrument of Dental Surgery, or who deals in patent remedies, shall be disqualified for membership."[19]

Significantly, the prohibition of patents was included under the
general rubric, "Dental Ethics," still another field in which the American Society of Dental Surgeons was forced to pioneer. The Society
claimed jurisdiction over the conduct of its members from the outset.

Article Seven of the constitution of 1840 provided: "Any member of the Society may be expelled for immoral conduct, malpractice in business or other sufficient cause, on motion of one member, seconded by another at any regular meeting of the society in which case a majority of three-fourths of the members present shall be required." For a time, the Society was content to operate under this vague standard. The resulting justice, however, was rather summarily administered. In 1845, for example, "a list of charges was brought by William G. Lord against J. O. Baldwin, of Newark, N. J., and said Baldwin was voted to be immediately expelled from the Society." Nor was this the end of the matter. The meeting directed that the action be published in the *Forcep*, and authorized Lord to publish the actions in the newspapers of Newark. There is nothing in the proceedings to indicate that Baldwin was apprised of the charges against him or that he or anyone else was heard on his behalf.[20]

Up to this time, the Society had limited itself to pronouncements on specific cases. In 1846, however, Amos Westcott proposed a committee to prepare a code of ethics by which the Society might be regulated in many particulars not specified in the constitution and by-laws. An editor of *The American Journal of Dental Science* dwelt at length on Westcott's proposal in a review of the 1846 meeting. "The history of almost every voluntary association proves that new and unexpected exigencies are constantly occurring, calling for some revision or amendment of its constitution or by-laws," the commentator averred. "We venture to assert [that] in nine out of ten [such cases], the exigency could have been provided for in a judicious code of ethics." Cone in his 1848 "Report," outlined the relationships a proper code should regulate. A dentist needed guidance, Cone declared, on his duties to his patients, on the duties of patients toward the dentist, on his duties toward other dentists, and particularly to members of the Society. Consideration should also be given, Cone thought, to "the obligations of the profession to the public, and the public to them." Subsequent revisions of the Society's organic law faithfully contained provisions on dental ethics, but specific questions, commonly relating either to patents or to the domain of advertising continued to vex the Society.[21]

John Allen ran afoul of the Society in 1847 not alone because he had patented his facial restorative device. The investigating committee reported that Allen had "made such use of the fact of a gold medal having been presented to him by this society, as the society do not contemplate in making such awards, and cannot approve or sanction." From the beginning the Society had sought to strike a balance between conferring prestige upon its members and granting them a distinction that they might exploit for individual advantage. Allen apparently abused the honor accorded him by the Society.[22]

At the suggestion of Amos Westcott, the session of 1845 adopted a resolution condemning resort to "letters of recommendation from divines, doctors of medicine, and, in short, all who are not well acquainted with dental practice." An editorial in the *Intelligencer* backed this proposal. "A moment's reflection ought to convince every one that such letters are worth nothing at all," the argument began. "It always seemed to us, whenever we saw them, as an implied acknowledgement of inferiority. We have seldom, if ever, known a man of genuine professional worth or eminent abilities, resort to such undignified means to obtain business."[23]

The proceedings continued to be enlivened by problems of professional ethics. At West Point in 1853, for example, "Dr. E. J. Dunning drew the attention of the society to a fulsome and offensive advertisement of one of its members." The broadside provoked the adoption of a strong resolution condemning "any member of this society who shall extol his own superior merits over a fellow practitioner in the public prints, or employs means of advertisement which may be regarded by the society as lowering the dignity of the profession, or compromising its character." An offender, the Society directed, should be impeached, suspended, or expelled. On the following day, Thomas Palmer was suspended from membership under the terms of the resolution. Almost as an afterthought, the meeting resolved "that Dr. Palmer be notified of the action of the society, and a copy of the law by which he was suspended transmitted to him."[24]

Affairs of this sort abound in the annals of the American Society of Dental Surgeons. The actions of the association were often abrupt and high-handed. All too seldom did the Society consider the rights of an alleged delinquent. Lying behind all of this there was an evident priority in the minds of the membership. Their concern, as John C. McCabe expressed it in 1843, was to establish "a band of union between worthy professors of our art, . . . designed to protect the gentleman, and the scientific practitioner, from the odium that should ever attach to the charlatan." In retrospect, the appraisal of the policies of the Society by Elisha Townsend and Joseph Foster seems remarkably accurate and succinct: "All the necessities of fraternization were acknowledged, and all [the Society's] general usefulness was appreciated, but the main interest of the emergency was the creation of a conventional tribunal, with its incident authority, to assume the responsibilities of the profession, and to establish and vindicate its corporate character." [25] It is because the leading members of the Society held this view of its functions that the evolution of its membership policies is of paramount importance in understanding the successes and failures of the first national dental association.

With neither the objective recognition of statutory sanctions, nor a traditionally recognized standard of training, the American Society of Dental Surgeons undertook single-handed "to give character and respectability to the profession by establishing a line of distinction between the truly meritorious and skillful, and such as riot in the ill gotten fruit of unblushing impudence and empiricism." This statement of objectives reflects the crusading fervor with which the founders approached their task. Thoroughly convinced of their own rectitude, they were equally sure that they truly represented the wishes of "all respectable and well informed Dental Surgeons." The organizers were so confident of their ground that they admitted to charter membership many dentists who were not present at that first meeting. One class thus enrolled were those unable to attend who had indicated their support of the movement by sending proxies or letters endorsing the project. The inclusion of these men seems legitimate enough, but the founders went beyond this category. They listed as charter members all of their colleagues who had been invited to participate in the Society whether their sympathies were known or not. One of the founders later declared that the principle for determining charter membership was even broader: "Each person present," he recalled, "was permitted to name such other gentlemen as

he considered would be a desirable acquisition, and they were enrolled, leaving it optional with them to continue their connection
afterwards." [26]

At one stroke the founders created for themselves an insoluble
difficulty. By their own definition, membership in the Society was to
be the mark of respectability and true skill. Implicitly, nonmembers
were "such as riot in the ill gotten fruit of unblushing impudence
and empiricism." But what if an undeniably respectable and skillful
practitioner refused to endorse the formation of the Society? The
founders were not long in encountering just this embarrassment. E.
B. Gardette of Philadelphia bore one of the most respected names
in American dentistry. He was "present by letter" at the foundation
of the Society. When the organization was completed, Gardette was
elected third vice-president for the ensuing year. He acknowledged
notice of this honor, but, as he later stated, deferred his decision until
he received extracts of the minutes of the meeting. Gardette then
forwarded his resignation, or "non-acceptance" to Chapin Harris,
who was corresponding secretary of the Society. "I had hoped," Gardette wrote, "that the character of my reply by letter to you in June
last, as well as my views previously expressed in conversation at my
house, would have led you to conclude that a society formed as this
has been could never receive my sanction, much less induce me to
accept a prominent post in it." Deeply aggrieved, Harris spread the
correspondence, with editorial comment, upon the pages of *The
American Journal of Dental Science*.[27]

Solyman Brown in New York had meanwhile encountered a similar
reaction on the part of John Trenor, M.D. Trenor had been recorded
as "present by invitation" and entered an objection. Brown's obliging
response was published under the caption "Important Announcement." "This is to inform our numerous readers and all whom it may
concern, agreeably with Doctor Trenor's request, that I am as happy
to state, as he possibly can be to have it known, that he was not personally present on that occasion." [28]

The tone of personal grievance exhibited by both Harris and
Brown in the face of the rebuffs by Gardette and Trenor foreshadowed yet another source of difficulty for the Society. It was already
evident that it could not hope, as Brown put it, "to embody all regular
and worthy dental practitioners." In their anxiety to establish and

maintain high standards of membership, there was some danger that the Society would come to represent a mere clique founded on personalities.

Unlike Gardette and Trenor, many dentists were offended because they had been omitted from the first enrollment in the American Society of Dental Surgeons. Solyman Brown hastened to inform this element that many "whose merits were not known to the individuals of the first convention . . . were providing themselves with the proper credentials for making known to the Executive Committee their just claims to fellowship." "Even without this precaution on their part," Brown continued reassuringly, "many will be elected at the next annual meeting who were forgotten, overlooked or unknown, at the last."[29]

It is plain that the members of the Society had designated themselves as the arbiters of the profession. Undismayed by nearly a decade of controversy, one of the founders, Joseph H. Foster, in 1849, described what must have been the dedication the founders brought to their self-imposed task. "That wisdom and knowledge derived from a deep and earnest contemplation of the subject, must dictate the imperative necessity of acting as public monitors—of sacrificing all feelings of individual love and affection . . . upon the altar of professional duty," he declared. "Let us then do our duty, regardful only of the interests, safety and protection of the millions who are so much dependent upon our professional good offices . . . fixed and unalterable in a determination to do effective service in the cause of humanity."[30] The evolution of the membership policy of the Society exemplifies this attitude to the full.

According to the constitution of 1840, the Executive Committee proposed new members at the annual meetings. The members then present balloted, two thirds being required for election. Applicants for membership were directed to establish by one or more of its members that they were well informed in the theory and practice of dental surgery, and possessed of an unexceptionable moral character. An applicant without acquaintance among the members of the Society might submit to an examination and present samples of his operations.[31] Practically, entry into the select circle was limited to those known personally to the membership.

The Society's promoters understood the responsibilities they had assumed. Eleazar Parmly warned his colleagues to exercise the utmost caution and diligence in assessing candidates for membership. At Boston in 1842, special committees were named to sit in Baltimore, New York, Philadelphia, and Boston to consider candidates' qualifications. In the following year, another committee undertook a review of the system with instructions to provide and recommend a plan for guarding the society from imposition in the admission of members.[32]

As a result of the findings of the committee and a sharp challenge from J. H. Foster, the 1844 meeting "barred a little more strongly the avenues of entrance to membership." From this date, written application had to be accompanied by the recommendation of at least three members of the Society. Access to the Society was being further restricted. At the sixth annual meeting in 1845, another constitutional revision was undertaken. At the same time, the session "declined, by resolution, admitting any members during the present meeting." [33]

At the New York meeting of 1846, the members adopted a series of amendments that made membership even more difficult to attain. All candidates, whether graduates of a dental college or not, were now placed on the same footing. The Executive Committee investigated all applicants. Members endorsing candidates now had to vouch for moral character as well as professional qualifications. A period of three years' practice was added to the requirement of two years' training in a college or the office of a preceptor. The new requirements demanded submission of applications six months before the regular annual meeting. At the session itself, balloting took place as before, but opposition by as few as one sixth of the members present constituted an effective bar to admission. The meeting that adopted these new provisions decided to allow all candidates the opportunity of withdrawing their applications. As a result, only one member was added to the rolls in the two years 1845 and 1846.[34]

The early membership policy of the American Society of Dental Surgeons was at first too lax and then too severe. Quite apart from other factors that were operating at the same time, the membership policy militated against the long duration of this pioneer organization. The policy was too lax, especially at the outset, when, as one of the founders later recalled, "a feeling of congratulation, of honor-

able pride, that we had assembled for the noble purpose of giving
character to the profession, an object worthy the high ambition of
its votaries—kindled in our hearts a generous, a charitable, but mistaken feeling of philanthropy, which induced us to extend the right
hand of fellowship to all whom we thought had claims to be considered reputable members of the profession." Spurned on the one
hand by such luminaries as Gardette and Trenor, and scandalized by
disagreement among the members on supposed fundamentals on the
other, the Society swung to the opposite extreme. It sought to follow
the advice of the father of the association, Horace H. Hayden. Hayden had warned: "Gentlemen, if you would make your society
respectable, and would have it esteemed so by the world, do not be
hasty in electing your members, but be careful and judicious in
selecting those whom you would admit into your ranks." [35]

Under the impulse of this injunction, the conditions of membership were made steadily more severe. Joseph Foster, a prominent
figure in the Society throughout its history, argued, "The more exclusive such an association—the more fixed and peremptory in its restrictions—the more exacting in its requisitions as to attainments and
qualifications of its members, the greater will be the desire and the
ambition of all good men and true to fit and prepare themselves to
unite with it." [36] Undoubtedly this consideration did operate upon
the dentists of the day. At the same time, however, the bias of the
additional qualifications tended to favor the personal acquaintances
of the members—and the graduates of the Baltimore College, which
until 1845 was the only regularly chartered dental school, and which,
in any case, was directed by the same group that had organized the
American Society. The requirements of preceptorial training under
men known to the members, and the location of the examining committees in population centers where the Society was already well-
represented carried further the tendency toward making entrance
into the Society a matter of personal connections.

Obviously, the consequence of this policy was to restrict the base
of membership too narrowly. The preponderance of number and
influence among the membership was concentrated on the eastern
seaboard. When the leading members fell out among themselves,
even the profession on the east coast came to be represented only in
a limited way. The long neglect of the West on the part of the Soci-

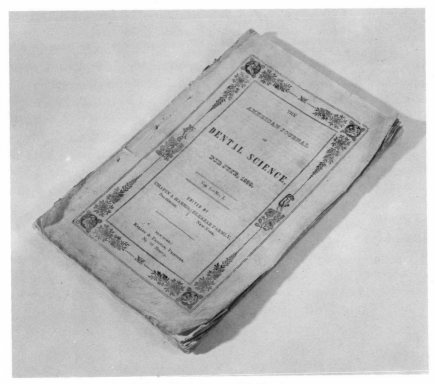

The American Journal of Dental Science, Vol. I, No. 1

ety, plus the flourishing character of organized dentistry beyond the Alleghenies, limited the influence of this purportedly national organization.

The very exclusiveness the Society came to assume handicapped its leadership of the profession, especially as the number of dentists increased and dental colleges and associations multiplied. The total membership at any one time never exceeded one hundred and fifty. Attendance at the annual meetings seldom, if ever, exceeded one fifth of that number. During the 1840's, the size of the profession more than doubled.[37] Although its limited numbers and its failure to expand prevented the American Society of Dental Surgeons from adequately representing the profession, other factors contributed to its failure to endure. Avowedly, the objects of the Society were "to promote union and harmony among all respectable and well informed Dental Surgeons" and "to advance the science by free communication and interchange of sentiments . . . between members of the Society," as well as to establish a line of distinction between legitimate operators and quacks. When the Society adopted a test by which to distinguish the truly meritorious and skillful from impostors, its selection proved unfortunate. In seeking to enforce its definition of a legitimate practitioner, the Society forgot its other objects. The line of distinction it chose and the manner in which it sought to impose it split the Society itself. The controversy so distracted the Society from its objects that union and harmony and the advancement of the science through free communication and interchange of sentiments took place largely outside the confines of the Society. As a consequence, it failed to profit from the very developments it had set in train. Progress in dentistry during the forties and fifties left the Society far behind.

The controversy that contributed most to the demise of the American Society of Dental Surgeons was the famous Amalgam War. In grappling with the perplexities of that problem, the Society showed fully the faults of its virtues.

Chapter IV   THE AMALGAM WAR

THERE IS SOMETHING of the inevitability of classic tragedy about the Amalgam War and its contribution to the unhappy fate of the first national dental association. The participants all acted decisively and honestly in accordance with their convictions. All the conditions conspired to carry the affair through its successive stages to its unsatisfactory conclusion.

It might be said that the Amalgam War began when the Crawcours arrived in New York. There seems little doubt that Parmly, Brown, and their fellows organized the Society of Surgeon Dentists at least in part to fight the incursions the Crawcours and their amalgam were making into the practices of the legitimate dentists of the city. This first known dental society succeeded in driving the Crawcours out of the country, but amalgam continued in use. "Our memories are still fresh with the recollection of those splendid hum-bugs, the Messrs. Crawcour," fumed Solyman Brown in 1839, as he noted that the "execrable material" was still in use. Amalgam was easier to manipulate than the other common filling materials of the day. Consequently, it appealed to the less well-trained operators. This factor led one survivor of the controversy to conclude that the filling "was almost entirely in the hands of a set of itinerating quacks, who knew not how to use aright this or any other substance for filling teeth."

67

Because of this association with poorly qualified operators, failures of amalgam plugs were frequent. Failures, too, were more readily noticed and more easily remembered than successful operations. The identification of the use of amalgam with quackery came naturally.[1]

At its second annual meeting, the American Society of Dental Surgeons first explicitly confronted the amalgam question. Joseph H. Foster propounded a question to the assembled savants. He admitted later, "I little dreamed that I had inadvertently thrown a firebrand, which would ultimately cause such an extensive conflagration." Foster asked if there were cases where teeth could be filled with materials other than gold and preserved long enough to compensate for the operation. The query was certainly innocent-seeming; yet it set off the Amalgam War.[2]

The American Society of Dental Surgeons was entirely unprepared to give a satisfactory answer to Foster's question. What made the Society's attempt to solve the problem disastrous was that it did not recognize that it was unprepared. Since, by the most optimistic estimate, it never enrolled more than one-tenth of the profession, it clearly lacked the numbers and prestige to impose its answer on the profession. At the same time, the Society lacked the scientific method and the scientific knowledge to devise an authoritative answer to Foster's question. Indeed, its faulty scientific knowledge and method combined to produce an answer that was incorrect.

The dental profession of the 1840's was probably not greatly different from a similar specialized group in any other age. There were those who considered that the ultimate in craft and wisdom had been attained. Such was the opinion of John C. McCabe, a pillar of dentistry in Virginia. In a paper read before his peers, McCabe declared,

> Do not think that it is my design to *lecture* the profession upon any one subject in the range of our science *proper;* older and abler hands have opened to our eyes the volume of their experience, enriched by the successive offerings of successive pilgrims, in the pursuit of professional knowledge, until the cry of "Eureka" has resounded from one chamber of the temple to all the rest. The harvest, which at one period seemed to be whitening beneath the sun untouched, has been gathered by the early reapers; and it would seem, now, we are compelled to pause, for there seems to be scarcely a grain left to the late gleaners in the field.

While few thoughtful dentists were ready to agree wholeheartedly with McCabe's analysis, there were many who considered the existing status of the science and the art entirely satisfactory.[3] There was an understandable tendency for these self-satisfied members of the profession to "put up the cry of 'Quackery' upon the introduction of anything new in mechanics or an improved remedy in disease," as a contributor to the *Dental Recorder* complained. Indeed, James Taylor, a moderate but forward-looking leader of western dentistry, proudly congratulated his colleagues upon their freedom from the distractions of innovation that harassed other departments of the healing arts. As he pointed out, "No Homeopathic dose will suit in the extraction of a tooth—no Hydropathic ablution can insert a set of teeth." [4]

Less obvious than the normally conservative temper of the profession, but equally significant in the history of the Amalgam War, was the influence of current scientific method. The dominant temper of the time favored empirical observation. In medicine, speculation was falling out of favor before the advance to prominence of clinical procedures. General principles took their validity from their alleged origins in observed facts. "All correct practice is based on correct theory, and correct theory is only attained by close observation and experience," a dental spokesman explained. Among dentists who considered such matters, there was substantial agreement upon the virtues of an empirical approach. "Experience aided by observation and comparison, has been the main object in establishing facts which have rendered the utility of dental surgery such as to deserve the gratitude of mankind, and elevate it to the dignity of a respectable, learned and responsible profession," a prominent dentist declared.[5]

For many who paid lip-service to the principles of observation and experience, the virtues of this method were obvious and simple of attainment. Others, more thoughtful or more cautious, were well aware of the limitations of a naive empiricism. "It is a principle of the human mind, to seek and determine a cause for every circumstance or fact as they may frequently occur, or be presented to human observation; and it is equally true, that the cause so determined is more frequently wrong than right," wrote one of the more perceptive critics of the day. Careful dentists warned against excesses of independent, "unassisted genius," relying on "sudden irradiations of intelligence." "To begin aright we must avail ourselves of the observation and experience of those who have preceded us in investigations," argued another commentator. "We must, however, carefully sift their *facts* from their *opinions*, and toil and delve after facts for ourselves," he warned, "lest we be led into erroneous views and practices by the errors of others, upon whose dictation we have too implicitly relied." [6]

To overcome the weaknesses inherent in individual research and observation, C. O. Cone of Baltimore made a proposal that members of the American Society of Dental Surgeons maintain statistical records of their cases. He presented an elaborate table on which all supposedly significant factors in a case could be recorded. Citing the august authority of Lord Bacon himself, Cone explained the need for keeping written accounts of their observations:

> Unless we make a written history of the case, we gather and recollect only such facts of the case in question, as may coincide with the impressions or prejudices; and, moreover, we are unable from memory alone to make that careful and close analysis of the different features which a case or cases present to establish scientific and correct conclusions. Hence it is that many false facts are established and considered invulnerable, to the exclusion of more simple and unostentatious truths. [7]

Cone and others perceived the pitfalls in a too-facile empiricism, but, though they warned of the dangers, they themselves fell victim to those very errors. In recommending his system for tabular collection of statistics by the entire membership of the American Society, Cone revealed that he had succumbed to an over-assurance that was as dangerous as the self-satisfaction displayed by the conservative element. He argued that his method appeared to be peculiarly adapted to the practice of the profession. Dentistry, he explained, was more definite in its practice, "more plainly presented to the senses," than any other department of medicine. He concluded that almost all the common phenomena of dental practice could be accurately described by "comparison with some familiar color or hue, or explained by some known fluid or solid, and measured by weight and capacity." [8]

This was a vain delusion that more than a generation had to labor to correct. It was particularly a handicap in connection with the amalgam problem. The descriptive terms Cone proposed were not precise enough for clear communication—and even this "system" failed of adoption. Then and thereafter for years to come, the dental

profession lacked an agreed nomenclature and system of classification that would permit an adequate exchange of information. At the
same time, the loose prevailing terminology tended to conceal these
faults.[9]

Many dentists strove to keep abreast of the latest scientific discoveries, especially in medicine. The respect with which dental practitioners received the opinions of medical authority was particularly
unfortunate in connection with the amalgam controversy. In the first
place, these were years of considerable change in medical practice.
Not only was there a veritable rash of curative sects challenging the
regular physician, but European developments brought heavy criticism to bear on the regular modes of practice, particularly current
American therapeutics. "If the whole materia medica, as now used,
could be sunk to the bottom of the sea," remarked Oliver Wendell
Holmes, "it would be all the better for mankind—and all the worse
for the fishes."

Not the least of the practices thus brought under attack was the
popular universal remedy, calomel, mercurous chloride. There was
no question but that calomel was abused. The medical historian,
Richard H. Shryock, has concluded that the abuse of this remedy
"was the cause . . . of almost as much promiscuous poisoning as was
ever credited to secret nostrums." For dentistry, however, the difficulty arose because the justifiable criticism of the medical uses of
mercurial preparations was extended by analogy to apply to the
various amalgams of which mercury was a constituent. Yet it is now
known that mercury, in the form in which it appears in amalgam,
is not absorbed into the body system.[10]

All in all, the contemporary situation in American medicine was
such as to betray many prominent dentists into an unwarranted feeling of assurance in their condemnation of amalgam as a filling material. Others, equally prominent, on no sounder scientific grounds,
had concluded the substance was harmless to the system and useful
for filling cavities. Neither side possessed the technical competence
to establish a convincing vindication of its position. Both sides saw in
the cases they observed the facts they wanted to see. Under these circumstances, it is hardly surprising that the amalgam controversy generated considerable heat and flared and sputtered its way to an
utterly unsatisfactory conclusion.

The question exhibited its characteristic qualities with the earliest exchange specifically addressed to it. One A. Clar of Pen Yan issued the challenge in a letter to the editors of *The American Journal of Dental Science* in November, 1839. Clar noted the charges against amalgam and acknowledged that if the allegations were true, the user was certainly guilty of quackery and fraud. But he demanded to know how amalgam produced the alleged ill effects. This query, as events soon proved, exceeded the capabilities of contemporary dental science. He asked how long the substance required to work its harmful consequences. And, he insisted, "Argument based on indisputable facts is desired; the dictum of no man, though grey in his profession, will be deemed sufficient." [11]

Enoch Noyes promptly picked up the gage. Noyes admitted, "That I shall be able to remove the doubts his enquiries would seem to imply is more than I dare anticipate, for he tells us that the 'dictum of no man, though grey in his profession, will be deemed sufficient.'" The condition made Noyes bristle. "The inference to be deduced from this, is, that he is actually ignorant and chooses not to be taught." With every evidence of exhausted patience, Noyes then tried to answer Clar's query by adopting all the suggestions Clar had made about the way in which the amalgam worked its harmful effects. The corrosion of the surface of the filling combined with the saliva to attack the teeth, Noyes said. The mercury in the filling "evaporated," permitting "the secretions of the mouth" to penetrate between the filling and the walls of the cavity where the decay then took place more rapidly than before, he thought. "At least this would seem to be the case from the fact that the teeth, after being filled with this amalgam, often decay faster than they did before." With somewhat less assurance, Noyes stated that the mercury in the amalgam also found its way to the stomach and thus into the body system. He theorized that it might influence the gums in this manner, although he admitted that he was not sure but that it acted directly on the gums. He did not presume that the uninjured teeth absorbed mercury, but he "would not like to hazard the assertion" that they did not. "The solution of this question, however, is of no consequence to the point at issue," he concluded. "As it regards the modus operandi, that is a matter of no importance. The fact that bad effects do result from the use of the amalgam here alluded to, in filling teeth, ought to be sufficient to deter every dentist from employing it for that purpose."

Noyes completed the anti-amalgam argument by offering three cases of bad experience with amalgam fillings that he had observed. One victim, he said, complained of sore gums and mercurial taste. Furthermore, "the secretions of [the patient's] mouth were so abundant that she was kept almost constantly spitting; and they were much vitiated and very viscid." Noyes claimed that the mercury from the amalgam fillings in another mouth had caused the patient's gold fillings to crumble away and come out. In the final case, amalgam had been used to fill a tooth to which a plate was anchored with clasps. According to Noyes, the mercury in the fillings had caused both the clasp and the plate to crumble.[12]

This brief exchange exhibited all the difficulties under which the controversy labored. Clar's statement reflected a helpless irritation at the variety of charges, some of them contradictory, amalgam opponents brought against it. He also felt the inadequacy of the explanations of how the mercury in the preparation worked its supposed ill effects. But Clar did not succeed in making the latter aspect of his challenge clear. Noyes's response showed all the characteristics to which Clar had objected. Noyes was evidently uncertain how the harmful results were produced. This made the final position he assumed all the more irritating. The problem of how the mercury operated, Noyes and the other antagonists of amalgam insisted, was a matter of no importance. The essential "fact" upon which they rested their case was the "bad effects" of the use of amalgam. Clar and the other inquirers could only sputter indignantly. No one explicitly retorted that if the opponents did not know how the amalgam produced its evil results, they could not know that the symptoms were to be attributed to amalgam. The contenders thus failed to meet the issue squarely—and additional sources of irritation soon further exacerbated the rivals.

The rivals faced what might be called the amalgam dilemma. The foes of amalgam could not allow any virtue to the controversial substance. In the back of their minds, there must have lurked the reasoning that if amalgam was a better filling than gold in any cavity, it was better in all cases, because it was cheaper, easier to manipulate, and hence easier on the patient. Accordingly, the critics of amalgam had to deny or explain away any reports of the successful use of amalgam under any circumstances. This necessity greatly simplified the problem of the amalgam critics.

Their opponents, on the other hand, did not try to take an extreme stand—and their moderation weakened their position. They did not ask the displacement of the accepted foil filling materials. Perceiving the advantages of amalgam, they only desired that it receive a fair trial. The advocates of amalgam could not and did not deny that the substance was largely in the hands of ill-trained practitioners. On the contrary, they attributed most of the alleged bad effects to the operator rather than the material. Furthermore, in cases where competent dentists had resorted to the substance, it had been largely as a desperation measure. "Amalgam has also been used, mostly, to fill the worst class of decayed teeth where the caries had progressed so far, and the surrounding parts had become so much diseased, that no treatment was proper but extraction," one of the proponents of amalgam argued. He pointed out that in such cases the condition of the tooth and mouth would tend to produce symptoms which might easily be mistaken for the constitutional effects of mercury. Because of these circumstances, he argued, "any candid and unprejudiced mind will readily perceive that with a fair trial, in the hands of men of good judgment, skill and scientific attainments . . . , the result might have been entirely different." [13]

The enemies of amalgam turned such statements against their authors with telling effect. As one righteous anti-amalgam hero said, "There are many who rank high in reputation in the community; as well as with the profession, who nevertheless have been in the habit of using it, as they assert, with great care and circumspection, who are ready to affirm and declare that the indiscriminate use of it is most decidedly injurious, and that there are but few cases in which it can be advantageous; they defend themselves for using what in the aggregate they allow to be an extremely dangerous article, on the same principle that the moderate drinker does the use of ardent spirits—'It does no harm to me or any one else as I use it.'" [14] Thus, it can be seen, neither side of the controversy could appear to advantage and neither had a prospect of convincing the other. Under these conditions, the good humor of the participants was bound to deteriorate.

Such was the setting into which Joseph H. Foster threw his fire-brand. Foster asked the American Society, assembled in their second annual session, whether there were cases of carious teeth in which gold foil could not be used that could be preserved with some other filling material. The Society appointed a committee to investigate the question. The committee considered all manner of filling compounds in which mercury was an ingredient. They declared "that the use of all such articles were [*sic*] hurtful, both to the teeth and every part of the mouth, and that there was no tooth, in which caries could be arrested, and the organ rendered serviceable by being filled, in which gold could not be employed." Foster's query thus received an unequivocal answer. The committee's condemnation of amalgam was explicit and categorical. The meeting unanimously adopted the conclusions of its committee.[15]

This statement of opinion apparently had no more effect in eradicating amalgam than had the strictures of individual authorities in the periodical literature of the time. Apparently some members of the Society itself began to investigate the possibilities of the new treatment. Accordingly, at the 1843 meeting, Chapin Harris proposed stronger measures. On his motion, the Society resolved, "that this society regards the use of mineral paste in plugging carious teeth as malpractice." Proof of its use by a member was now grounds for expulsion. At the same time, the Society sought additional confirmation of its position. The Harris resolution requested the submission of data concerning amalgam to the medical society of Onondaga County, New York, which was investigating the material.[16]

Thereafter, the rigor of the anti-amalgam campaign increased. At the 1844 meeting, the American Society found that its resolution of the preceding year had not stamped out the use of the article within its own ranks. The meeting therefore directed the recording secretary to warn every member charged with using amalgam that the Society had pronounced its use malpractice and that the next meeting would consider the offender's case.[17] Evidently feeling was running strong within the organization. The "union and harmony" of the first national dental association was collapsing.

Early in the New York meeting of 1845, John B. Rich proposed that the membership resident in New York and Brooklyn be interrogated "for the purpose of ascertaining from each whether he had used any amalgam in the course of his own practice, or approved of its use, and if so, whether he had used it within the last twelve months." As the reporter for the *American Journal* noted, " a spirited debate ensued." The issue was beclouded because two points were under discussion, the right of the Society to demand information of this nature from its members and the propriety of using amalgam.

The enemies of amalgam asserted the broadest rights of the Society. The advocates of this position were led by Eleazar Parmly. Amos Westcott and J. B. Rich supported him. Both journals reporting on this session sympathized with the views of the anti-amalgam faction. Their accounts of the debate are not very revealing. Nothing is said of the arguments used by Parmly and his cohorts. The bias of the journals apparently led them to assume that their case was convincing. The adherents of the pro-amalgam side tended to deny the right of the Society to quiz its members' practice. This group had two doughty champions in Elisha Baker and Solyman Brown. Both men insisted the Society could not inquire into its members' methods. Baker also spoke on behalf of amalgam as "occasionally admissible." Brown held that "no one ought to be required to pledge himself not to use any article, as his conscience might demand that he should use it." The majority, however, favored the adoption of Rich's resolution.[18]

In keeping with this decision, a committee visited the members of the Society living in New York City and Brooklyn. The committee reported that ten of those interviewed never used amalgam, five occasionally used it, but would agree to abandon the practice, while six recalcitrant operators acknowledged approval of the controverted article.[19]

These findings provoked further stringent action against the users of mineral paste, adamantine cement, succedaneum, diamond cement, lithodeon, alabaster cement, Chinese cement, in short, any amalgam whatever. The terms of the condemnation were stronger than before. Amalgam was pronounced not only unfit, but dangerous, and its use was again declared to be malpractice. On this occasion, the bitter critics insisted on further measures. A majority of the twenty-nine members present decreed that "any member of this Society who shall hereafter refuse to sign a certificate pledging himself not to use any amalgam, and, moreover, protesting against its use, under any circumstances, in dental practice, shall be expelled." The members were allowed thirty days in which to comply with this mandate.

Before the Society adjourned, an additional measure broadened the campaign against amalgam and its users. The Society endeavored to enlist the public on its side. The meeting prepared an open letter to be published in the newspapers and periodicals distributed throughout the country. The document declared that the purposes of the Society were "the mutual improvement of its members, and the protection of themselves and the public against the quackery and empiricism which are the disgrace of the profession." The letter then went on to explain that the Society sought to further its objects by exposing "one of the base deceptions by which individuals calling themselves dentists [were] grossly imposing on the community." The American Society thus proclaimed its abhorrence of amalgam "by the use of which thousands of valuable teeth are annually destroyed, and immeasurable evils result to the community at large, which can never be repaired." In conclusion, the letter announced the action of the Society against its members who might in the future be guilty of using the objectionable substance.[20]

No doubt the anti-amalgam faction had scored a notable victory. They had captured the American Society of Dental Surgeons. This, they thought, would assure their ultimate triumph. One of them "expressed the hope that the action of the Society at this meeting on this subject would be efficient, positive, and final, that no more of their time might be consumed by it."[21] A vain hope, as the events of the ensuing years proved.

The actions of the majority at the 1845 meeting split the Society and the profession. The heat generated by the temper of the discussion even flares up from the pages of retrospective accounts of the session. Joseph H. Foster, for example, reportedly "treated the subject with an ability and earnestness calculated to force every living quack to abandon his way, and have rendered the prospect of a resurrection exceedingly uncomfortable to dead ones." This was perhaps the most harmful aspect of the course taken by the controversy. For the claims to social and professional respectability of many opponents of the policy were as good as those of its advocates. Yet the strictures of the anti-amalgam spokesmen made no distinction among amalgam users. Many who used it undoubtedly "possessed neither scientific nor artistical skill in the use of gold, nor common honesty as men," and hence used amalgam in the worst possible manner. But such characteristics could not fairly be ascribed to the leading dentists who asked a "fair trial" of the substance. The bitterness thus engendered disrupted the profession for many years.[22]

The ensuing annual meeting, convened at New York in 1846, heard a report that must have provoked feelings of dismay. Amos Westcott, the recording secretary, summarized the results of his correspondence concerning the amalgam protest and pledge. The whole number composing the Society at the time the resolutions were passed, was one hundred and thirty-four. Of this number, seventy-two had complied with the mandate of the association. Among the remaining sixty-two, six had indicated their willingness to conform by returning the pledge and protest after the expiration of the time-limit or by claiming they had not received the documents from the recording secretary. This left a substantial minority of the membership, some fifty-six all told, who had been automatically expelled according to the resolutions of 1845.

Westcott, commenting on this aspect of the matter, insisted that their failure to comply with the directives of the Society was "as good evidence . . . that they did not receive the circular, as that they are friendly to the practice against which the protest was made." Indeed, Westcott said he found on the list of non-signers many whose anti-amalgam sentiments were well known. Subsequently, Westcott went even further in his interpretation of the list of delinquents. "When this list was presented to the Society, it was found to contain many, nay, to be composed mainly of those whose opinions and practice . . . were wholly averse to the use of amalgam." The original measure had not anticipated "this unpleasant exigency."

Something had to be done to retain such a substantial portion of the membership. The matter baffled the parliamentary resources of the session. A committee deliberated overnight, without success. It appeared that the Society had been caught in its own web. Another day and a half was devoted to seeking "some plan by which the Society could at once be protected against [the use of amalgam by members], and at the same time do justice to many who would innocently suffer by the unmitigated action of the resolutions." At length the meeting determined to rescind all previous action and begin over again. "We retract nothing as regards our sentiments," the members insisted, either in relation to the use of amalgam or the power of the Society to take action against it. They were determined, the members declared, to be free of the "odium necessarily attached to this reprehensible practice," while rendering "equal and exact justice" to all members of the organization. To fulfill this purpose, the session adopted a new pledge and protest, which was to be sent to all those who had failed to respond to the original. The net result was to defer final action until 1847.[23]

At the Saratoga Springs meeting in the following year, Amos Westcott announced, "The number reported as delinquents at the meeting of 1846, or on the original protest, was fifty-six. I am happy to be able to state that this list is now reduced to twenty-one." The number of dissenters had evidently decreased, but the problem of the remaining rebels proved vexing. The recalcitrant members included some of the most respected and influential dentists in the country, among them Elisha Baker, one of the founders of the Society, James Taylor, a prominent leader of western dentistry and soon to be editor of the *Dental Register of the West*, and Charles C. Allen, who later became the second editor of the pioneer dental periodical, the *New York Dental Recorder*.

The presiding officer appointed a committee, headed by Chapin Harris, to report some plan of disposing of the amalgam question at this meeting. After a period the committee requested inclusion of members holding differing views. As a result, two stalwart opponents of the Society's policy were added to the group. The proposals that were finally submitted to the full meeting were definitely moderate. The report opposed expulsion of any member who was not in the practice of using or recommending the use of amalgam for filling teeth. In this way, the committee sought to avoid the unpleasant necessity of discharging those members who denied the Society's power to regulate matters of individual practice. The committee rec-

ognized that the act of expelling some of its members would tend to
undermine both the status of the Society and the strength of its stand
against amalgam. The committee declared that it was "the duty of
every member, who has the usefulness of this Society at heart, either
to acquiesce in its doings so far as his practice and influence is [*sic*]
concerned, or quietly to retire and resign his membership." This
plaintive request that the dissenters abandon their position was without effect.[24]

That the session appreciated the gravity of the step they were taking and understood that it probably would provoke considerable
adverse opinion was clearly implied by the care with which they proceeded to carry out their decision to expel any defender of amalgam
from their ranks. Charles Allen received every consideration. Allen
claimed two years previously to have signed and adhered to a pledge
that he would neither use nor recommend amalgams for dental purposes. He still, however, protested against the action of the Society
as unconstitutional. When Allen read this pledge, the Society found
it unsatisfactory. He was directed to prepare another. In the end, the
meeting accepted Allen's revised pledge.

The semi-official reports of the proceedings do not reflect the extent
of the Society's concession to Allen. His revised pledge, according to
his own account, read:

> Two years since I felt exceedingly unwilling to abandon the use of amalgam,
> but as many of the members of this society who have used this article more than
> I have, and for whose opinion I had the highest regard, then decided to use it
> no more, nor to encourage its use, and as I did not wish to impose the slightest
> obstacle to the success, union and harmony of this society, I cheerfully con-
> sented to do the same, hoping that all the members would feel the importance
> of making mutual concession, if they would be a happy, useful and prosperous
> society. That concession I consider binding upon me so long as I remain a mem-
> ber.

If Allen's testimony is to be believed, and the anti-amalgam forces
did not challenge this pledge, the friendly journals gave a distorted
account of the proceedings. On the basis of Allen's pledge, it is probable that more of the dissident members would have been willing
to remain with the Society.[25]

The majority accepted Allen's assurance that another delinquent
was sound on amalgam. Another dissenter claimed "that he had occasional calls for amalgam fillings, when the patients would have it,

and that he had sometimes used it where he thought it was for the benefit of the patient." He offered a compromise pledge averring that he regarded amalgam as not free from objection and that he did not recommend or use amalgam as a substitute for gold. The meeting unanimously refused to accept this proposition. The majority did not, however, revenge itself on this independent member. He was allowed to resign his membership.[26]

The case of Elisha Baker apparently roused the deepest feelings at the meeting. Baker had been detained in New York on the first day, so consideration of his case was deferred until he was present. After Baker arrived, he was given the floor. He challenged the actions of the Society in the amalgam question as unconstitutional and criticized the session for expelling members while possible defenders were absent. He then spoke in defense of amalgam. There was apparently no further discussion. The report of the proceedings states, "After Dr. Baker had concluded his remarks, it was moved and seconded that Dr. Baker be expelled." Baker objected to the resolution of expulsion because it implied that he used amalgam exclusively. One of the anti-amalgam faction pointed out that they might accommodate Dr. Baker by expelling him for refusing to join the Society in its protest against amalgam. He was accordingly removed from the rolls on that ground.[27]

Most of the other dissenting members were expelled, either on the grounds of their use of amalgam, or because they refused to endorse the Society's protest. Some of the more prominent rebels, who had persisted in ignoring the documents sent to them, were given additional time.[28]

Having completed the purge of the active membership, the survivors determined to make a sweep of the honorary members as well. Most of these dentists were Americans practicing in Europe, or were known to Americans through their publications. The triumphant anti-amalgam faction instructed the corresponding secretary to obtain "their views respecting the employment of amalgam for stopping teeth, and if now using it, their intentions with regard to its future use in their practice." The action of the meeting in the case of C. Starr Brewster left no doubt about the reaction to be expected upon an unsatisfactory response. Brewster, an American practicing in France and England, had publicly acknowledged his occasional use of the "paste." He had also stated that most of his European colleagues resorted to amalgam from time to time. The meeting therefore decided, "in view of good and sufficient evidence," that he be no longer considered an honorary member.[29]

All the care with which the majority at the Saratoga Springs meeting had implemented their determination to eliminate amalgam practitioners failed to forestall the storm that broke about their heads. Conditions were now such as to give the fury full play. A new dental periodical with a fearless editor began publication in the autumn of 1846. This was the *New York Dental Recorder*, guided by J. S. Ware. The *Recorder* became an outlet for expressions of dissatisfaction with the policy of the American Society of Dental Surgeons. Beyond the mountains, the *Dental Register of the West* began publication in the fall of 1847. The chief editor was James Taylor, who held a moderate position on the amalgam question. Taylor was assisted by B. B. Brown of St. Louis, who was expelled from the Society at the stormy meeting of 1847. In the pages of the dental journals and in the newspaper press, the controversy erupted with a force that divided the profession and, eventually, shattered the American Society of Dental Surgeons.[30]

The actions at the 1847 meeting were attacked from several different points. Critics vehemently denied the right of the session to make the decisions it reached. The first reason advanced was that the policy had been imposed by a minority of the Society. One critic vowed, "It is a matter of the deepest importance to every member to preserve the character of the profession as well from the tyranny of the few as the charlatanism and quackery of the many." [31]

The charge was certainly true. The total attendance at the meeting was between twenty-three and thirty, approximately one-fourth of the membership.[32] Moreover, the expulsions required the support of only two-thirds of those present, that is, between fifteen and twenty votes. One member, who was expelled at this meeting, claimed that the action was taken by a session at which only thirteen members were present. This small number allegedly decided upon the expulsion of several of the members by the narrow margin of nine in favor and four against the measure.[33]

The critics also attacked the wisdom of the policy. They denied that it would produce the desired effect. "Every formula which requires the members of a learned profession to be pledged like lost drunkards at a temperance meeting, is . . . an outrage . . . and revolting . . . to the personal dignity of the gentleman and the scholar," one opponent insisted. All attempts to dictate the practice of the profession, interfering with the free exercise of individual judgment "must terminate in arrant quackery and force the society into the unenviable position of being the laughing stock of the more intelligent and respectable portion of the community," he warned.[34]

Amalgam opponents used the press to denounce amalgam users as quacks and charlatans, but were deeply hurt when charged with impugning the reputations of those who disagreed with them. In response to one such complaint, Eleazar Parmly insisted on his and the Society's right to express their views of amalgam and those who made wholesale use of it. Parmly denied resorting to "any personal 'epithets,' except in the case of the notorious swindlers, the Crawcours." In a righteous peroration to this defense, Parmly thundered, "The Society will at all times claim the right and privilege of expressing fearlessly to the public throughout the land its honest convictions, founded on experience, of the use and abuses in professional practice, leaving each 'operator on teeth,' whether he has assumed the title of Doctor or not, the undoubted right and exclusive privilege of applying to himself as much or as little of the Crawcourian character as his practice and his conscience tell him he is entitled to." [35] Small wonder that feeling ran high in a controversy conducted in this way.

The insoluble character of the question as the profession confronted it was reflected by parallel statements from each side. Edward Taylor wrote, "If the society is constituted of members who are only to be restrained from malpractice by a solemn and formal pledge, . . . the sooner it disbands the better." Amos Westcott retorted, "If the American Society of Dental Surgeons have [sic] no authority to proscribe quackery among its members, it has no object, and the sooner it ceases to exist, the better." [36]

Inevitably, the controversy found its way into the newspapers. Some of the newspaper discussion was merely rancorous, but one lively incident was exploited to the fullest. This case concerned the death of a man allegedly caused by amalgam fillings that had been placed, and removed, some seven years previously. The patient supposedly had swallowed some of the amalgam. Both sides of the controversy leaped into the fray, summoning chemists and physicians to testify, and dispatching investigators to the scene. The exchange pursued an inconclusive course until the participants (and, no doubt, the spectators) wearied of the game.[37] One observer concluded the affair had become "disreputable to all concerned," and tended "to bring the Dental Art into disgrace and ridicule with the public."[38]

The irreconcilable attitude of the anti-amalgam faction provoked a reaction from their opponents that widened the breach in the profession. A correspondent of the *Dental Recorder* suggested the formation of another society. The editor of the *Recorder* feared the effects of such a move. He explained, "We have an Anti-Amalgam Society in the country now, and to establish at this time an association of Amalgam Dentists would savor too much of party, and would only serve to separate still wider the breach that has already been made in the profession." The editor's plea was without effect. The disgruntled elements met in November, 1847, and organized the Society of Dental Surgeons of the State of New York.[39]

Although this New York society failed to outlive the organization it sought to displace, its founding symbolized the defeat of the anti-amalgam policy of the American Society of Dental Surgeons. The action of the American Society provoked widespread opposition in the profession—and it was far outmatched in numbers. The policy also alienated many who felt that the characteristics of amalgam could not be settled by opinion and authority.[40] Discussion of the question soon degenerated into a discreditable exchange of personalities. Precipitation of the controversy in 1847 dealt the American Society a blow from which it never recovered.

By the time of the ensuing meeting, at Saratoga Springs in 1848, the full effects of the amalgam policy were becoming apparent. Only twelve members answered the roll call when this ninth annual meeting convened. The Society, however, was still troubled with the amalgam affair. The official report noted that the first order of business was the disposition of some cases left over from the preceding year. On behalf of one of the delinquents, a member testified that the defendant had complied with the requirements but that the letter had miscarried. His case was accordingly deferred again. Another individual had been out of the country for two years. Disposition of his case, too, was laid over. Chapin Harris declared in defense of James Taylor that the latter had assumed his original protest of 1845 sufficed. Harris said that he had good reason to believe Taylor was right, both in theory and practice, upon this subject. The meeting decided to find out and put the decision off for another year. There was some unpleasant business that could not be deferred. The Society received a number of resignations. Three of the four acted upon at this time had been delinquents in 1847.[41]

Just at this time, too, the Society faltered in the regularity of its sessions. The annual meeting scheduled for 1849 was deferred until the spring of 1850.[42]

When the deferred session at last convened in the Lecture Hall of the Baltimore Dental College, the amalgam controversy took a new turn. Elisha Townsend interrupted the regular proceedings and "gave notice that he wished at the proper time to present a subject . . . on which a Committee might be called for." The meeting promptly suspended the regular order of business to hear what Townsend had to say. His subject was "The Propriety of Rescinding the Amalgam Pledge."[43]

Townsend's speech was eloquent and full of home-truths, but it was phrased with superb tact. He argued for repeal of the amalgam resolutions first on the grounds of policy. "Five years of experience, under the sharp discussions and sharper government of this question, must have pretty well served all the purposes of such a measure," he reasoned. "If five years have not done it, fifty cannot." He continued, "If it compels nobody and convinces nobody, it must either be repealed as inexpedient, or left to grow obsolete upon your records—wear out it must, either because all resistance ceases, or because the resistance maintains its ground."

The doctor then suggested that the prohibitory measures had been mistaken. "I do not think questions in natural science can be settled and decided by the legislation of majorities," he declared. Townsend hastened to still the opposition his implicit criticism might well

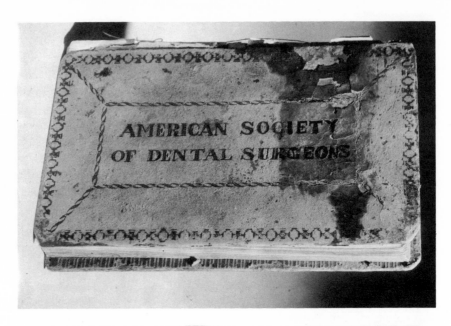

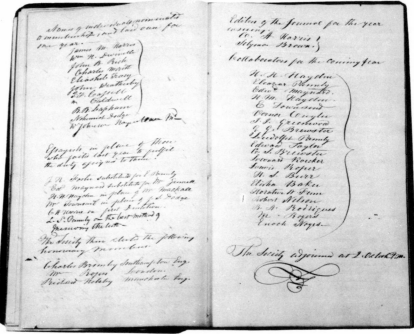

Minute Book of the American Society of Dental Surgeons

arouse. He acknowledged the right of the association to take action in its own defense. He carefully identified himself with that action. Then he launched into an eloquent defense of freedom of investigation.

"There has been enough of book burning, and heretic roasting, and creed crushing," Townsend argued. In this section of his brief, he advanced directly to the heart of the Society's great error. "If men will judge and govern other minds by their own, then the unknown comes to be the untrue, and stupidly enough, without pretending to know everything, they decide on the assumption that they do," he observed. "Wait till nobody disputes your point, and then seal up your decree; then only it will not be wrong, it will only be useless, and that is the best thing that can be said of settling questions by opinion of authority."

After this devastating blast, Townsend recurred to the worst consequences of the policy. With the anti-amalgam resolutions in effect, he pointed out, the Society had its "doors barricaded against the entrance of the freshest and boldest spirits who would seek our association." He went on, "My ultimate aim and wish is to relieve the association . . . from the incumbrance of regulation which now regulates nothing needing restraint, and restrains only the progress and prosperity it was designed to promote." He went on, "To me the time is fully come to let down the bars and to admit men, young men, who will not endure the muzzle." [44]

Townsend first urged that someone "whose convictions against [amalgam] are the deepest" assume the initiative in carrying out the suggestions in his speech. Then he withdrew the proposal. He urged "that it abide a year's dispassionate reflection, and the issue and decision will be right and prudent, and true, too, I cannot doubt." No less staunch opponent of amalgam than Amos Westcott moved the appointment of a committee. Townsend became a member of the committee to consider the suggestions he had made. Within six months, at the annual meeting for 1850, convened with Townsend himself, as vice-president, in the chair, the American Society of Dental Surgeons abandoned the anti-amalgam policy. [45]

The new turn in the course of the society was a personal triumph for Elisha Townsend. To this first national dental association, it represented a two-fold failure. The active leadership of the American

Society of Dental Surgeons had sought through the prestige of the organization to eradicate a practice they regarded as vicious. The effort had failed. In the process of abandoning the unsuccessful campaign, the Society failed again. To eliminate the use of amalgam, the association had sacrificed many of its other objectives. It had denied itself the respect of a substantial portion of the profession because it sought to settle a scientific question by the force of legislative fiat. The manner in which it resigned the policy cost it the respect of additional numbers. The reasons alleged for rescinding the amalgam resolutions were patently false. The action, according to the *American Journal*, was "based upon the belief that the resolutions had accomplished the object for which they were designed, and that there no longer existed any necessity for their enforcement." When the action was taken on these grounds, one of the most fervent supporters of the Society, John B. Rich, resigned in disgust.[46]

Chapter V   THE END OF THE AMERICAN SOCIETY

THE FAILURE of the American Society of Dental Surgeons in the amalgam controversy marked the beginning of the end for this first of national dental organizations. From the spring of 1850 to its dissolution in 1856, the association was preoccupied with efforts to establish itself as the leader and spokesman for American dentistry. The members of the Society displayed considerable vigor, enterprise, and shrewdness, but the incubus of the history of its first decade was too great. It gradually became evident that only a new and different association could win the support of the profession rent by the bitterness of the amalgam controversy.

For several critical years, beginning in 1845, the rolls were closed, or virtually closed, to new members while the Society fought the Amalgam War. At the instance of J. B. Rich, the session of 1845 admitted no new members. In the following year, the Society revised its membership qualifications in such a way that only one candidate could be registered. The meeting of 1847 discovered only four applicants "eligible to the honor" of membership, and of these only two were able at that time to sign the constitution and thus become full-fledged members. At Saratoga Springs in 1848, attendance had fallen off to "less than a baker's dozen, and no new candidates for admission." The ensuing meeting was deferred from August, 1849, to the following spring. One new member was elected at that time.[1] The dearth of new applicants reflected a debility that justified fears for the future.

The Saratoga Springs meeting in the summer of 1850 provided other evidences of the declining vigor of the Society. This was the session that abandoned the publication of _The American Journal of Dental Science_ to the private endeavor of Chapin Harris. The thin attendance of recent years led to the consolidation of the offices of recording and corresponding secretary. Although, in the past, the latter office had been compensated, this practice, too, was dropped at the 1850 meeting. The important standing Committee on Practical Dentistry was at this time reduced to one member. The diminution of attendance and the cutting off of access to membership were justifiably attributed to the explosive issues raised by the amalgam dilemma.[2]

Confronted with the disastrous consequences of its anti-amalgam policy, the Society sought to regain a position from which it could claim leadership of the profession. There were two lines of thought on the problem. One faction wanted to maintain the distinction the founders had tried to identify with Society membership. This group sought the answer to the Society's difficulties in constitutional revision. At the Baltimore meeting in 1850, while Townsend was working toward a repeal of the amalgam policy, S. P. Hullihen sponsored a special committee to review the membership provisions of the constitution. The deliberations of this committee left no trace on the records of subsequent meetings. Later in the year, at Saratoga Springs, J. H. Foster proposed a committee to consider the articles of the constitution relating to membership. This committee reported that it was inexpedient to effect any change in the membership policy at that time. A new committee was appointed at the 1851 session to consider constitutional reform and report at the next meeting. In 1852, this committee reported progress and was continued. Before the convention adjourned, however, Hullihen moved that the existing committee be discharged and another one appointed for the purpose of drafting a new constitution. The new constitution reported by Hullihen's committee was amended and adopted at the West Point meeting in 1853.[3] The new instrument failed to satisfy the Society.[4] When the deferred 1854 session finally met at Cincinnati in the spring of 1855, it determined to consider dissolution of the Society on the ground that further revision could not rehabilitate it.[5]

Meanwhile, another faction of the Society, under the urging of Elisha Townsend, had been seeking a fundamental redefinition of the role of a national professional organization. The basis of Townsend's conception of the association was inclusiveness, whereas that of Foster, Hullihen, and their confreres was exclusiveness. Townsend summarized the differences between the two points of view in his address at the Cincinnati meeting in May of 1855. "In authorship and in professional teaching a score or two of able men might be sufficient for a country and an age, but the purpose of a national society is necessarily the aggregation, or at least the thorough representation, of the entire fraternity, in one organic movement," he claimed. "I venture the assertion that the proper and principal qualification of a National, or State, or County Society of professional men engaged in practice, is even more a question of numbers than of standing and talent, provided only that standing and talent are embraced within the number."[6]

The desire for a more open policy on the part of the Society stemmed from two related lines of criticism that had been levelled at it for several years. Within its own ranks, it was charged, the Society had failed to exhibit the breadth of concern demanded by its objects. "The association is designed as a national institution, administering to the interests of the most distant and remote of its members; but to make it effective and useful to its full extent, these interests must be represented by its members, and the doings of its meetings free from local favoritism," the editor of the friendly *American Journal* asserted in 1847. Some years later, urging attendance at the Philadelphia session by "members from the southern and western states," the *Journal* again referred to the provincial bias of the association. "Heretofore [southerners and westerners] have complained, and we admit with some show of justice, that the meetings have been held too far north, and refused to attend on that account." There was warrant, then, for charging that the Society's policies did not adequately represent its own membership.[7] It had no valid claim to speak for the profession.

In the eyes of the majority of practicing dentists, who were not members of the Society, it had become a "mere clique of self-constituted exclusives." Many detractors considered the organization ridiculously presumptuous. The editor of the *Dental Recorder* found the attitude of the Society toward its honorary members during the amalgam controversy hilarious. "What a 'pretty figure the Society cuts' in directing their erudite corresponding Secretary to catechise such men as Cartwright, Nasmyth, Tomes and others, concerning their practice—and requesting *'definite'* answers!" The defenders of the Society merely reiterated their self-righteous stand.[8]

At the height of the Amalgam War, a physician, Henry James Brown, submitted to the *Dental Register* an analysis of the proper role of a professional association. Brown implicitly criticized the amalgam policy of the American Society as he wrote that those "who claim for voluntary associations more than an advisory prerogative, have fallen into the error of attempting to make those obedient to laws who have had no part in their formation." Brown insisted that a professional organization could exert only moral influence. "The united voice of an association is entitled to the respectful considera- tion of the whole profession, in the sense of that of any one man of respectable standing, but when it is attempted to coerce obedience, common self-respect revolts as against the pretensions of a vain man, who has quite forgotten his place." The work of professional reform, Brown reasoned, could be accomplished only by the united efforts of the entire body of the profession. "The intrigues of party, the cabals of colleges, and the ceaseless quarrels of individual practi- tioners, must give place to a pervading sense of high-toned integrity," he concluded.[9]

The exclusiveness and presumption of the Society were also the ground for a second type of criticism. This line of argument held that the Society's policies inhibited rather than fostered advancement of the science and the improvement of the profession. In retrospect, one complainant dubbed the American Society "a species of 'Mutual Ad- miration Society.'" None but the favored few were permitted to share its benefits. He went on, "Thus those who made new discoveries or improvements threw around themselves the garb of secrecy, com- municating only with a few personal friends, and thus placed an ex- tinguisher over the light which should have been allowed to cast its genial rays far and wide, brightening up the dark corners and dreary wastes of ignorance in the profession."[10] That the amalgam controversy had distracted the members from their discussions of "practical subjects," was obvious to many contemporaries.[11]

Developments in the profession during the forties had brought another aspect of the exclusiveness of the American Society into prominence. This was the problem of the relationship of the Society to the nascent dental colleges and to other respectable dental associations. Chapin Harris repeatedly urged the importance of extending special consideration to the graduates of dental colleges. C. O. Cone found the Society's role as the patron to the dental colleges a reason for special satisfaction. "It extended the demand for instruction by the necessities it imposed on members and candidates," he claimed. The promotion of the Baltimore College of Dental Surgery, Cone boasted, had been a "favorite object" of the association. Yet, by the mid-point of the century, in part due to the anxieties created by the amalgam controversy, Harris and his supporters had been unable to obtain favored treatment for the holders of collegiate diplomas.[12]

Equally pressing by 1850, was the question of the relationship of the Society to other dental organizations. In the beginning, the founders of the association apparently contemplated its fostering a series of regional satellites. Article Three of the original constitution authorized each of the vice-presidents to convene the members of the Society residing in his vicinity. These groups were empowered to elect necessary officers and transact business of concern in their area. The constitution required that these regional organizations report their proceedings regularly to the parent Society. Since none of the annual transactions carried the doings of any such auxiliary society, it would seem that this authorization was never acted upon.[13]

Through the middle forties, Chapin Harris and others turned their attention to the possibility of forming state societies that would serve as subsidiaries of the American Society. At the Baltimore meeting in 1843, Harris spoke hopefully of the prospects of a network of constituent state organizations. "I doubt not that it will receive the attention of this association, and be annually recommended until the escutcheon of dental surgery in the United States, shall boast as many stars as the banner of the Union, and until this body, sustained by twenty-six state societies, shall assume the station in this department of science which the American Congress sustains in the political relations of the country."[14]

Not all of Harris's colleagues were as sanguine as he regarding the possible benefits of local associations. Amos Westcott spoke for a substantial element of the Society when he estimated that "at least three-fourths of these societies would be composed of a majority of those having no claim to skill or science."[15]

In 1844, the matter of state auxiliary associations was debated at length. This session considered the appointment of a committee to devise a plan for organizing a network of subsidiaries. If the Society adopted such a course, however, the records do not reveal it. At the same meeting the Society did adopt a resolution recommending that the members organize state societies "not only for the purpose of accomplishing local good, but also for that of ultimately becoming auxiliary to the American Society of Dental Surgeons." C. O. Cone later noted that, before the American Society took effective action toward the organization of state or local auxiliaries, "other state societies were formed, absolving the Society from any future action on that point."[16]

By mid-century there were several active local or regional associations. The most impressive dental society, in terms of numbers, scope, and activity, was the Mississippi Valley Association of Dental Surgeons. Founded in the summer of 1844 in Cincinnati, the Mississippi Valley Association was the vehicle for much of the vigorous growth of the dental profession in the West. Shortly after its organization came the founding of the Ohio College of Dental Surgery and, somewhat later, the inauguration of the *Dental Register of the West,* both under the aegis of the Mississippi Valley Association.[17] The vigorous development of professionalism in the trans-Allegheny region bade fair to overshadow the contentious centers of the East.

The earliest of the seaboard societies was the Virginia Society of Surgeon Dentists, founded in 1842. It is uncertain whether it persisted much beyond the mid-century mark.[18] Following the energetic precedent of the Mississippi Valley Association was the thriving Pennsylvania Society of Dental Surgeons.[19] The enterprising dentists of Philadelphia soon gave every sign of establishing their city, rather than Baltimore or New York, as the outstanding center of dentistry in the coastal region. New York City, in particular, had been badly divided by the amalgam controversy. It was the site of an organization of amalgam dentists formed in defiance of the edicts of the American Society. Many of the well-known practitioners of the metropolis were associated with this Society of Dental Surgeons of the State of New York. This dissident group appears to have been, in part, a successor to an already-existing city organization.[20]

These developments of the first decade of organized dentistry were only the beginning of a rich flowering of new societies that characterized the fifties. In the winter of 1852-53, for example, the *Dental News Letter* reported the founding of a society in Allegheny County, Pennsylvania, and a city society in Brooklyn. The middle years of the decade witnessed the organization of many new dental associations.[21] Under the circumstances, if the American Society was to establish its leadership over the professional dental organizations, amicable relations had to be established with its contemporaries.

After the repeal of the amalgam resolution, Townsend turned his attention to the need, as he saw it, for broadening the appeal of the Society by opening the meetings to non-members. At the Philadelphia meeting in 1851, Townsend adopted a suggestion of the *Dental News Letter* and sponsored the invitation of the dentists of the city "to attend the sittings of the society." [22] By 1853, this practice had become fixed in the usages of the Society so that to ask the profession in the vicinity to the meetings was referred to as the "usual" and "customary" procedure.[23]

This increased cordiality toward the profession outside the fold could not of itself strengthen the Society. Some mitigation of the requirements of membership was needed also. And this the Society was unable to agree upon. As a result, the membership increased at a trickle instead of a flood. Two new members were admitted at Saratoga Springs in 1850. One candidate was entered on the rolls in 1851. The transactions for 1852 reported no new members. Then there was a grand rush of four new members added in 1853. Measured by its accomplishments in securing new members, the opening of the meetings to outsiders was an obvious failure.[24]

Townsend also sought to improve the relations of the Society with the other dental organizations and dental colleges. In 1851, he offered a resolution that aimed to ease the membership restrictions and, at the same time, to establish amicable connections of mutual respect with existing dental associations. The proposal would have amended the membership article of the constitution to provide "that all delegates appointed to represent recognized Dental Colleges and Associations of Dental practitioners, organized for scientific purposes, shall be admitted to all the rights and privileges of active members of this Society, as fully as if they had been elected to such membership by ballot." Townsend's argument on behalf of this measure indicated his conception of the role the American Society should play in the profession:

> The name and the attitude we take, assume to fraternize the men and centralize the movement by which our profession is to be carried forward to its destined position in the world of science; and it is incumbent upon us to adjust and address ourselves to our function by every proper means that promise to promote our aim. The adoption and publication of this amendment in connection with our other action on kindred points, I conceive will indicate the liberal and cordial spirit which animates us, and will be received as an earnest overture to the professional brotherhood, everywhere, for that correspondence and co-operation which must answer to the achievement of our great design.

According to Townsend's view, the first object of the Society, to establish a line of distinction between the qualified practitioner and the unqualified pretender, had been accomplished. The need now, he felt, was to unify the profession. The time for a suspicious and rigorous policy was now happily passed. "The attitude of offensive and defensive war should be changed in all points, so that no prejudice or suspicion shall be allowed to remain, that we are taking more care of our character and caste than of the great interests of the profession," he declaimed. Townsend believed that the members of other dental organizations would enter the fraternity of the American Society only as equals, not as suppliants. "Such men as there is any interest or honor in inviting, would not come to us as guests to receive our hospitalities," he protested. "They would come, and we would receive them, as equal members, on the level platform of a broad brotherhood that exchanges honors and benefits evenly." [25]

The same opposition that prevented substantial alteration of the constitution caused Townsend's proposal to be laid on the table. [26]

Thus, a move that might have converted the American Society into a representative body was never adopted.

The attendance at the annual sessions continued small. When the West Point meeting convened in August, 1853, there was no quorum, and the session adjourned overnight. By the following day, enough members had arrived to justify terming the attendance "pretty good." The 1854 convention was scheduled to meet in Cincinnati. Because of rumors of a cholera epidemic, the meeting was postponed until the spring of 1855. Nine members met, "together with many other members of the profession." [27] These heard from the president, Elisha Townsend, a sympathetic description of the situation of the American Society and an eloquent plea for a new order.

"The American Society was organized, like the Constitutions of the older States, in the midst of a revolutionary struggle," Townsend pointed out. The founders, he allowed, "did their work with pure hearts, fervently, and noble fruits have been harvested of their right hand planting; they have ripened richly for our use, and it is for us to plant them now in a larger field." Shorn of the rhetoric, Townsend's argument rested on the changes the preceding fifteen years had wrought in the profession and its status in the eyes of the public. "The exclusion and exposure of quackery was the exigency of those days, and numbers was a consideration secondary to all the other objects of association," he disclosed. Townsend enumerated the measures and the results of the Society's campaign against quackery, not the least of the latter being a "narrowing of the membership in proportion to the rigidness of its discipline." He demanded, "The society did its work, but is it not also obvious that it has almost lost its capacity for the work that is before it?" In brief, Townsend proposed that the Society's "position in the profession should be changed from exclusiveness to inclusiveness." [28]

The Committee on the President's Address recommended that a meeting be called to consider the dissolution of the Society. All of the members present participated in the discussion of the report. The result of the debate was a unanimous resolution directing the president to summon the Society to Philadelphia "on the day previous to the holding of the meeting called by a number of dentists of that city." This was a reference to the movement to displace the American Society with an association organized on a more open basis. Townsend complied with the resolution, and the Society accordingly convened in Philadelphia on August 1, 1855.

Although only ten members answered the roll call, they discussed the propriety of dissolving the Society during the morning, then placed the matter in the hands of a committee to report in the afternoon. After the recess, the committee announced that they "thought it inexpedient to dissolve the Society at present, and ask of the Society leave to report at the annual meeting of 1856." The session granted the committee's request and empowered it to do anything "so as to perpetuate and place this Association upon a permanent basis, and to suit the views of the Profession generally." After deferring the regular annual meeting for 1855, the session adjourned to determine the fate of the Society at the New York meeting in the following year.[29]

The erratic scheduling of meetings, the scant attendance, and the desperation move granting blanket authority to a committee to remake the Society, all foreshadowed the demise of the first national dental organization. The end came at New York in 1856. In the course of the proceedings of the second annual meeting of the American Dental Convention, Elisha Townsend reported that the American Society of Dental Surgeons had voted unanimously in favor of dissolution. According to the *Dental Register,* the announcement was received with applause. An embittered observer commented, "Only seven members of the society attended the Cincinnati meeting, and these naturally, thought it quite time to abandon a charter under which so little good and so much harm to the profession had been produced, and which had seen its hopes and its promises dwindle into lamentable insignificance, the sad results of a bad beginning in a 'National Convention' at New York, succeeded by an endless chapter of blunders, of undignified quarrels and gradual dilapidation."[30]

A chorus of discontent followed the demise of the pioneer national dental organization. "The American Society dragged its slow length along for many years and finally died, without doing much good, except to stimulate, perhaps, a general movement of societory formations under more favorable auspices," grudgingly acknowledged the *Dental News Letter,* a prominent sponsor of the Society's successor. These observations were perhaps overly hard on the backers of the first attempt at professional organization. More just were the regrets voiced by the *Dental Register*. "The only arguments used, we believe, in favor of dissolution were, that the progress of the profession had rendered such an organization no longer necessary; that it had served the purpose for which it was organized; and, that a new organization, on a more liberal basis, would better subserve the present wants of the profession." In another comment, the *Register* suggested, "Let its departure be regarded as a resignation, not as a dissolution." [31]

As the reactions to the passing of the Society were mixed, so, too, were the explanations advanced for its failure to endure. It is from conclusions reached by dental leaders on this point that the explicit lessons of the career of the American Society can be learned. In general, there were two basic observations made regarding the fate of the American Society. The first category held that the great mistake had been in membership policy. A capital spokesman for this point of view was J. H. McQuillen, later powerfully influential in the organization of the American Dental Association. McQuillen declared that "the society, while losing some members entirely, and the interest and sympathy of many others, made no effort to secure the young talent and energies of the profession, and failing to receive fresh additions to its ranks, it ceased to grow, and, in accordance with an immutable law of nature, repair not being equal to waste, death ensued as a necessary sequence." [32]

The irreconcilable opposition to a more generous membership policy repeatedly prevented accommodation in this direction. Furthermore, many contemporaries held that the policy of the Society had been rather too generous than too narrow. The membership clauses of the constitution were "never scrupulously observed," one critic noted. "Hence, many were brought within its portals utterly destitute of science and even of moderate excellence as practitioners; consequently, they were incapable of aiding the promotion of any of the objects which the originators of the movement had in view in its formation—the advancement of dentistry and the elevation of its respectability." Once such an ill-qualified operator gained entry into the

Society's ranks, this observer reasoned, it was easier to introduce many such, so that ultimately the transactions of the association were so burdened with these incompetents it, "from mere inanition, ceased to exist." [33] The constant vacillation in membership policy due to the perplexities induced by the callow state of the profession contributed largely to the failure of the American Society of Dental Surgeons, but the uncertainty of the situation confused the lesson and dimmed its impact.

The second line of criticism carrying a lesson to the successors of the American Society of Dental Surgeons is less clearly formulated. The complaint appears to have grown out of a conception of professional organization that emphasized two aspects of association. The first of these conceived the role of organization as educational, the second as fraternal. The position was enunciated by the *Dental News Letter:* "First, that new facts may be discussed and elucidated, and thus much information obtained; and, secondly, that by the interchange of sentiments and opinions, the courtesies becoming the members of a liberal profession, may be enjoyed." Those holding this view of the purposes of the organization were perturbed at the Society's preoccupation with questions of constitution and legislation. Amos Westcott responded to such critics. "It was necessary to occupy the time in this way till the organization and structure was complete, as to finish a ship before it was sent out to contend with the ocean's storm, and to be an instrument of profit." Westcott readily admitted that these political concerns had retarded the "attainment of some of her professed objects." [34]

This line of reasoning related the first category of criticism to the second. For the major preoccupation of the procedural debates had concerned the details of membership policy. The object of the policy was to draw a line of distinction between the quack and the legitimate operator. This problem was the crux of the difficulty. "An exceedingly delicate judgment is requisite to determine what is quackery," a physician wrote in the *Dental Register.* He then went on to point out that the application of medical and dental knowledge necessitated considerable freedom. "In their use men must think, and every man must think for himself." [35]

Looking back on the fate of the American Society after almost two additional decades of experience, Amos Lawrence, retiring president of the American Dental Association, appraised its actions:

Eleazar Parmly Elisha Townsend

James Taylor S. S. White

Early Leaders in Dental Organization, Education, and Publication

The mandates and required pledges of the society in question were intended to correct certain practices and abuses which were thought to be pernicious, and threatened to become too widely prevalent. No society of our profession was ever organized by better men, nor men influenced by purer motives, than were those of whom I would make honorable mention. Yet it was intolerant of opinion which was its apparent, fatal mistake, expressed in over-abundant legislation, which is not education; nor can it, if sumptuary in character, entail any advantage upon the members of scientific or other associations of men; for the consent of the governed is an important element for consideration in the art of governing.

On the same point, Lawrence observed, "The old 'Blue Laws' of Connecticut were considered well adapted to their time and place; perhaps they were, but it is difficult for us now to imagine any such time or place on this continent or any other." [36]

Yet, it is difficult to see how the founders of organized dentistry could have dealt differently with their problems, given the limitations under which they labored. The American Society of Dental Surgeons rose—and fell—for the advancement of the dental profession. In the words of one of its staunchest defenders, "It could hardly be expected that the first attempt at organizing and conducting a national society should be faultless, yet it has at least served the purpose of a standard to rally under till a more perfect one could be reared." [37]

Chapter VI   THE AMERICAN DENTAL CONVENTION

THE MOVEMENT to supersede the American Society with a new and different organization found its leadership high within the ranks of the Society itself. Elisha Townsend, president during its last years, reasoned that the times had rendered the Society obsolete. The need now, Townsend believed, was to broaden the base of operation, to reorganize the national association of dentists to make it comprehensive and representative of the whole professional talent of the nation. "It cannot answer the best and broadest of its aims in any other way," Townsend insisted. The tiny remnant of the Society that attended its waning sessions dutifully echoed Townsend's views. They agreed that the profession now occupied "a very different position from that which it did when this society was first organized; that however admirably adapted the organization was then for the work assigned it, yet having accomplished, as we believe, that work, and been of vast service to the profession—a broader basis for action" was needed.[1]

Although the Cincinnati meeting of the American Society endorsed its president's recommendations, the process of dissolving or reconstituting the pioneer national dental association was slow. Townsend and the others who sought the advancement of the profession, if necessary at the expense of some of its venerated institutions, could

103

not wait. The summer, 1855, issues of the dental periodicals carried a "Call for a Dental Convention" that aimed to establish a national professional dental organization on a new basis.

Coming, as it did, from the Philadelphia group, which had been agitating under Townsend's leadership for a more inclusive basis of association, the call reflected its sentiments. The summons recited the changes the profession had undergone since the establishment of the American Society—"the elevated standing which it has taken among the sister branches of remedial art; the vast improvement in its educational methods; the great numerical increase of practitioners, and, especially the enlarged liberality of professional sentiment which has grown with its growth." All these considerations, the call declared, demanded a new national dental organization. "Our proposition is, therefore, made to our brethren everywhere, to meet in the spirit of professional brotherhood, and organize such an association as shall be best fitted to satisfy the requirements of the fraternity, and give the best direction to its efforts for advancement in all usefulness and honor." The call then set the time and place of the proposed meeting. The site chosen was Philadelphia, home of a majority of the impressive array of signers of the call.[2]

The dental press gave the call a cordial reception. The reaction of J. R. McCurdy, editor of the *Dental News Letter,* was representative. "It is hoped that there will be a large attendance—that every state will be represented, as the subject is an important one and well worthy the consideration of the profession," he wrote. "The character of the gentlemen having the matter in charge is sufficient guarantee that everything will be done to secure a pleasant and profitable meeting."[3]

As it turned out, the convention drew an amazing response, surprising and gratifying the most sanguine of its promoters. On the appointed day, some eighty to one hundred dentists ("probably the largest meeting of dentists ever held in the world," one reporter thought) convened for the purposes outlined in the call. With a minimum of confusion, and a surprising unanimity of sentiment, these men organized the second national dental association, the American Dental Convention. The majority of those in attendance came from Philadelphia and vicinity, but there was a liberal representation from New York and from the Ohio Valley, while some dentists from as far away as North Carolina and Louisiana to the south, and from New England to the north, signed the roll.[4]

In many ways, the proceedings were remarkable. The *Recorder* noted a "fact, unprecedented . . . in the history of Dental Associations, that none of its originators accepted official positions." Nor was this the extent of the promoters' self-denial. They represented at best a minority on the two major committees of the convention, the nominating committee and the constitutional committee consisting of one member from each state represented at the meeting.[5]

Less surprising, perhaps, than these demonstrations of humility by the founders, was the structure of the new association. In many ways, it departed widely from the precedents of the American Society. The American Dental Convention represented Elisha Townsend's conception of what a national dental society should be. Article Two stated its purposes:

> The association is intended to promote professional and personal intercourse among those who are engaged in the cultivation and practice of dentistry throughout the world; to advance the cause of dental education, and systematize and strengthen the exertions of its friends, and, by a mutual interchange of opinions and experience, to advance knowledge and liberalize the relations of its members.

In accordance with these intentions, the membership requirements were made as simple as possible. Any member of the convention then sitting and "such other practitioners of dentistry and auxiliary branches of science" as might be elected could become members of the American Dental Convention upon signature of the articles. Election could be obtained after nomination by any member of the Convention and acceptance by majority of those voting on the question.[6] The editor of the *Forcep* demonstrated the liberality of the founders' intent when he announced, "We will take pleasure in proposing any gentlemen for membership who will authorize us to do so." [7]

The simplicity of the remainder of the document was in keeping with the determination of the Convention to attend to professional rather than procedural and legislative business. Before each annual session adjourned, the president was required to appoint a Committee on Business that would decide upon the topics to be discussed at the next meeting, assign papers, and so forth. To distribute the control broadly, each state represented at the meeting named one member of the Business Committee. The constitution granted the president some discretion in determining the program. The Convention, nevertheless, reserved to itself the right to alter and amend the program devised by the Business Committee.[8] There could be no question of the determination of the Convention to keep control down on the floor rather than at the chairman's lectern.

Before commencing discussion of practical matters of technique and treatment, the Convention took note of the need for a national society to have the strong support of a widespread network of local organizations.[9] J.F.B. Flagg sponsored a resolution proclaiming the Convention's advocacy of local associations. The ultimate objective in fostering a sound foundation at the grassroots was shrewdly expressed by the editor of the *Dental Register*. "With our present feelings we should like to see State and Local associations with delegates to a national society," he wrote. "This would then be what its name imports; yet until the former become more general, the latter is to some extent impracticable." While the Convention could hardly do more to found local societies than had its predecessor, it may well be that the circumstances were more favorable at this time. Whatever the reason, there can be no doubt that the years following the organization of the American Dental Convention witnessed the founding of many new local, state and regional associations.[10]

Once organizational affairs had been disposed of, the Convention turned its attention to the primary purpose for which it had been founded. The temperate tone of the practical discussions that occupied the balance of the formal sessions excited much comment in the dental press. "There never has been as large and as harmonious a meeting of the dental profession in this country as this proved to be," declared the *News Letter*. The *Recorder* agreed. "We certainly never attended a meeting of Dentists where so many subjects were so sensibly and harmoniously discussed, and where so much good feeling and generous hospitality was exhibited." [11]

According to the reporters, there had been some apprehension that the affair would not come off so smoothly. Not only were the wounds of the amalgam controversy still sore, but the pundits had also anticipated trouble from discussion of the many other controverted materials and modes of treatment then being considered by the profession. "It was to be expected by many that the subject of chloroform in dental surgery would find its way before the Convention, incidentally or otherwise; but, owing to good management, or the great interest of other discussions, it failed to come up," one annalist commented. He explained part of the mystery himself in describing the procedural regulations that governed the discussions. "The adoption and enforcement of the 'five minute' rule, gave all an opportunity to express their opinions upon the subjects discussed, and effectually put a stop to those long-winded philosophers, whose labored efforts are so effectual in wasting time, crushing inquiry, tiring hearers, and disgusting sensible men." In addition to avoiding controversial subjects, and restraining loquacious and prolix remarks, the planners made positive contributions to the *bonhomie* of the meeting.

Undoubtedly much of the good feeling was stimulated by a "collation" in Parkinson's saloon at which the Philadelphians were hosts. In the course of his welcoming remarks, Dr. Townsend confided that it was "the most ardent desire of his heart to see the profession united and meeting together in harmony for the interchange of ideas."

Whether the reason was good management, or good feeling, or a combination of these virtues, the first Convention succeeded in stilling any fears that it was in the hands of partisans. The editor of the *Forcep* assured his readers, "It is not composed of, or intended to supersede, the American Society; it is not amalgam or anti-amalgam, wedded to sponge gold or foil, continuous gum or gutta percha; is not the offspring of any college, association, or clique, and will not debase its 'high intent' for the purposes of personal ambition." Another chronicler concluded, somewhat prematurely, "The experiment has proved in the highest degree successful, and the originators of the move have reason to be proud of the benefit which they have been instrumental in conferring upon a most important branch of science." [12] "We had our fears that the enterprise would not succeed —indeed we were not prepared for such a demonstration, and consequently we have been most agreeably disappointed," the *News Letter* confessed. "And we now firmly believe that the Convention will be a permanent institution; and that it is well calculated to do much good none can deny." The career of the American Dental Convention thus began on a note of high promise and hope for the future.

Good feeling persisted to the very eve of the Convention's second annual meeting. The *Register* urged its "readers of the South and West" to attend. "The fullest report that the journals can give, is at best but a meagre outline of the progressive truths eliminated by the discussions. We feel assured that those who do so, will return to their patrons with refreshed energies, renewed vigor, and enlarged ideas of professional truths." Among the seaboard reviews, the *American Journal,* published in Baltimore, and the *Recorder,* emanating from New York, showed less enthusiasm. The *Dental News Letter,* coming out of Philadelphia, was more deeply committed to the new organization. It announced that "the profession generally are respectfully and earnestly invited to be present." It hoped for "a monster meeting —productive of great good, socially and professionally." [13]

From the *Recorder* came the first indication that there were possibilities of dissension beneath the tranquil surface of the profession. "Our city is soon to be honored by the presence of the Dental Profession 'en masse,'" the June issue announced. The editor promised further information in the next number. In the meantime, he endeavored to stir the New Yorkers into action. "We surmise that Philadelphia will be largely and ably represented; our Philadelphia brethren are used to working together," he began. "They are thoroughly organized and will in all probability succeed in electing one of their number President, and will generally manage affairs to their own satisfaction, while we of New York will have an excellent opportunity of learning how all this is done." [14]

Here was the beginning of a genuine rift in the newly cemented unity of the profession. From Philadelphia came an alarmed denial. "The idea propounded in certain quarters that this is a work, and that a locality, in which Philadelphia and Philadelphians are to preponderate, does great injustice to the very catholic spirit in which the movement was conceived," a correspondent of the *News Letter* protested. The Convention "is a meeting of all, and for all; the natural 'primary assemblage' of the craft; and he does it dishonor who neglects to give to, and get from it, all the advantages which such a liberal intercourse insures," the writer declared. He invoked the aid of everyone "anxious to elevate and advance a profession capable, in its special but acknowledged claims, of such undoubted power in the alleviation of human suffering." He concluded, "In such a cause results are everything—persons and places, comparative trifles."[15] In this atmosphere the second session of the new organization convened. The honeymoon was over.

In many ways, the second session of the American Convention built yet higher the esteem hopefully granted it at its organization. The attendance dwarfed the record-shattering numbers of the organizational meeting. The practice of a large convivial dinner meeting was continued. About 350 members partook of the hospitality of Messrs. Jones, White, and McCurdy, a dental supply house predecessor to today's S. S. White Co. S. S. White gave "a forcible dissertation on the union of the Science and Art of Dentistry in their aesthetical as well as their physical relations," a topic obviously dear to a manufacturer of artificial teeth. "The company did not separate till after midnight."[16]

The advancement over the first session was not solely in terms of numbers and sociability. In one field of action, the attempt of the second Convention to outdo the first occasioned some embarrassment. The membership clauses of the constitution offered admission to "practitioners of dentistry and auxiliary branches of science" upon nomination and acceptance by a majority present in the Convention.[17] Under the circumstances, however, with an attendance more than twice as large as at the original session, the constitutional procedure required considerable time-consuming formal activity in order to enroll all applicants.

Daniel Neall of Philadelphia sought to eliminate the difficulty by proposing a resolution that would admit "all practicing members of the Dental profession who may be present, and feel desirous of co-operating with us." Since this move would violate the constitution, Dr. McQuillen recommended the suspension of the membership articles. This suggestion was adopted, whereupon Neall renewed his proposal and it carried.

This did not fully solve the difficulty, for now a member rose to inquire if the action of the Convention had also seated "gentlemen engaged in auxiliary branches of the profession." There followed an unseemly wrangle that further delayed proceedings and lacerated feelings. The confusion and indecision of this membership episode brought no credit to the Convention. "One thing we could desire," sighed the *News Letter*, house-organ of Jones, White, and McCurdy, "is that the discussion which occurred in the first morning's proceedings in reference to membership and admissions from auxiliary branches, were blotted out, or rather, had never occurred." [18] There were, no doubt, many friends of the Convention who echoed the sentiment.

The second Convention followed the first in urging the formation of local societies. [19] This desire to further local and regional professional association held great promise for the future. But, given the membership policy of the Convention, the conversion of that body to an assembly of delegates was highly improbable. Membership could not easily be restricted to delegates and the large numbers in attendance made it unlikely that delegates of local societies could dominate the deliberations.

In two important areas of professional development, the American Dental Convention assumed national leadership at its second annual meeting. One of the most significant services the association could perform related to the encouragement of innovations in techniques and treatment. Exponents of "auxiliary branches of science" peopling the Convention prevented adoption of a policy favoring the dentist and the public over the inventor and manufacturer. Nonetheless some valuable steps were taken toward a professional policy regarding new devices.

The problem appeared innocently enough. The New York session adopted a statement on the allocation of credit for new improvements. "In the opinion of this body, the credit due for new discoveries or useful modes of operating, belongs more to those who have given those improvements to the profession, than to those who pretend to have discovered the same at a previous period." The next move, in view of the educational purposes of the Convention, was perhaps inevitable, yet could not help but bring trouble upon the Convention. The meeting resolved to "request the members of this Convention and others, who have anything new or useful, to present them at the next meeting." [20]

It was desirable to solicit information about new developments. But the solicitation implied that the Convention might be called upon to evaluate the innovations presented. Furthermore, the invitation to display new improvements could readily be abused. The mere exhibition of a device at the Convention might be exploited by its proprietor as an endorsement. If this difficulty were avoided, other problems remained. Assuming that the Convention undertook to pass upon the merits of the improvements brought forward, how was this to be done without creating dissension? Through the years the Convention would grapple repeatedly with this problem.

The Convention took the lead in another area of professional concern at its second meeting. This was the problem of competition among dentists in the matter of fees. The subject was introduced by a long paper on "Professional Fees," by Elisha Townsend. Townsend's remarks inspired the appointment of a special committee, which acknowledged the importance of the subject and took due account of its complexity.

Notwithstanding the technical difficulties militating against any national fee schedule, the committee ventured to formulate principles for the guidance of the profession. They insisted upon a "fair and liberal fee" for professional counsel and advice. The dentist's charges for services rendered, the committee recommended, should be "such that he shall be well paid for all the time and the best skill he can expend on an operation, and which shall be an inducement for further excellence." Furthermore, the committee averred that preventive measures were "of equal, yea, more value to our patients than that which may arrest or cure." Adoption of the committee report prompted one of the members to return to the subject later in the session. He sponsored a committee to consider the expediency of adopting a scale of minimum prices. A committee was appointed and charged to report at the next meeting. The leadership thus given to the profession induced a number of local and state societies to establish fee bills in the following years.[21]

Late in the year 1856 came the beginning of the sort of attack to which the Convention was peculiarly vulnerable and which eventually led to its supersession by the American Dental Association. An anonymous "Buckeye" delivered himself of some sarcastic "Random Thoughts" regarding the proceedings at New York.

"Buckeye" struck first at a particularly sore point, the Convention's attempt to avoid the rigidity of the structure of the American Society. "Buckeye" called the attention of his readers to "the great advantages derived from combined effort." "It will be seen that the association got itself organized and ready for business, in the short space of five hours from the time the president took the chair," he explained. "Now, no one would be silly enough to believe that this could have been done, had not a few of the most kind-hearted and able-bodied members zealously went [sic] to work, 'moving,' seconding, offering amendments, appealing, making long speeches, etc." The timing, "Buckeye" reasoned, was just right. To get underway in less time might have caused too great a shock, while a longer delay might have alienated the less patient attendants. "Each fragment was held back till just the exact time, and then quietly slid into its proper niche," he recounted admiringly. "We trust it can be 'put through' without such mighty efforts next year. If it can not, it is to be hoped the same force will be on hand, lest raw recruits might fail."

The critic next turned his satiric gaze upon the manners of the debaters. "Buckeye" particularly admired "the beautiful and professional (?) application of the 'self-puff and reciprocal tickle.'" In this department, he made a recommendation: "In the event of a social entertainment at a future meeting, would it not be well to erect a power grindstone, for the accommodation of those who have axes to grind. . . . When an ax has been badly roughened by the quarrels of rival choppers, it grinds harshly on the feelings of a social assembly."[22] This dubious expression probably referred to the long-run effects of participation in the meetings by dental suppliers, a problem that long vexed the leaders of organized dentistry.

When the American Dental Convention met for its third annual meeting in Boston in 1857, the pattern established by the preceding sessions was repeated. The attendance was again impressive, although precision regarding the numbers, as usual, was impossible. Sociability once again figured prominently in the activities of the gathering. The hosts regaled the visitors with a hilarious excursion in Boston Harbor. Altogether, it was a splendid outing, featuring songs, speeches, and general good fellowship.[23]

The question of membership again occasioned perhaps the most spectacular activity. W. W. Allport, the corresponding secretary, explained that his circular notice of the meeting had proved confusing to some recipients:

He meant by 'practicing dentists,' to convey to those who received the circular, the idea that any one could become a member of the Convention who wished. He did not mean that every one could vote without complying with the requirements of the Constitution. It seemed to him proper that every member should sign the Constitution, and pay his proportion of the expenses.

This elicited an eloquent rejoinder from James Taylor:

He thought they did their best to make every dentist in the United States, Europe, Africa and Asia, understand that he was a member as soon as he came here. . . . So far as signing the Constitution was concerned, he thought that was done simply to get the names of those present, and no man was compelled to pay one dime toward the expenses. They took it for granted, and he hoped they always would, that the body of dentists was ready and willing to meet all the expenses that might be incurred.

According to the report, Taylor's spirited remarks provoked applause. Whether the pleasure was prompted by the absence of compulsion to share in the expenses, or by Taylor's ringing declaration of faith in dentists, does not appear.

Elisha Townsend was so moved by the demonstration that he advanced an astonishing idea. He proposed "that they do away with the Constitution altogether, and invite every dentist, everywhere, to become a member." Townsend was supported by William H. Dwinelle, who also suggested that membership include anyone who had ever been a practicing dentist. Not to be outdone, Townsend stated that he should like to see gentlemen connected with other scientific professions in the Convention. He explained that he had learned a great deal in reference to his own profession, from men who knew nothing at all about it. They had given him the results of their investigations, and he made an application of them which they did not dream of. This seemed to be Townsend in a different mood from the one who had opposed the admission of men connected with the auxiliary sciences at the previous meeting.

The conduct of the chairman was different, too. He ruled that a non-practicing dentist could vote on the pending question. Thereupon Dr. Townsend's proposal was adopted. The Convention had done away with its constitution! Townsend then confessed "that this was what he aimed at two years ago, but to speak the whole truth about it he was afraid to undertake to start the movement without something that looked like a piece of red tape to tie up the members."[24]

In other respects, the meeting was not quite so happy. The Business Committee, charged with directing the program, failed, "worse than failed, to perform the principal duty assigned them." Not only did the Committee neglect to publish the topics for perusal in advance of the session, they were unprepared when the Convention was ready to begin the practical discussions that comprised the bulk of their concern. Small wonder, as the *American Journal* complained, that the Convention was not "conducted in a manner altogether best calculated to secure the largest possible amount of practical and accurate scientific information." "It is not to be expected," commented the *Register,* "that men can speak as directly to the point, and as profitably to themselves and others, when totally unprepared, as when they have carefully studied the subjects before them, and selected the language in which to present their views of them." Although the criticisms in both the *Journal* and the *Register* were moderately expressed, their dissatisfaction with the quality of the discussions was plain.[25] Soon the opposition was to become even more outspoken.

The Convention occupied itself with another of its self-made troubles while it waited for the Business Committee to complete preparation of the program. A Doctor Weiber of Paris had transmitted to the president a specimen of a new preparation of gold for filling teeth. The chair proposed that a committee be formed to test the material fairly and thoroughly.

The suggestion set off a lively discussion. A dentist from Boston insisted that the question was one for the whole membership to determine. The Convention, he argued, was not a "Mutual Admiration Society." The gold should be appraised in an open and democratic manner. This position was ably upheld by John Allen of New York, who had had a somewhat unhappy experience with the American Society in a similar matter. Allen declared that "a resolution ought to pass, to the effect, that they would not endorse any improvement brought before them; but that they would examine it, each man looking upon it with reference to its merit or demerit, but not that they were to endorse or reject it as a body." The problem was at length tabled on the motion of Dr. Allport.[26]

Forewarned by the uproar created by the question of Dr. Weiber's gold, the Business Committee persuaded the Convention that "persons having mechanical means or appliances to present . . . [should] deposit them in a separate room for examination."[27] This expedient proved to be the most satisfactory way of dealing with new innovations for many years.

While the Convention met one grave problem by avoiding its settlement and indulged in another practical discussion of dubious merit, on one issue it committed a serious mistake. Christopher W. Spalding of St. Louis pointed out the need for a uniform nomenclature and suggested a committee on the subject to report at the next meeting. Spalding's proposal met opposition. One dentist claimed that Harris's dictionary served the purpose adequately. Spalding denied that the dictionary solved the problem. In the face of criticism, however, he withdrew his proposition.[28] Unfortunately, Spalding was right. The discussion of both mechanical and operative dentistry was gravely hampered by the inadequacies of the nomenclature. J. Richardson of Cincinnati expressed some alarm. "The almost unintelligible descriptions which immediately preceded, and which unquestionably provoked the motion, should have suggested to that body the propriety and the wisdom of devising some means to abate, in some degree at least, that insufferable proclivity to a sort of *hotch-potch* use of descriptive terms so common among writers." The author then offered an array of examples, drawn from the reports of the Convention and recent journal articles, of the misuse of terms applicable to mechanical dentristry. Richardson was not the only thoughtful dentist who was perturbed by the distressingly casual usages of much current technical discourse.[29]

Bound up with the controversy over a formalized nomenclature was a more profound disagreement regarding the proper objects of dental investigations and disquisitions. Many active practitioners held that their concern should lie wholly with matters of practice and technique. Others felt that such exercises were barren without knowledge of the scientific principles underlying them. As time passed, this division within the profession became more and more pronounced.

Happily, the Convention performed with real credit in other directions. The assembly showed an awareness of the importance of opposing patent abuses. Dr. Dwinelle brought before the Convention the case of a patented improvement, "which he said had been used by the profession long prior to the date of said patent." One of the Convention, Dwinelle announced, was being sued for violation of the patent. The session resoundingly indicated its sympathy for the victim and offered aid. Subsequently, the offer of aid was rescinded on the grounds that the action would prejudice any assistance they might be called upon to render as witnesses in the suit. In later years, the Convention did, nevertheless, extend financial aid to the defendant in this suit.[30]

One of the actions taken by the Convention at its third meeting, perhaps the most interesting and significant, was that relating to research. The chief exponent of the idea was Jonathan Taft. At his instance, Alvan Blakesley of Utica presented the conception to the Convention. Blakesley was convinced that there was a definite way of getting at the matter of diseased teeth, and the remedy. He thought the problem must be bound up in the effect of foods upon the teeth. He proposed, therefore, that the Convention "institute a fund and employ one or more competent persons, whose time should be occupied in the analysis of the various grains and vegetables in their natural state and after they were cooked."

Blakesley admitted that he had no knowledge of these matters. He lacked the time to undertake the investigations himself. He wanted all this matter put into such a condensed shape, that in a few minutes he could ascertain all he wished to know. The speaker declared that he was willing to be taxed from ten to fifty dollars a year to promote an object of this kind. The proposition was greeted with applause. Taft spoke on its behalf. "Everyone could see the propriety of this, and the beneficial results that would accrue to the whole profession if Dr. B.'s suggestion was carried out," he exclaimed. "Take, for instance, decayed teeth," he went on, "Did not the discussions of the last three days show that there was no fixed opinion with regard to the cause?" Taft was sure that the facts could be discovered, "if some one would take hold of the subject, and work away at it until he had attained the truth of the matter." "A hundred good objects . . . [are obvious]," he declared, "[that] would be subserved by this."

The proposition undoubtedly pleased a majority of the auditors. There were, however, some objections. One dentist remarked sourly

Jonathan Taft   J. H. McQuillen

that Dr. Johnson's "Chemistry of Common Life," contained "all the information desired on this subject." Another objected, "with all due respect to the gentleman who had introduced this resolution, and to those who had advocated it," that the idea came too late. "Now the field had been gone over, the science of chemistry had been very fully developed with reference to every branch of art." Opposition came from other directions as well. One critic objected that the scheme would restrict the freedom of the Convention. This dentist "wanted one society in the country, where every man could come in and speak his thoughts, and when he went away, profit by what he had learned." It was not clear whether the speaker feared that discovery of the truth would leave them with nothing to talk about or he really opposed the check that rigorous methods would put on speculation. Perhaps he merely felt, as some of his colleagues did, that the hiring of a research specialist would discourage private investigations.

A member of practical bent suggested that it was easier to pass resolutions than to raise funds. He wanted to know how the funds were to be raised. There was no use, he thought, in adopting the policy unless they could finance it. Optimistic answers to this latter objection were readily forthcoming. Advocates of the scheme were sure that widespread support was to be had for the asking. Taft was certain the Convention "could easily find ten men who would give from ten to one hundred dollars a year." He added that "he was astonished that any man should think that the science of chemistry was now perfected . . . when they came to bring chemistry to bear upon their profession, and saw how little was known on the subject, and began to open their eyes to the fact that they knew nothing at all." Loud applause endorsed Taft's description of the sorry state of dental chemistry. The Convention then resoundingly adopted the policy and resolved to appoint a committee to oversee the work. As an afterthought, the Convention even established the committee and authorized it to solicit contributions from "all members of the Dental Profession."[31]

This decision precipitated widespread discussion—and disappointingly little action. "Every one will perceive at a glance, the objects aimed at in the above resolutions," the champions thought. "It is to open up the hidden treasures of the collateral sciences, and make them tributary, more than hitherto, to the dental specialty, and to bring to full view, things that have as yet been seen only in the dim and uncertain twilight, as well as to bring forth, from total obscurity, agents, processes and principles, that shall develop our young science with far greater rapidity and certainty than heretofore." The foes of the measure scorned the scheme as a "most preposterous thing, . . . the most humiliating confession of [the profession's] imbecility." "Shame on the men who could vote for such a resolution," cried its adversaries. "Have we come so low as to be mere mechanics, leaving the scientific part of our work to some man or other who does the thinking for us for dollars and cents?"[32]

Since the Convention had granted the authority for the raising of funds for the project, the partisans of the scheme could afford to be temperate in their response to criticism. "It is not supposed for a moment, that by the above arrangement everybody is going to quit studying," they replied. "By no means. Every one will do all he can, and be encouraged to do more thinking than before, from the fact that if he has but time to sprinkle his thoughts on paper, and send that to the committee or experimenter their value will be at once thoroughly and efficiently tested by careful experiment."

Confident of their rectitude, the friends of the research project set about raising the funds. They even optimistically selected a scientist and obtained his consent to conduct the investigations and experiments.[33] To no avail. Many assurances of support and approbation came into the hands of the committee. The North Carolina State Dental Society recorded its approval.[34] Some four thousand circulars were addressed to the members of the profession, so far as their names and addresses were known. In response, the committee received promises of cooperation, commendation "in the highest terms"—but "small remittances." At the Cincinnati meeting of the Convention in the following year the committee conceded that the response had been discouraging. They blamed the failure of the scheme on "the peculiar character of the times" resulting from the onset of the economic Panic of 1857.[35]

From the time of the Boston meeting, outspoken criticism of the Convention became more common in the dental press. There were complaints of the haphazard discussion, the incongruous mixture of sense and nonsense, that characterized the technical portions of the proceedings. That the complaints were not unwarranted, even the staunchest supporters of the Convention had to admit. The crux of the difficulty seemed to be a lack of organization, which hampered the endeavors of the ablest members to direct the discussions along fruitful lines. The severest of the critics readily allowed that meetings of the practitioners of any scientific pursuit, "if properly conducted, must of necessity tend to elevate the profession in the eye of the world." To accomplish this end, the meetings should be organized on as liberal a basis as the nature of the science would permit. Up to this point, critic and defender were in agreement. But here the critic insisted: "Such conventions cannot possibly fulfil their purposes if they are without system or rules."[36]

In some of the critics, there was already evident a desire for a more exclusive organization on the grounds that this would tend to enhance the value of its proceedings. "If, in the organization of societies for the advancement of dentistry, high professional qualifications were required as a test of membership, their transactions would certainly be more interesting and instructive, and as a consequence, productive of more good," the *American Journal's* editor expostulated. "We trust the day is not distant when such an association of dentists shall be formed. . . . In the meantime, we trust the American Dental Convention will adopt a constitution and laws for the government of its proceedings." [37]

Although the beginnings of a desire to supersede the American Dental Convention may be discerned by the spring of 1858 in such comments as those just noted, the Convention still had valuable work to do and systematic efforts to form a new society did not appear until the following year. In the meantime, the American Dental Convention held its fourth annual session and for the first time met to the west of the Appalachians. As there had been at Boston, there was some falling off of numbers from the high figure established at the New York meeting. Perhaps, as one observer believed, "the deficiency in numbers was more than compensated for by the earnest spirit manifested by those assembled." The shortage was in considerable degree due to the very small attendance from the seaboard. Since the West and Southwest held a majority of the membership, the elections and appointments to office reflected this bias. The leading candidates for the presidency were both from the Mississippi Valley. The executive committee drew four of its five members from west of the mountains. Even the site for the next convocation seemed to indicate the preponderance of western votes. [38]

Some of the business of the Convention was not without interest. One member proposed that the executive committee seek fare concessions from the railroads, alleging that this was already the custom of the roads with regard to "Conventions,—religious and secular." The session heard a discouraging report relative to the progress of the great scheme for establishing a paid research scientist. And most significantly, at the urging of H. J. McKellops of St. Louis, the Convention, following the leadership of the Western Dental Society, appointed a committee to memorialize Congress "on the necessity of appointing dentists for service in the regular army."[39] This was the inception of a long struggle. The assumption of this responsibility by the profession in the interests of the nation has been a function of organized dentistry ever since.

S. S. White found the Cincinnati discussions "somewhat remarkable." "The interest . . . almost amounted to enthusiasm in both speakers and listeners," he wrote somewhat ambiguously. He thought "the debates were of a higher character, and gave evidence of a more extensive knowledge of the subjects under discussion, and a more earnest and philosophic spirit of inquiry, than most of those which had preceded them."[40]

Although there were those whose satisfaction with the discussions at Cincinnati was more qualified than White's, the dental press generally was pleased. The *Register* reviewed the professional results of the Cincinnati meeting with complacency. "A great many new ideas were advanced, some of them very valuable, and a few otherwise. There were no startling new developments, but many new particulars, and shades of difference in practice, and special manipulations, that will be very valuable to those who heard them and improve thereby." The writer emphasized these virtues of the Convention in exhorting the laggard element to give their support to the organization.[41]

In spite of the bright outlook fostered by these indications of improvement in the quality of the Convention sessions, an influential faction in the profession was unimpressed. These dentists felt that the American Dental Convention did not and could not answer the true needs of dentistry. The efforts of these men through the winter eventuated in a call for yet another national dental organization, the American Dental Association, to which the present society of the same name traces its origin.

International Hotel, Niagara Falls, August 3, 1859

Smithsonian Institution, Washington, D. C., July 31, 1860

Sites of the First Meetings of the American Dental Association

Chapter VII   THE AMERICAN DENTAL ASSOCIATION

THE MAJOR STEPS by which the organization of the American Dental Association was effected were relatively simple. The dissatisfaction of some prominent dentists over what they considered the deficiencies of the American Dental Convention resulted in consideration of a different expedient. The proposals for a new organization did not apparently menace the continuance of the existing national society. Hence even the most devoted adherents of the Convention viewed the new movement without antagonism. The element seeking a new form of national organization was thus able to operate in the open. The principal landmarks along the path are abundantly clear.

The campaign that resulted in the establishment of the American Dental Association began in the spring of 1859. The April issue of the *Dental News Letter* carried an article by J. H. McQuillen, writing under the pseudonym, "Junius." Dr. McQuillen set forth a series of objections to the American Dental Convention and advanced the principles upon which, he thought, a proper national dental organization should rest. The basic conception related to membership policy. According to McQuillen, the members of the national body should be representative of the *organized* profession. The new association would be composed of delegates chosen by the membership of the local and state societies and the faculties of the dental schools.[1]

McQuillen, meanwhile, had circulated a memorial among Philadelphia dentists advocating the establishment of a national association upon a representative basis. At a meeting of the Pennsylvania Association of Dental Surgeons on April 6, 1859, McQuillen brought the matter before that organization. J. Foster Flagg sponsored a motion to put the society behind the movement. As a result, the president appointed McQuillen and Flagg to correspond with the colleges and societies on the subject. A fortnight later, they reported favorable reactions from twelve of fourteen societies addressed. The memorial now having the signatures of "a number of practitioners in different parts of the Union," the Pennsylvania Association directed the committee to send copies to the dental journals for publication.[2] Accordingly, the summer issues of the dental press carried a "Call for a National Association on a Representative Basis."

There were eighty-nine signatures to the document. Thirty of these, by far the largest number from any single city or state, were Philadelphians'. The major cities of the central valley supplied most of the remainder. Eight Cincinnati dentists endorsed the call. Cleveland furnished seven, as did Detroit. Chicago and St. Louis each had eight names on the list. Indianapolis contributed four signatures. The remainder of the signers showed a scattering distribution with Ohio and Pennsylvania supplying fifteen names. There was one lone signer from the South. None came from any of the eastern seaboard centers other than Philadelphia.[3]

Publication of the call elicited lively discussion among the profession. The Cincinnati Association of Dental Surgeons aired the subject fully upon receipt of word from McQuillen and Flagg. While its reaction was favorable (the members present signed the call), the society confided the appointment of delegates to a committee with power to act at discretion.[4] Editorials appearing in two successive issues of the *Register* showed the ambivalence of the Cincinnatians. "T." declared, "We consider the formation of the contemplated Association, an event in the Dental Profession in the United States, and one that will influence it much in the future. It is a matter in which all should feel interested and be represented as far as possible." In the next issue, "W."[5] expressed some doubts. "As to the formation of a delegated National Society, we have only to say that the idea, if properly carried out, is a good one. Such an organization is not at all incompatible with the continuance of the Convention, or, if it is, we are opposed to it, at the present time." For all their reservations about the matter, the Cincinnati dentists acted vigorously to ensure adequate representation at the proposed meeting. Both the Mississippi Valley Association and the Ohio Dental College Association held special meetings to choose delegates to Niagara.[6]

The Pennsylvania society, which, of course, had been privy to the scheme from its inception, convened in mid-May to select its representatives. The president of the Indiana association, J. F. Johnston, handled the matter somewhat differently. Johnston received the communication from McQuillen and Flagg and signed the call. Presumably he also secured the signatures of some of his Indianapolis colleagues. He did not consider that he had the authority to convene a special meeting of his society. He did not, he said later, deem it advisable or necessary, even if he had the power. Instead, he conducted a poll by mail of his membership. And he headed the Indiana delegation to Niagara himself.[7]

By whatever means they were chosen, twenty-six men from eight dental societies and two colleges gathered at the International Hotel in Niagara Falls on August 3, 1859. The turnout was hardly cause for elation. Although McQuillen and Flagg claimed to have received favorable responses from twelve societies, only eight sent delegates. Since the instigators of the move had corresponded with fourteen organizations, this means that only a little more than half of the existing associations were represented. Furthermore, the representatives who did appear constituted only about half of those chosen. The Pennsylvania society, for example, chose eight delegates and granted them authority to name substitutes. Nevertheless, only four members attended from that organization.[8]

Moreover, the roll reveals a pronounced regional bias. A scant five of these men represented the entire eastern seaboard. They were all Philadelphians, four from the Pennsylvania Association and a faculty member from the Pennsylvania College. Two men participated from the Pittsburgh society. St. Louis sent two emissaries; the Western Dental Society two. J. F. Johnston and two colleagues spoke for Indiana's state organization. Two delegates represented the Mississippi Valley Dental Association. The largest block of delegates was credited to the Ohio Dental College Association. This body registered seven men. The local society in Cincinnati sent two delegates; the Ohio Dental College faculty one. It is apparent not only that the Middle West dominated this initial assembly of the American Dental Association, but that the most significant dental group represented at the meeting was Cincinnati. This included not only the local society but also the Ohio Dental College and the Ohio Dental College Association, comprising the owners of the college and its alumni, which met annually in Cincinnati. Here, likewise, the Mississippi Valley Association of Dental Surgeons customarily convened.

Thus, although Philadelphia might claim the initiative in the movement for a national representative association, Cincinnati plainly dominated the first meeting.[9] Nevertheless, the eastern contingent could hardly have complained of the way the proceedings developed. In spite of the fact that the Ohioans had viewed the proposal for a new society with some misgivings, no doubts or disagreements marred the record of the Niagara meeting. Implementation of McQuillen's scheme was virtually unopposed.

After the session was organized, its first move was the selection of a committee to draft a constitution for submission to the convention and for final adoption at the next annual meeting. It was at first proposed that this committee consist of one member from each delegation. Johnston, however, led a move to reduce the group to a more efficient three-man panel. McQuillen appropriately headed the group. He was aided by William Wright of Pittsburgh and James Richardson of Cincinnati. The session accepted the report of the constitutional committee. Then, on the motion of James Taylor of Cincinnati, the meeting referred it back to the committee with instructions to mature and amend, if necessary, and publish in the journals. Next, the convention fixed the time and place for its next meeting. The question of the permanence of the organization was thus implicitly answered in the affirmative, apparently without any debate or discussion. Briskly, the founders disposed of the remaining business. They urged the formation of societies where none existed so that the next meeting would be more fully representative; they stipulated that delegates must be "practitioners of Dental Surgery," and fixed the proportion of delegates to members; they assigned five of their number to prepare papers to be read at the next meeting. Then the first meeting of the American Dental Association adjourned.[10]

True to its instructions, the Committee on the Constitution published a draft of the document in the dental press in the autumn issues of 1859. Opinions of the proposals, both criticisms and rebuttals, appeared in abundance. Much of the debate revolved, as always, around the question of membership policy. The comments of "Junius," which had launched the debate in the preceding spring, recalled the earliest days of organizational history when he declared, "Every member of the profession, fully impressed with the dignity and importance of his calling, must deplore the inferior qualifications of many who have been long engaged in practice, and of numbers of those who annually enter the ranks of the profession." McQuillen's Philadelphia colleague, Flagg, struck the same note, expressing the concern of many dentists about the undiscriminating character of the American Dental Convention. Even more reminiscent of the American Society was the editorial comment in the *Dental News Letter:* "We shall always hold it to be necessary, that our profession shall have some great head, some flag to march under, some mark of distinction by which to identify the fully competent from the tyro or indolent and wilfully ignorant. A standard of qualification must some day be established." The principal characteristic that differentiated these strictures from those of an earlier day lay in the fact that the later examples did not impugn the motives of those they criticized.[11]

The critics of a new society on a representative basis also felt the resemblance to the original American Society. The memory of that ill-fated venture remained fresh in the minds of the profession. Jonathan Taft, for example, believed that the scheme was "invested ... with an air of aristocratic exclusiveness, ... [and, therefore,] would create ill-feeling and jealousy on the part of a large class of practitioners." Another critic claimed that the reliance for membership upon local societies, far from obviating the charge of exclusiveness, would aggravate it. "Local societies are all cliques, (I guess they don't claim to be anything else,) and their representatives would necessarily partake of the same."[12]

Others pointed to the unequal distribution of local organizations as fostering division in the profession. McQuillen had tried to avoid this difficulty by providing for members by invitation from sections of the United States not otherwise represented at the meeting. But this feature, too, roused the old suspicions. "What shall be taken as an evidence of a dentist being in *reputable* standing from sections of the country not otherwise represented?'" queried one skeptical journalist. "There are many dentists of reputable standing in more ways than one, who are not capable of representing their profession at a national society." Another doubter expressed the positive side of the criticism. Could it be possible, he asked, to have a national association hedged in by a constitution and laws which would avoid discrimination among membership applicants of equal merit? [13]

Dentists constructively concerned with the problems of organized dentistry recognized the membership dilemma clearly. Somehow a mode or modes of organization had to be devised that would do two seemingly contradictory things. A national society had to serve as a unifying force in the profession. It must also be so constituted that it could justly claim to be the spokesman for American dentistry. At the same time, in the interests of efficiency as well as prestige, it could not comprise the entire profession. To accomplish its business, its numbers had to be relatively small. It had to base its membership qualifications on high standards, standards that many dentists, to whom it had to look for support, could not meet. In the deliberations of the Cincinnati society concerning the proposed representative association, Charles Bonsall defended the American Dental Convention as indispensable to the interests of the profession. Nevertheless, Bonsall recognized that the Convention was not perfect. "If it was faulty in its organization," he declared, "it was in being too democratic, as its predecessor was too strict or exclusive." Somehow the balance had to be struck.[14]

This was the virtue, in McQuillen's eyes, of the basis he proposed for the American Dental Association. "To give it stability and character, and deprive it of any approach to a clique, the proper basis of such an organization would be a representative body, composed of delegates that have received their appointments from permanently organized Dental Societies, and regularly constituted Dental Colleges." [15] Indeed, such an arrangement appeared to have many advantages that earlier systems of membership had not enjoyed.

None of the contemporaries formulated the argument in so many words, but it must have been evident that a representative basis neatly avoided the difficulties of the exclusive-or-inclusive dilemma. The proposed organization would be exclusive and would have the prestige that exclusiveness might be expected to give it. Yet, because it did not control the selection of its members, it could not be charged with being a self-perpetuating clique.

Only one observer noted a significant characteristic of the projected organization that later was to create difficulties. An anonymous correspondent of the dental press summarized the membership dilemma as it had emerged during the consideration of the new plan. "The charge of *exclusiveness* has already been made—and some little feeling on this ground has shown itself—which charge is based partly on that feature in the proposed Constitution which provides for 'members by invitation,' and partly from an impression that it is gotten up in opposition to the American Dental Convention, and, also, that it is not so democratic and *inclusive* as the latter body." The writer then probed the possible shortcomings of the representative association. He feared that a difficulty might arise because the few associations and colleges of that day might fail even to take up their full representation. Alone among the commentators, this reporter noted the tendency, under the proposed organization, to place control of the policies in the hands of the permanent members, who attained this status after service as delegates, rather than in the hands of the delegates fresh from the grass roots of the profession. And even this shrewd analyst failed to appreciate the difficulties inherent in this feature of the scheme.[16]

As a matter of fact, by far the greatest emphasis in these debates was on the encouragement a national association of dental societies would give to local organization. "Junius" insisted that this factor overcame the objection that his scheme was premature because there were not yet enough local bodies to form a group of delegates of any size. This drawback would decrease each year because of the stimulus such an association would give to the development of local societies. A contributor to the *American Dental Review* reasoned that the direct tendency of such an organization would be to create new state, county, and city associations. Indeed, many spokesmen urged the formation of local and state societies to broaden representation in the new organization. A correspondent of the *Dental Cosmos* explained that the existing societies of the middle west, such as the St. Louis and the western associations, failed to represent the profession adequately. "Who? Alas, of all the dentists in the State of Illinois, Chicago included, generally attend the meetings of that [Western] society?" [17]

One critic thought local organizations tended to elevate standards in the profession. McQuillen, too, believed that improvement in the quality of dental services would come by means of local societies because dentists would be stimulated to study and investigate the science, and practice the art with increased benefit to their patients. Furthermore, the exchange of views in local organizations would improve the ability of dentists to communicate their findings in a clear and comprehensive manner. [18]

One author, who was distressed by the poor qualifications of many practitioners, thought that mere membership in a local society should not suffice to admit a delegate to membership in the national association. Some external test of capability should be required; otherwise, he pointed out, the national society would not be better than the character of the local societies sending delegates. [19] For most dentists, however, the suggestion of a national association of dental societies had the desired effect. McQuillen exhorted the unorganized areas not "to remain, as doubters and tide-waiters, in a state of glorious and masterly inactivity," but to set about at once the business of organizing to insure their representation in the new society. And many other voices were raised on the same theme. [20]

The debates over the proposed constitution displayed some uncertainty regarding the relationship of the national organization to the profession.

Jonathan Taft and J. H. McQuillen exaggerated the force of the pronouncements of a national association in spite of the adverse experiences of the American Society of Dental Surgeons. James Taylor, on the other hand, went to the opposite extreme and minimized the influence that a national organization could exercise provided it understood its limit. According to McQuillen, the Association would possess a combination of the qualities of a supreme court and of a legislative body. "Consisting of delegates, representing on a liberal scale every interest of the profession, . . . it would exercise an influence and wield a power possessing all the force and energy of a government." [21]

Taft, in the course of the Cincinnati society's examination of McQuillen's suggestions, discussed the relationship between the Convention and the proposed representative body. The two organizations, he thought, could exist without conflict because the Association would probably be concerned with adjudication of questions which were outside the functions of the American Convention. He argued that the new society would be "a tribunal of last resort for the decision of matters that could not be authoritatively settled elsewhere." This conception of the role of a national dental organization smacked strongly of the views of the defunct American Society. Taylor pointed out that the fatal mistake of the pioneer association had been to sit in judgment on the "right of private opinion." He doubted that dentists were any more tolerant of aggression in that direction now than they had been.[22] The best evaluation of the society's role in this connection came from an editor of the *Dental Register*. In response to the query whether the new association would make laws for the profession, he replied, "It most certainly will not, at least farther than to lay down rules of ethics and recommend them, leaving it to the enlightened judgment of the members of the profession whether they adopt them or not." The editor then stated the principles that ought to govern this limited conception of the legislative prerogative. "Any such rules and regulations adopted, should so harmonize with reason and good sense, as to recommend themselves to the good judgment of all."[23]

While much of the discussion of McQuillen's plan dealt with procedural matters, these were all subordinate to the various conceptions of the service the new society could perform for the profession. In general, these ideas fell into two categories. The first concerned the improvement of the standards and quality of the profession itself. McQuillen and Flagg complained that the American Dental Convention had not stimulated such advances. Another practitioner admitted that the Convention was not competent to undertake scientific investigation. Its purpose, rather, was to raise the level of competency in the profession by instructive discourse on practical points.[24]

Among the advocates of a new association who desired higher standards, the sentiment constantly emerged that dental knowledge on the strictly scientific level was grossly inadequate. The importance of mere handicraft dexterity should not be exaggerated. A critic spoke scornfully of the devotion of the Convention to "that mighty subject of filling teeth." An opponent of the representative scheme contended that matters of practice could not be settled by legislative fiat in the existing state of dental knowledge. "We know but little about the causes of caries and some other diseases of the teeth; and as to their treatment, we are nothing but empirics." [25] No stronger criticism of dental science was voiced by any contemporary. This comment from the opposing camp indicates the deep consciousness of the inadequacy of dental knowledge.

McQuillen dwelt at some length on the scientific advantages sure to accrue under the scheme he proposed. He argued that the delegates would be chosen for their abilities and attainments. If these superior dentists divided the dental field among them for investigation, their findings would elevate the professional standard by developing a more accurate science and a more perfect art.

He then emphasized the influence that group enterprise would have on the individual practitioner. "The combined influence of national and local societies would develop that desire for mental cultivation, literary research, and scientific investigation so much needed on the part of individual members of the profession." [26]

One aspect of the discussion was the comparatively small interest displayed in the importance of the relationship of organized dentistry and the community. From time to time a critic of the Convention would complain that the inanities of some of the discussions did the reputation of the profession no good. For the most part, the spokesmen of the profession regarded the public benefits from dental organizations as being, at best, indirect. It was argued that properly conducted dental societies would instruct the practitioner as to the qualifications that would merit the respect and confidence of the "intelligent portion of the community and the profession." McQuillen insisted on regular additions to the national organization of "the young and growing intellect of the profession." This was necessary, he explained, to "enable it to command not only the respect of the dental profession, but the votaries of other sciences."

Proponents of the representative type of organization emphasized that they were following a form devised by "some of the brightest and best minds of our country . . . the American Medical Association." The reforms in dental organization were urged because they would establish dentistry as "a liberal profession." The frequent recurrence of the emphasis on professional status in contrast to the incidental references to public welfare clearly indicates the priority of the former in the minds of the dentists.[27]

Occasionally, the debate over the proposed American Dental Association lapsed almost into bitterness. "Bourbon" suggested in the *Register* that "his excellency the Grand Duke of *Tusc*-any" be called to preside over the new society. "He certainly would purge the association of its 'democratic' element, and place it at once on a high and honorable basis." "E.T.," in the same organ, questioned the maturity and deliberation alleged to undergird the proposed constitution. Even if there had been nothing to distract or divide the attention of the founders, he doubted that a truly satisfactory document could have emerged in so short a time. "But when it is remembered that the American Dental Convention was in session, that the place was *Niagara*, with all its attractions, and Blondin besides, it would be unreasonable to expect a suitable report from *any* body [*sic*] on such short notice." [28]

Criticism in this vein goaded McQuillen into an indignant defense of the proposed organization. Particularly cutting was his reaction to the charge of exclusiveness. "He who objects to the establishment of such an organization, on the ground that it is anti-democratic and exclusive, fails to remember that where a large number are interested, and it is impossible for the entire body to meet, that a representative basis is absolutely demanded, and that such representation is *eminently democratic,* and only exclusive so far as the wilfully ignorant are concerned."

These examples from both sides of the controversy awakened echoes of the exciting, but unedifying, feuds of an earlier day, and indicated the divisive possibilities in the situation.[29] Fortunately, a considerable number of dentists viewed the possibility of rival national organizations with more equanimity. Some even denied that the Convention and the representative Association would be at all competitive. "If the Convention does not meet the wants of a large portion of the profession, why not at once form a National Society? and let all who wish to join do so, and then abandon the Convention, or still continue with it, and be a member of the society also," one such dentist suggested. Being a member of the one should not disqualify one for membership in the other. Editorials in the *News Letter* and the *Register* also strongly favored continuance of both national organizations.[30]

Much of the discussion preceding the inauguration of the American Dental Association dwelt on considerations of practical politics. On the eve of the Niagara meeting, the *New York Dental Journal*, faithful to the interests of its constituents, thought that the movement was "impolitic," on the grounds that the Middle Atlantic and Eastern states lacked organizations and would thus be unrepresented. "If this change is made . . . , it will be justly regarded by many as an effort calculated to create a sectional spirit of rivalry and divide our common interests by geographical lines." The *Journal*, for itself, disavowed such suspicions, but it insisted that the charge of sectionalism would be made. It hoped that a national organization would be deferred until the wishes of the profession throughout the country could be made known.[31]

The desire to be represented in any national organization of dental societies stimulated activity in local organizations throughout the country. Local societies were formed in both the city and state of New York during the year following the Niagara convention, but they failed to yield delegations to the Washington meeting in 1860. According to one source, the lamentable "finessing of some two or three members of the New York City Society" prevented the latter's participation. Kentucky dentists inaugurated a state society, whose delegates appeared at the 1860 meeting, but no other new state dental associations from the West sent representatives to Washington. A regional organization, the Northern Ohio Dental Association, came into existence in Cleveland. It chose delegates, but their names do not appear among those in attendance at the Washington meeting. A representative of the newly-established Mad River Valley Dental Association participated in the deliberations. And a local society in the host city seems to have been formed for the occasion. Georgia dentists organized and dispatched a delegate to Washington. The Michigan State Dental Association, which had been in existence since 1856, sent a spokesman to the Washington meeting. On the other hand, only six of the eight initiating societies, and only one of the two colleges, had delegations in attendance when the American Dental Association convened in 1860. Twenty-three dentists, in all, par-

ticipated. On this occasion, the Philadelphia contingent, eight practitioners from the Pennsylvania society and one professor from the
college faculty, was the largest, but delegates from the interior valley
numbered eleven, almost exactly half of the convention. The failure
of a delegation from the Ohio Dental College Association to make
an appearance cost the Middle West its dominant position. Efforts
to bring the organization to maturity over the winter had not been
conspicuously successful. Nonetheless, the present-day American
Dental Association traces its origins in a direct line back to those
inauspicious conclaves at Niagara Falls in 1859 and in Washington
in 1860.[32]

As mentioned previously, the Committee on the Constitution published a draft of their document in the dental press during the
autumn of 1859. The debate, besides arguing the merits of the proposal in general terms, also narrowed to deal with specific provisions
of the document and their implementation. The constitution echoed
the proposals of J. H. McQuillen in his "Junius" paper. The members
of the representative organization were to be exclusively practitioners of dentistry. Three categories of members were provided for:
delegates of local dental societies, members by invitation, and permanent members, the latter class to consist of those who had served
as delegates. The members by invitation were to represent sections
of the country lacking local organizations to sponsor delegates.[33]

This scheme for membership for the new Association was openly
borrowed from the "Plan of Organization" of the American Medical
Association. According to "Junius," this plan of membership had been
successfully used by the physicians for many years, but the plea that
the dentists should emulate their scheme became a source of further polemics in the debates over the suggested constitution. The
significance of the controversy—and the dependence on the structural details of the medical organization—can be fairly accurately
described.[34]

The American Medical Association emerged from the deliberations of a national convention of delegates from local societies and

medical colleges that met in New York in 1846 and completed its deliberations in Philadelphia in 1847.[35] Thus, while it was not so old as the earliest national dental society, the experience of a dozen years under the scheme had fully exhibited its features. Yet, by accident or intent, McQuillen, in his proposals for a delegated society, overlooked a very significant feature of the membership provisions of the American Medical Association. McQuillen followed the physicians' "Plan of Organization" correctly in providing for three classes of membership: delegates, members by invitation, and permanent members. He failed, however, to note that the original "Plan of Organization" denied permanent members the right to vote on questions before the Association. Such was still the phraseology of the "Plan of Organization" of the A.M.A. in 1859 when McQuillen prepared his "Junius" paper.[36]

McQuillen's plan for the American Dental Association, in contrast, granted full participation in the society's activities to the permanent members. This feature was noted and commented upon in the dental press during the winter of 1859-60 while the project was gestating. "The only thing that looks like trouble ahead in the membership is that every delegate becomes a permanent member, having a right to attend all the meetings and vote on all questions, etc.," wrote "Reviewer" in the *Cincinnati Dental Lamp*. "Once a member, always a member—I am not prepared to say that this is wrong, . . . yet the practical working of the system must be to give many of our local societies a full representation." In 1863, this point was fully discussed in the Pennsylvania Association of Dental Surgeons. Some members objected to the re-election of former delegates. It was urged that such re-election was in direct opposition to the design and interests of the Association, by limiting the number of its members and the extent of its influence, and in preventing the attendance of those who were desirous of becoming members and participating in its deliberations.[37]

Whatever doubts there may have been about the manner of designating permanent members, the dental association's constitution, adopted in 1860, placed permanent members on an equal basis with delegates. For many years these men, rather than the delegates, governed the Association, supplying the majority of its officers and much of the substance to the scientific discussions.

In the remaining articles of the first draft of the constitution of the American Dental Association, there is relatively little that can be traced directly to the "Plan of Organization" of the American Medical Association. The membership article of that document stated that its members "shall collectively represent and have cognizance of the common interests of the medical profession in every part of the United States. . . ." A portion of the dentists' constitution follows this phraseology almost exactly. Article Two, stating the objects of the Association, concludes with the words "to collectively represent and have cognizance of the common interests of the dental profession in every part of the United States." The source of the phrase seems evident, but the conception is hardly unique. The idea must surely have found some expression in the dentists' code whether the physicians' plan was consulted or not.[38]

In any event, not all the dentists of the day were impressed by the achievements of "the brightest minds of the country." And one defender of the proposed constitution of the American Dental Association ventured to suggest that the dentists' scheme was superior to that of their medical colleagues. Defending the constitution against the charge of "verbosity," he declared, "This charge falls to the ground when it is known that the proposed plan is half the length of the constitution of the American Medical Association."[39]

We have seen that a substantial part of the debate over the new organization centered on its role in advancing the scientific standing of dentistry. Some of the arguments hopefully suggested that the American Dental Association be made the instrument for this purpose. "For, as those branches of professional knowledge are pursued which require the higher faculties of the mind for their development, so will dentistry be entitled to a place among the liberal professions," argued the editor of the *American Journal.* "The observance of this truth, the violation of which has heretofore justly caused the dentist to be looked upon as a mere craftsman, deeply concerns all future advancement."[40]

McQuillen's Committee on the Constitution met these aspirations by providing the machinery by which they might be realized. A series of standing committees were created in order to investigate the existing state of dental science and techniques.

These committees divided the field among them in a fashion calculated to reveal the existing state of dental science and technique. The scheme contemplated annual reports on dental physiology and dental chemistry, embracing, if practicable, the results of original investigations. Another category subsumed dental pathology and surgery. This committee was to study every thing that appertained to pathological conditions of the teeth and adjacent tissues, and the remedial agencies embraced under the head of operative dentistry. Innovations in the latter field, if expedient, were to be tested and reported on each year. Another technical committee took cognizance of mechanical dentistry. The committee was to receive plans, improvements and specimens submitted by inventors desiring to bring them to the notice of the Association, and was authorized to reject those they might deem unworthy of presentation. To foster improvements in dental science and technology a committee on prize essays was also to be established. In its keeping, subject to the ratification of the Association, were two annual prizes "consisting of medals not exceeding in value fifty dollars each." Additional permanent committees were to be the watch-dogs over the progress of dental education and dental literature.[41] The machinery for leadership in dental science and technology was thus tentatively established.

The proposed machinery for achieving these objectives was received in some quarters with considerable misgivings. The editor of the *Vulcanite*, B. W. Franklin of New York, was particularly skeptical of the possibilities of scientific achievement from the new organization. "'The elaboration and development of the science of our profession' can only be accomplished by a 'National Society' composed of delegates," he wrote, paraphrasing the reasoning of the friends of the movement. "If this be true," he went on, "then it is manifest that we have a mine of hidden talent in our profession which the annual gathering of the American Convention has never been able to bring to the surface." He insisted that the Convention represented as much ability in dental science as the Association was likely to be able to muster. In the November issue of the *Vulcanite* he delightedly mocked the scientific endeavors of the Washington meeting and concluded: "When the time shall come that ignorance and empiricism shall give way before the light of true knowledge, the members of our profession will naturally come together in local societies by the law of affinity, and not till then. . . . this was not, is not, and will not be the case for a long time to come."[42]

PART TWO

Developing Concepts
of Professional Leadership
(1860 – 1912)

WITH THE INAUGURATION of the American Dental Association, the history of organized dentistry entered on a new phase. For the ensuing half-century the Association endeavored to attain primacy among professional dental organizations. At the same time, it sought to establish itself as a body literally representative of American dentistry. In the process it was necessary to devise techniques that would permit it to operate as the spokesman for the profession without, at the same time, provoking divisions that would foster the rise of rival national groups. Beginning with one rather narrow definition of its functions, through the years the American Dental Association forged a new and different conception of its role in the profession. By the close of this period, the re-organization of 1912 revealed an American Dental Association closely akin to the organization of today.

Annual Session of the Association, Niagara Falls, 1864

THE ELECTION of Abraham Lincoln in November, 1860, was quickly followed by the secession of the states of the Deep South and the outbreak of war. Up to this time there had been little reflection in dental literature of the rising political excitement of the country. Such comment as had existed indicated a desire to suppress the divisive elements in the nation. During the secession winter, and on the eve of the outbreak of fighting, even the *Southern Dental Examiner,* published in Atlanta, betrayed no particular sectional animosity.[1] The April number printed and commented favorably on the circular of the American Dental Association urging local organization of the profession. The note stressed the need for organization in the Confederacy, but showed no antagonism towards the North.[2]

After the outbreak of fighting, feelings intensified. A number of professional organizations abandoned their plans for meetings in the summer of 1861, among them the American Dental Association.[3] On the other hand, the American Dental Convention went ahead with its plans. The *Dental Journal* acknowledged that many had urged the abandonment of the approaching meeting, but added, "We have considered the matter seriously and earnestly, and really, we cannot find in those events any excuse for what we must consider a dereliction of our professional duty."[4] The Convention accordingly met as planned.

When the session convened, it was officially discovered that the chairman of the Executive Committee, F. Y. Clarke, of Savannah had "seceded." His letter announcing this fact closed with the militant declaration, "We are having warm times here, and now learn that a force of 20,000 Federals are off the harbor. They are fools if they attempt to land at Fort Pulaski, as we are prepared to give them a warm reception." The corresponding secretary of the Convention, who had received the letter from Dr. Clarke, stated that he took the secession flag and with his revolver put five balls through it, saying, "This is the way we intend to treat traitors." [5]

In spite of the tensions of war the profession maintained a fair equanimity. Professional activities continued. Organization work resumed and spread. In the summer of 1862, both the Convention and the Association met. Inaugurating the Cleveland meeting of the Association, Dr. Atkinson merely alluded to the unsettled state of the country as the reason for the cancellation of the previous year's assembly. The balance of the session passed without overt notice of the war. [6]

The editor of the *New York Dental Journal* considered the meeting of the Convention that summer one of the most interesting of all the meetings. "Taking into consideration the serious condition of affairs at the present time, . . . with rebellion at home, and possibly foreign war staring us in the face from abroad; with high prices, enormous taxation, and all the necessary adjuncts of great national crises on every side; it was, indeed, wonderful that so many of our profession could be brought together to calmly discuss matters appertaining to their profession," he marveled. [7]

The Convention did not confine itself exclusively to professional matters. The dentists announced their patriotism and devotion to their country. The occasion of this avowal of patriotism was rightly captioned an "Enthusiastic War Meeting." While a specially appointed committee was drafting resolutions reflecting the sentiments of the assembled dentists, a glee club from a nearby village regaled the meeting with a "patriotic song, sung by three voices—the sentiment of which was admirably adapted to the occasion, while the manner in which it was sung reflected great credit on the musical ability and culture of the performers." Following the martial music, a cannon in front of the hotel boomed loudly, and drums and fife infused spirit into the meeting. The dentists were now ready to transact business.

The conclave assured the federal government of its support "in all the measures it may in its wisdom adopt for the suppression of this most unholy rebellion." Under the urging of the fiery B. W. Franklin of New York City, the dentists declared that the purpose of the war was "the permanent establishment of free institutions over the entire territory of the United States." This was a point that was not decided upon by Lincoln's administration for another month.[8] In pursuit of this objective, Franklin's resolutions declared that the extermination of "the entire race of rebels . . . would find justification on the ground of having a decent regard for the rest of mankind."[9]

The profession as a whole was, of course, much affected by the war. The October, 1862, issue of the *Cosmos* was delayed because of the absence of part of its staff "in the service of the State as militiamen, or in attendance upon the wounded of the late battles."[10] Dental luminaries, like George Watt, co-editor of the *Dental Register*, John Toland, the well-known proprietor of a supply house in Cincinnati, along with many less well-known practitioners, saw active service as surgeons, line officers, or in the ranks.

While the dentists were proud of the valor of their colleagues, they were more concerned, professionally, with the status of dentists in the eyes of the military. The national associations in the North collaborated in seeking the appointment of dentists in the Medical Department of the Army. This movement had actually begun before the outbreak of the war, but the onset of fighting lent new urgency to the subject. The dental and medical press carried articles stressing the importance of sound teeth in fighting men, and emphasizing the deleterious effect of life in the field on the teeth. The American Dental Convention established a committee on the question of seeking the appointment of dentists in the Army and Navy at their session in New Haven in 1861. After due deliberation, the committee concluded that they needed more time than could be given during the meeting. The Convention obligingly continued the committee, vesting it with discretionary powers.[11]

When the American Dental Association resumed its sessions in 1862, a scant dozen delegates and but three permanent members presented themselves.[12] This handful of enthusiasts apparently took no action on the problem. The eighty-odd members of the Convention who gathered in Trenton Falls, New York, in the same year heard a disappointing report from their committee on dentists in the armed forces. The committee reported that there were too many difficulties in the way of pushing the matter at present to admit its successful prosecution. J. D. White, a member of the committee, had, however, received an encouraging letter from the Surgeon-General. Another dentist had discussed the matter directly with that official and had received the same impression, while yet another member of the Convention had received word even more favorable to the project from the same source. The Convention enlarged and continued the Committee, and at the same time constituted each member "a special committee to prosecute this matter." Jonathan Taft reported that officers in the army wanted to have dental services available to the troops. He advised that dentists should take advantage of needs that might arise for their services, and urged the necessity of legislation to authorize the appointment of dentists as assistant surgeons.[13]

Nothing had been accomplished by the time the associations gathered for their meetings in the summer of 1863. The two national dental organizations directed their committees to cooperate in advancing the campaign to obtain the appointment of dentists in the armed services. During the next year the dentists met with a great deal of opposition in the Medical Department. After discussion, the members of the American Dental Association came to the conclusion that some other means must be resorted to, to bring about the desired end.[14]

On the side of the Confederacy, the picture was much the same. W. H. Morgan related that dentists were detailed in the Confederate hospitals, and much good was accomplished in that direction. Assignment of dentists to the troops in the field was urged in the South as in the North, but when the war ended dentists had received official recognition in neither army. In the North S. S. White had interviewed President Lincoln concerning the matter. Not surprisingly, the President referred Dr. White to the War Department. After consultation with the acting Surgeon-General, Dr. White reported that nothing could be done while the armies were in active operation. If the war should last until winter and the armies go into winter quarters, something could probably be accomplished.[15]

The condition of the teeth of the men in the service was apparently miserable, but the sorry state of affairs was not entirely caused by life in the army. Dentists were appalled by the high rate of rejections and exemptions from military service from the recruits' failure to meet even the prevailing low dental standards. A recruit had to have six opposing front teeth "to bite the cartridge" in order to pass and secure a surgeon's certificate for admission into the service.[16] It was estimated that rejections ran as high as forty per cent. This figure was much too high, but the careful comparative study undertaken by John R. Lewis showed that nearly one-fifteenth of all exemptions in 1863 were for dental reasons, while those in 1864 ran nearly ten per cent. Once the soldiers were on active duty the need for dental services remained great. A southerner reported that when Sherman's army came into Savannah, "there was enough work to employ one hundred dentists for six months." The need was so great that charlatans followed the armies pretending to practice dentistry. One such was reported who prepared his cement by the wholesale quantity in a tin cup, enough to last all day.[17]

Part of the 1864 meeting of the American Dental Association was devoted to a discussion of how this need might be met in view of the opposition within the War Department. The report of the discussions on this question shows that the dentists canvassed the problem thoroughly. One difficulty arose from the opinion that one half of the services rendered by a dental practitioner would be of such an expensive character that the government would be unwilling to assume such a great additional expense. This was the conclusion of James Taylor. Dr. Taylor advocated that medically educated dentists enter the army as surgeons or assistant surgeons, but that no one should be admitted in such a capacity unless evidence of dental education was provided. This, Taylor insisted, merely asserted the equality of dentistry with the medical profession, "which our present standing unquestionably warrants." Many members suspected that "the opprobrium of opposition to this humane movement" should be placed upon the medical profession. Like Taylor, supporters of this view tended to believe that dentists with a medical background were more competent to discharge the duties pertaining to the post of surgeon than that officer himself.

Of the opposition within the Surgeon-General's domain there was no question. Dr. Shepard recounted his efforts to secure permission to visit a regiment in the field where a number of officers desired treatment. He related that the colonel regarded the regiment as his special domain, and had promised him special protection whether or not his visit was endorsed by the Surgeon-General's office. Dr. Shepard suggested that dentists by-pass the Surgeon-General's office. The military establishment in those days was such that "a permit from the governor in the state in which they resided would suffice to authorize dentists' practicing among the troops from the state."[18] Shepard's scheme found acceptance among the membership, but it is difficult to determine how widely the idea was applied.

On the home front, dentists suffered the inconveniences of civilian life in wartime. A notable feature of the situation was inflation. Rising prices led dentists to adjust their schedules in localities where organization had progressed to the point of adopting fee bills. The operation of the conscription act, plus the departure to the army of many medically-trained dentists, created a shortage of dentists in many localities—and lucrative practices for those left behind. Urging attendance at the Philadelphia meeting of the American Dental Association, the corresponding secretary observed, "Although society is much disturbed by the terrible troubles of the nation, yet money is abundant, and business in the aggregate has suffered but little."[19]

The government's search for new sources of revenue to feed the insatiable maw of the war machine brought difficulties to many dentists. Many new excise taxes were levied, and dentists had to take out a license costing ten dollars. In this connection another problem arose that was to plague the dentists again in later years. Some Internal Revenue Collectors insisted that the preparation of dentures was a manufacturing operation, and sought to exact an additional ten dollar fee, plus a three per cent levy on the value of the output. The alert Philadelphia practitioners managed to obtain a decision from the Collector there which held that "a dentist having paid his license, has no further tax to pay. Operations upon the mouth do not place a dentist in the category of manufacturers: neither does the construction of artificial dentures for his own patients." [20] Securing an official determination that mechanical dentistry was not a manufacturing operation proved a significant landmark in the establishment of professional status for dentists.

Dentists in the South found their lot in the post-war period not altogether happy. The *Dental Register* recounted the misadventures of a Dr. Berry, who had been practicing in Mississippi. Berry returned to Cincinnati poorer to the tune of about ten thousand dollars, which he lost in some manner not specified. "He looked," said the *Register,* "somewhat as though he had passed between the upper and nether millstones." Dr. Berry's northern background evidently had done him little good among the Mississipians. "He says that he met with no very direct manifestations of hostility; except that being two or three times invited out to be hung might be so regarded (this may require a stretch of the imagination, however)." The *Register* concluded that Berry had been very fortunate in making his escape from that land of terror and desolation.[21] The fire-eating southerner, F. Y. Clarke of Savannah, who in the early days of the secession had promised the Federals a warm reception, apparently underwent a change of sentiment in the course of time. He greeted and served the dental needs of Sherman's forces when they captured his city. He confided to the Boston meeting of the American Dental Association in 1866 that he had been persecuted at home for his Union sentiments.[22]

During the Civil War period and on into the post-war era, the dental profession faced problems over scientific standards similar to those that had vexed earlier generations. In 1863, a contributor to the *Dental Cosmos* presented the situation in a form that had become almost a cliché. "In our profession, all are dentists, from those possessing the highest degree of worth and talent to those whose lack of skill compels them to deal in plastic materials, and whose proficiency is mainly manifested in extracting—unjust fees from their patients' pockets," he complained. "Let us unite in drawing a line of distinction between the worthy and the unworthy, the skillful and the empiric." [23] By the 1860's not only the statements of the problems, but also the solutions had achieved a traditional formulation. The principal device of professional advancement, many dentists agreed, was education. Dental spokesmen defined education loosely, including as its agents the journals and societies, as well as the colleges.[24]

Both the problems and their solutions, of course, were much more complicated than the standardized formulations indicated. Nor were the dentists of that day deceived by the hackneyed phrases. Still, such statements do serve to emphasize the continuity of professional history while they also help explain the recurrence of old problems and their equally venerable remedies. Changes in the social environment of professional life alter the appearance of the perennial problems and evoke new solutions—or necessitate the reformulation of tried ones. These conditions provide the movement that gives professionalism a history.

One of the most persistent examples of this sort of thing in the history of organized dentistry is the question of the relationship between the skills and techniques of everyday practice and the theoretical and scientific learning upon which practical success depends. The conflict was thoroughly aired in a debate between members of the American Dental Association at Chicago in 1865. One delegate, "a simple man in the profession," he styled himself, complained that the session had been too much "absorbed by matters outside of the legitimate objects for which the Association had assembled." The speaker acknowledged that there were relationships among the various parts of the human body. But, he went on, "I have never treated corns, nor diseases of the eye, nor do I ever expect to do it." This dissident one found support from a Dr. Perkins of Albany. "It appears to me that too much time is spent in these continuations of dentistry," Perkins declared. "I am one who comes here to learn of what is essential to my success in practice on what comes every day within my operations." Called to order on the grounds that he was introducing "matters not relevant," Dr. Perkins grumbled, "I am very much inclined to the opinion that it would puzzle the Doctor to furnish evidence of it." [25]

J. H. McQuillen stood forth to champion the opposing view. The Association, he maintained, was not established for the purpose of confining its attention exclusively to the consideration of the dental organs. McQuillen argued that a broader viewpoint and more profound knowledge enabled a dentist to expand his usefulness. He added that "it is owing to the disposition on the part of the profession in the present day to become thoroughly acquainted, not only with our specialty, but every thing that appertains to it, that has elevated our calling from a mere mechanical occupation to the position of a liberal profession." [26]

The most vocal leaders of the profession agreed with McQuillen's stand on this point at least. The issue provoked fairly constant discussion throughout the period. Most of the argument came from the advocates of scientific discussion, perhaps because they encountered passive, though apparently silent, resistance. T. L. Buckingham, for example, spoke up on behalf of a broader basis of discussion on practical grounds. He asked that the profession turn to fundamental principles. "And as we have to operate on living tissue, both in its normal and abnormal conditions," he argued, "a few minutes devoted to its development and structure may be profitably employed." [27] A great deal of the scientific and theoretical discussion within the profession maintained a reasonably intimate connection with the everyday problems of dental practice.

Some dental leaders, however, held to broader interests and sought to carry their fellows along with them. It would be hard to say which of the sciences commanded the greatest attention among these men. References to leading chemists, physiologists, biologists, even geologists and "natural philosophers," of the day came readily to the lips of the dental scientists. Nor were their concerns restricted to the application of scientific discoveries to dentistry. Undoubtedly the most spectacular scientific development of the Civil War era was the promulgation of the Darwinian theories of the origin of species. Dentists, in common with the rest of the educated community, were divided on the implications of Darwin's doctrines for conventional religion. At the Saratoga meeting of the American Dental Convention in 1873, the President, I. J. Wetherbee of Boston, devoted his opening address to Darwin's work on the origin of man, criticising it, and attacking many of that author's theories.[28]

T. L. Buckingham of Philadelphia deplored the Spencerian popularization of Darwin as "the worst kind of philosophy that was ever preached, materialism, which existed before Christ." [29] Buckingham's remarks were prompted by some statements of J. H. McQuillen, Buckingham's arch-rival in Philadelphia dentistry. McQuillen presenting the position assumed by the less belligerent apologists for the new discoveries, argued that previous experience suggested that the alleged discrepancy between scientific discoveries and the Bible was to be found not in fact, but in man's interpretation of Scripture. Citing the earlier controversies that had arisen over the differences between the geological age of the earth and the Biblical account of creation, McQuillen pointed out that "now pious, learned and eminent divines, in place of opposing the geological record, draw some of their strongest arguments from it in support of the Scriptures." [30] In another debate on the same subject, McQuillen referred to Agassiz's formulation of the historical "rule" regarding the reception of novelty: "Whenever a new and startling fact is brought to light in science, people first say, 'it is not true;' then, that 'it is contrary to religion;' and lastly, 'that everybody knew it before.'" [31] McQuillen referred to the piety of many of the leading scientific pioneers and then concluded: "To my apprehension, the investigations at present progressing . . . are not in abnegation of, or in opposition to, a great creative power, but [are] only trying to discover His grand truths; and I hold that the geologists and other scientific men, who, in a reverent spirit, prosecute their studies and give instruction from the book of nature, are as much worshippers of God, as much teachers of God's truths, and as usefully employed, as those who teach from the written record." [32]

As editor of the *Dental Cosmos*, McQuillen gave space in its pages to correspondence from his friend, F. V. Hayden, the naturalist, archeologist, and geologist, who was then leading one of the four great exploratory and mapping expeditions in the trans-Missouri West. [33] Not only McQuillen, but other leading dentists of the time were acquainted with the work of prominent contemporary scientific figures. Not the least interesting of these men was John William Draper.

Draper's role as philosopher and historian served to identify him in the eyes of the public, but the dental world knew him in his professional role as a physician, pioneering in blood chemistry and physiology. [34] The dentists were naturally in closest touch with scientific advances impinging more or less directly on their own specialty. Thus, Oliver Wendell Holmes's fame among the dentists arose from his work as a scientist-physician rather than from his public role as humorist and poet.

More directly relevant to dental interests were the advances during the third quarter of the century in the fields of biochemistry, physiology, and pathology. These discoveries affected the line of attack on the problems of dental caries. The scientific debaters in dental meetings appealed to the authority of Justus von Liebig, pioneer organic chemist and predecessor of Pasteur in the study of decay and fermentation. Liebig's teachings, however, may well have confused the understanding of caries etiology.[35] Another great scientist of the mid-century, whose influence on the history of dentistry has not been clearly defined, was Rudolf Virchow. Virchow's studies of cellular pathology concerned disease and diseased tissue from the point of view of cell structure and cell formation.[36] Concentration on cellular studies, coupled with limited developments in microscopy, produced a number of lively controversies in the areas of dental histology, embryology, the etiology of dental diseases, and dental physiology.[37]

Dental interests were not confined to medico-biological subjects, nor were they restricted to a narrow concentration on the individual patient. Dentists debated the value of environmentalist theories to explain what they seem to have regarded as the endemic character of dental caries in the United States. Such concerns help account for their frequent appeals to the writings of Humboldt. Some dentists at least understood the limitations of much of this sort of theorization. In the session of the American Dental Convention at Long Branch, New Jersey, in 1875, one speaker attacked the suggestion of a member of the National Academy of Medicine of France that attributed the prevalence of caries to the changed climate resultant on migration from the Old World to the New. The critic declared that data to confirm or refute the hypothesis were lacking in view of the dearth of knowledge of the dental history of the American Indian. Julius Chesebrough made a beginning toward a study of the relation of environment to the incidence of caries in a pioneering statistical study of 1864.[38]

In spite of the vogue of evolutionary thought, McQuillen enjoined the profession to be skeptical of a too-ready reliance upon fragmentary remains as indicating evolutionary changes. Such data, he warned, require careful and exhaustive confirmation. Conclusions too quickly adopted often had to be altered or abandoned. He reminded his hearers that the anatomical peculiarities which, from time to time, had been pointed out by anatomists as distinguishing and reliable characteristic traits, proved not unfrequently to be of no value when subjected to a rigid and extended examination.[39]

In addition to their human susceptibility to the more fashionable scientific vogues, dentists betrayed some enthusiasm for less sophisticated medical fads. At the American Dental Association meeting in 1864, one speaker ventured an apologetic endorsement of homeopathy, a popular medical cult of the time. Another semi-medical obsession that flourished in the post-war years was first brought to public attention by Sylvester Graham. Graham's contention was that modern developments in milling technique had resulted in the elimination of most of the food value from flour. Graham sponsored his own variety of flour, which is still with us in Graham crackers. John Allen of New York, for example, was a supporter of Graham's position. He informed the Society of Dental Surgeons of the City of New York that he had some "families who are feeding their children on coarse flour not deprived of the bran, in accordance with his instructions; and results have corroborated the idea that the hull of the grains contains the lime-salts essential to teeth and bones."[40] A Dr. Wardle told the Odontographic Society of Pennsylvania that "The young of this age and climate are brought up on candies, sweetmeats, and confections with pastry made from flour passed through a thirty-nine bolting-cloth, and the miller complained of because he does not produce it still finer. From these and other causes are the inhabitants of this region cursed with bad teeth." Amos Lawrence warned that current practices in milling were violations of chemical laws. "The bone-making portions of the grain being removed in preparing the fine, super-fine, and double-refined flour, the result is: we eat the

Annual Session of the Association, Boston, 1866

unhealthy 'superfine,' and feed the *best* to filthy swine." Lawrence declared this practice was foolish "in view of the claim to superiority we set up against the hog." Other dentists through these years labored the theme that "civilization is the enemy of health." [41] By the middle seventies, nutritional studies had progressed so that the bodily requirements of phosphorus and mineral elements were better understood. Still, John Allen complained: "We bolt and sift out of every barrel of flour forty pounds of essential elements, the mineral which we need for building up the bones and teeth. As a result we see the deterioration of the teeth." [42]

Even the most determined advocates of scientific advancement in dentistry found the going occasionally difficult. At the meeting in 1868 scientific and technical matters were crowded off the agenda owing to the great amount of pressing business. The supporters of science also had to contend with the temptations that presented themselves to turn the annual meetings into holiday recreations. Writing in anticipation of the Cincinnati meeting in 1867, one dentist lamented, "We can eat and drink, and 'laugh and grow fat' at home; but we cannot there interchange scientific thoughts with the leading minds of the profession within the space of a few days." [43]

Such lamentations came from dental leaders who believed in the educational function of dental organization. Taft once observed, "The fact of associated effort becoming so general is an evidence of an increasing desire for knowledge."[44] In view of the scientific attainments of Taft, Buckingham, McQuillen, and Atkinson, a quartet of indefatigable visitors to local and state society meetings, it would seem that these men were as busy disseminating the findings of dental science as they were spreading the gospel of associated effort. In a report on his visits to local societies, Atkinson mentioned only the scientific discussions. "My intercourse among the various societies has been very pleasant, especially in the South," he related. "There they fight and quarrel, and say I'm wrong, and all that; but when I convict them they are convicted all over. . . . But these New England fellows are hard to convict. They think they are the 'hub,' you know, and when you show them the truth they say, 'that's so,' and all that, but they are only convicted on the surface. If you go back to them after while, you'll find them sunk right in the old ruts again."[45]

The opportunity for self-improvement offered in "demonstrations by clinics, illustrations by the microscope, and exhibitions of instruments and appliances" formed a major inducement for attendance at dental meetings. The argument was placed on a very practical level, ". . . there is none who can afford to stay away from these conventions. If anyone is poor in professional attainments, this is one of the best means of securing confidence and influence; and with these anyone can command money."[46] In 1864 the Association decided to include clinics as part of the regular program.[47] This decision of the war years was unsuccessfully challenged early in the seventies, on the ground that "the association could not afford to flitter [sic] away its time in manipulative exercises, which can be carried on in local societies."[48] Whether clinics should be part of the activities of the national body remained an open question, but there was no doubt of the value and acceptance of the use of clinics for educational and philanthropic purposes among the local societies. William H. Atkinson warmly supported the clinics as the best mode of education for dentists, where oral instruction could be immediately followed by demonstration. Atkinson proposed the establishment of a fund to finance clinics in every locality where enough dentists could be got together to make it interesting.[49]

Chapter IX   PROBLEMS OF DENTAL EDUCATION

THE CONCERN of dental organizations with the education of dentists
was not confined to the dissemination of scientific lore and practical
technique at their meetings. The dental societies were likewise concerned with the formal institutions of dental education. Hardly any
question provoked more lively and extended discussion through the
years than the standards and content of dental collegiate instruction.
The associations were concerned with the standards of dentistry and
those of their membership—they sought to establish a public measure of competence and respectability—and they recognized that their
influence as spokesmen for the profession could influence the practices of the dental colleges.

Development of the societies and of the colleges, as dental leaders
saw it, was interrelated. "A professional wall is now being built up,
in the shape of Dental Colleges and Associations, and we hope it
will be built so high and strong, that none can scale or break it down,
but that all who enter will be compelled to do so through the legitimate and well-guarded gate-ways," wrote Jonathan Taft in the mid-
sixties. It was agreed that the associations could not by themselves
protect their ranks "against improper intrusions." [1] Some standard
of qualification independent of the membership of dental societies
seemed necessary.

155

An obvious measure of competence that met these specifications was the possession of a diploma from a dental college. To decide upon this test, however, was to introduce complications. What was to be done about the cases of competent and respectable practitioners of long experience whose training had been entirely under the preceptorial system? There were still many dentists who found the acceptance of students in their offices a profitable supplement to their income. Also, the American Dental Association's control over the qualifications of its members was indirect. Too stringent membership requirements might result in withdrawal of local societies. The American Dental Convention, of course, had an even more tenuous hold on its membership, which had to be renewed each year. Finally, resort to the diploma as an index of ability imposed the necessity of supervising the standards of the institutions granting the degree.

For all these reasons, the local and state societies frequently preceded the national organizations in adopting educational qualifications for their membership. Even these organizations found it expedient to provide for a transitional period before requiring a diploma as an absolute standard. In 1866, for example, the Missouri State Dental Association adopted a resolution stipulating that all dentists should insist on a minimum period of two years' office training. (This was the standard that had been suggested by the A.D.A.) In addition, the Missourians demanded that the preceptor exact a pledge from his prospective student that he would also graduate from a dental college before entering active practice.[2] The Central States Dental Association, organized in 1866, incorporated a similar provision in its by-laws. The membership clause of the regional society required graduation from a dental or medical college plus one year's practice, or six years' service as "a respectable practitioner." It added that "if the candidate [for membership] commences practice after this date, he must invariably be a graduate."[3] The Michigan Dental Association incorporated similar resolutions in its by-laws in 1866. In this case, the term of preceptorship was extended to three years. Graduation from some regular dental college was required of candidates for membership entering the profession after this date.[4] The Southern Dental Association determined that its members must have a degree or have practiced ten years. In the latter event, the additional safeguard of a three-fourths vote of the members present was imposed.[5]

The official position of the American Dental Association was not quite as rigorous. Dentists were requested to insist on a full two years' preceptorship "and for no consideration" to accept an applicant unless the student agreed to graduate from a dental college before practicing. Simultaneously a suggestion was made "that the people should demand of all those who hereafter enter upon the practice of dentistry that they shall hold a diploma from a Dental College, as the first requisite to public confidence and patronage." [6] The results of these suggestions seemed to bear out McQuillen's dictum that the Association "could not assume to *dictate* terms to the profession, but the *recommendations*, emanating from a body composed of delegates from local societies established in every section of the country, should carry with a moral force which would be overwhelming and irresistible." [7] The Committee on Dental Education urged in 1867 that the Association take the further step of requiring every candidate to become the recipient of the title of Doctor of Dental Surgery before being admitted to the roll of membership in any society, general or local. Ultimately, time and circumstances would force the Association to make this requirement, the Committee argued. "At present we have no fixed professional standard by which a man is to be measured—no rule which any one is required to comply with before he is to be recognized as a Dentist. . . . and therefore, *any* one and *every* one who chooses may hang out his sign, and set up his claim, not only to *be* a Dentist, but also to be recognized as such by others." [8] The obstacles to the adoption of strict standards were still too great. The final acceptance of the diploma test was yet far in the future.

For the most part, the national society confined itself to the exertion of moral pressure and the passage of resolutions "recommending" educational reforms. The 1866 session, for example, appointed a committee to prepare a circular containing suitable suggestions on the subject of accepting students. The circular then was to be distributed among the profession for the consideration of every dental practitioner in the United States. The committee energetically carried out its assignment. It even sketched the specific studies to be followed during each year of pupilage in order to "produce greater uniformity and better results . . . and thus prepare the student to receive his lectures with more profit to himself, and not less honor to the profession whose vital interests," the committee averred, "we aim to cherish." [9] The recommendations were not always so specific. There was apparently a widespread desire to elevate the standards of education preliminary to undertaking dental studies. These related to the subjects and skills commonly associated with a general education.[10] Some educational reformers advocated eliminating the substitution of practical experience for course requirements, a system that, according to one writer, "was inviting students to impose their ignorance on the public." [11] Others urged that the colleges undertake the gradual enlargement of their curriculum of study. Ordinarily the direction of enlargement was toward the inclusion of more specifically scientific and medical studies. But this was a trend that awakened old fears for the integrity of dental education, and excited old antagonisms.[12]

Rarely through this period was the opportunity offered for the American Dental Association to act directly and explicitly to influence the course of dental collegiate instruction. The reports of the standing Committee on Dental Education mostly viewed with alarm or pointed with pride. On one occasion, the Committee's grounds for satisfaction proved to be unwarranted. In 1867, its report took "much pleasure in reporting that gratifying evidences exist of increased prosperity in the educational department of our profession." The facts cited were the establishment of a new dental school in St. Louis and the organization of an association of the faculties of the dental colleges "having in view greater uniformity in the rules and usages of the different schools, and concert of action among them for the general advancement of Dental education." [13] Neither of these developments lived up to the Committee's expectations.

According to the constitution of the American Dental Association, each dental college faculty was entitled to send one delegate to the annual sessions. When the representative of the new St. Louis Dental College presented his credentials, they were challenged. The chair appointed a committee of five to investigate.[14] The committee brought in a blistering report charging that the school had been "conceived with very discreditable motives" and deserved the "strongest condemnation and rebuke." Recognition of the delegate from the St. Louis Dental College, the committee concluded, "would be setting a dangerous and mischievous precedent that would lower the standard of dental education, and put quacks and mountebanks in the highest places of trust and honor in the profession." The meeting accepted the report and adopted a resolution endorsing the maintenance of high standards of dental education.[15]

The Association of the Colleges of Dentistry, whose establishment was reported with such optimism by the Committee on Dental Education in 1867, had a short and unhappy history. A group of professors, representing all the regular schools then in existence except the Baltimore College, held a private conference during the Boston meeting of the American Dental Association in 1866.[16] This small group took the preliminary steps toward formal organization, including consideration of a draft preamble and constitution. It was agreed to meet later in Philadelphia to complete the organization. In the autumn of 1866, representatives of all the dental colleges in the United States gathered and formed the Association of the Colleges of Dentistry. A total of sixteen professors, representing five dental schools, agreed upon the structure of the organization.[17]

The organizational meeting proceeded to adopt a number of desirable measures. They agreed to abandon the practice of considering one session in a medical school as the equivalent of one dental college term. Two years' preceptorship, plus two full courses of dental college lectures, became the standard requirement to qualify for the degree examination. A graduate of a medical college with a year's preceptorship and a single course of dental lectures qualified for examination. It was also agreed that seven years' practice equalled one course of lectures, but the applicant had to submit to an examination before his acceptance as a student. The professors also agreed upon a date in the course-year after which new students would not be admitted. They were unable to agree, however, upon a proposal to extend the term to five months from the generally accepted four. Nor were they amenable to fixing the tuition at $120 for the first course of lectures and $115 for the second.[18] The conferees then adjourned to convene the following spring.

At the spring session in 1867, the united front of the colleges was broken. Meeting at the Philadelphia Dental College, the Association found two occasions for disagreement. The first of these was the appearance of a new applicant for membership. Professor Homer Judd, representing the newly-established Missouri Dental College of St. Louis, asked admission to the Association. A committee of Barker of the Pennsylvania College, Kingsley of the New York College, and McQuillen of the Philadelphia College, after some indecision, admitted Judd only on condition that his school provide chairs for qualifying aspirant practitioners in operative and mechanical dentistry.[19]

The second divisive issue proved more difficult to surmount. Indeed, it apparently was fatal to the Association. The controversy arose when a sort of advisory and condemnatory rule was suggested. According to this proposition, the practices of one of the member-schools, the Pennsylvania College, were criticized. The rule stated: "Regarding the education of the profession as the primary and only object in the establishment of dental colleges, therefore, Resolved, That while this Association does not forbid, it cannot approve the conferring of degrees upon persons who have not complied with the regulations agreed upon by this body, with the exception of gentlemen who have distinguished themselves as contributors to dental science."[20]

The immediate cause of the rift in the Association of the Colleges of Dentistry at the spring meeting in 1867 arose when, in January, 1866, the Pennsylvania College announced a rule whereby its faculty offered "to examine and graduate any good, respectable dentist" who had been in practice since 1852, provided the candidate met certain conditions. These stipulations included proof of his length of practice and his good standing, the submission of an acceptable thesis and of satisfactory specimens of his workmanship, and, finally, the successful passing of examinations in the several specialties of the faculty.[21] Presumably, the rule of the Association of Dental Colleges that made eight years' practice the equivalent of one course of dental lectures justified this practice of the Pennsylvania College. When the matter came to a vote by colleges, the Pennsylvania College found the other four schools solidly aligned against it on two different versions of the resolution. "Immediately after this vote, the faculty of the Pennsylvania College of Dental Surgeons announced, through their dean, that the passage of this resolution rendered it necessary for them to withdraw [from the College Association] . . . alleging for this movement their conviction that it is a rebuke upon their past practice . . . and also a restriction upon their intended future course in this respect."[22]

The action of the Association and the reaction of the Pennsylvania College precipitated a bitter controversy. The *Dental Register* sorrowfully noted the unwillingness of the Pennsylvania College to join with the other schools to "present a united front, a uniform curriculum, a co-operation of action, that cannot fail to increase their influence for good." The editor even counted the fledgling Missouri College on the side of the Association. "We take it for granted that the Missouri College . . . will place itself squarely on the platform of advanced and united Dental Education." The comment continued sadly, "We are sorry that the brethren of the Pennsylvania College thought it best to go out into the cold, and hope they will reconsider the matter, and come along with us, for we 'will do them good.'"[23] The newly re-established *American Journal,* edited by F.J.S. Gorgas and others of the faculty of the Baltimore College, opened its pages "to any communications on either side of the question, which shall be written with fairness and courtesy." Speaking, however, "as friends of education, and Professors in a Dental College," the editors lamented and disapproved "the Secession of the Pennsylvania College." Not surprisingly, the Odontographic Society of Pennsylvania endorsed the regulations and by-laws adopted by the Association.[24]

Almost alone, the Pennsylvania College defended itself through the pages of the *Dental Times.* The defense showed considerable rancor. "Unknown" greeted the reappearance of the *American Journal* with scorn. "Index" attacked "the croaking members of the 'dental fraternity'" who had complained of the College's actions. The "croakers," the writer suggested, consisted of two classes. The first had obtained their degrees when it was easier to obtain a degree than to undergo a strenuous tutelage or they held "honorary degrees." The second had never received "honorary degrees" and were "aware of their inability to successfully pass the ordeal requisite to procure a proper college certificate." Buckingham bitterly criticized McQuillen's alleged arrogance. "Now everyone knows that the *Cosmos* is the dental world, and that the editor, like Atlas, sustains the world on his shoulders, and when he takes up his pen to write on dental education, the little boys must get out of the way, for he is about to show the elephant." Buckingham charged McQuillen had indulged in the very practices he now deplored. Even some of the faculty of the Philadelphia College were said to lack the coveted degree.[25]

The movement to unite the colleges to establish and maintain standards apparently sundered on the rock of this controversy. The hopeful comment of Taft that the foundation of the Association was the most important step taken by the profession for many years proved unjustified.[26] The Association of Dental Colleges disappeared from the pages of the dental journals after the reports of its spring meeting in 1867. On the whole, the controversy provoked by the action of the Association was not very edifying. It did, however, underscore the complexity of the problem the profession faced in endeavoring to distinguish the able from the incompetent practitioner. Pursuit of a solution to this dilemma revived the difficulties inherent in trying to make society membership a measure of respectability. And it re-introduced the profession to the tribulations consequent upon adoption of legislative regulation of practice.

The failure of the Association of Dental Colleges thrust the problem of educational standards back upon the American Dental Association. Education had been a subject of concern to the Association from the outset. One of the permanent committees established by the constitution of 1860 was charged with submission of an annual report on the state of dental education.[27] This report was discussed at the annual sessions, and interest ranged from the desirable preliminary qualifications through relations between preceptorial and collegiate instruction to the length of the school term and the manner of determining the fitness of a candidate for the degree.

Preparatory education before undertaking dental studies furnished a starting point for discussion of the problem. Jonathan Taft advocated drastic action in 1864. "Our Colleges should at once, without fear or favor, institute preliminary examinations, and admit no student to their halls, who can not stand a thorough test."[28] In 1867 the report of the committee demanded at least sufficient literary knowledge to enable the student to speak and write grammatically, and to pursue the study of the sciences with understanding. More skill and learning in this direction was necessary, and a later committee report elaborated arguments for a broad preparation in general education.[29] Not only was such training needed to pursue dental studies, but "complete success in our practice and operations on the teeth" frequently depended "upon a superior general education." "The *refining influence*" of a "*liberal education*" was emphasized, for "our profession must be brought up to the test standard of a 'learned profession,' or it will lose much of the power and influence which it has already gained."

To buttress these theoretical or idealistic advantages of a sound educational background, the report offered a materialistic argument: "As the aggregate of those who employ our services, and sustain our profession, possess a greater amount of refinement and wealth than do the patrons of any other profession, education, refinement and skill, or any other quality that contributes in any degree to palliate human suffering, will be sought after, and its exercise rewarded; so that, if education imparts confidence, and confidence renders our operations less painful and more perfect, our services become more valuable, and will command a higher price."[30]

The Association continually urged high standards of preliminary education. As late as 1879, an attempt in the American Dental Association to define adequate preliminary education as the equivalent of graduation from the Boston Grammar School failed.[31]

A thorny problem for the Association was the control of preceptorial training in dentists' offices and the relation of this training to collegiate education in dentistry. In 1860, the colleges, according to one informed estimate, supplied only about one tenth of the new men entering the profession each year. A later estimate placed the figure at less than half.[32] While the proportion of college trained dentists undoubtedly increased through the years, the majority of dentists were still trained in the offices of established practitioners. The system of office training presented serious drawbacks, but the Association could hardly take extreme measures against the method that had trained the great mass of its potential constituents and that represented a lucrative source of supplementary income to dentists. "We live in a busy age; it takes but a little while to become a grandfather in dentistry," one observer remarked. "That is, to send out a student who in a short time will have sent out his student." Accordingly, the Association confined itself to recommendations that preceptorial training be supplemented with collegiate work.[33] However, preceptorship did not escape criticism. Fiery George Watt of Xenia, Ohio, who served off and on through these years as one of the editors of the *Dental Register*, asserted that the colleges, by recognizing practice as equivalent of a certain proportion of collegiate training, "bribed" the student to slight his education. This was "inviting students to impose their ignorance on the public." The 1866 session of the American Dental Association adopted a resolution instructing a committee to draft suitable suggestions upon the subject of accepting students.[34] In the following year, the committee brought in an extensive report that recommended the specific studies to be followed by the students during the period of their tutelage under a preceptor, thus fitting them better to profit by their collegiate training.[35] Even so, the preceptorial system enjoyed a relative immunity from criticism that did not appear in the attitude of the members of the Association toward the college system, the favored object of so many dental reformers.

Wearied by the attacks on the colleges, McQuillen exploded at the Detroit meeting in 1874: "Why not criticize the private preceptors in their unquestionable failure to perform their duty? For the vast majority of accessions to the ranks of the profession come from private offices." [36] There was, no doubt, considerable justice to McQuillen's charge. At the same time, the preponderance of office-trained dentists in the profession enjoined considerable caution in attacking the system.

Perhaps McQuillen's testy challenge prompted W. W. Allport to offer an amendment to the constitution requiring delegates who entered the profession after the adoption of the amendment to be graduates of a dental or medical college. When the amendment came up for a consideration at the next session of the Association, it gave rise to considerable discussion. Little of the debate has survived, but sufficient information is available to indicate the general lines of argument. Some speakers claimed the amendment signified a tendency toward exclusiveness. W. H. Atkinson opposed the proposition on this ground. He held that the colleges were not yet strong enough, nor advanced enough, to lead the profession. He insisted that the standard must be accomplishment, rather than the attainment of a degree.[37]

Another faction claimed that the amendment did not go far enough. I. J. Wetherbee of Boston argued that the American Dental Association was not sufficiently exclusive. It was failing to aid the public in discriminating among dentists. "The larger part of the people . . . call on the first man whose shingle they meet," Wetherbee objected. "This association is a stumbling block to our advance. It is composed of graduates and non-graduates. Change the constitution, and allow no delegate to come here who is not a graduate, and you will have set an example to the whole country."[38] Upholding this position, W. H. Morgan urged that in the future no delegate be accepted who did not hold a diploma. This precipitate assault on the preceptorially-trained dentists may have frightened the opponents of the amendment requiring all new dentists to have degrees. Morgan withdrew his suggestion and the gradualist amendment passed.[39]

In taking this step, the national organization in a sense followed the lead of the younger societies of the states of the middle west. As far back as 1866, the Central States Dental Society and the state association of Michigan had written the diploma requirement for membership into their constitutions.[40]

The decision in favor of collegiate over office training merely transferred the center of discussion. Consideration now turned to what was to be taught in the colleges. Many of the recurrent problems of defining the qualifications for the profession again found an airing. One aspect of dentistry as a profession that was fully explored in this controversy was the question of the relationship between operative dentistry and mechanical dentistry. This distinction is one that is difficult to make today. The line of demarcation was not altogether clear to the men of the nineteenth century. In a general way, mechanical dentistry referred to the portions of practice concerned with prosthesis, replacing missing teeth with artificial dentures, while operative dentistry held sway over the balance of the dentist's work. Another way of making the distinction would be to say that mechanical dentistry covered the portion of the dentist's work performed in the laboratory and at the workbench; the work at the chair was operative dentistry.[41] Any desire to exclude mechanical dentists from the professional ranks ran headlong into the fact that orthodontists and oral surgeons also spent long hours in the laboratory or at the workbench. Frequently, indeed, the skilled prosthetician served as ortho-

dontist and oral surgeon as well. Mechanical dentistry, as confined to
the preparation of artificial dentures, came under reproach during
the sixties and seventies, largely because of the widespread use of
vulcanized rubber in dentures. "Many persons engaged in the manufacture of artificial dentures were such poor operators, so illy prepared to perform good work, that even the average dentists felt
ashamed to call him [sic] by that name, so he was called 'cheap John'
and 'tooth carpenter,'" recalled a writer of the eighties. Another
writer described the operations of these men: "They make Mr.
Green's, Miss Prim's, and Mrs. Brown's dentures all alike, with blocks
from the same mould, or single teeth arranged with true mechanical
precision." The manipulation of rubber seemingly required less skill
than the earlier metallic restorations. Similarly, rubber was cheaper.
The development of the vulcanite base also fostered the rise of chains
of "dental parlors" dedicated to wholesale extractions and the replacement of the natural teeth with artificial ones.[42] Other abuses
were due to the fees and licenses demanded of the dentists by the
holders of the patent on vulcanized rubber originally granted to Nelson Goodyear in 1851. After 1864 the Goodyear Dental Vulcanite
Company, holder of the so-called "Cummings Patent" on the process
of denture making from vulcanized rubber, required all dentists to be
licensed and to pay royalties. The license fees ranged from twenty-
five to one hundred dollars a year. In addition each dentist was required to pay a royalty on each denture.

The use of rubber as a substitute for gold placed the price of dentures within the reach of large numbers who could not afford the
more expensive materials, but the charges on processing the plates
threatened large numbers of dentists with bankruptcy. Various
groups were formed for legal action, including the United States
Dental Union of Boston, the New York Protective Union, and the
American Dental Protective Union. They carried the case to the
Supreme Court of the United States, but lost their appeal. In an
effort to evade the fees, some dentists began to use celluloid. Efforts
by the company to protect its revenues were defeated in the U. S.
District Court of Baltimore in 1879 which refused an injunction to
prevent dentists from using the substitute. Tragedy entered the conflict in 1879. A Josiah Bacon had gotten control of the patents and
contrived a new system of office licenses which affected about five

thousand dentists. His threats and warnings to those who refused, resulted in his murder by an outraged dentist named Samuel P. Chalfont who had been taken to court on charges of evading the fees. Relief came to the harassed profession only after the patents expired in 1881.[43] All of these factors tended to discredit mechanical dentistry.[44]

Some dental educators proposed that training in mechanical dentistry be confined to the period of preceptorship. One such observer felt that while training in mechanical dentistry should not fill, as it tended to do, too large a portion of that office and instruction time, the office was the place for such training, not the college. Not enough time for it could be found in the crowded college curriculum. Early in the eighties there was still sentiment in favor of dropping instruction in mechanical dentistry from the collegiate curriculum. Truman W. Brophy, reporting on behalf of the American Dental Association Committee on Dental Education, said, "We believe that the cause of dental education would be greatly advanced if the learning of mechanical dentistry were not made compulsory in our colleges, and the time now devoted to it were spent in the pursuit of medical studies."[45] "Is dentistry, then, a liberal profession?" rhetorically asked a dental spokesman of the day. He answered, "Yes, certainly, if the majority of its members are men of liberal education. . . . But skill without education, art without science, cannot be called a profession."[46]

The practical and mechanical side of dentistry, however, did not lack advocates. The *Cosmos* editorially warned the profession that "there is danger that in the laudable ambition to justify the doctorate by medical culture the necessity of handicraft may be to a great extent neglected."[47] For all the variations of opinion, mechanical dentistry remained of interest and concern to the members of the profession. The sixties and seventies saw a number of important innovations in prosthetics and in the related area of orthodontics. With the development of the collar crown in 1883, mechanical dentistry stood on the threshold of yet greater achievements. However, patents on the gold crown and other processes held by the International Tooth Crown Company resulted in a new wave of exploitation of dentists similar to those in the earlier vulcanite controversy. By 1886 dentists were being issued licenses and charged fees totaling

$100 to $500 a year. Various forms of intimidation including legal action caused widespread protests. Finally J. N. Crouse, a former president of the American Dental Association, succeeded in rallying the profession. In 1888 he formed the Dental Protective Association and collected some $60,000 to fight the exploiters. He not only aided the dentists in suits brought against them, but he instituted legal action which resulted in forcing the crown company out of business. In this action he was assisted by the Association which gave him $1,000 in 1889.[48]

An observer in the early eighties noted with satisfaction, however, that "the prosthetic section [at the annual meeting of the American Dental Association] was as well received, and called forth as much attention and earnest discussion as any other section." [49]

A major factor behind the movement to eliminate mechanical dentistry from the collegiate course involved the perennial question of the relation of dentistry to medicine. Through these post-war decades the usual mixed pattern of amity and asperity characterized the relations between the two fields. Many dentists felt that the physicians did not have sufficient respect for the dental art.[50] Nevertheless, physicians visiting or practicing in the cities where the American Dental Association convened were often asked to meet with the Association. In 1867 a resolution to this effect met objections on the ground that no such invitation had been extended by the Medical Convention to the dentists. However, the resolution was adopted.[51] The friendly relations between the dentists and physicians culminated in 1881 with the inauguration of a section on dental and oral surgery in the American Medical Association to which dentists holding the M.D. degree were eligible. That same year American dentists participated in the International Medical Congress in London.[52]

The relationship between the two associations has been concerned continuously with problems of education. Some wrongly maintained that special schools for dental education were founded because the medical schools refused to give dental instruction. "How enthusiastically did the late Chapin A. Harris, he whose name we all love and venerate, with his associates, labor to establish a department of dentistry in a medical college in Baltimore," Truman W. Brophy declaimed in 1881. "And no doubt those of our elder brothers with us to-day who knew him well could relate to us the expressions of bitter disappointment that fell from his lips when he saw that his fond and just desires in the interest of suffering humanity, owing to the opposition of the medical faculty, could not be realized." Brophy, indeed, blamed this apocryphal event for the estrangement of the two fields. Atkinson, too, claimed that bad feeling now constituted an obstacle to adequate medical instruction for dentists.[53] N. S. Davis, M.D., addressed the American Dental Association at the 1865 meeting in opposition to excessive specialization. He like others favored a general medical education, implicitly for dentists as well as physicians.[54] The contemporary dental reaction to these overtures by the physicians was cautious. The dentists countered Dr. Davis's arguments for general education by insisting on the virtues of specialization.[55] C. W. Spalding spoke for the American Dental Association Committee on Dental Education in 1867. He acknowledged that it might be argued that both physicians and dentists should be fully prepared in the branches of science taught in both medical and dental schools. He noted, however, that preparation for such requirements would be entirely impracticable without greatly extending the period of pupilage of both schools. It was therefore evident that the differing needs of the two specialties dictated different methods of instruction.

In the sixties, leaders of dental education advocated an expansion of the curriculum by the addition of relevant subjects that were also found in the catalogues of medical schools. James Taylor proclaimed as he welcomed the American Dental Association to Cincinnati, shortly after the physicians had also met in that city, "In looking over the curriculum of our Dental Colleges, we are rather disposed to think we shall soon absorb or lay under contribution every department of medical science."[56] Through the seventies, sentiment among the dentists began to run again in the direction of a closer relation between medical and dental education. "If we are not medical specialists we are a set of carpenters," declared Homer Judd of St. Louis before the Southern Dental Association. "Other specialists must be M.D.'s before recognition by the medical profession, and we have been more recognized than any other specialists, and better treated than we deserve. The opposition to teaching the strictly medical branches in medical colleges has passed away." Professor Austin argued before the American Academy of Dental Science that lack of medical education was one obstacle to recognition of dentistry as a liberal profession. A speaker before the Southern Dental Association advanced the proposition that "when dentists become M.D.'s they will be better dentists, and the M.D. when he understands more of dentistry will be a better physician." The *Philadelphia Medical Times* warned editorially, "If dentists are ambitious to be considered medical specialists, they must undergo a general medical education. An individual dentist who has taken the medical degree may assuredly be received as a brother practitioner, but a simple D.D.S. never."[57]

Thomas Fillebrown of Portland, Maine, inaugurated a program to persuade medical schools to add chairs of dentistry to their faculties. Dentists had long advocated the inclusion of rudimentary dental instruction in the medical schools—arguing that the physicians did not know enough about dental disorders to send their patients to dentists.[58] The suggestion had never had any appreciable effect. Now some dentists embraced the idea with enthusiasm—for the better instruction of dentists. Fillebrown's proposition was endorsed by the American Academy of Dental Science in 1876. At Chicago, in 1877, Fillebrown, a member of the committee on education, brought his scheme before the Association. He moved the adoption of a preamble and resolutions embodying his proposals. The preamble declared dentistry to be a medical specialty. The first resolution acknowledged a sound and thorough medical education to be essential to successful dental practice. A second resolution stated that for the best interests of the profession of dentistry, medical schools should expand their curricula to include instruction in dentistry, "in order that it may be placed on an equality with other specialties of medicine." The Association discussed the suggestions and then suspended the rules to bring the matter to a vote. The preamble and the first resolution were adopted, while the proposal to turn dental education over to the medical schools was rejected. Undismayed, Fillebrown brought the defeated resolution forward in the following session, where it was again the occasion of lively debate before being voted down for a second time.[59]

W. W. Allport of Chicago also advocated the combination of dental with medical education. He led the movement to establish a section on dental and oral surgery in the American Medical Association. He also felt that the two objectives, medical education for dentists and medical recognition of dentistry, were related.[60] Here and there minor beginnings in this direction took hold. Two prominent instructors left the Baltimore College of Dental Surgery to join the dental department of the University of Maryland, where they would be connected with one of the oldest university-related medical schools.[61] Among the dentists as a whole, however, the movement found little sympathy. The proposition was again agitated at the Cincinnati meeting of the Association in 1882. The sentiment of the profession for maintaining separate identity was too strong, a reporter noted with satisfaction. "The feeling was almost unanimous that dentistry was altogether too large to be made the tail end of the kite of medical practice." [62]

The dentists found reasons stronger than sentiment for maintaining their independence. The situation of medical education scarcely warranted abandonment of the sound foundations of the dental college system. The medical faculties followed the lead of the dentists in trying to establish an association of medical schools.[63] The effort seems to have produced mixed results. A decade later, an advocate of dental independence warned that there was "no controlling or supervising power over all those [medical] colleges." "The majority of the medical schools (by the showing of the medical journals) are not so enviable in their reputation as to offer inducements for entering into relations with them," he warned. Other dentists, however, claimed the Association of Medical Colleges had produced a healthy effect upon medical education.[64] The president of the American Dental Association expressed dissatisfaction with the dental instruction offered in the medical schools. "The late movement on the part of some of the medical schools in instituting additional chairs for the purpose of giving instruction in dentistry would be entitled to more confidence and favor had the medical profession shown any appreciation of the requirements of the dentists in the field for study which dentistry offers." This, he pointed out, "is made patent by the fact that upon a partial and very limited medical education, its colleges are yearly conferring degrees in dentistry with all of the rights and privileges pertaining thereto, while the ophthalmologist, dermatologist, obstetrician, and gynaecologist, as well as the aural surgeon, must all take a full course of medicine and receive the degree of M.D. before they can be recognized in any of the above specialties."[65] Robert Arthur undertook a selective survey of dental education in the middle seventies. He reported that even in the university-related schools, where access to instruction in medicine was presumably easier than in the case of the independent dental colleges, medical instruction was a "kind of pabulum." Furthermore, he charged, "it is done at the expense of that technical instruction which is so strongly contended . . . is its great essential."[66] The problem of relations with medicine remained open.

This provisional settlement in favor of continued dental independence lent urgency to the educational problem. Not only was it necessary to consider content and standards for dental instruction, but the means of enforcing these had to be determined. Efforts on the part of the American Dental Association—and other dental organizations —to this end were not notably effective. In 1883, the Association resolved, "That the interests of the profession and advanced dental education both demand that all dental educational institutions shall require that every student, before being admitted to examination for the degree of Doctor of Dental Surgery, shall have taken two full courses of lectures."[67] H. A. Smith, in his presidential address, alluded to the experience of the American Medical Association. The physicians had discovered that there was no power in the association to coerce the colleges. He quoted the wry conclusion of the president of the American Medical Association: "The plan of making war directly upon the medical colleges, endeavoring to compel them to conform their practices to our theories, or else surrender the prerogatives to which they had been so long accustomed, was altogether a mistake." Here, said Smith to the dentists, "we have an instance of history teaching by example."[68] W. H. Morgan, an outstanding Tennessee practitioner, active in both the Southern and the American organizations, ruefully acknowledged the limitations on society action against the schools. "The schools do not belong to the associations," he said, "and the associations are not the profession." Experience, both in the dental and medical organizations, enjoined caution. Public opinion, the dental leaders reluctantly admitted, had the final say in the matter.[69] And the people had begun to have their say by adopting legislation regulating dental practice.[70]

The movement toward statutory regulation of dentistry, as in the past, was viewed with mixed feelings by the dental profession. In the post-war decades dentists soberly weighed again the advantages and disadvantages accruing from dental legislation. Many spokesmen welcomed the intervention of the state. The *Dental Cosmos* reasoned that since the public had no means of judging between the competent and the incompetent dentist, they should, in justice, have some guarantee of qualification.[71] At the same time, it was recognized, the people did not always desire such protection. "Ours was a government of the people and by the people, and it was notoriously impossible to secure the enforcement of any law which did not meet popular approval," reported an Illinois dentist. "It was difficult to convince the people that they needed any protection. . . . The reply was always ready, that the people were abundantly able to protect themselves, and that if they chose to employ quacks, they alone would suffer, and it was nobody's business." [72]

Regardless of their point of view, commentators were agreed upon one point. Dental legislation would make it possible to advance dental education. "When laws regulating the practice of dentistry are made and executed in all the States, then we can more effectually aid the colleges and hold them responsible for the professional attainments of incoming practitioners," explained Truman W. Brophy for the American Dental Association Committee on Dental Education. He believed further that the law would be productive of good, and especially that its moral influence would be very beneficial in inducing proper preparation on the part of new recruits.[73]

Most of the dental legislation adopted during these years required graduation from a dental college, although some allowance was also made for office-trained applicants to qualify by examination.[74] As a result, dental organizations found their relations with the colleges complicated rather than simplified by the intervention of the state—

and the need for regularization of dental education was even more urgent.

Many of these early statutes placed new and additional responsibilities upon the dental societies. In Ohio the state society or one of its auxiliaries could issue a certificate of qualification, prerequisite to entering practice in Ohio, if the applicant was not a graduate of a regularly-organized dental college. In New York, Pennsylvania, and Georgia, the state societies chose the board of examiners who determined the right of the applicant to enter practice in the state.[75] In virtually every case, the holder of a degree from a dental or medical school held an advantage over the office-trained candidate seeking to enter practice. Because of this provision the dental societies found themselves concerned not only with the qualifications of individual applicants, but also with the credentials of the college in which the applicant had been trained. "Is it to be taken for granted that all the dental colleges now existing, and those of the future, are to be considered reputable without question?" asked the American Dental Association Committee in 1882.[76] The actions of the various state boards were not consistent. A college diploma accepted in one state might be rejected in another.

The situation called for some fixed and recognized standard to which the curriculum of a given school could be referred. It seemed that action by the national organization of the dental profession could fulfill this function. The Committee on Dental Education, under the chairmanship of J. N. Crouse, recommended in 1882 that the Association sponsor a society of the dental colleges.[77] The suggestion found widespread support in the profession. On the eve of the 1882 meeting of the American Dental Association, the *Dental Register* had urged representatives of the colleges to use the occasion to begin organizing such a society. "It would seem eminently fit that such an association should be organized and made to subserve the interests of the profession, as well as similar organizations promote the welfare of general education, and some of the special systems of education."[78] The dental spokesmen appreciated the difficulties in the way of achieving such an organization, but they insisted that the time was more favorable than it was likely to be in the future.[79] The 1882 session adopted a resolution favoring the formation of an association of dental colleges for the purpose of securing concerted action as to

Annual Session of the Association, Niagara Falls, 1886

what shall be required of students. The resolution offered the support of the Association: "In case such an association is formed, no college refusing to abide by the action of the College Association shall be recognized by the American Dental Association." [80]

Between the 1882 and 1883 meetings, the founding of a national organization of state examiners altered the situation. The Association now hoped by working through the examiners to achieve its purpose. The Association felt that a new vehicle was now at hand to assist in elevating dental educational standards. The National Association of State Boards of Examiners established a minimum length of the course leading to the degree of Doctor of Dental Surgery. It insisted that only regular dental colleges should grant degrees or titles. It urged states without dental legislation to push the adoption of laws regulating dental practice, and it resolved to furnish all state societies with copies of a worked out legislation, so that uniformity of laws, as far as practicable, would be attained.[81] The American Dental Association could do no more than endorse the measures of the examiners.[82] During the following year, a National Association of Dental Faculties was accomplished. Henceforward, it appeared, these two new organizations would bear the major responsibility of the profession toward dental education.

In these post-war years, the American Dental Association had a contradictory record in relation to developments in professional education. The Association assumed the function of determining the educational policy of the profession. Yet the structure of the profession, and the role of the Association in it, limited the effectiveness of any action the organization might take. Other societies, with lesser stature and narrower scope, could, and often did, adopt policies in advance of the national body. When the first association of dental schools was founded, the American Dental Association could do little to sustain it and nothing to prevent its collapse. The profession looked to the states to control access to the dental field and to influence educational practices. Inevitably, in this situation, the state and local societies assumed a more significant role than that of the national organization. The needs of state-regulated dentistry fostered a new national organization with the specific function of dealing with these problems. The National Association of Dental Examiners was in a better position to influence dental education than the American Dental Association. The Association's sponsorship of a new society of the country's dental faculties introduced yet another complication into the relations of the profession with its schools. By the end of this period, the Association's influence on dental education had to be expressed indirectly through two new national organizations capable of exercising a greater degree of direct control on the schools than the Association could hope to have.

Chapter X   PROFESSIONALISM IN THE GILDED AGE

As NEW RIVALS of the American Dental Association appeared, an old one was passing from the scene. The American Dental Convention experienced a decline from the vigor it had displayed during the Civil War and finally expired in 1883. Earlier histories of dental organization have dealt principally with the American Dental Convention solely as the predecessor of the American Dental Association. In doing so they have neglected most of the history of the older society. The American Dental Convention lasted for nearly a quarter of a century after the formation of the American Dental Association.

Initially, there was some antagonism between the older society and the new one. The ill-feeling seems to have been confined to a few prominent individuals rather than to any deep-seated sentiments of rivalry among the members of the two organizations. Leading figures of the American Dental Association also frequented the sessions of the Convention.[1] The Convention commanded strong loyalties. In 1866, for example, William H. Atkinson, first president of the American Dental Association, provoked a heated debate in the Convention by demanding to know whether the Convention was to be kept up or to become obsolete. The supporters of the Convention leaped to its defense. John B. Rich, who had played a prominent role in the American Society of Dental Surgeons before its demise, spoke elo-

177

quently on behalf of the Convention. "This Convention was formed to bring together men who would not otherwise meet. It was the first scientific convention for the exchange of opinion and advancement of the dental profession." Rich and the other advocates of the Convention suggested pointedly that the Association wished to destroy its rival. Atkinson beat a hasty retreat, but plucked up his courage again in 1868 and proposed dissolution of the Convention. Again, the Convention's supporters insisted that it must continue.[2] It was evident that suggestions of adjournment *sine die* would not succeed so long as substantial numbers of dentists felt that the Convention filled a need of the profession.

The Convention's leaders sought to establish relations with the American Dental Association. The session at New York in 1866 debated whether or not to send delegates to the representative society. Opponents of the idea argued that the constitution of the American Dental Association precluded admission of representatives from the Convention on the ground that it was not a local society. This view failed by a close vote and delegates were chosen. The Convention's representatives did not appear at the Boston meeting of the Association in 1866, nor did they attend in the following year. In 1868, however, J. G. Ambler, C. S. Weeks, and A. Starr presented credentials as delegates from the American Dental Convention.[3]

The appearance of representatives from the Convention nearly disrupted the session. The Credentials Committee accepted the Convention delegates. This portion of the Committee's report occasioned some debate and was finally found unacceptable. Now it became necessary to appoint a special committee to consider the question. A majority of the special committee decided the delegates were not entitled to membership, principally because the elder society was not sufficiently restrictive in membership policies. A lively and occasionally bitter discussion followed. The report of the majority was stigmatized by one of the opponents as a shameless and shameful production, and the motives of those preparing it attributed to personal objections. After spending most of the afternoon debating the problem, the assembly at length adopted the minority report, which stressed the permanent character of the Convention, by a vote of 56 to 51.[4] The delegates representing the older society were accordingly admitted to the ranks of the Association.

The decision by no means ended the division in the meeting. A move to seat delegates from Canadian societies occasioned a similar dispute. The Canadians were denied membership, but were admitted to the floor for the current meeting. Opponents of the Convention used the occasion to reopen the membership controversy. Another special committee, this one headed by J. H. McQuillen, was named to investigate the report of the Credentials Committee. The McQuillen committee presented a lengthy report that denied the Convention's right to representation and challenged the seating of a delegate from the Delaware Dental Association on the ground that he had retired from practice. Further haggling resulted in the adoption of the report only as it applied to the future.[5]

McQuillen continued the battle in the pages of the *Dental Cosmos*. Admission of the delegates from the Convention violated the constitution, he fumed. Such actions menaced the prosperity of the Association. McQuillen found the Convention's lax membership policy most objectionable. "As an illustration that no discrimination is exercised with respect to the admission of members, it is only necessary to direct attention to the fact that at the meeting of the Convention held some years ago, provision was made by which persons engaged in the manufacture of the various articles used by the profession were made eligible to membership. Admitting the right of the Convention to representation opens the door to these." The editorial vocabulary apparently could not produce a satisfactory noun. Mention of dental manufacturers and dealers recalled the incident of seating a nonpracticing delegate from Delaware, who kept a dental depot and "who came to the Association making a display of his wares." The annual meetings, McQuillen allowed, offered a good opportunity for dentists residing far from population centers to make contact with representatives of manufacturers. Yet these agents, he argued, have no right to force themselves into the Association as members, for they come there on account of individual interest, not to advance the objects of the Association. Two committees had tried, and failed, to indicate the dire consequences of these two violations of the constitution, "subverting the very genius of the organization." McQuillen then proceeded to mark out a highly ambitious role for the national organization. "A common mistake with respect to the Association is to regard it merely as an annual gathering of the profession for an

interchange of views on scientific and practical matters connected
with the principles and practice of the profession. This is a prominent
and important object; but in addition, as a *representative* organization, it partakes somewhat of a *legislative* character, whose *suggestions,* not to say rulings, affect the *present* and the *future prospects*
and welfare of the profession." McQuillen heaped scorn on the Convention, as a society willing to take in anyone, however unfit to practice the profession. He then wrapped himself and the Association in
the flag of "our own great and glorious country," and appealed to the
constituents over the heads of the delegates. The local societies, he
felt, would not countenance the actions of their misguided delegates.
Another session, he implied, would see the Association return to the
"path of righteousness." [6]

The 1869 session of the American Dental Association convened at
Saratoga Springs, a favorite site for meetings of the Convention. The
address of welcome was delivered by J. G. Ambler, perhaps the most
prominent leader of the Convention. Ambler alluded only in passing
to the controversy. "This Association, the eldest child of the American Dental Convention, has now reached its ninth birthday," he
declared. "It is breeched and booted, and claims the ability to fight
its way to that bright castle in the distance, unassisted even by its
venerable mother." There does appear to have been some debate as
to the application of the resolutions of the preceding year. This
prompted a member to offer a resolution regretting the misunderstanding and deploring "an ex post facto interpretation of the laws
which disqualify [*sic*] a delegate for membership in 1869 who was
acknowledged to be a member in good standing in 1868." The move
was tabled. Back home, triumphant, McQuillen remarked on "the
regularity and harmony which characterized the proceedings . . . ,
so markedly in contrast with the preceding meeting." It proved con-
clusively, he announced, that the differences at Niagara were due to
"a violation of, or in fact, *an utter disregard of the constitution.*" [7] The
Convention did not again send delegates to the Association.

Through the seventies, for the most part, relations between the
two societies were amicable. So far as the Convention was concerned,
its attitude was conciliatory. J. G. Ambler, staunchest of the Convention's champions, sounded a characteristic note of sorrow that the
younger society lacked due respect for its elder. "A society additional

is not necessarily a society oppositional," he declared. "Without one disparaging word or thought towards the American Dental Association, but with the best wishes for its success and hearty prayers for its usefulness, hoping it may live a thousand years, yet we desire also to live and to be respected and honored as its sire." [8] Ambler boasted that the Convention adhered to the same code of ethics as the American Dental Association.[9] William H. Atkinson, first president of the American Dental Association, sought to serve as peacemaker. To play this part, he overcame his modesty and accepted the presidency of the Convention. "All the good of association that is capable of coming to us, is marred if we set ourselves up one against another," he explained. "Last year I was notified that they proposed to elect me President of the American Dental Convention. I said, as my custom is, 'If you elect me, I will not serve.' But wanting things to go on harmoniously again, I reconsidered and accepted." [10]

The Association, while tolerant of its rival, remained aloof. Anticipating the Centennial Exhibition at Philadelphia in 1876, the Convention appointed a committee to confer with representatives of the Association regarding a joint meeting on that occasion. The Association rejected the proposal.[11] William H. Atkinson, presiding at a joint meeting of the Convention, the Southern Dental Association, and the Maryland and District of Columbia Dental Society in 1877, seems to have somewhat extended the mandate of an American Dental Association committee to include consideration of a union of the Convention, the Association, and the Southern Dental Association.[12] A committee for the Convention was appointed. The Southern Dental Association also seriously considered union. In 1878, the three societies met simultaneously in Niagara Falls. The Association apparently took no notice of its rivals. The executive committee of the Convention decided that it was inexpedient to hold a separate meeting, but nothing came of the unification movement.[13] In the following year, again at Niagara Falls, the president of the American Dental Association, H. J. McKellops of St. Louis, who was also prominent in the Southern Association, renewed the subject of consolidation. Listing the three major dental organizations then in existence, he urged their unification to strengthen the whole profession.[14]

The assembly decided on a special committee "to devise means to secure the concentration of the entire strength of the profession in one truly national body." The special committee deliberated. It consulted with the committee from the other organizations. At the Boston meeting of the American Dental Association in 1880, the special committee reported: "Your committee desire nothing more than that the whole profession should be united under one banner, but they are unable to see in what manner this object can be attained, unless the members of the profession throughout the country come to this Association with proper authenticated credentials from their State or local Societies. . . . Your committee, therefore, believing that the American Dental Association possesses all the requisite qualifications of a truly national body, would respectfully recommend that it take no action which would in any way tend to impair its usefulness or terminate its existence."[15]

The American Dental Convention, in the meantime, continued to meet. Its deliberations, in the judgment of Jonathan Taft, "carried the standard of American dentistry high in the van of professional science." Consisting, as it often did, of the same prominent membership as the American Dental Association, its scientific discussions, insofar as they were reported in the press, were of comparable stature. The Convention showed concern with the same order of problems that preoccupied the Association. It discussed problems of dental education and exhibited the same differences over the questions of rigid time requirements versus accomplishment and relations with medicine that divided the American Dental Association. The perennial problem of fee schedules was aired here. The Convention likewise gave serious consideration to the best means of instructing the public in the rudiments of dental lore.[16] The close similarity of the programs of the two organizations raised the question of the need for the continued existence of two purportedly national societies.

While the American Dental Association insisted that the dentists come to it in order that the whole profession should be united under one banner, the American Dental Convention actively sought union with other societies. In so doing, it gradually destroyed itself. The Convention met with the Southern and District of Columbia and Maryland societies in 1877. In the following year came the ill-fated pilgrimage to Niagara Falls. In 1879, the Convention named another committee to confer with committees from the American Dental Association and the Southern Dental Association. The former remained uncooperative. While the American Dental Association gathered in Boston in 1880, the Southern Dental Association, temporarily operating under the title of "National," and the American Dental Convention held a convocation in New York. Again, the Convention transacted no significant business. There was apparently no meeting in 1881. A session was summoned for 1882, but the journals did not receive a report of the proceedings.[17]

The end came in 1883. While the demise was spectacular, it hardly became the dignity of the second ranking national dental organization. Through the years, J. G. Ambler of New York became the dominant figure in the Convention. At this final session, however, the president, the fiery F. Y. Clark of Charleston, and Ambler, as chairman of the executive committee and treasurer, had a disagreement over the program. The argument descended into a bitter wrangle over the finances of the Convention. Ambler reportedly insisted that past records should not be available to the Convention since "every Convention ended with itself." Ambler's critic retorted that, "if such was the case, then the debt of several hundred dollars, which Dr. Ambler claimed was due him by the Convention, was not a proper subject for the consideration of the Convention, as it was contracted in years past to publish Dr. Ambler's speeches (?) [*sic*] and his poetical quotations." Further acrimonious exchanges resulted in the adoption of a motion to adjourn *sine die.* This proposal, observes the reporter, "was unanimously agreed to, with the exception of the Treasurer [Ambler]. So expired the American Dental Convention. Peace to its ashes."[18]

At the same time, another venerable dental society, the Mississippi Valley Association of Dental Surgeons, seemed also in danger of dying of general debility. Two reasons for this decline were offered by the observer who reported it. First, he blamed the proliferation of state and local societies, "yet scarce dry behind the ears," which the Mississippi Valley Association had fostered. Second, the reporter observed that the society had fallen into the hands of its older members, swollen with self-importance, who distracted the sessions with "their own impotent twaddle or that of some windy edition of antiquity."[19] Anticipation of the passing of the Mississippi Valley Association was decidedly premature. The society continued in existence for more than a decade before expiring.

The accounts of the meetings of the American Dental Association are sprinkled with reports of the growth of organized dentistry. In 1876, for example, a committee claimed a sevenfold increase in local organizations over the ten represented at Niagara Falls in 1859. E. T. Darby, in his presidential address in 1884, announced that there were a hundred. A more careful survey, conducted by the Section on Education, Literature, and Nomenclature in 1890, found "not less than ninety nor more than one hundred dental societies—strictly speaking and excluding alumni and other kindred organizations—in the United States."[20]

Inasmuch as it was dependent for its membership upon the local and state societies, the American Dental Association encouraged the founding of such organizations. A comittee on state and local societies was a more or less constant feature of the Association's structure. Much of the activity of the Association was confined to exhortation, but certain leading members of the Association worked diligently to extend the network of dental organization to the borders of the nation. Scarcely a dental meeting along the eastern seaboard was spared a visit from William H. Atkinson. Atkinson must stand high on any list of colorful personalities that have enlivened the dental profession. He possessed qualities that the profession of the late nineteenth century could not ignore. His scientific interests were broad and he unabashedly proclaimed his findings and his theorizings, as well as those of others, in a rich and intricate oratory that impressed, even if it did not always enlighten, his auditors. On one occasion, "the doctor's dissertation was so full of technical language, that it sounded like the rattle of musketry on a frosty morning." The report relates that Atkinson used a familiar term four times "and four times the auditors had spasms of an awaking consciousness."[21] Blended with his science was a morality that has since become referred to as Victorian. In addition to these qualities, his stature as a practitioner and as a leading figure in organized dentistry contributed to an irrepressible outspokenness. Atkinson was ready with a decided opinion on practically any subject. "Anaesthesia is death in the ratio of its manifestation," Atkinson once announced. Before the American Dental Association he backed an opinion with a wager. "I offer a Delmonico dinner and a pair of clean sheets at my own house, and a week's lodging, for a specimen of hyperostosis, or so-called pericementosis, upon a tooth that has never lost its occlusion. Thumb-suckers and mouth-breathers are the people who have those troubles." While these characteristics did not save him from criticism, they commanded, even from his critics, a respect that with the passing years was more often than not tinged with affection for one of the fathers of American dentistry.[22] Whether he spoke formally on the subject of dental organization, or advised and negotiated privately, Atkinson's ubiquitous attendance at dental meetings exercised a profound influence on behalf of professionalism.

Less spectacular, but far more influential, in fostering the establishment of dental societies was Jonathan Taft. Whereas Atkinson's interest in dental organization seemed incidental to his devotion to scientific enlightenment, Taft was primarily concerned with the practical consequences of establishing dental institutions. He traveled far and wide to aid in the founding of local and state societies. Scarcely less significant was his activity on behalf of collegiate dental education. Dean for many years of the Ohio College of Dental Surgery, he gave up the post to become the first dean of the dental school at the University of Michigan, a pioneering state-supported and university-related college, a position which he held until 1903.[23] The fruits of the labors of Taft and Atkinson and their colleagues of the American Dental Association were the numerous local, district, and state dental associations that dotted the eastern half of the country by 1890.[24]

On the other hand, there were some services to dentistry that the American Dental Association could not, or would not, perform. In response to these needs, new organizations, some of them claiming national scope, came into existence. The earliest of these societies was the American Academy of Dental Science. Founded in 1867, the primary interest of the Academy was in the elevation of dentistry through education. With the passing of time, the direction of this concern turned toward amalgamating dental with medical education. In the eighties, the American Academy of Dental Science was the principal agency through which this sentiment found an outlet.[25] In anticipation of the centennial year, 1876, the Academy decided to present, in some suitable manner, the claims of dentistry, or, more properly, of "oral science," at the Philadelphia celebration. A committee of the society labored through the winter on the project, soliciting the aid of representative men throughout the country. In February, they published an appeal to the profession at large for "facts relative to the early history of the profession in this country, as to individual practitioners, and the efforts at securing a suitable and thorough education in this specialty of medicine that have been made." The resulting work, "a free gift to the profession," appeared in the autumn as *A History of Dental and Oral Science in America.*[26] Although it drew speakers from other parts of the country and exhibited a general rather than a local interest in dentistry, the American Academy of Dental Science remained throughout its existence primarily associated with Boston.[27]

The Academy is not to be confused with the American Academy of Dental Surgery, a New York society. Not much is known about this organization. It appears to have been founded as a rival of the American Dental Convention during a period when the latter was largely dominated by the elders of the New York profession. This Academy may have grown out of an attempt in 1867 to confine the Convention sessions to New York City and to change its name to the American Institute of Dental Science. The Academy of Dental Surgery aimed at the younger men in the field to draw out their latent talent and make dentistry a satisfactory and remunerative field for the brightest intellect. This association also favored a professor of dental surgery in every medical college.[28]

In brilliance of scientific contributions, these organizations were all overshadowed by the New York Odontological Society. Founded in 1867, the Odontological Society aimed at healing or bridging the breaks that gravely divided the profession in New York. The Odontological Society obtained articles of incorporation from the state, one of the first dental associations to take this step. The major concern of the society was to promote "mutual professional improvement." To this end, the membership was small and select and the programs were confined largely to the discussion of papers presented by members or guests imported from a distance because of some particular contribution they could make. The Odontological Society, in common with the other professional organizations of the day, wrestled with the problem of professional education. Unlike the two academies, however, the Odontological Society advised dentistry to steer clear of the uncontrolled and chaotic medical college system.[29]

Through the latter part of the nineteenth century the proceedings of the Odontological Society of New York furnish an excellent index of the interests and the stature of dental science and technology.

In the early eighties, a new organization appeared that represented a potential challenge to the American Dental Association's national leadership. The movement originated in 1879 when the Southern Dental Association and the American Dental Convention appointed committees to organize a truly national society. The American Dental Association reluctantly followed suit. The three committees met at Saratoga Springs in August, 1879. This conference discussed the problem and designated the several chairmen as a subcommittee to meet in the spring of 1880. The subcommittee met and determined to summon a mass meeting of dentists in New York at a time when the Southern Dental Association and the American Dental Convention were also scheduled to meet there. The American Dental Association had planned its meeting for Boston during the week preceding the contemplated mass convention. Both the Southern Association and the Convention proved ready to merge their identities in a new national society, but the American Dental Association remained doggedly independent. The promoters of the new organization refused to be discouraged by the rebuff. The older societies continued their separate existence, but the new National Dental Association of the United States of America was launched.[30]

The new society boasted a number of features which anticipated later developments in organized dentistry. To make the association the representative body of the American dentists, the founders provided for annual meetings in different cities, and quadrennial meetings in Washington. The country was divided into regions and the time of the annual meeting held in each was to be fixed "on account of climate." The higher offices of the organization were rotated among the several regions. The plan also provided for establishment of permanent headquarters in Washington. Subsequently, Washington became the site of biennial sessions, and an invitation to attend was extended to foreign dentists. The scientific aspirations of the National Dental Association impressed the medical press: "The Association aims at high scientific work, and will arrange at once to secure governmental recognition to the dental profession, and help from it in studying ethnological peculiarities in their relation to dentistry. The Smithsonian Institution promises aid in this direction." [31]

All of this organizational activity among the dentists represented only a specialized facet of a hectic vogue that swept the country in this epoch. New associations ran the gamut from fraternal and social orders, like the Knights of Pythias and the Elks, through professional and trade societies, to labor and farm organizations, like the Knights of St. Crispin, the Sovereigns of Industry, and the Patrons of Husbandry. According to one historian of American society, nearly five hundred secret societies arose during the last three decades of the nineteenth century. During the same period, about half that number of learned societies appeared.[32] Farm and labor organizations, societies working for the amelioration of social evils, and special political pressure groups were apparently uncounted and presumably uncountable.

Within the medical field, the proliferation of societies reflected increasing specialization.[33] The development of these specialties raised problems of professional unity and problems of education that were also reflected in the field of dentistry. Some of the difficulties tended to bring the two branches of the health sciences together, while others tended to drive them apart. The "regular" practitioners in both fields, for example, united in warring on the phony diploma racket. During this era, when professional education and professional degrees were beginning to assume considerable legal significance, and before educational standards and the educational system had been adequately regulated, the establishment of colleges and universities solely for the purpose of selling degrees was a lucrative enterprise. Philadelphia was one center for these illusive schools. In 1880, by spending a few dollars in fees and postage, a Philadelphia newspaper editor accumulated an impressive array of diplomas, including doctorates in law and medicine, and similar acknowledgment of his learning in "electro-therapeutics" and sacred theology.[34] The problem was particularly uncomfortable for the dental profession when these diplomas were dispensed abroad, bringing the legitimate schools into question and damaging the repute of American dentistry. In spite of the danger, the profession was slow to rally. The battle to stamp out fraudulent schools was a long one, not finally won until the end of the century.[35]

The establishment of a section of dental and oral surgery in the American Medical Association gave medical recognition to dentistry that was coveted by many dentists. W. W. Allport, who served as chairman of the Niagara Falls meetings in 1859 that had led to the founding of the American Dental Association, was, in the 1870's, an outstanding spokesman for uniting medical and dental training. In the late eighties, Allport reacted against the mechanical and practical emphasis in dentistry. In his presidential address he urged a program to bring dentistry closer to medicine. "As handicraft-manipulative skill has well-nigh reached its limits in dentistry, upon the more thorough and appropriate medical education of those who may hereafter enter upon the practice of dentistry must its advancement and greater usefulness mainly depend. To this end, therefore, let this Association, grasping the strong right hand of the American Medical Association, in friendship extended,—by resolutions, provisions for membership and by every other means within its power,—direct its great moral influence." [36]

The difficulties experienced by the dental and medical men in achieving some sort of professional organization were not unique. The legal profession, for example, was only beginning its development. The American Bar Association was not founded until 1878. A historian of American law, Professor James Willard Hurst, has described the vicissitudes of the lawyers in terms of problems with which the reader of this history is already familiar. The organized bar was weak because of the ill-considered adoption of the practice of a select instead of an all-inclusive membership; it was weak, also, because it failed to solve the characteristically American problem of federalism. This result, Hurst explains, followed from nearly a hundred years' neglect of admissions to the profession, of explicit standards of professional conduct, and of any form of professional discipline. The history of organized dentistry is also a history of the struggle to solve these problems. But the similarities do not end there. The concern of the Bar Association through its early years, Hurst reports, was directed toward the improvement of legal education and standards for admission to the bar. "Thus from the start the new body attended to a public service function; the emphasis was significant even if for the first generation nothing happened beyond a few committee reports." These features are paralleled in the experience of American dentistry. On the other hand, the organized bar failed to attain the statutory control over admissions that some dental societies enjoyed.[37]

Among the professionals there was a mixture of motives underlying the drive toward organization. First of all, associated effort was desirable to control and limit access to the profession. Professor Austin told the American Academy of Dental Science, "Gentlemen, I call upon you, first of all, to establish your metes and bounds, and inclose your domain. . . . Then, with some hope of general adoption, can you frame a code of professional ethics, and encourage gentlemen to enter the profession by guaranteeing them the courtesy due to gentlemen." The latter part of Austin's exhortation indicates a second motive, the desire for prestige and social recognition—or, among those who already had these, the desire to maintain them.[38] In keeping with this impulse was the heightened sensitivity concerning advertising. The American Dental Association determined in 1888 that it was unprofessional to use on cards or signs anything except name, title, and address. Nathan Smith Davis voiced the suspicion that medical specialties constituted disguised advertising.[39]

This craving for social recognition is related to another important impulse, the desire for fraternal relations with fellow practitioners.[40] Often these professional gatherings merely furnished a pretext for a gala outing, with or without the family. The editor of the *Herald of Dentistry* presented this idea after the Saratoga meeting in 1884. "So far as an unprejudiced looker on could form an opinion it would seem that most of the members were in the condition of the American in Europe who when asked 'if he came with his wife, or was he traveling for pleasure;' [sic] answered that 'he was traveling for pleasure, his wife was in America.' Most of the Western dentists wanted the next meeting in the extreme East, while the Eastern men wanted the extreme Northwest." [41] In the mid-nineties, after a session at Asbury Park, an editor complained that summer resorts made poor sites for the meetings because the members were forced to scatter all over the town in search of lodging at reasonable prices, destroying the possibility of social intercourse.[42] Presumably, he spoke for a minority, for in the nineties the Association met twice at Saratoga, twice at Old Point Comfort, twice at Niagara Falls, and once at Asbury Park. Only the site of the 1898 session, Omaha, could not rightly qualify as a resort. The 1893 meeting was in Chicago for the Columbian Exposition. This practice was understandable, if not always leading to outstanding scientific sessions. Philadelphia's Centennial Exposition drew both the American Dental Association and the Convention, while the Southern Dental Association went to Atlanta during the Cotton States and International Exposition in 1895.[43]

Whatever the locale, the assembled dentists were apparently sedate. Little information on the informal diversions that attracted the members has survived. One reporter observed that the dentists were "like the cattle that have been shut up all night in the barnyard, as soon as the bars are let down they scatter to feed." He noted, however, that "as there was a camp meeting going on in one place and a temperance meeting in another, they were probably not idle."[44] A frequent practice among the practitioners and dental dealers of the host city was to treat their guests to a tour of interesting local sights. At Cincinnati, in 1882, "the Association was invited to proceed to the Zoological Garden for a special entertainment." Reaching the Garden must have been an adventure in itself: "Cars were provided which took them through Eden Park to a station on the Cincinnati Northern railroad, where a train was waiting to convey them to the Garden."[45] The report does not indicate the homeward route. At Boston, in 1880, the hosts outdid themselves. On the second day, "the members of the association, with their ladies, were driven through the suburbs of the city." The tour featured a glimpse of the Washington elm and Harvard University, before the guests were returned safely to their hotels. The next day's entertainment was even more elaborate. The party, again including the ladies, sailed down Boston harbor to Deer Island, the location of the city reformatory for children. The guests inspected the place and listened to "musical exercises by the inmates." Next, they "partook of an elegant collation." The occasion was climaxed by "a humorous speech" by the mayor of the city, "to which Dr. Marvin responded happily on the part of the guests."[46] One, at least, of the meetings of the Southern Dental Association seems to have had exciting moments. The site was Baltimore. Leaving the convention headquarters, the assembly marched behind "Minnick's band" to the Light Street wharf, where they took a boat to the Pavilion Retreat. There they partook of a soft crab and chicken dinner, which they devoured, we are assured, "with remarkable relish." The reporter tells us "there was a commendable absence of anything spirituous at the dinner, though there was a profusion of fluids on board the boat." The dinner was followed by a further cruise on Chesapeake Bay. The affair ended as it had begun: "The excursionists after landing again formed into line, and accompanied by the band, proceeded to the Carrollton Hotel." [47]

The festive nature of the sessions of the American Dental Association did not fail to meet with opposition. In 1886 the Association resolved to "discountenance" in the future "the giving of banquets, excursions, entertainments, etc., by local professional societies or individuals" at the annual meetings.[48] The reasons for this decision are a matter for conjecture. The resolution may have been a belated result of the effort of the Women's Christian Temperance Union in the preceding year to persuade the Association "to pass certain resolutions." The session had tabled the suggestions "not because the Association did not sympathize with the objects of the resolutions, but because the consideration of such matters was entirely foreign to the purposes of this organization." [49]

The argument on the virtues of association that figured most prominently through these years was economic. To say this is to say that the dental profession shared the preoccupation of the rest of American society in that era.[50] Dental discussion of the relation of the economic motive to dentistry reflected the terms in which American society in general was debating the relation between the economic motive and American ideals.

Perhaps the most striking feature of the economic changes in the nation during the latter part of the nineteenth century was the growth of business combinations. Small units banded together to gain the increased strength that larger capitalization could afford. Likewise competition could be suppressed or obliterated by means of "pools," "trusts," and other forms of combination. The fringes of dentistry, at least, experienced a vogue for adoption of the corporate form. In years following the Civil War there was a resurgence of

large-scale dental establishments similar to the firms of the Crawcours and Mallans before the war. Whereas the earlier institutions
seem to have been principally concerned with comfortable cavity
filling, the new dental corporations emphasized inexpensive dentures. A natural concomitant, or antecedent condition to this enterprise was indiscriminate extraction. Both features, "relieving our
unfortunate fellow beings of important and valuable organs by the
wholesale," and the replacement of these with artificial dentures,
roused the antagonism of the regular practitioners.[51]

The vogue for business combination evoked varying reactions
among the dentists, as it did among the rest of the population. In the
early eighties, following the death of Samuel S. White, the company
he had founded to produce dental materials merged with the competing Johnson Brothers firm of New York. The reaction of the profession to this development was mixed. While some dentists feared
the rise of a monopoly that would use its position to raise the prices
on dental goods, one observer, at least, reported that he had experienced "instead of an increase, . . . from month to month, a gradual
reduction in the prices of all dental materials." Shortly after the
merger of Johnson Brothers and S. S. White was consummated, another development aroused the apprehensions of the practitioners.
The American Dental Trade Association was founded in 1882.[52]
Anticipating an adverse reaction from the profession, the Trade Association published an elaborate apologia that presented the standard
arguments on behalf of business combinations. The arguments may
all be classified under the head of "the evils of competition." The
Trade Association proposed to establish a one-price system for the
same goods, regardless of the dealer making the sale. This arrangement would do away with the injustice of one dentist negotiating a
more advantageous price for his materials than another in the same
city. Similarly, the Association promised to adopt a standard schedule of discounts for cash purchases. Its prospectus explained, "Believing that, as a rule, it is no kindness to the average professional man
to induce him to incur debts beyond his needs for a moderate and
reasonable time, the aim of the Association will be rather to offer
inducements for cash transactions than to endeavor to make sales by
offers of unreasonable credit." The Association disavowed any attempt to fix prices. It hoped to avoid "the inevitable tendency of an

eager competition for cheapness toward depreciation in the quality of the goods offered," by providing "assurance to each customer that he is paying the same price for the same goods that his neighbor pays."[53] In short, competition among the manufacturers was to continue; competition between dentists and suppliers, being wasteful, was to be eliminated.

The new system had its defenders. "In Dentistry, as in every other business or profession, there must be a head," wrote the editor of the *Herald of Dentistry.* "Without a leader there can be no system or organization, and the profession would be compelled to rely solely upon the individual efforts of its members for its promotion and support, for the advancement of the science and the improvement of appliances. . . . Each Dentist cannot, nor would if he could, make his own implements and materials; and how can they buy without there is some one to sell?" The writer denied that the combination had abused its power. He derided the prospects of a successful producer's cooperative to combat the Association. "We wish it all success; but, as it has been tried in nearly all other branches of industry . . . , and proved in each case a signal failure, and as the Dental profession is composed of many men of many minds, we fear that there will be too many 'bosses' and an inevitable and early dissolution." The *Herald's* editor insisted that the opposition complained merely because the manufacturers were doing what everyone wanted to do. "We are monopolists; so is all the world. . . . Where is the dentist who would not, if he could do so profitably, employ a hundred assistants?" he demanded. "Why, then, cry monopoly?"[54]

This advocate spoke for a minority. Most dentists were likely to complain of "the domineering tendency of the trade concerns . . . , this gigantic 'trust,' which is grinding at the very foundation of professional liberty."[55] One such dentist wrote hopefully, "If the independent dealers will hold out, the dentists will surely come to them in time, for they will not tamely submit to an extortion more conscienceless than the monopoly established by the Goodyear Dental Vulcanite Company. If we are relieved from that soulless corporation only to be subjected to a Combination yet more detestable, there will be another professional war." The solution in the face of combination was a counter-combination. "It is high time for dentists to begin to form corrective confederacies and associations; and for dental societies, which assume to look after the interests of the Profession, to take a hand in the fray and speak out in tones unmistakable." [56]

The dental societies occasionally spoke out. The tone tended to be moderate, if not ambiguous, when they addressed the dental trade. Relations between the American Dental Association and the trade were often friendly. At the Minneapolis meeting in 1885, the Parke, Davis Company supplied "the elegant programmes" for which they received a special vote of thanks. [57] For years the S. S. White Company produced the *Transactions* of the American Dental Association. The main consideration involved was the right to publish any or all of the papers read at the session in the *Dental Cosmos* before they appeared in any other place (including the *Transactions*). Louis Jack attacked this practice bitterly in a paper before the Association in 1889. "The essential spirit of professional ethics is such a consideration for the interests of others as to lead one to prefer the good of another to his own benefit," Jack said. "The general tendency of trade is to secure the good of the individual to the disadvantage or the injury of others." On this account, he reasoned, the S. S. White Company was unfit to lead dental journalism. Dentistry, Jack concluded, could not claim to be a true profession until it had its own journalism. Jack's cause was taken up by W.C. Barrett, himself a former dental editor. Barrett criticized the policy that slammed "the doors in the faces" of the journals, "for the sake of saving a few pitiful dollars." Barrett claimed that he had not written for the sessions because as an editor he could not even publish his own articles. There were a number of other able writers, he declared, who felt the same way. Barrett made it clear that he was attacking the system rather than the house of S. S. White. In rebuttal, J.N. Crouse recounted the background of the arrangement. "I know something about publishing the *Transactions* of the American Dental Association on our own hook. We have been there. We were bankrupt for years." [58] The White Company was offended. The Company addressed a long communication to the next annual session in which the history of the relationship was reviewed. The Company insisted that the arrangement was a large expense for which the only compensation was the right of first publication in full of the papers read before the Association. The Company concluded by hoping that a more satisfactory arrangement could be made. One of the members immediately offered a resolution acknowledging the Association's debt to the Company, disavowing sympathy with the imputations in Jack's paper and Barrett's remarks, and expressing the hope that the arrangement might be continued. Another member suggested a committee to review the matter before the Association took action. The committee reported fuller resolutions that were of similar tenor. The adoption of the report was reconsidered the next day and the matter ended with the adoption of the original conciliatory resolutions.[59] The S. S. White Company was sufficiently mollified that it continued to publish the *Transactions* for another generation.

The Association had some little trouble controlling the activities of dealers whose exhibits distracted the members from the deliberations of the society. Although resolutions were adopted in an endeavor to regulate the exhibitors, the problem continued to harass the management of the annual sessions.[60]

Toward business combinations outside the dental field the dentists showed no forgiving spirit. In 1873, the assembled dentists labelled a revision of railroad passenger policy as short-sighted, arrogant and selfish. Certain roads had abandoned their generous excursion-rate practices and had demanded full fare to and from the convention sites. Condemnatory resolutions scourged the railroads for failing to recognize that the convention delegates attended "at great personal sacrifice for the benefit of humanity and the general public good." The dentists believed that their work in advancing the cause of civilization benefited the railroads "(which depend upon the increase of civilization for their welfare)." [61]

There was among the dentists, as there was in the country itself, great pride and satisfaction in the material strides the nation had made since the Civil War. The observations of two leading dentists at the height of the period linked the growth of the profession with the achievements of the age. J. B. Patrick of the National Dental Association noted, "The age in which we live everywhere witnesses the crystallization of ideas." "Each specialty has its Columbus," he declared. "Scan the field of medicine, anatomy and physiology, and recall the many departments into which it has been subdivided, and on which are at work some of the grandest intellects," he invited his auditors. "Mark the labors of the engineer, the bridge, the railway and tunnel builders, the men who are making steam and electricity handmaids of the people's growth, and leaving an impress deeper than ever was cut before in the history of mankind." Patrick pointed to the achievements of Edison in the incandescent lamp and the generator. "Observe the perfection of travel on your elevated railroads, the bridging of the East River, the tunneling of the Hudson, the opening of the Suez Canal, the boring of the Alps between Italy and France, in short, turning the eye on every side and where in a similar period of the world's history have grander results been achieved?"[62] The presidential address of E. T. Darby before the American Dental Association in 1884 was equally exultant and recited a somewhat different catalogue of accomplishments: "What stupendous events have transpired since this Association was organized! . . . Almost a generation has passed away; the infant child has become the stalwart man. The population of the United States has increased from thirty to fifty-seven millions. A terrible Civil War has been fought, and enemies have become friends. The Atlantic cable has been laid, and the electric spark is darting from continent to continent. The Pacific Railroad has been built, and the locomotive whistles from Maine to the Golden Gate. Our country has celebrated its National Centennial, and we are elated with laudable pride because we have been honored by all the nations of the earth. The electric light, and telephone, and phonograph have been introduced, and the arts and sciences are proclaiming each day new discoveries." Darby then recited the impressive accomplishments of dentistry through the same years: a trebling in the numbers of dentists, a rise in the number of dental societies from twenty to one hundred, a seven-fold increase in dental colleges, widespread adoption of legislation regulating dental practice, the growth of an extensive literature.[63] It is hard to recapture the wonder with which the people of the late nineteenth century reviewed their times. This feeling of optimistic self-satisfaction and the confidence their undeniable accomplishments generated constitute a characteristic of that era that must be appreciated if the age is to be understood. This self-confidence, this recognition of tremendous achievements, instilled a complacency with status quo that was a formidable obstacle to reform.

And there was need for reform. For all its remarkable triumphs, late nineteenth century society had its faults, as many people of the time recognized. "The prevailing standard in medicine and, alas! in dentistry is unprofessional, it being 'money and preferment' rather than 'excellence and efficiency,'" William H. Atkinson complained. He added, "The so-called professions are but excerpts of societary unity." [64] A. H. Thompson compiled a more elaborate, and more scathing indictment of his contemporaries based on an examination of education. "Young men essaying to enter the dental profession seem to be actuated mainly, if not solely, by the desire to acquire an avocation which appears to be lucrative," Thompson said. "This being the motive . . . it is but a natural sequel that they should desire to be 'put through' and equipped with all necessary (and no super-fluous) knowledge, within the least possible period of time, to the end of 'getting to work to make money.'" Thompson found three reasons for this lack of concern with the finer scientific aspects of the profession. The major cause he attributed to a fault of American society. "This is all the outcome of the American epidemic rush after money, and the fanciful estimate of the value of money as a factor in human happiness, and the exorbitant money-value placed upon time." As this characteristic affected dentistry, Thompson was inclined to lay the blame at the door of "the irregular or lay element of the profession." But there was yet another source to the difficulty. "Another powerful factor is at work counteracting the dissemination of the taste and desire for higher professional, as well as for higher literary and general education in this country, i.e., the pseudo-education, misnamed practical, of the common-school systems of the various States." Thompson's trenchant analysis condemned the system of emphasizing a few minimum skills "considered essential to business and every-day life, and the acquisition of a little stock of miscellaneous historical information," and turning out the products as "educated." "The result is that the mass of the young men and women of this great nation are but half-educated, or, rather, half crammed, and totally uneducated; they have acquired just enough of knowledge to inflate their ignorance and create a contempt for further study, and not enough to have reached the safety-line where they can look inwards upon their own ignorance and outwards into the illimitable and humiliating expanse of the unknown beyond." [65] Thompson was overly pessimistic. Dentistry shared in many of the significant scientific developments of the late nineteenth century.

Chapter XI   DENTISTRY AND SCIENCE

THE VICTORIAN ERA was as rich in technological advance and scientific discovery as it was prolific in voluntary organizations. Probably the scientific study that had the widest impact in the world of science and in discussions of public policy was the Darwinian theory of the origin of species, arising from the struggle for existence. The application of Darwinian principles to the analysis of human society divided dentists as it divided the rest of nineteenth century society. Some attacked the novel theories on the grounds of their menace to traditional religion and morality. Others defended the new discoveries and tried to reconcile "scientific" and "revealed" truth as they were then understood. The public airing of Darwin's theories influenced the vocabulary of discussion even when it failed to affect the content.[1]

Much of the proof of the origin of species and related ideas depended upon geological and anthropological evidence. Because of the durability of the dental organs, much of this study required examination of ancient, often fossilized, teeth. This fact created a situation made to order for the interested dentist. If he wished, he could stand in the front line of scientific investigation. After listening to a paper by A. H. Thompson on "The Dentition of the Felidae," at the 1891 meeting of the American Dental Association, W. C. Barrett commented on this fact with considerable pride. "There is nothing scien-

199

tific about filling teeth, that is merely professional work," he said. "But when we consider dentition in its broadest sense, in all the vertebrate and invertebrate world, then we reach beyond mere professional bounds and emerge into the grand domain of general science."[2]

The connection of dentists with ethnological or anthropological investigations was more or less continuous from the post-Civil War period to the end of the century. In the beginning, the dentists defined their interests in these studies broadly. The National Dental Association of the United States sought "governmental recognition . . . and help from it in studying ethnological peculiarities in their relation to dentistry." The 1882 session of the American Dental Association considered subsidizing a scientific tabulation of the skulls of the various collections held in this country. Passed in the morning, the scheme was reconsidered and rejected in the afternoon.[3]

The Association did not again take up the matter until 1889. In the meantime, individual dentists had begun to work on various collections throughout the country. Preliminary findings seriously undermined the theory that caries was peculiar to civilized man. In the spring of 1889, the Illinois State Dental Society decided to collect a fund for conducting a survey of the pre-historic crania in the United States. When the aid of the American Dental Association was requested, the request was granted. The project was carried forward for several years. Additional funds were appropriated. The study was completed in 1894. In 1896, however, the project was in arrears to the dentist who prepared the report. Copies of the study of pre-historic crania did not sell well. In 1897, the Publication Committee of the Association reported that it had persuaded a dental manufacturer to bear the expense of distributing the remaining copies to the profession generally. The report explained that in this way they might reach some parties to whom they might prove valuable.[4]

Other scientific developments of the period struck closer to the main concerns of dentistry and commanded correspondingly more sustained interest. This was a period of uncertainty and flux in American medical thinking. "Even on apparently the simplest subjects there is dispute and doubt, darkness and lack of knowledge," a contemporary complained. In part, this was a result of the conservatism and skepticism of many of the leading physicians of the day.[5] The other side of this coin was the excess of enthusiasm that led many to claim too much for each new discovery.[6] Furthermore, as one historian of medicine has noted, "The practice of healing was plagued by a variety of quack methods, but even 'regular' medicine had in many respects advanced very little, and neither the bewildered sufferer nor the conscientious physician had any real way of knowing what was quackery and what was not."[7] This uncertainty was the price of progress through these years.

American dentists were well aware of the general condition just described. One dental educator exactly captured the character of the age. He said, "When we are reproached with the uncertainties of medical science, and are pointed to the constant changes occurring in her theories and practice, how absurd then to attempt to deny them. Just as all of the physical sciences are changing and advancing, just so with medicine."[8] In such a situation, dogmatism was an insufferable handicap. "We need to be eclectic,—willing to gather suggestions from any source; always open to conviction, ready to investigate theories advanced, and then to adopt such modes of practice as may best suit each individual case presented to us for treatment," one dentist declared.[9] The position was excellent for a transitional stage in medical and dental progress, although it lacked the apparent security of unwarranted certainty. One dentist lamented, "We all seem to have our own peculiar mode of treatment in these cases; if this is the case we are the greatest set of empirics the world ever saw."[10] Yet at that stage of knowledge, dentists, like the physicians, could only be empirics.

The appreciation of the bacterial origins of some diseases introduced a powerfully upsetting factor in medical thinking during the post-Civil War period. In Europe, the development traced its history back into the early years of the century. A series of important discoveries in the realm of techniques, such as improvements in microscopes, the development of solid-culture media for the convenient isolation of particular strains, and the development of differential staining of specimens by means of aniline dyes, cleared the way for the rapid advance in bacteriological knowledge that characterized the late nineteenth century. Many significant discoveries had already been made by the 1870's, but the American medical profession remained relatively indifferent to the possibilities of the new knowledge until after the Philadelphia Exposition.[11] Studies by American dentists attempting to apply the bacteriological theories to dental practice, in the form of antiseptic techniques and in the etiology of oral diseases and infections, were thus well abreast of the more advanced segments of American medicine.

In the early phases of the dental reception of the new ideas, the crudity of the microscope, the influence of folk-lore and outmoded speculation, and the consequences of analogy based on inadequate information, contributed to misleading one of the pioneering dental researchers, J. H. McQuillen. McQuillen spoke about "oral parasites," before the Southern Dental Association. "In the mouth of man and lovely woman these parasites move and have their being," he said, while the stomachs of his auditors no doubt churned. It was not yet clear whether these organisms were animal or vegetable, McQuillen acknowledged. Nor had it yet been established whether these little beings were active in the decay and destruction of the teeth. Analogy and the novelty of the microscopic organisms tempted the speaker to compare the deposition of tartar on the teeth and the building of a coral reef. McQuillen concluded his remarks by apparently repudiating the parasitical theory. "The first element of decay is chemical decomposition," he said.[12] Later researchers were to show the ambiguity, and hence the inadequacy, of this statement.

Theories attributing dental caries to bacterial origins began to appear among European students in the 1870's. An early study along these lines by T. Leber and J. B. Rottenstein, published in 1867, appeared in an American translation in 1873. In 1880, Greene Vardiman Black published a preliminary report of his investigations.[13] The International Medical Congress, held in 1881, brought forth a number of refined statements of existing theories, including a "septic theory," enunciated by Arthur S. Underwood and W. T. Milles. These English dentists concluded that "caries is absolutely dependent upon the presence and proliferation of organisms; that those organisms attack first the organic material, and, feeding upon it, create an acid which removes the lime salt; and that all the difference between caries and simple decalcification by acids is due to the presence and operation of germs." [14] The first publication on the subject by Willoughby D. Miller appeared in German in 1882. In the years that followed, papers by Miller were published in rapid succession in the *Independent Practitioner* and the *Dental Cosmos*. Miller's writings treated the whole caries problem exhaustively. He managed to demonstrate the complicated interrelationships among a host of factors contributing to caries in the teeth. As they related to the rising science of bacteriology, his experiments showed that acids acting to decalcify the teeth (the first stage in the development of caries) were generated by microorganisms growing in a medium of carbohydrates.

The theoretical assault on caries etiology stimulated studies of the proper mode of treatment. In this area the prominent role belongs to G. V. Black. A series of papers through the eighties culminated in his series in the *Dental Cosmos* on "The Management of Enamel Margins." Black's work represented only a part of a vast body of material compiled through these years relating to cavity formation, methods for retention of fillings, the devising of inlays, and the shaping and finishing of fillings. What made Black's contribution significant lay not so much in his presentation of novel methods, but in that he, at last, supplied "scientific reasons . . . for methods that [were] familiar to every practitioner, and which he [had] worked out for himself by actual experience at the chair . . . too often at great cost not only to himself but to his confiding patient also." [15]

Medical advances encouraged parallel work in other fields of dentistry as well. Improvements in microscopy, mentioned above, and subsequently the application of photography to histologic researches fostered impressive advances in this field.[16] By the end of the century the discovery of roentgen rays opened the door to still more avenues of knowledge in dental science. The use of generalized anesthesia in dental operations continued to be the subject of much debate. There was disagreement over the best agent for this purpose, as well as over the methods of administering the anesthetic.[17] At the same time, interest in local anesthetics grew. And, by the end of the century, appreciation of this subject had grown to the point that dentists discussed the possibility of limits to the usefulness and the potential dangers of deadening pain sensations.[18] Some fields of oral disease, however, stubbornly refused to yield to the new techniques. In dentistry, as in medicine, the barriers resulted from a lag in therapeutic techniques.[19]

There were areas of investigation in which dentistry enjoyed an advantage over medicine. Some aspects of dental practice depend upon mechanical contrivances or on the physical properties of certain metals and minerals. In this area of dental research there could be precision and certainty that were not available elsewhere in the practice of the healing arts. W. H. Morgan spoke in defense of this aspect of dentistry. "Is not the man who can calculate the strength of that column and the weight it could bear as much a scientific man as the man who would give you a dose of calomel and tell you it would operate upon your liver, but he did not know how? . . . Medicine as it is taught in the present day is to a very large extent a science of unascertained truths based upon theories that are plausible but not demonstrable."[20] The practical field was one in which American dentistry had always shone. The late nineteenth century was particularly rich in innovations on the technical side of practice.

The age saw the development of electricity from a laboratory curiosity to a powerful and pervasive servant of civilization. In its application to dentistry, electricity went through much the same progression. The period saw the application of electrical power to dental engines, to the operation of furnaces, and to mallets for packing gold in cavities.[21] By the end of the century electricity was an accepted aid, if not an absolute necessity, in the dental office and laboratory.

In the development of materials for packing cavities there was yet another area in which, to a certain degree, precision and certainty could be reached. During the seventies, J. Foster Flagg and others propounded the "New Departure." Christened perhaps after the political movement of the same name among the Democrats of the day, the dental "New Departure" renewed the former campaign favoring amalgams as suitable filling materials. The movement revived old antagonisms and old attitudes. Jonathan Taft, for example, remained unalterably opposed to amalgams. He refused even to experiment with the compounds.[22]

For dental science, the most interesting aspect of the renewal of this old controversy was the stimulus it gave to a more precise examination of the characteristics of the various competing substances. As early as 1873, Ambrose Lawrence of Boston related "an interesting experiment to prove that amalgams do not shrink after being placed in the cavity of a tooth." Lawrence's apparatus consisted of iron tubes into which he packed the amalgam "in precisely the same manner" as he would fill a cavity in a tooth. A little tincture of iodine was placed over the filling. A small force-pump with a gauge for measuring the pressure was attached over the plug. The other end of the iron tube went into a solution of starch, which would instantly react to any iodine that passed the plug. Lawrence reported that the amalgam plugs resisted the "immense pressure of 66 4/15 atmospheres to the square inch" without permitting any of the iodine to leak around the plug. Lawrence explained that amalgam had been supposed to shrink in bulk because mercury, in passing from a fluid to a solid state, decreased in specific gravity. Lawrence pointed out that the reduction in specific gravity did not necessarily mean a reduction in bulk, citing the example of water passing from the liquid to the solid state.[23] Lawrence's experiments were not definitive either in theory or in execution. Their significance lies in that they show an anxiety to settle the controversy by demonstration rather than by argument. Through the remainder of the century, other dentists pursued this and other aspects of the amalgam problem far more exhaustively and far more ingeniously.

In 1874 the New York Odontological Society listened to reports of two elaborate researches in the amalgam problem. The members of the Society were overwhelmed by these exhaustive studies, evidencing, as one of them said, "patient and persevering research." Dr. Flagg was not so impressed. The results, he declared, "were all bosh, bosh, though we were led to believe that that meeting was the culmination of all dental science." Flagg complained that the findings ignored the variability of amalgams. He said he had packed one thousand tubes, and found that some fillings leaked while others did not. Flagg mentioned two variables that were significant. The first was the manner of packing. The filling must be placed dry. The second, he said, had to do with the preparation of the amalgam: "Amalgam ought not to be washed; if it was, the tubes would leak."[24]

These studies triggered an epidemic of tests of the various amalgams on the market.[25] One manufacturer, at least, finally tired of requests for samples for testing. There were too many variable conditions involved for the untrained experimenter to be able to produce valid results.[26] One consequence of this renewal of interest in amalgams was a vogue for copper amalgam. Copper amalgam's desirability hinged on its antiseptic qualities as well as its physical characteristics.[27] Successive refinements in experimental technique led up to publication of G. V. Black's elaborate researches beginning in 1895.[28] The great Illinois dentist thus closed the century by completing a series of studies on the several aspects of caries and its treatment.

In fields more directly involving the patient there was also progress. The problems of regulating the size of the dental arch and the positions of the teeth in the arch received much attention. The discussion revealed a division between those favoring extraction to relieve crowding and the pioneer orthodontists who advocated the use of appliances in the mouth.[29]

Of progress in dentistry there was an abundance. But a disturbing question haunted the promoters of societies. What shall be the relationship of the organization to research and advancement? Until the late nineteenth century, the principal means by which special societies—and the larger society of which they are a part—had contributed to the advancement of knowledge was by recognition of accomplishment. Within special organizations the nature of recognition ranged all the way from the mere acknowledgment of achievement through the awarding of a medal, to payments of money. In the broader society of the general population recognition seldom went so far as the latter form. Recognition was granted and ingenuity and industry were rewarded by extending, for a limited period of time, a monopoly of the use of the invention, a patent. Dental organizations used these means of recognizing accomplishment from the beginning.

The American Dental Association and its contemporaries continued to use this mode of advancing the art and science of dentistry. The Association, for example, acknowledged the debt of the profession to William H. Atkinson for introducing the use of the mallet for condensing gold fillings.[30] In the sixties, a young dentist by the name of S. C. Barnum contrived and presented to the profession the rubber dam, a device that helped the dentist exclude saliva from the tooth and filling while the cavity was being packed. A member of the Association described the innovation in 1865.[31] By 1870, the Association had decided to recognize Barnum's achievement. At Nashville, the corresponding secretary of the Association was instructed to frame an appropriate resolution of thanks for "his generous gift to the profession." In addition to this, three leading members of the Association offered to bear the expense of a medal to be presented to Dr. Barnum by the Association.

Nor did this appear to be adequate acknowledgment of the profession's debt. One of the members elaborated on the situation confronting the society. They had discussed denying membership to anyone holding a patent. "Now what encouragement has [Barnum] for his present to the profession, which would have been a fortune to him, if he had chosen selfishly to patent it?" The discussion then turned to the collection of a purse to be presented to the inventor. A pro rata assessment of the membership was proposed—and opposed. There was not even complete agreement that the gift should be made. One member opposed a precedent of this kind. Another retorted that this was just the sort of precedent they should wish to establish. The latter view prevailed. A resolution appropriating $1,000 to Dr. Barnum passed.[32]

The next problem was to carry out these decisions of the 1870 meeting. The resolution of thanks was beautifully engrossed, at an expense of $25, and duly dispatched to Dr. Barnum. The special committee charged with procuring a medal reported. The *Cosmos's* reporter was quite impressed:

This medal was a most magnificent one, weighing 75 dwts., of full 18-carat gold. . . . Upon one side was a most exquisitely engraved monogram of the letters "A.D.A." and the words, "American Dental Association, organized Aug. 3d 1859." Upon the reverse was an equally elegant engraving of the monogram, "S.C.B." and the words "Presented by the American Dental Association to Dr.

S. C. Barnum in appreciation of the great value of his invention of the Rubber Dam, and of the true professional spirit in which it was given to the world, A.D. 1870."

The reporter added, "The engraving would bear the closest inspection with a magnifying-glass. The medal was donated to the society by Drs. Cushing, Allport, and McKellops, and was procured by them at a cost of $200." The last portion of the honors to be awarded Dr. Barnum, appropriating a purse of $1,000, lagged. In 1873 one of Barnum's admirers secured the appointment of a committee to take the matter in hand. Thereafter the affair dragged on for more than two years before the subscriptions had been paid up and the funds delivered to Dr. Barnum. Resolutions of thanks and the presentation of medals apparently were more popular modes of recognizing innovations than the awarding of purses.[33]

Consideration by the American Dental Association of cash prizes for work on special problems failed as often as not. In 1867 the Association tabled a proposal to offer a prize of $5,000 for "a perfectly plastic material that shall be in every respect equal to gold as a filling for decayed teeth, and shall more nearly approximate the tooth in point of color." Twenty years later, a scheme to award a prize "for a dental cement which shall most nearly approximate gold in resisting the action of the secretions of the mouth and most nearly approach the color and non-conductive properties of the natural teeth" withered without bearing fruit.[34]

An outstanding example of the difficulties encountered when the Association attempted to foster dental research by means of prize offers involved the perennial problem of dental caries. The story begins in 1882. H. A. Smith, president of the Association in that year, persuaded the Association to offer a prize for the best paper, based upon strictly original investigation, related to the etiology of dental caries. He explained, "True dental science may include much more, but certainly it means no less than that when the specific disease which we denominate dental caries is recognized, the efficient causes producing the symptoms shall be known and demonstrable."

At the meeting of the following year, the special Committee on Prize Essays announced they had received but one paper—one by Willoughby D. Miller. The Committee said that while the views contained in the paper were not original, many of his experiments, which were in detail and made for the purpose of confirming his theory, had not been previously published. On this account the Committee recommended awarding the prize to Miller. The Association endorsed the Committee report. On the last day of the session, according to the *Herald of Dentistry*, after the greater part of the members had dispersed to their homes, "a tricky minority upon some trivial plea obtained a reconsideration, and the doings of the Committee and everything connected therewith were thrown out." [35]

This was a somewhat biased version of the episode. On the motion of Atkinson, the Prize Essay Committee was directed to again report on the matter in 1884. Nothing came out of the Committee the following year. The subject languished for three more years before it was renewed by the Section on Pathology and Etiology. The report of this Section in 1887 declared that the failure to carry out the terms of the prize offer placed the Association in a false position. The reconsideration and subsequent neglect of the matter, the report confessed, seriously compromised the honor of the Association. The Section urged that the money set aside for the purpose be paid over to Dr. Miller. [36]

By the late nineteenth century, ordinary citizens and scientists began to consider that the advancement of knowledge and the pace of discovery might be encouraged by subsidizing research, that is, by rewarding the innovator in advance. In the role of patron of research, both government and private agencies were expected to take part. The question of the relation of the federal government to scientific research appeared in many different aspects during the late nineteenth century. It received correspondingly numerous answers. No clear policy was enunciated—none can be deduced from an examination of the many episodes that raised the problem in a practical way. [37]

The tale of federal relations directly with medicine is checkered. The successes of John Shaw Billings in connection with the establishment of the Army Medical Museum and Library, for example, stand in contrast to the unhappy story of the short-lived National Board of Health. [38] Official interest in medical matters was largely confined to the control of epidemic diseases, which, in turn, was related to the growing public health movement in the country. Public health concepts—and dental thinking—were not yet sufficiently refined for these developments to have much significance for dentistry. Dental concern in this area related primarily to public instruction in the rudiments of

dental embryology, anatomy, and hygiene. Not until 1887 did the
American Dental Association begin the campaign for instruction in
these matters in the public schools.[39]

The dental connection with the history of science in the federal
government during this epoch was confined to three areas independent of those that have already been mentioned. Organized dentistry
sought the cooperation of the federal government in studying the
dental condition of the various races of men for the light such research
might throw on the connections between civilization and caries. Then,
too, dental leaders were aware of the advantages that might accrue to
dentistry if the movement to establish a National University in Washington succeeded. Although the National University scheme came to
naught, dentists sought to persuade the Association to take advantage
of the great facilities being developed in Washington with the growth
of the size of the federal government. A suggestion "for the establishment of a National Dental Academy, Museum, and Library" was presented as early as 1888.[40]

In 1895 the campaign began in earnest. Williams Donnally, a Washington dentist, read a paper announcing "An Opportunity for a Great
National Museum." Donnally reported that John Shaw Billings had
invited the dental profession to adopt the Army Medical Museum and
Library as its own national depository. The invitation was readily
accepted by the session. In addition a committee was appointed to
work with the Museum managers "in enriching its stores of dental
literature and museum specimens, especially by appealing to dental
societies and individual members . . . for material assistance." The
effort to build up the collections of the Army Medical Museum and
Library by these means continued in the years following.[41]

By 1897, the Association was ready to take the next step in exploiting to full advantage the splendid facilities being developed at the
Museum and Library. The Committee report in that year pointed out
that the scientists on the staff of the institution could not adequately
serve the interests of dental science due to lack of specialized training.
"The needs of dentistry in this respect could be met by a few well-
qualified persons pursuing the scientific subjects of dentistry, if such
persons were supplied with ample facilities and freed from the exigencies of private practice," the report explained. The Association accordingly asked the government to employ a dentist in the Army

Medical Museum and Library.[42] So began the campaign to find a place for dental research in governmental laboratories.

The late nineteenth century was also the age in which the sciences began seeking lay support for their investigations. The physicians achieved some success in this direction during the period, but dentistry had to wait until after the turn of the century before any substantial program based on private funds could be inaugurated. On the other hand, in subsidizing research on the basis of its own resources, dentistry preceded the medical profession.[43] The latter did not begin to discuss the problem until 1890, while the American Dental Association addressed itself to the question in 1885. A committee of the Association advised:

In view of the fact that This Association has funds on hand which should be employed for such purposes; that it is a scientific organization depending upon original research for all the progress it is to make; that its members have neither the time nor the means to conduct investigations which will contribute to that progress, except in a meagre and incomplete manner; and that the prestige, dignity and usefulness of this Association are being compromised by the lack of originality in its papers and reports: Your committee would respectfully recommend that appropriations be made for the prosecution of original investigations, to be conducted under the auspices of various [scientific] Sections, for the benefit of the Association and of the profession at large.

The Association decided to allow each of three sections two hundred dollars to be expended in original research.[44]

The leaders of the American Dental Association believed that the latest advances in dental science should be reported at its meetings. "We should be so enamored of purely scientific matters that we should take up anything else with great reluctance," said President W. C. Barrett.[45] To carry out this ideal presented many problems. One aim of the constitution was to organize in such a fashion that the entire field of dental progress would be covered and reported at the annual meeting without duplication of effort. In the beginning this was accomplished through the appointment of a series of standing or permanent committees. In the middle seventies, the Association decided that this method was inefficient. A committee report in 1878 explained, "By the plan of annual committees, members are appointed thereon in many instances without having been consulted, and thus placed in charge of subjects not consonant with their tastes or inclinations, and with which they are frequently not familiar."[46]

Advocates of reform urged adoption of the plan in vogue in the American Medical Association. The new arrangement proposed division of the membership into permanent sections, each section having jurisdiction of a field of dentistry analogous to those under the charge of the old standing committees. The difference in the new arrangement lay in the provision that members were to choose the section with which they would affiliate. Membership in the sections was to continue from year to year, which would, it was thought, permit greater efficiency in compiling the annual reports and greater accuracy in reporting the consensus of the profession. Finally, the committee advocating the section system argued, "the talent and ability of those members who will naturally gravitate to each section will, if not immediately, yet in a short time, give to its dictum on the subject under its charge that type of authority that is now accorded to the writings of Agassiz on Natural History, Liebig on Chemistry, Huxley, Leidy, and Marsh on Comparative Anatomy and Physiology, Tyndall on Physics, etc." The new system was put into effect in 1878 with the understanding that if it proved unsatisfactory the Association would return to the old arrangement.[47]

Although the Association did not abandon the plan for sections, the system revealed a number of faults that provoked intermittent criticism and required frequent amendment. One difficulty arose from the expansion of dental knowledge and of particular fields so that the number of sections and the fields under their supervision had to be constantly adjusted. Experience soon proved that under the plan for sections, as under the old committee system, much of the work was done by a few—or not done at all. While some complained that the concentration in sections diminished the interest of the general sessions of the Association, another element in the society retorted that scientific knowledge could only be advanced by meeting exclusively in the sections—mass meetings provoked political controversies—and "science does not, cannot flourish in crowds."[48]

To make the Association the scientific leader in the profession involved other problems as well. Some division of labor within organized dentistry was clearly desirable. Discussion of how this division was to be accomplished exposed a long standing rift in the ranks of the Association. It was again the contest between theory and practice. "We are not supposed to come here to consider elementary subjects," W. C. Barrett admonished the 1886 session. "This is not an experience meeting, and the relation of long-winded incidents of office practice, with elaborate details of birth, parentage, and social standing of our patients, is out of place." Barrett's views accorded well with the earlier proposition to eliminate clinics from the annual sessions.[49]

Another source of complaint regarding the level of discussion at the meetings of the national organization related to the lack of novelty and originality displayed in the papers. Charges were frequent that the scientific level of American dentistry lagged far behind the practical, although some optimists professed to see improvement as the years went by.[50] Yet, toward the end of the century, a leading dentist warned that the existing membership policy did not bring the best scientific minds to the national meetings.[51] One scheme to improve the significance of national gatherings proposed the circulation of topics for discussion among the local and state societies each year. The annual section reports would then be compilations or syntheses of the results of the work in the local and state organizations. Instituted in 1892, the program at first yielded discouraging results, perhaps because the 1893 meeting dealt with strictly business affairs of the Association. By 1895, however, cooperation among the state and local societies was improving and the report of the committee on the project was optimistic.[52] The fact remained, however, that many prominent dentists were dissatisfied with the scientific quality of the deliberations of the American Dental Association.

Society work in the scientific realm had not kept pace with the technical and scientific development of the dental profession, a critic charged. "The real progress of dentistry is exclusively due to the work of individuals and largely independent of any society efforts," he declared. "There has been no attempt made, so far as we are aware, to crystallize this isolated scientific element into one body. It remains as it began, without organization and often without encouragement."[53] The implication was plain. The founding of another national organization for the scientific elite of the profession was imminent. Yet, one of the main excuses for the unsatisfactory quality of American Dental Association meetings offered by the defenders of the Association was that other national bodies, meeting at the same time drew off attendance from the sessions of the Association. The search for a solution to this difficulty occupied much time in the deliberations of the American Dental Association.[54]

Perhaps too much time was given to such questions. For another complaint against the American Dental Association as the century drew to an end held that political considerations dominated the organization. Through the middle years of the eighties a decline of interest and attendance at the national meetings occasioned some alarm. A special committee investigated but could make no recommendations for reform.[55] Nonetheless, an observer speculated in 1889 that perhaps the American Dental Association had "passed the perihelion of usefulness" and was tending to decay and extinction. This awful prospect he attributed to politics:

> There are two prominent disintegrating forces at work and have been seriously undermining the foundations for a long period. They are briefly:—(1st) the stringency of constitutional enactments and the combined determination of a few "learned in the law," to enforce these to the bitter end; and, (2nd) the annual effort to make this convention a political machine in which the legitimate work of such a body is subordinated to the struggle of rival factions for control of the presidency.[56]

Whether such charges were justified or not, they presaged a movement for political reform in the waning years of the century. In part, then, to clear the way for placing the American Dental Association at the head of dental science in America, something had to be done in the way of reorganization.

Chapter XII   A NATIONAL DENTAL SOCIETY

THROUGH the late eighties and nineties, many thoughtful observers remarked the apathy that seemed to afflict the meetings of the American Dental Association. After a disappointing session at Saratoga in 1889, a correspondent of the *Odontographic Journal* attempted to explain the malady. He hinted that there might be a conspiracy to supplant the existing society with a new one. This writer was not alone in fearing a movement antagonistic to the American Dental Association. Another correspondent declared that the sundry proposals to change dates of the meetings, to separate sessions of the faculties' and examiners' organizations from those of the American Dental Association, and to hold memorial meetings and international congresses were "all malicious, and intended to disrupt the membership of the Association—in fact to accomplish what has been frequently said recently—to disband the Association." [1]

When the critics did not darkly warn of subversion against the very existence of the organization, they tended to attribute the difficulties to political factionalism. One commentator charged that "The American Dental Association was a sufferer for years from this affliction, . . . The presidency was to many more important than the work the members met to accomplish, and long anterior to the annual gathering more attention was paid by opposing forces to securing the coveted prize than to scientific work needed to make the meeting of permanent value." There was enough reality to the charge to bring denials from some supporters of the Association.[2] To some the situation suggested the probability that national associations had had their day, and that in the future the real work of the profession would be accomplished by local organizations. Many observers reached a similar conclusion on this point. Opinions on the respective roles of the local and national societies ranged from the extreme view that would have turned all professional responsibilities over to the local societies, to the opposite extreme that would have relegated discussion of clinical problems and matters of manipulation to the local associations, reserving "scientific" matters to the national organization. The function of the state society was also examined during the discussions. The main argument on their behalf was the important relationship of these organizations to admission to the profession. State societies were well situated to influence state dental legislation and membership on boards of examiners.[3]

The functions of the examining boards had significance beyond the state borders. In the interest of winning greater mobility for dentists, the profession desired co-ordination among the state boards of examiners. This was partially achieved with the establishment of the National Association of Dental Examiners. But the desire for greater facility in interchange of licensure was also related to the problem of dental education. In this field, too, there was a national policy-making body. The immediate problem was to co-ordinate the work of the educators and examiners. It is interesting that an Association committee on the subject did not envision the role for the American Dental Association. "Let us, as an Association and as individuals, work to harmonize the labor [of the faculties and examiners]. In union there is strength. Can we not secure this union by a Committee, either National or State, to assist in the examination of students? By such a union we should soon have harmony of action in our State laws." Other dental spokesmen assigned the function of promoting national uniform dental legislation to the American Dental Association.[4]

This conception of the Association as a national legislative force raised an old problem again. Was the Association to be the scientific head of the profession or the representative spokesman for the material and social interests of the country's dentists? Contemporary practitioners saw a conflict between the two functions. And the Association at that time seemed to fill neither part well. To represent the profession before the country and the government, the Association would have to increase its rolls appreciably.

Precise figures of membership are difficult to secure. The fragmentary statistics do, however, tell a consistent story. An investigation by the Section on Education, Literature, and Nomenclature produced these findings: "1. That the American Dental Association is not a truly representative body of the profession. 2. That its membership is too small to accomplish what it should." [5] Five years later, W. C. Barrett came to the same conclusions. "The American Dental Association comes the nearest to being a true National Association of any society that we have among us. It has about two hundred and fifty members. What kind of representation is this? That is one in every two hundred and eighteen of the dentists of America." Supporters of the American Dental Association agreed that a membership of at least one thousand must be attained before the Association could lay claim to a representative character. [6]

There were, on the other hand, many leading dentists prepared to argue that the national body could not become large without losing effectiveness. Their reasons were many. One faction believed that a large society entailed an unwieldy organization. B. H. Teague spoke for another group when he claimed that distance was a great hindrance to a full representation in a national assembly. A supporter of this view said, "There are many lustrous gems in our profession whose incomes will not admit of their taking two and three thousand mile yearly trips. Shall wealth and location determine who shall legislate for all?" Proposals to concentrate or centralize the profession ran into other prejudices as well. One ready answer to these debaters was the device of shifting the meetings from place to place. But, the critics replied, such a practice meant only that the local element inevitably dominated the meetings and this destroyed the continuity of the policy discussions. [7] Even more appealing were the arguments that emphasized sectional pride and sectional differences as justification for sectional organizations. This sentiment rested not only on regional loyalty but on a long-standing tradition of American political thought that, in the name of states rights, suspects any concentration or centralization of power. [8]

The centralizers or nationalizers had much on their side. They enlisted "progress" in their camp. "The spirit dominating the mind of the sectionalist is not the spirit of progression, but of retrogression," one of this group declared. Concentration would make the profession "a power that could make itself felt in legislation and scientifically." Furthermore, dental science had international significance. The American part in the development of dentistry must be upheld and advanced. This could only be done by concentrating the front of the American profession in one organization.[9] Insofar as dentistry claimed to be a learned profession, it could not lag behind other professions in seeking international recognition for American accomplishments.

The attitude of American dentists toward their colleagues in foreign countries revealed the same mixture of feelings that characterized the first tentative ventures of the United States into world affairs. The United States ratified the International Red Cross convention in 1882. The gesture was symbolic of American emergence from a continental preoccupation, a change from "isolationism" to "internationalism." America participated in other international conferences through these years: on weights and measures, patents and trademarks, copyright, and suppression of the slave trade.[10]

The Centennial of Independence, celebrated at Philadelphia in 1876, stimulated American dentists, as it did their fellow countrymen, to exhibit their accomplishments for foreign approbation. The American Dental Association began planning for the occasion as early as 1872. The promoters of the affair hoped to attract to the meeting of the Association at that time "a number of our professional brethren [from abroad]." The assembly at Philadelphia proved not quite so cordial as the advance notices implied. Eight foreign dentists satisfied the Executive Committee and were invited to seats upon the floor and to participate in the discussions. The program of the meeting, however, was devoted entirely to contributions by members of the Association.[11] The affair was hardly an international congress.

The hopes for international recognition and cooperation, first expressed in connection with the Philadelphia Exposition, did not diminish. American dentists accepted gratefully the invitation to participate in the International Medical Congress in London in 1881. In 1885 a committee was appointed to consider the feasibility of holding an International Dental Congress in conjunction with the 1887 session of the Association. This proposition failed to yield any results. The Section on Dental Education, Literature, and Nomenclature in 1887 urged the Association to take the initiative in the formation of an international congress. Again the society failed to act. In 1888, the joint session of the American and the Southern Associations accepted an invitation to participate in the Paris meeting of the American Dental Society of Europe in 1889. The whole movement for international dental organization approached its climax when plans were laid for an International Dental Congress in connection with the World's Columbian Exposition in Chicago in 1893.[12]

The failure of many of these proposals to produce results was indicative of opposition among many of the members of the profession. Here and there voices were raised in active protest. A correspondent of the *Dental Review* explained, "I disapprove of all the various means which are employed to weaken the meetings of the association by entangling it with International Medical and Dental Congresses. With the former it cannot consistently affiliate unless it wishes to destroy its identity; while to the latter it needs to give nothing but its sanction." Other critics professed to doubt the scientific value of such conclaves. One such dentist insisted that there had been too many participants. "The most convincing example of herculean effort without a corresponding equivalent in results had recently been given the world in the Columbian Dental Congress," he said.[13]

American dentists showed a lively interest in dental developments abroad during these years. The American Dental Association exchanged friendly and fraternal greetings with kindred organizations elsewhere. Occasionally practitioners bound for Europe received credentials as delegates to overseas societies. Foreign dentists merely received the privileges of the floor at meetings of the Association. From developments abroad, American dentists may first have heard of dental service in the primary schools. The method of manipulating gold formulated by Wilhelm Herbst came to the attention of American practitioners through G. V. Black's translation.[14] Relations with the profession in Great Britain were particularly close. This may have been due to the common language, for American dentists found foreign tongues an obstacle to reception of European innovations. The editor of the *Dental Cosmos* derived from a British example a means of turning into a useful channel the "enormous" sums American dentists spent yearly on the printing of the proceedings of their meetings, most of them of little or no value. The editor proposed to imitate the British Medical Association and distribute a journal to all society members. "By massing numbers, it becomes possible to furnish a costly journal at a very small price per copy." [15] It was many years before the American Dental Association was able to adopt this practice, although some state societies began to offer a subscription to an "official" journal during those years.

Efforts to bring about closer relations between American and foreign dentistry ran afoul of the prevailing sentiment of nationalism. A southern opponent of union between the American and the Southern professional societies declared, "I should be far more decided in my opposition to 'combination and consolidation' were the parties of the second part England, France, Germany, Spain, or Spanish-America." Such negative expressions of national pride were relatively few, but doubtless many American dentists shared the sentiments of the contributor to the *Medical Record* who dreamed of a utopian condition in the year 2000 when "the opinion of the retiring, common-sense, professional neighbor will be as worthy of at least as courteous a reception as that of some unknown Herr Professor, with an unpronouncible name, from the middle of one of the southern provinces of Austria." [16]

Advocates of international professionalism found an excellent argument for international cooperation in the vexing question of a standard nomenclature. In the years following the Civil War, one of the outstanding leaders of American dentistry, William H. Atkinson, served as chairman of the American Dental Association committee on nomenclature. Atkinson submitted a series of reports on the subject. Like most of the ventures to which Atkinson set his hand, nomenclature received bold treatment. Instead of following the expected line of attack and attempting to systematize the existing vocabulary, Atkinson adopted a radical approach. He would bring all the nomenclature of science and philosophy into a single unified system with a

Site of the Philadelphia Centennial Session, 1876

new universal artificial language, "Alwaso." All knowledge would be subsumed under a new science, "universology." Atkinson's prestige and the portentous way in which he presented his reports cowed any opposition until 1882. In that year the contentious George Watt led a movement that halted Atkinson's program in mid-career.[17]

By coincidence, at the same time that the action of the Association forced the adoption of a more orthodox approach to the problem, the National Board of Health managed to convene an international conference intended to produce a more uniform nomenclature. From the deliberations of this body came the International List of Causes of Death, an important move forward in the effort to secure adequate mortality statistics. The dental profession did not take any decisive steps in this direction until after 1887. In that year the Section on Dental Education, Literature, and Nomenclature reported receipt of one lone paper. This annual report stated, "To our knowledge, not a

single article has appeared on the subject anywhere in our literature."
The Section outlined the importance of the problem.

> There are no rules governing the phraseology of diseases; there is no universal system of giving the anatomical description of the surfaces of the teeth. In the present state of affairs, it is almost impossible to describe certain conditions in a sufficiently lucid anatomico-physiological manner, so that on the mind of every hearer the same ideas would be impressed.

The report concluded that nothing comprehensive or definitive could be accomplished without an international conference. This argument was repeatedly used in the following years on behalf of organizing an international dental congress. As late as 1895, a dental editor complained of the absence of agreement on the subject. Nomenclature, he pointed out, "cannot be changed by essays, however learned they may be." [18]

Satisfactory solutions to all these many problems could be reached only through reform of the mechanisms of dental organization. In the last years of the century there were two movements looking to this end. One pursued fundamental reform. The other sought first to bring the profession under a single head. The former movement became enmeshed in the latter. Its objectives were not accomplished until the new century was well underway. The latter movement resulted in the union of the Southern Dental Association with the American Dental Association. The history of relations between these two parallel institutions and their eventual amalgamation brings into focus many illuminating features of rising American nationalism and lingering American sectionalism that characterized the late nineteenth century.

Declarations of intersectional amity began among some dentists, as they did among some portions of the rest of the country, when the guns ceased to fire. But the strains and hatreds engendered by four bitter years of bloodshed proved sufficiently strong that the Southern Dental Association was founded, although some individuals belonged to both societies and the two societies exchanged delegates with fair regularity. Not until the end of Reconstruction, marked by the with-

World's Columbian Dental Congress, Chicago, 1893

drawal of federal troops from the South, did the bitter memories of the war years begin to fade. The Southern Dental Association announced its 1876 meeting to be held in Nashville and "cordially invited" all dentists of good standing in the profession to be present. Northern dentists ungrudgingly acknowledged the initiative of dentistry in the Confederacy in "the late unhappy civil war." The South, they pointed out, had showed commendable consideration for the health and welfare of her soldiers in providing some dental care through the appointment of army dentists. By the eighties, a president of the American Dental Association felt he could refer to the conflict and its aftermath in a catalogue of American achievements. "A terrible civil war has been fought," he recalled, "and enemies have become friends." When the two organizations held a joint meeting in 1888, the president of the Southern joked about the conflict in a debate on educational policy. "Editor Sudduth speaks about secession of the specialists from the general profession," he said. "We once tried secession, and it is not very popular in this country." On the eve of the union of the two societies, two leaders, one a northerner, the other from the South, appealed to "the common patriotism of any learned profession." They urged the session to "join hand in hand" "for the advancement and development of the proper fraternal feeling . . . obliterating all sectional lines and objectionable sectionalism." [19]

Exhortations to obliterate sectional animosity were accompanied by deeds. In 1878, as a conciliatory gesture, the Southern Dental Association went to Niagara Falls in the hope of effecting a union with the American Association and the American Dental Convention. A southerner, H. J. McKellops of St. Louis, presided over the American Dental Association in 1878–79. He renewed the plea for national unification in his presidential address. [20] The Southern Dental Association changed its name to the National Dental Association in that year in an effort to broaden its appeal and forward the movement toward union. The American Dental Association refused to support the program. When the unification movement produced yet another national professional society, the new National Dental Association of the United States, the Southern Association resumed its sectional name.

The next move toward unification came from the southerners. H. J. McKellops, as president of the Southern Association, "extended . . . a most hearty invitation," to the American Dental Association to meet with the Southern at Lexington, Kentucky, in 1884. He assured the session that "'the latch-string would always hang on the outside.'" The gesture failed to attract the American Dental Association.[21]

In 1886, H. A. Smith of Cincinnati initiated a move for a joint meeting with the Southern Association at Asheville, N. C. The invitation was issued, but during the year a majority of the officers and executive committee, foiled in their effort to postpone the meeting for a year, changed the place of the meeting to Niagara Falls. At the 1887 session of the American Dental Association, the corresponding secretary read a joint letter from the Virginia State and the Southern societies inviting the American Dental Association to meet with them at Old Point Comfort. The Association appointed a committee to confer with the Southern Association regarding a joint session in 1888. This committee met with the Southern Association at Old Point Comfort. Here some southerners evidenced opposition, but a meeting was agreed upon.[22]

The two societies met together at last in 1888 at Louisville, Kentucky. The American Dental Association extended an "earnest and friendly greeting" to the host society and gratefully stated their "appreciation of the hospitality." The joint meeting memorialized Congress, requesting the removal of all tariff duties on imported dental and surgical instruments, apparatus, and supplies. The address by B. H. Catching, president of the Southern Dental Association, set off an argument that crossed sectional lines because it raised the perennial question of the relation of dentistry to medicine, but there were no displays of purely sectional antagonism.[23]

At the close of the meeting, the retiring president of the American Dental Association hailed the session as "the beginning of our friendship." He added, "Let us not hear or know that there is such a part of the country as North or South. Let us all feel that we are brothers, that we are working for the general good; and let us work as harmoniously as it is possible for brethren to work together." President Catching of the Southern Association echoed the sentiment: "We have cultivated friendships, we have formed attachments, and I do hope that we will never find anything to estrange us, and that we shall all live in one common country, engaged in one common profession." A Doctor Storey summed it all up: "Behold how good and pleasant for brethren to dwell together in harmony!"[24]

The next few years showed that reconciliation of North and South was not the only obstacle to national unity in the dental profession. Many dentists considered distance to be an obstacle to national meetings. Since local dentists attended in greater numbers than those from remote parts of the country, there was a tendency for the meeting site to remain in the same vicinity. The American Dental Association, for example, met west of Niagara Falls only nine times in the years between 1870 and 1897. The Southern Dental Association attempted to solve this problem in 1882. In that year, the area from which the Association principally drew its membership was divided into four districts. A constitutional amendment provided for rotation of the annual sessions among the four regions.[25]

In addition to the problem of distance, there was the tenderness of sectional pride, which was by no means confined to the South. In the ranks of the American Dental Association, the West exhibited characteristics similar to those of the southerners.[26] There were, for example, complaints that the Association slighted the West in choosing the sites for the annual meetings.

A corollary of this line of attack was the recognition that for all its pretensions of national scope, the American Dental Association was really an eastern sectional society. An analysis of the membership of the Association in 1890 revealed that 136 of its 175 members came from the eastern states. Regional sentiments among the members of the American Dental Association constituted as great an obstacle to national unification as did southern particularism.[27]

Spokesmen for the South, however, developed the most elaborate arguments on behalf of regional divisions within the profession. "Sections differ in wealth, manners and customs," wrote one advocate. "It is well, that those of like life should meet together. Climatic influence has its bearing even on scientific topics." The Southern Dental Association commanded 'its sentimental supporters too.[28] W. W. H. Thackston well represented the conservative leadership that combined intense attachment to the regional society with suspicion of change. In a paper read before the Virginia State Dental Society in 1895, Thackston declared that the existing two associations rested on the existence of two separate and distinct sections of the country. He reiterated that "these two Associations have adapted and suited their methods and measures to the tastes, the genius and needs of the sections they represent." Thackston conjured up a picture of a "colossal, ponderous and overgrown 'combine,'" that would dominate the profession. He raised the specter of the southern contingent in "the position of a helpless and hopeless *minority* in a great, overgrown and arrogant organization, without sympathy or congeniality, with manners and customs different, and with interests and purposes often antagonistic and conflicting." "Human nature is about the same now that it was in historic, and most likely, in pre-historic days," he warned. "The love and quest of *power* still prevails, and the *perversion* and *abuse* of power is to-day *no* rare or unusual incident." Thackston urged his followers to proceed cautiously before abandoning the old institution for the obvious risks of the new.[29] It was against such sentiments that the drive for a reorganization of the national dental societies had to advance.

The need for reconciliation of regional loyalties, as well as the more objective problem of geographical distance, made this problem dominant over other problems facing organized dentistry through these years. Omnibus suggestions designed to eliminate a whole array of difficulties began to appear early in the nineties. Perhaps the first was that enunciated by A. W. Harlan in his presidential address before the American Dental Association in 1891. Harlan's recommendations resulted in the appointment of a committee that produced an elaborate proposal for constitutional revision. In 1896, A. H. Thompson presented a similar scheme. But these suggestions were all sidetracked in deference to the more immediate importance of uniting the two great sectional societies.[30]

B. Holly Smith explained the difficulties in trying to supersede the existing organizations. "A national would, in my judgment, be weakened in authority and lessened in influence if it did not definitely and upon terms of equality extend its jurisdiction through state organizations to every section of our country," he said. Smith went on to argue that this end could not be accomplished without uniting the American and the Southern societies because each held the loyalties of state associations that would not surrender their interests in the existing organizations.[31] The leaders, with this factor well in mind, were able to make progress toward unification despite the distractions of appeals for reform in other directions.

After the joint meeting at Louisville in 1888, the union movement lay dormant for several years. Relations between the two societies were cordial—with reservations. Members of the Southern Dental Association took part in the session of the American Association in 1890. Southern representatives also joined in supervision of the work of the Dental Protective Association. A proposal for the two organizations to promote jointly an international dental meeting in conjunction with the World's Columbian Exposition at Chicago, however, encountered opposition.[32] The distractions of the approaching congress and the deliberations of a committee on constitutional revision deferred further action on union until 1894. At the Old Point Comfort convention in that year, Thomas Fillebrown sponsored a resolution calling for a committee to confer with a similar committee from the Southern Association on the subject.[33] The committee was unable to carry out its mandate because the Southern society held no meeting between the two sessions of the American Association. The committee did, however, find a considerable pro-union sentiment among the members of their own organization. The president of the American Dental Association in 1895 was J. Y. Crawford, a southerner. Crawford recommended continuance of the committee in order to give the Southern Association "an opportunity, if it so desires, to appoint a like committee." Crawford closed his first term of office urging that the American Dental Association "become a truly representative body, knowing no North, no South, no East, no West." Crawford was re-elected and the committee was continued.[34]

During the ensuing year, the committees from the two organizations were unable to meet. Correspondence between them, however, resulted in a suggestion from the Southern Dental Association that the two societies meet at the same place and time in 1897 for the purpose of concluding the matter one way or another. President Crawford devoted his annual address to the problems. The first arose from differences among the state laws governing dentistry. The second was the problem of union. He linked the two together in the conclusion of his argument. "The uniformity of laws is one of the reasons that could be offered at this time for creating out of the two organizations that are now in existence . . . one national organization." Crawford's successor, James Truman, assumed the chair optimistically. Truman said, "I am satisfied that when we meet next year at Old Point Comfort the hope of many years of my later life will be accomplished; that we shall join hand in hand with our Southern brethren, and come up as one body to carry on this great work in the future." [35]

And so it happened at Old Point Comfort in 1897. Almost anticlimactically, the old sectional division in the profession was closed. The committee proposals had received a thorough airing in the dental press during the year. Nor did they contain any particular surprises. A new name, "distinctly national," would avoid any appearance of favoring the American over the Southern. The plan envisioned division of the country into three sections through which the annual meetings would rotate. Three vice-presidents, representative of each section, served under a president chosen from the region in which the meeting had been held. Each great region could organize a branch society, electing officers and meeting its own expenses. State societies would send delegates to the branches, but membership in a branch meant membership in the national organization. The American Association's system of scientific sections carried over, but the president appointed the chairmen rather than leaving these important posts to the chance of election within the sections. The scheme represented a nice amalgam of suggestions that had long been current in the profession.[36]

The American Dental Association session, convened at the Hotel Chamberlain, found little to do. The Southern Dental Association acted first. Its president then sat beside the president of the American Dental Association while the last business under the old form of government was transacted. When these matters had been disposed of, the American Dental Association moved across to the Hygiea Hotel, where the new National Dental Association began its career.[37]

A reporter commented on the great occasion with some amusement. "Everything had been prepared in advance, the wires had all been laid, the ways properly lubricated, and the launch was accomplished in about as indifferent and perfunctory a manner as ever such an important movement knew at its inception." Interestingly, the union convention was under the chairmanship of "that old veteran in society and professional work, Dr. John B. Rich." Rich ruled the convention with a stern hand, brusquely setting down every attempt at diversion from strict business. One determined debater "indignantly demanded to know if the members there had any rights whatever, and was informed that there were as yet no members, and of course they had no rights, and he must at once take his seat." Such treatment of the august dental statesmen, says the reporter, put the convention "in capital humor." The chairman then ruled that every word of the proposed constitution and by-laws be read. After listening to this lengthy document, "the formerly riotous assembly was as tame as a cosset lamb, and ready to agree to anything." All opposition was stilled and the new society was set in motion without incident. The reporter concluded in some awe of the presiding officer: "Czar Reed [then the iron-fisted speaker of the House of Representatives] was a child to Chairman Rich." [38] This account of the historic meeting may have been colored by the bias of the observer, but the fact of the matter was that the new constitution represented no essential change from the old regime. The great problems facing the profession at the turn of the century remained to be solved.

Chapter XIII   CURRENTS OF REFORM

THE YEARS at the turn of the century were years of transition for many
aspects of American life. Victory in the Spanish-American War formally introduced the United States to the status of a world power. This
victory, while it did not permanently add Cuba to American territory,
brought the United States a measure of responsibility for the fate of
the new nation. The Treaty of Paris, moreover, brought Puerto Rico,
Guam, and the Philippines under the sovereignty of the United States.
Just before the war broke out, the Hawaiian Islands had been an-
nexed. Not long after the turn of the century, the Panamanians re-
belled against the Colombian government and asserted their freedom.
Secretary of State Hay immediately, some said precipitately, recognized Panamanian independence. Simultaneously, he negotiated the
Hay-Bunau-Varilla treaty with the new republic, giving to the United
States in perpetuity a ten-mile-wide zone across the Isthmus. The
years that followed witnessed American interventions on behalf of
peace and good order here and there through the Caribbean Basin.
On a wider stage, too, the United States asserted its claim to a larger
role. American marines participated with the forces of other powers in
relieving the besieged western legations during the Boxer Rebellion
in China. President Roosevelt assumed the lead in negotiating the
end of the Russo-Japanese War in the Treaty of Portsmouth. He acted

231

decisively in the deliberations of the great powers of Europe at Algeciras. These few years demonstrated that the United States had entered the world scene to stay. This momentous step brought awesome responsibilities. American statesmen now had to absorb notions of global strategy and great-power diplomacy at the same time that they endeavored to learn how to apply American principles of government to the administration of poverty-stricken peoples of radically different cultural backgrounds.[1]

Nor were the changes on the domestic scene less bewildering. Wartime prosperity, plus the excitement of empire, plus new gold discoveries, temporarily stilled agitation of currency problems, while the problems themselves remained unsolved. The national economy embarked on a giddy course of booming prosperity and wracking panic. In the wake of the distresses of the Panic of 1893, economic recovery, encouraged by the war with Spain, and aided by a benevolent Republican administration and a sympathetic Supreme Court, fostered a wave of business consolidations, mergers, and combinations that assumed a magnitude previously unknown to American experience. Between 1898 and 1904, 236 corporations were organized with a total capitalization of more than six billions of dollars. The whole development was epitomized in 1901 with the organization of the United States Steel Corporation claiming $1,400,000,000 of capital. By this time six major groups controlled almost all of the nation's railway mileage. Monster combinations dominated most of the important sectors of the economy. Towering over the whole loomed the great financial giants, the House of Morgan and the Rockefeller interests. Accompanying the near-absolute control of the few over the domestic economy was the beginning of the flow of American funds overseas— following the flag into the Caribbean and the Orient and striking out on its own paths into the European marts. The consequence of these economic developments was a revolutionary turn in American economic life. New institutions bore familiar names but behaved in unfamiliar ways.[2]

The new gigantism in business and finance aggravated the problems already raised by the late-nineteenth-century urban agglomerations. American institutions for contending with social problems, the political parties and other organizations, confronted the necessity of rethinking their roles to fit a changed America but dimly understood.

Private groups, ranging from the radical Industrial Workers of the World to the National Child Labor Committee, organized to grapple with one facet or another of the new problems. They contended with the evils of intemperance; they fought for the rights of women; they wrestled with the inequities of capitalism—or of labor organizations. One and all, in one fashion or another, they called for the intervention of the government to redress injustice. The political campaigns to bring about these reforms are called in American history the Progressive Movement; their age the Progressive Era.[3]

The established departments of the executive branch were renovated and new government bureaus, agencies, courts, and commissions in the cities, the states, and the federal government proliferated in response to the demand. The old Departments of State and War experienced changes. During the administrations of Theodore Roosevelt, the energetic Rough Rider and his associates, particularly Elihu Root, William H. Taft, and Henry Cabot Lodge, shook up the traditional offices and inaugurated sweeping reforms. The diplomatic service gained status and a beginning was made toward establishing a professionally trained corps. The poverty-stricken and corrupt consular service was reconstituted.[4] In the meantime, similar broad changes altered the outlook and operation of the War Department. By 1903, the office of Commanding General had been replaced by that of Chief of Staff and the various staff bureaus, which had previously been semi-independent, had been consolidated into a unified structure with clear-cut lines of responsibility and authority. Provision had likewise been made for the continued professional education of officer corps and for continuous planning for war.[5]

While Secretary Root forged a "new" army, the medical department underwent few changes. By exploiting the scandalous situation that developed during the Spanish-American War, however, dentists at last won appointment as contract dental surgeons in 1901. The contract surgeons had no military rank or status. It was a situation that was far from satisfactory to the profession.[6] Committees on Dentists in the Army and Navy continued to be appointed by the National Dental Association through the first decade of the century and after. Repeated efforts to promote legislation to enhance the status of dentistry in the armed forces failed. Part of the difficulty may be attributed to lack of unity among the members of the profession. Yet another source of trouble was the surgeon general at the head of the respective medical departments of the two services. Once the obstacle of the surgeon general had been surmounted, the dental representatives encountered the opposition of Secretary of War Root (and subsequently that of his successor, Taft) and of Secretary of Navy Moody. Then members of Congress had to be wooed and won. Not until 1911 did the dental profession secure legislation leading to commissioned rank for dentists in the army. Further legislation had to be passed before dental officers won even a semblance of equality with officers of the medical corps.[7] It seems fair to conclude that dentistry did not gain much from the reformation of the army. Indeed, the advancement of dentists to commissioned status seems to have occurred outside the main currents of the reorganization of the service.

In addition to renovation of the traditional departments, offices and bureaus of government, new ones especially suited to the demands of the new economy, appeared. In 1903, in the field of trust control on the national level alone, a new Department of Commerce and Labor, with full cabinet rank, was augmented by the Bureau of Corporations and the Commerce Court, created especially to try causes arising from the regulatory legislation. The states established industrial commissions to study the social, physical, and economic problems that suddenly seemed to have acquired a new urgency.[8] Public utilities and railroads likewise received increasing attention from commissions formed earlier by aroused state legislatures.

The increasing complexity of life in an industrialized society, plus expanding discoveries in the scientific realm, necessitated the collection of information and the setting of standards before the regulatory responsibilities of government could be carried out. Consequently, new service agencies of the government appeared and old ones assumed new functions and new importance. The Marine Hospital Service, for example, found, as a result of legislation in 1901, that its Hygienic Laboratory had acquired new duties and that the agency itself had become the Public Health and Marine Hospital Service. In the following year, the Hygienic Laboratory was charged with establishing tests and licensing manufacturers of serums, antitoxins, and the like. Similarly, in 1901, the National Bureau of Standards came into existence with responsibility, among other duties, for standards of weights and measures, which previously had somehow been managed by the Coast and Geodetic Survey. In the same year, the Bureau of Census attained permanent status at first under the Department of the Interior and subsequently in the Department of Commerce and Labor. These are but a few examples of the ferment of reorganization and novelty that affected the federal government during the Progressive Era. On the state level, the picture might readily be duplicated.[9]

Similar innovations arose in the nongovernmental sectors of American society. A multitude of private agencies appeared, dedicated to the collection and distribution of information, or to agitation for the reform of abuses. Most of these ventures were small in numbers and resources, and relatively narrow in their range of interest. As in the case of the domestic economy, the most spectacular activities were those of the giants. Recent economic developments had produced huge individual fortunes. The holders of some of them sought to apply their wealth to the amelioration of the problems of the new society their activities had helped to create. This movement had its origins before the turn of the century with the establishment of the Johns Hopkins University, the Rockefeller gifts to the University of Chicago, and similar benevolences. About the time that Andrew Carnegie disengaged himself from the industrial wars with the formation of the United States Steel Corporation, a new era in philanthropy began. Early in 1902, Carnegie established the Carnegie Institution of Washington for the encouragement of research. This occurred shortly after the Rockefeller giving had taken a new turn. A board, headed by the great physician, William Welch, had received $20,000 for distribution in individual grants for medical research in 1901. In 1902, the Rockefeller Institute for Medical Research was established. The decision, as in the case of Carnegie, had been in favor of an independent organization rather than for the endowment of an existing teaching institution. Not only was the institutional basis of these research organizations new, but so also was the conception of subsidizing research in progress in contrast to the traditional method of rewarding accomplishment with medals and prizes.[10]

The National Dental Association sought to take advantage of the new developments to encourage fundamental dental research. The Niagara Falls meeting of 1902 appointed a Committee on the Carnegie Institute for this purpose. At Asheville, N. C., the next year, the Committee chairman reported some difficulty because the Carnegie Institution considered that the Rockefeller Institute for Medical Research covered the medical field. B. Holly Smith of Baltimore reported, however, that he had learned from Daniel Coit Gilman, president of the Johns Hopkins University and president of the Board of Trustees of the Carnegie Institution, that requests for funds from individual dentists would be considered. The National Dental Association Committee reported that it had contacted a number of dentists engaged in research. At that time, the Committee found, none had applied for Carnegie aid although some dental researchers planned applications. Some state societies also appointed committees to investigate the possibilities in Carnegie research grants. The report of the Committee advised caution in pushing applications for dental research grants. It pointed out that there was too much at stake to risk losing out by asking too much. The Committee recommended that aid be sought for an index of dental literature. This was the only specific project that won the committee's support. For the time being, the committee urged that individual dentists make applications that would be processed through a committee of the National Dental Association. For the long run, the Committee favored establishment of a fully equipped laboratory staffed by "men selected for their devotion to science and proved ability as investigators." [11] After this high point, the campaign lagged. The National Dental Association sought funds for dental research by other means and from other sources.

In the meantime, the American Medical Association had begun a program to foster research within its ranks. The movement had its origins in a declaration of policy adopted at the meeting of 1898. It did not bear fruit, however, until the establishment of a permanent Committee on Scientific Research financed by the Association itself. Grants at first amounted to no more than $100. With the passing of time, the research program sponsored by the American Medical Association expanded, but the entrance of the Rockefellers and other philanthropists into the field limited the need for funds from the medical association.[12] Dentistry, on the other hand, was not so fortunate. Dental leaders issued periodic pleas for greater research activity and support. Not until 1908 did the National Dental Association establish a permanent Committee on Scientific Research modeled on that of the American Medical Association.[13]

Similarly, the dental campaign for government aid to research had more difficulty than the medical campaign. Developments in the Army Medical Corps, as well as in other government agencies, led naturally to medical research.[14] The need for investigations in the dental field was not so obvious. The main emphasis among the dentists for a research connection with the government was on the National Medical Museum and Library, where a beginning had already been made. Endeavors to secure federal support for a dental investigator there failed.[15] Although organized dentistry did not share significantly in the expansion of either federally or privately sponsored research, enough has been said to indicate its participation in the moves in that direction during the Progressive Era.

Formation of the great trusts and the reform movements to study and control their excesses had one feature in common. Both developments envisioned greater centralization of power. Such a motive also characterized many other developments of the period. Not least interesting of these was the long campaign to reform the National Dental Association.

The agitators scarcely paused when the American Dental Association combined with the Southern Dental Association. On the eve of the consolidation, one editor warned that mere union and a change of name would not suffice. He proposed a more radical step, a change in the very basis of the national organization. The change to come with union, he warned, might be the last such opportunity for a generation. Another writer observed that the new constitution incorporated no essential change, although, he noted wryly, "any alteration must be for the better."[16]

Even James Truman, retiring president of the American Dental

Association, and a leading promoter of the consolidation, acknowledged that the new organization needed perfecting and only after
further reform could hope to usher in a dental utopia. Nor was dissatisfaction with the machinery of organized dentistry confined to the
leaders of the profession. A sampling among dentists in Illinois revealed deep-seated discontentment among the rank-and-file practitioners. The complaints voiced by these average members of the
profession, some of whom belonged to dental societies, while others
lacked affiliation with any association, indicated a widespread belief
that the chief purpose of the professional societies was "politics" and
the self-aggrandizement of the active workers, whom many of the
critics regarded as mere covert advertisers. The charge of a preoccupation with politics and office was by no means confined to dentists of
no prominence. Similar charges were made on the editorial pages of
the leading journals of the time.[17]

On other points there was less agreement between the two extremes of the profession. The Illinois critics of organized dentistry
objected to the theoretical character of much of the discussion at
society meetings. They demanded more attention to practical educational papers. A corollary of this complaint was the charge that the
societies provided too little return for the expenditures of time and
money that membership entailed. It was this utilitarian bias of the
rank and file that led James Truman to lament, "The altruistic side of
dentistry needs cultivation, but it will never assume large proportions." Some of the less-well-established practitioners fretted under
the restraints of the Code of Ethics. " 'The Boston Dental Parlors' and
similar affairs get the most work, and the only way to fight them is to
meet them on their own grounds," one such dentist declared. Confronting the unethical operator from day-to-day was no simple matter.
"The idea that 'Cheap John' does poor work, etc., is a mistake. He is
up to date; he buys the best goods and gets the latest appliances."[18]
Comments of this nature indicated the depth of the division within
the profession. They showed the great educational effort that would
be required before the full strength of the profession could be marshalled on behalf of elevated principles of dental practice as well as
scientific advancement.

A vigorous movement was under way in Illinois to bridge the gap.
The fruitful center of this development was Chicago. At this time

Chicago was experiencing a considerable renaissance in the healing arts. A progressive educational establishment communicated its virtues to medical organization. The Chicago Medical Society grew prodigiously in the later years of the century—multiplying its membership threefold during the eighties and nearly doubling again in the nineties. By the end of the century Chicagoans dominated the state medical society.[19] In consequence it is difficult to determine whether the innovations in membership provisions, which were to be of such crucial importance in the reform of the healing professions, first occurred in the state or the city. It matters little. The central feature to be noted in the changes that occurred in both medical societies was the provision that membership in a local or specialist society entailed membership in the state or city organization. Dues were collected only at the lowest level, in the local or specialist group, and a portion of these moneys was then forwarded to the superior association. This relatively simple device solved at a stroke two problems that had been perplexing dental promoters since the beginning. The first of these was selective recruitment in significant numbers. The second involved the maintenance of a large dues-paying membership without demanding attendance at the annual meeting of the organization.

Accompanying the ferment in the world of medicine was a like phenomenon in Chicago dentistry. Chicago was the home of G. V. Black, perhaps the best-known dentist of the day. Scarcely less well-known were C. N. Johnson, J. N. Crouse, W. H. G. Logan and many others. The reputations of this galaxy of great dentists rested on broad foundations: They were renowned as teachers, administrators, writers, and organizers. The dental school of Northwestern University and the Chicago College of Dental Surgery stood high in the ranks of the nation's dental colleges. Some of the best dental journals were edited and published in Chicago, for example, the *Dental Review* and the *Dental Digest*.

Chicago dentists likewise took the lead in organizational work. Even before the union of the American Dental Association and the Southern Dental Association was accomplished, the Chicago Odontographic Society began efforts to form auxiliary societies in nearby towns, "for their own good and that of the whole people they serve."[20] The Chicagoans' energy soon communicated itself to the state society. In the spring of 1904, the Odontographic Society of Chicago adopted resolutions citing the resurgence of the Illinois Medical Society, describing the methods used by the physicians, and urging similar action by the state dental organization.

A committee appointed by the Odontographic Society presented the resolutions before the ensuing meeting of the Illinois State Dental Society. At the same time, the Chicagoans produced an elaborate survey of the status of organized dentistry in Illinois. Application of the system devised by the medical society to the existing array of local and district dental societies in Illinois would, the committee estimated, augment the membership of the state association by about 300 per cent. Increased organizing activity in moribund areas promised further accessions of membership. With the state society strengthened in this fashion the committee believed improvements in the status of the profession could be achieved, first, through stricter enforcement of existing dental legislation and, second, through the enhancement of the quality of the technical and scientific work accomplished and reported before the state society. In addition to these benefits, the committee argued that strengthened organization would tighten enforcement of the ethical code. Finally, the reformers urged that improvement of the profession, in both social standing and scientific knowledge, would arise from the increased contacts among the practitioners of the state.[21]

After the presentation of the Odontographic Society's resolutions, E. K. Blair of Waverly, chairman of a committee on increasing the membership, appointed at the preceding meeting, reported. His committee had, he stated, "found a general sentiment existing among the members favoring an enlarged membership." Encouraged by this news and with the support of the Odontographic Society of Chicago, Blair said, the committee had issued a circular letter to all known Illinois dentists urging them to attend the meeting and inviting them to join the state society. Blair's report also included some recommended amendments to the constitution. Furthermore, the committee announced that the state medical society had offered to federate with the dental association for purposes of wielding a larger legislative influence. In conclusion, the report argued that the proposed amendments were no novelties. The details had "been parts of the constitutions of ten or fifteen state medical societies for years and have proved very acceptable."[22]

Site of the Old Point Comfort Session, 1897

The discussion that followed the two papers was generally favorable. C. R. Taylor of Streator, however, urged caution. "Is it not possible that we can gain the end by some other means?" The suggestions, he pointed out, were fine, but not necessarily the only way. They involved a considerable risk. "It means either a grand success or a disastrous failure." In Ohio, Taylor said, membership was considered permanent. "If a man does not attend the annual meeting he does not pay any fees, and it works admirably whenever the question of legislation comes up." The meeting ignored the rather flimsy reservations of Taylor and adopted the amendments recommended by the Blair committee. Soon after, C. N. Johnson of Chicago proposed a resolution of thanks for the efforts of the Odontographic Society. Next, Arthur D. Black offered amendments to the constitution and by-laws. These, too, were adopted.[23] The *Transactions* did not print the specific proposals of the two reform committees, only the constitution as amended. Consequently, there is no way of distinguishing between the suggestions of the Black committee of the Odontographic Society and the recommendations of the Blair committee of the state organization. There was probably no material difference between them.

The reorganization proposed was fundamental. Under the prevailing system of membership, a dentist became a member of the state association by election at the annual meeting. This affiliation might or might not involve membership in a local or district organization. Under the new arrangement, the applicant had to belong to a local society in order to become a member of the state society. The American Dental Association had overcome the problem of determining the qualifications of candidates for membership by accepting delegates from approved societies. In this fashion, the difficulties inherent in selecting qualified (ethical) members were shifted to the local, district, or state organization. The Illinois reform embodied the same principle. Local societies, representing the profession in a single county of the state, could obtain charters as components of the state dental association on application following adoption of an acceptable constitution. The new arrangement went further. The American Dental Association had built its roster solely from delegates sent by the lesser organizations. On this basis, the rolls could grow only as rapidly as new delegates attended the annual meetings. The Odontographic Society plan made *all* members of component societies automatically members of the state association. The drastic effect on the list of members is evident. The new system surmounted the obstacle of the payment of dues to two societies by reducing the amount of the state society dues from five dollars to two. The secretary of the local society collected the dues for both associations in a lump sum and forwarded the state's share along with a list of paid-up members. The by-laws directed that "every reputable and legally registered dentist shall be entitled to membership." The plan also provided for appeal to the executive council against a component by an aggrieved individual.[24]

The reformers perceived that the membership would ultimately grow to the point where it would become unwieldy for conducting the business of the Association and legislating for the profession. Eventually, they knew, it would be necessary to turn these matters over to representatives of the membership. Thus, A. D. Black reported, the business affairs of the state medical society were in the hands of an executive council, similar to the one then functioning in the state dental association. No change was needed here. In the matter of legislation for the society, however, a "house of delegates," consisting of representatives elected by the components in numbers proportionate to the size of the component's membership would later handle these functions. "By this arrangement the entire business of the society is transacted by men especially appointed to do that work, and the majority of the members are not required to lose so much time from the papers and other scientific work in which they are more interested," Black explained. The committee's suggested amendments did not include the establishment of a house of delegates on the argument that the size of the membership did not yet require it. Thus, for the immediate future, the alterations in the constitution of the state society would involve merely provisions for the establishment of component societies; for the recognition of the role of the existing district societies, and for the new membership plan. The main problems related to fostering new associations in counties having none. The executive council directed the appointment of a committee on organization and revision of the constitution. Black was named chairman.[25]

The committee set vigorously to work, with immediate results. Within the first year, no section of the state had less than thirty-five per cent of the dentists enrolled and three had exceeded eighty per cent. The increased membership encouraged passage of a long-desired dental bill in the state legislature. Although dues had been reduced as part of the new arrangement, and in spite of the heavy expenses of promoting organization and membership, the treasury showed a net gain of $700. C. N. Johnson, in his presidential speech, claimed "more than double the number of members belonging to any other dental society on the continent."[26]

There was much yet to be done in Illinois—and other currents of reform and innovation were flowing in the National Dental Association.

Site of the Cleveland Session, 1911

Cleveland Square, 1911

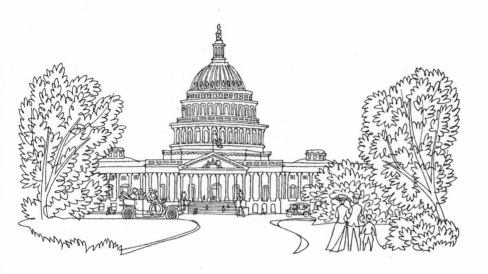

Chapter XIV   PROGRESSIVISM IN THE ASSOCIATION

ONE OF THE STRONGEST FORCES for change in American life at the turn
of the century was the impulse toward philanthropy. Many factors
contributed to this development. There was growing concern over
the casualties of the economic struggle for survival, although many
observers argued that help merely prolonged the suffering of the
unfit. The charitable urge was not limited to financial giants, economists, and social philosophers. The American churches in this period
demonstrated a growing interest in social questions. From still another
direction, the settlement house movement and the teachings of the
Fabian Socialists in England brought other Americans into charitable
activities. Furthermore, participation in the sundry humanitarian
crusades of the day undoubtedly turned American thoughts to more
general philanthropic endeavors. Political reformers and labor leaders
campaigned to persuade business and government to care for the
wounded of the battle for existence. All of these elements contributed
to a widespread development of charitable activities in many different forms.[1]

The impact of this phenomenon on the National Dental Association
may be found in the beginnings of organized efforts to aid dentists
who were suffering misfortunes due to age and infirmity or to
natural catastrophes. Interest in such matters appeared periodically

245

through the later years of the nineteenth century. In 1892, for example, the American Dental Association heard of the unfortunate plight of W. H. Dwinelle, an innovator in orthodontics and one of the first generation of leaders in dental organization. Aid was generously rendered.[2]

Most instances of charitable activities by the profession before the twentieth century involved individual cases. Ordinarily, these measures were informal and unorganized. The national association served mainly to publicize the needs of worthy persons whose problems were then handled by individuals or voluntary committees. The approach remained the same when the profession confronted major catastrophes involving many practitioners in a stricken community. Assistance to the victims of the Chicago Fire of 1871, as a matter of fact, was undertaken on the initiative of the supply house of S. S. White and administered through White's Chicago branch.[3]

In common with other facets of American life in the Progressive Era, the charitable activities of dentists took on a more formal aspect after 1900. Several presidents in their annual addresses urged the adoption of a regular plan to assist members and former members in distress.[4] Such suggestions found a sympathetic hearing, but the limited treasury blocked measures beyond the appointment of committees to consider the problem. The hurricane and flood in 1900 that devastated the Texas port of Galveston inspired the National Dental Association to make a small contribution to ease the difficulties of practitioners whose equipment had been destroyed or damaged in the disaster.[5] The Galveston disaster aid seems to have been the first instance of such action by the Association.

It was the San Francisco earthquake and fire in April, 1906, however, that aroused the dental profession to extraordinary efforts and stimulated the establishment of a permanent program. The spectacular nature of the catastrophe and the magnitude of the devastation that followed it undoubtedly excited the sympathies of the profession. More than five hundred of San Francisco's five hundred fifty-nine dentists lost their office equipment in the disaster; two lost their lives. As had been the case in the past, informal groups collected and dispatched funds and equipment to the scene. Chicago dentists and dental supply houses sent $3,000. Later in the year they mailed another $500 to the Relief Committee. Theirs was the first of numerous contributions from individuals and societies. The Committee of Fifteen for the Fourth International Dental Congress transmitted $750 from its funds through the president of the National Dental Association. The National Dental Association, acting officially through its president and executive committee, also contributed relief funds from the treasury. Such was the generosity of the profession on this occasion that the funds collected by the San Francisco Dental Relief Committee exceeded the needs of the disaster victims. Altogether the Committee received more than $15,000 of which they disbursed more than $11,000. At the 1907 meeting of the National Dental Association, the Committee presented a report of its activities indicating the source and the use made of the funds they had received. The balance remaining in the fund, nearly $4,000, the Committee turned over to the National Dental Association in trust for use as a National Relief Fund. The Committee stipulated that the principal be retained for disaster relief; the interest, they decreed, might be used for the relief of superannuated dentists in distressed circumstances.[6] The profession could no longer put off determining a definite philanthropic policy.

The Executive Council advised acceptance of the trust. They recommended that the Council administer the fund until some permanent policy could be devised. The money was delivered to the custody of the treasurer of the Association and he was placed under bond. With exception of an appropriation of $250 from the interest to make a contribution for an international memorial to Willoughby D. Miller, the matter rested until 1911. In his annual address, the president, Edward S. Gaylord, reminded his colleagues of the obligation imposed by the action of the San Francisco Dental Relief Committee. The Committee on the President's Address concurred:

The question of a relief fund for indigent and aged members of our profession has long enough been held in abeyance. The frequent spectacle of elderly and infirm dentists being thrown on the mercy of the world, to eke out a miserable existence in their declining years, has been presented to us in a manner to arouse the profession, and it is high time that this association should take some action to organize a movement and start a fund under proper supervision, to be used for this and other charitable purposes.[7]

In accordance with these recommendations, the Executive Council decided to appoint a committee to solicit funds. The resolution charged the same committee with oversight of the funds. The Executive Committee was authorized to contribute annually to the relief funds such amounts as they felt could be "judiciously spared." The terms of the resolution concerning disbursements conformed with those of the San Francisco grant so that the initial gift became the nucleus of the proposed philanthropic fund. Before the Executive Council, at the following session, the committee reported a conflict between the advancing movement for reorganization of the Association and the committee's own proposal to increase state organization dues for the relief fund. The Committee on the President's Address recommended another committee to harmonize the two movements. And so the matter stood until after the reorganization in 1913.[8]

Progressive America was not only concerned with relieving the victims of catastrophe. In numerous ways, voluntary organizations sought to help our citizens meet the demands of a new and strange society and to help them forestall difficulties before they arose. The renewed vigor of the temperance crusade in the years leading up to World War I belongs to this class. Among these organizations were many voluntary health societies which united the efforts of physicians and interested laymen in drives for funds for research and treatment of special medical problems. A prominent and appealing example of this variety of organization was the National Tuberculosis Association, founded in 1904. Arthur H. Merritt brought this particular crusade before the National Dental Association in 1908, and won specific endorsement of the movement.[9]

Many of the humanitarian campaigns for reform or amelioration of the age turned, as so many American enterprises do, to the educational system to augment and perpetuate the advances they sought in legislative regulation. The early years of the century saw the renewal or intensification of the drive for vocational education, "manual training" for boys and "domestic science" for girls. The reasoning behind the movement held that the schools should provide such training to enable their graduates to lead more productive and efficient lives as adult citizens. This approach blended naturally with the mounting concern for public health provoked by the crowded living conditions in the giant urban centers. A considerable part of the energies of the public health movement were directed at better sanitation in connection with the manufacture of food and drugs and in the directing of truthful labelling of the products. But this approach was not enough unless the consumer had been educated to know what was good for him and how to preserve his health. Hence both the preparation for adult life and the aspirations of the public health movement encouraged the introduction into school curricula of elementary courses in "hygiene" and physiology.[10] American dentistry seized on this development as an aid to broadening popular education regarding dental health.

This facet of dental care is a recurrent feature of the history of the profession. The dentists' experience in this field was not very happy until the waning years of the nineteenth century when some of the afore-mentioned factors began to operate. During the Progressive Era the dental hygiene movement gained additional momentum. In 1900, Richard Grady secured the appointment of a committee of five to consider the expediency of introducing dental hygiene into school programs. The committee's report at the following meeting was optimistic. In 1902 the campaign faltered, but thereafter enthusiasm mounted with accomplishment.[11] Accounts crowded the pages of the dental press. More and more frequently the annual reports of the committee announced the adoption of dental hygiene programs in various cities.[12] Welcoming the Association to Boston in 1908, Governor Curtis Guild, Jr., boasted of the legislation in his state requiring all school children to undergo dental examinations. After some difficulties, the Committee on Oral Hygiene produced a short pamphlet that won the approval of the Association.[13]

By the end of the first decade of the century, the advocates of the oral hygiene movement could claim that their views were fully justified. Amazing reports came from various cities as the results of examinations of school children became known. W. G. Ebersole of Cleveland declared that seventy-five per cent of the children examined needed dental care. T. W. Brophy of Chicago reported, "In the city of Chicago there are 400,000 children. We are attempting to give dental care to these children, and to provide free dental service for those who are unable to pay for it. How many dentists do you suppose will be required to care for 400,000 children? There are not dentists enough in the states of Illinois, Wisconsin, Iowa, and Missouri to do it." Herbert L. Wheeler of New York warned, "There are not enough dentists in America to attend to the carious teeth in the city of New York alone, and unless we arrive at the point where it will be possible to prevent some of this trouble, the situation is hopeless." [14]

This appalling prospect directed attention to preventive measures among adults as well as children. In discussions of this aspect of the movement, as in other theoretical essays of the times, lingering confusions from the great debates of the late nineteenth century on evolutionary theory occasionally emerged. For example, the chairman of the Committee on Hygiene in 1905 declaimed, "The generic history of a species discovers that the initial status of progeny is determined by the degree of development attained by its progenitor; while the life-history of an organism shows that subsequent development is fixed by environment." The orator linked this doctrine with an environmental theory of the causation of dental caries. He insisted, however, that the vanguard of dental thinking went beyond this position. He elaborated the doctrine as he saw it:

Conserve every organ or part thereof which can be made tolerable to the system. Restore, so far as possible, all lost contour, in such a way that it will most nearly perform natural functions and dwell in harmony with nature. And institute a regime that will provide normal environment and require functional activity. The ultimate outcome of this system will be intrinsic immunity. [15]

Much the same thought still prevailed in 1909. "It would seem logical that greater immunity should follow a typically normal development of tooth tissue and the ideal arrangement of the teeth in true anatomic form and relations," said a commentator. "This ideal is the inevitable conclusion of every follower of the new school of oral prophylaxis, and one comes to feel that restorative achievement only, while of the greatest value and service when needed, can never satisfy the higher conceptions of duty to humanity." [16]

On a more mundane level, these inspiring thoughts induced a renewal of the perennial attacks on American eating habits. "In this peculiar age of American enterprise, a man will go to the breakfast table, put his newspaper up in front of him, and attempt to read while he is eating," one reformer complained. "Can one read the sickening details of some horrible murder while he is trying to eat, and produce that salivary fluid so necessary to digestion?" The same commentator favored the application of Theodore Roosevelt's principles of "strenuous" living to eating as well. The critic invoked two prominent examples to support his position. "Can you imagine a more anomalous circumstance than stomatitis in the mouth of Theodore Roosevelt? If Horace Fletcher is ever troubled with aphthous ulcers, I'll surrender my theory." [17] What red-blooded American of that date could ignore such an appeal? It seemed to one ardent promoter of the oral hygiene movement that after nearly a decade of discouragement there were grounds for optimism. He exulted, "Humanity is awakening to its distressed condition, and is standing with out-stretched arms imploring aid; and the public press is deeply interested and is lending valuable cooperation." [18]

The proponents of the movement assigned various reasons for their success and advanced differing arguments in seeking the support of the profession. As has been the case with most changes in dental practices and organization, the relation of the proposal to activities in the medical profession was a popular argument. Early appeals for cooperation from medical schools rested on this basis. Medical cooperation would help the dentists toward "our Ultima Thule, preventive dentistry," a committee reasoned. "Our new specialty of oral hygiene brings us nearer to medicine than we have ever been before, and our inspection of the teeth of children in our public schools and our interest in the condition of the teeth of the very poor will help to bring us recognition as a specialty of medicine from the world at large, as well as from medicine itself, whether we wish it or not," another spokesman said. [19]

Supporters of the oral hygiene program also resorted to the appeal of philanthropy. Indeed, one active worker claimed that the initiative in the drive came from outside the dental profession. "What has been accomplished in New York has been done by charitable organizations and through men who have been interested in social settlements and in the physical development and welfare of the people, and the education carried on in this way has aroused the public to such an extent that they are beginning to criticize the dentist, many times unjustly of course, because he has to be educated as the public is educated." Another asserted, "It is the duty of the organized dental profession both toward themselves and toward the community, (a) to make every person able to do so pay for his dental work, and (b) to see that no person needing dental work and unable to pay goes without it." [20]

On the other hand, one of the most voluble spokesmen of the movement, Walter G. Ebersole, insisted that the work "had been chilled and retarded in its action by 'philanthropy'—philanthropy, abhorred by the self-respecting poor, deplored by the middle-class, and despised by the rich." In this view, the chill had been broken by "the heat and warmth of education," which appealed to the rich, the middle-class, and the poor alike. Ebersole, and others like him, attributed the new popularity of the oral hygiene drive to the arguments appealing to education or to economic motives. "It is beginning to be understood that in a state where enormous sums have to be spent for hospitals, sanatoriums, and general places of recuperation, it may be more economical to prevent the distribution of conditions that make these hospitals and human repair shops necessary than to permit the destruction to occur and attack the question of repair afterward." [21]

Whatever the reasons might be, there could be no argument that by 1910 the oral hygiene campaign had reached a stage where it threatened to overshadow the other phases of dentistry and to assert its independence of the National Dental Association. At the annual meeting in Denver, the Oral Hygiene Committee offered a report whose tenor brought a vigorous reaction from some of the Association's steering committee, the Executive Council. A prolonged debate aired the various aspects of the oral hygiene program. Reluctantly, the Council agreed to support the continued work of the Committee. The Council warned, "we would suggest that the scope of the work in the future be conducted along lines and under such rules and regulations as shall be formulated by the committee and approved by the Executive Council." Although the decision of the Executive Council commended the energy and enthusiasm of the Committee, the attitude of the Committee's report engendered antagonisms that continued to simmer for several years after the Denver session. The Publication Committee considered omitting or editing the report as it would appear in the printed *Transactions*. Rumors drifted through the profession that the oral hygiene enthusiasts might form a separate national society.[22]

The aggressive actions of the oral hygienists constituted only one of a number of developments that directly challenged the place of the National Dental Association at the head of the profession. The problem of patents posed another threat to N.D.A. leadership. When the amalgamation of the American Dental Association with the Southern took place, the former, after contributing to the treasury of the new society, delivered the balance remaining in its treasury to the Dental Protective Association to help defray the expense of its titanic contest with the International Tooth Crown Company. "The cause of the Dental Protective Association [is] the cause of the profession," the Executive Council declared in 1900. Victory over the International Tooth Crown Company concluded the particular reason for the existence of the Dental Protective Association—and marked the beginning of the troubles of John N. Crouse of Chicago, who had devoted much of his time and had sacrificed his practice to the battle. The National Dental Association was grateful. Crouse was permitted to reorganize the Dental Protective Association as he saw fit. He was also authorized to enlist as many of the profession in the organization as he could. In an effort to recoup his fortunes, Crouse formed the United States Dental Supply Company. He contemplated profitably supplying the dentists of the country by underselling the regular supply houses, which, he claimed, charged exorbitant prices. As an inducement to join the new Dental Protective Association, Crouse offered to sell to its members at a ten per cent discount. At about the same time, Crouse also established the *Dental Digest*. This journal was to be free of the taint of a connection with the commercial supply houses or manufacturers. Through the early years of the century, Crouse regularly appeared before the Executive Council seeking the privilege of publishing the *Transactions*. The variety of Crouse's activities in his struggle for financial well-being must have placed a considerable strain on the gratitude of the National Dental Association.[23]

While the Dental Protective Association and its proprietor sought prosperity in commercial ventures, other representatives of dentistry joined in the contemporary movement looking to reform of the patent laws. An outspoken advocate in this cause was Rodrigues Ottolengui, editor of *Items of Interest*. In 1902, Ottolengui, on behalf of the New York State Dental Society, appeared before the National Dental Association to outline an amendment to the patent laws prohibiting "granting of an objectionable class of process patents relating to dental practice." The national body adopted resolutions in support of the proposed legislation, appointed a committee, and largely forgot about the problem for five years.[24]

In the meantime, William H. Taggart, a Chicago dentist of considerable mechanical ingenuity, labored on his experiments. His success was to raise the problem of patents yet again before the profession. Taggart was grappling with an exceedingly vexing problem. He sought a new means of making small precision castings. Existing methods yielded products that were somewhat distorted because of the expansion of the mold when the hot metal was introduced. A similar minute distortion occurred as the casting cooled and contracted. After some years of labor contriving and refining his apparatus and technique, Taggart appeared before a dental meeting in New York City on January 15, 1907, and demonstrated his casting process. Publication of Taggart's innovation created an immediate sensation in the profession. His discoveries enabled the dentist to do two things. In the first place, the practitioner could now cast a gold filling that would fit snugly in the cavity. This eliminated the need to condense gold foil to make the filling. The precision casting also made feasible the construction of secure anchorages for removable restorative devices.[25]

One contemporary development enhanced the desirability of the latter application. Dr. William Hunter published a paper in the English medical publication, *Lancet*. In this essay, Hunter emphasized the systemic relations of the dental organs and pointed out that many fixed dental prosthetic devices constituted menaces to health. In the hands of the sensational journals of the day, Hunter's warnings became a wholesale condemnation of current American dental practice. The public tempest stirred the profession. Dental journals published temperate defenses and joined in the condemnation of the excesses that gave rise to the complaints. The plain fact of the matter was that much of the prosthetic dentistry of that day was unsanitary. Many dentists anchored fixed bridgework on roots and snags of teeth from which the vital pulp had been removed. Frequently these "bridge abutments" became the seat of infection. Some dentists were more concerned with the engineering problems posed by prosthetic cases than with the effects on the patient. It should be noted, on the other hand, that observations like Hunter's had long been current in dental literature. Nonetheless, the spectacular nature of the popular response to Hunter's essay aroused new interest in removable prosthetic contrivances. Taggart's process held out the possibility of anchoring such appliances without the necessity of killing a sound tooth to do it.[26]

It is not surprising that the profession greeted Taggart's invention with delighted enthusiasm. A contributory factor was undoubtedly the impression that Taggart had donated his discovery to the dental world. This was a misunderstanding. Taggart held patents on his mechanisms and on the procedures for their use. He apparently expected to compensate himself through manufacture and sale of his machines. When it appeared that Taggart's production could not keep up with the demand for his machines, impatient dentists began to experiment with substitutes. They soon discovered something that Taggart had failed to discern. The substance from which the mold was made in his process held the chief key to the success of precision casting because it did not become distorted by heat. In other words, the elaborate machinery that Taggart had developed was not necessary to the successful casting of a small inlay. Taggart turned then to the procedure involved as the last redoubt from which to defend his discovery and realize some returns from it. He offered to issue licenses authorizing the holders to exploit his process. He threatened offenders who failed to secure a license with prosecution.[27]

The crisis following the beginning of the contest over the Taggart patents was particularly bitter. When the Dental Protective Association was called upon to lead in the defense against Taggart's prosecutions, Crouse advocated instead a licensing agreement he had negotiated with Taggart for the benefit of members of the Dental

Protective Association. It was, as M. D. K. Bremner, himself a leader in the fight against Taggart, has said, an arrangement that would have been profitable both for Crouse and for Taggart.[28] Crouse was not the only former opponent of patent rights who spoke up in defense of Taggart's position.

Three men who had worked on the Association's Patent Committee differed among themselves. Rodrigues Ottolengui adopted Taggart's cause. One dental leader noted wryly, "In the days of Dr. Ottolengui's editorials against process patents Dr. Crouse was not sufficiently aggressive to suit the editor, and now they have both had a change of heart simultaneously." Ottolengui had been a member of the Patent Committee of the National Dental Association for several years. He and his colleagues had spent much time seeking clarification of the patent laws at a time when the whole patent system was undergoing congressional review. One of Ottolengui's associates in the campaign, Emory A. Bryant, told of their problems. "With all these favorable conditions confronting Dr. Ottolengui and myself," Bryant recalled, "we were compelled to drop the agitation owing to lack of support by the dental profession." Bryant was distinctly an individualist and it was more or less accidental when he spoke for any substantial number of the profession. A Washington practitioner, Bryant was also a patent attorney and an active, and independent, lobbyist on behalf of commissioned status for dentists in the armed forces. Subsequently, he became one of the first commissioned members of the Navy Dental Corps. Although he continued to work for suitable legislation, Bryant insisted that the profession could not legitimately attack the Taggart claims since it had not supported the earlier campaign for revision of the patent laws. "If we are not interested enough to obey the laws, then to be consistent we should go into the stealing business out-and-out," he said.[29] A third member of the Patent Committee was Mark F. Finley. Finley was also from Washington. He served as president of the National Dental Association in 1905-1906. It was Finley who tried to rouse the Dental Protective Association to action and who led the defense against the Taggart patents when Taggart brought his first suit in Washington. Finley's position more nearly represented the official attitude of the National Dental Association.

The division among the active workers on the patent problem

symbolized the situation in the profession as a whole. Taggart found support among his fellow Chicagoans. In New York, Ottolengui spoke for a number of dentists who backed the Taggart claims. The official position of the Association was reflected in instructions to the Patent Committee in 1911. The Committee was told to seek "such legislation as will not permit the granting of process patents on any method which has to do with the healing art of medicine or dentistry, except such as can be manufactured and placed on the market for sale." Bryant headed the Committee through the next year. At the 1912 session, he reported minor success. He said he had persuaded Senator Henry Cabot Lodge of Massachusetts and Representative E. Y. Webb of North Carolina to include in identical bills clauses prohibiting the granting of process patents in medicine and dentistry. Bryant outlined a procedure by which the patent problem might be brought under control by the Association regardless of the fortunes of the legislation before Congress. He suggested that innovators and journal editors protect their material by depositing it with the Commissioner of Patents. In this manner, no manufacturer or later discoverer would be able to claim a patent on the material or devices so covered. Next Bryant urged that the Association adopt a resolution declaring the patenting of any method or device "not adapted to be put on the market and sold" to be unprofessional conduct. Accordingly, H. J. Burkhart introduced an elaborate resolution, reproducing the language of the proposed statute. The 1912 session adopted the resolution. Thus, five years after Taggart presented his patent applications, the official policy of the National Dental Association was set down. The declaration was, of course, too late to affect the course of the Taggart affair. Richard Summa of St. Louis gave the reason behind the orthodox stand. A process patent royalty was a tax upon the manipulative skill of the workman, he said. "This strikes at the base of human liberty; it seriously interferes with the development and progress of any vocation." [30]

Emotions aggravated and complicated the professional schism. Ottolengui read an elaborate paper demonstrating the justice of Taggart's position. Ottolengui's style was not calculated to moderate the feeling on the question. He invoked the magic associated with the slogans of Theodore Roosevelt in defining ethical conduct: "Epigrammatically we may declare that ethics means to render unto every

man a 'square deal.'" Ottolengui went on to complain that the ethical
rule in regard to dental patents remained unwritten. Thus, "each self-
styled ethical gentleman may write or read the rule to suit his own
purpose, such purpose being largely dependent upon how deeply
asleep his sense of honor may be, and to how much of the song of
the broomstick siren he has harkened." Ottolengui argued that this
state of affairs made it difficult for dental inventors to "protect themselves, their heirs and assigns, as do other inventors." Under such
conditions, there seemed to be little reason for "men of genius" to
labor on dental problems, since their reward was likely to be "professional ostracism." Ottolengui cited a long list of dental patent holders
including such illustrious names as Edward H. Angle, W. G. A. Bonwill, Truman W. Brophy, William Crenshaw, G. V. Black, and J. N.
Crouse. He next tried to show that the Taggart patents were not included in the objectionable class to which the earlier rubber and
tooth-crown claims had belonged.[31]

Ottolengui's essay, as might have been anticipated, provoked excited charges and counter-charges that failed to promote a reasoned
solution to the basic problem. Opponents of the patent claims assumed an attitude of outraged righteousness. This, in turn, goaded
Taggart's supporters into bitterly sarcastic retorts. M. L. Rhein, an
outstanding New York practitioner, took the floor to excoriate Ottolengui's critics. "To my amazement two gentlemen occupied this
platform and have done what they could to give an excuse for the
dentist to be a common thief, nothing less," he said. "Are the products
of a man's brains any less tangible than the contents of his pocket-
book?" More temperately, J. P. Buckley of Chicago reviewed the
argument:

Dr. Head made the statement that when the matter of justice involved one man,
justice should be done to that man, but if justice to this man produced wholesale
wrong to a large number of individuals, the interests of that man must not be
considered, or justice must not be done to that individual. I have no doubt that
the sentiment back of a statement of that kind is correct, but wherein lies the
wholesale wrong done by acquiescing to the demands, if demands you call it,
made by Dr. Taggart?[32]

Taggart himself took the floor briefly. His discussion elaborated on
the questions raised by Buckley. Taggart admitted that some of his
friends had urged him not to seek a process patent "because it was
such a humanitarian process, and humanity should be given its bene-

fit, and no one man should reap the reward." His response, Taggart said, had been "almost prophetic." " 'If this is a humanitarian process, and you dentists would band yourselves together to give it to humanity, I will give it to the world for nothing, but I do not propose that you forty thousand people should consider yourselves humanity as against eighty-five millions in the United States.' " [33] With such convictions of rectitude on both sides of the issue, the prospects for a reasonable settlement were dim indeed.

The depth of feeling stimulated by the debate created a perilous situation for the National Dental Association. The intensity of sentiment in the profession tended to inhibit official action by the Association to settle the controversy. More than this, it also hampered efforts to grapple with other problems when one proposed solution became associated with a given stand on the Taggart question.

From another direction the perpetual subject of educational standards emerged again to demand the attention of the National Dental Association and to divide its councils. For a time, the Association refused to recognize its involvement. At the 1903 session, for example, the chairman of Section II of the Association, which was concerned with dental education, literature, nomenclature, histology and microscopy, acknowledged that the problem of education would probably never be solved, but he found nothing to command the attention of the society. "The National Association of Dental Faculties and the National Association of Dental Examiners can safely be allowed to guide thought and action in the future in their respective lines, for each body has now demonstrated its worth to American dentistry, and that in no uncertain manner." Behind the tranquil facade, however, trouble was brewing in several quarters. Education held the key to the ultimate objective of state interchange of licenses, a cherished goal of the Association. The attainment of uniformity, according to a committee report on the subject, would require the participation of representatives of the national professional organization. It is perhaps significant to note that the plan called only for minority repre-

sentation for the National Dental Association on the national examination committee.[34]

As the conception of a uniform licensing procedure germinated,
sentiment in the National Dental Association seemingly favored leaving the initiative in the matter to either the National Association of
Dental Examiners or the National Association of Dental Faculties.
At the same time, National Dental Association officials did not hesitate to claim credit for the accomplishments of the profession in educational matters. Reviewing the situation in 1910, President Burton
Lee Thorpe observed, "From our National Association has evolved
the present systematized collegiate course, largely owing to the National Association of Dental Faculties, also the present dental laws,
mainly due to the efforts of the National Association of Dental Examiners, both being the offspring of this parent organization." The committee on Thorpe's address found "a crying need for reform" in
education. They agreed with the speaker, however, in concluding
that "much has been accomplished in the past through the combined
agency of the National Dental Association and its outgrowth, the
Dental Faculties and the National Association of Dental Examiners."[35]

There was much agitation concerning the standards of admission
to dental schools during this period. This question, too, drew the
National Dental Association into the educational arena. The Association's interest stemmed from its desire to promote interstate reciprocity in licensing. For the National Dental Association the problem
of admission standards presented two contradictory appeals that had
to be reconciled. The Association wanted to promote high admission
and instructional standards in order to assure reciprocity with states
having rigorous statutes. Nevertheless, it also sought a system of
reciprocity whose rigors would not preclude the participation of all
dentists eligible for membership in the National Dental Association.
Furthermore, the national society for the profession could hardly
avoid involvement in the affairs of the examiners' and dental faculties'
organizations so long as the former hoped to have the assistance of
the latter in enlisting a larger membership.[36]

While the National Dental Association tried to steer clear of the
touchy questions involving educational standards in the United
States, it was forced to meet the problem on the international level.

Some American institutions made a lucrative business of selling diplomas to European would-be practitioners. The appearance in Europe of ill-qualified dentists bearing diplomas issued by American "schools" cast doubt on the quality of all American degrees. This was a challenge to the whole machinery of organized dentistry in the United States. At the turn of the century the National Dental Association established a committee on international relations in connection with diplomas. The findings of this committee demanded intervention of the national body, for the report showed apparent collaboration between one of the objectionable colleges and the state board of examiners. The National Dental Association referred the information to the National Association of Dental Examiners.[37] Simultaneously, the National Association of Dental Faculties was aroused.

At the annual session in 1901, the National Dental Association heard the American consul in Munich recount his battles on behalf of legitimate American practitioners abroad. At the same time, the Association determined to prosecute the diploma mills. The sum of one thousand dollars was appropriated for the purpose and a resolution invited state and local societies to join in the crusade. Recognition of the seriousness of the problem was not universal. Another point of view at the same meeting held that no National Dental Association action was called for because the efforts of the Dental Faculties' committee and of the reputable American dentists in Europe were driving out the charlatans. The optimistic forecast proved unwarranted. The efforts of the Faculties, the Examiners, and the National Dental Association were coordinated in 1905 by the appointment of a committee whose membership accorded representation to all three bodies. The session gratefully acknowledged the continued aid of the United States government. And it appropriated funds to help meet the deficiency in the fund devoted to prosecution of the diploma mills. By 1907, the campaign had succeeded. The committee having the matter in charge reported, "all seems quiet along the line." [38]

The passing years brought more and more indications of the necessary involvement of the National Dental Association in matters of education. Increased professional concern with broader dissemination of the results of research raised again the problems of nomenclature. In this field, too, the necessities of the moment demanded greater efforts from the National Dental Association. As channels of information, the societies could not ignore their duty in this respect. "Every state and local society should have an active committee [on nomenclature], which might also serve in the capacity of an essay committee, and see to it that all papers to be read before the society, and all published matter, should conform to the system adopted by the National Association," one writer recommended. "The relation of the latter to subordinate bodies may well be the same as is maintained by the French Academy to the lesser lights of France." [39] Try as they might, the leaders of the National Dental Association could not dodge the educational problems of the day.

The manner in which the problems confronted the professional leadership increased their complexity. There was strong suspicion in the country against anything having the taint of commercialism. In the medical and dental fields, this popular crusade found expression in drives against proprietary colleges and supply house journals. Dr. William Welch, whose personal influence as one of the nation's outstanding physicians and medical educators was buttressed by his advisory role in the Rockefeller Foundation, argued strongly on behalf of university affiliation for medical schools. A movement in this direction during the early years of the century was publicized and accelerated by the publication in 1910 of Abraham Flexner's report on medical education sponsored by the Carnegie Foundation. [40]

In dentistry, the drive against the proprietary schools had the added prestige of association with the parallel campaign in medical education. At the Boston meeting of the National Dental Association in 1908, representatives of five university-related dental schools met to consider the question of organization. James Truman of the University of Pennsylvania Dental School offered a draft constitution for the proposed society. The conferees deliberated briefly and then adjourned to meet again in Philadelphia the following year. At that time, the original five schools, California, Michigan, Minnesota, Pennsylvania and Harvard, plus Iowa, founded the Dental Faculties Association of American Universities. The constitution stipulated that membership in the Association should be limited to schools that were "an integral part of state universities or of chartered universities of equal standing . . . , holding membership in the Association of American Universities, demanding graduation from accredited high schools, or the equivalent amount of education, for matriculation."

The founding schools sent notice of their actions to the secretaries of state universities, the National Association of Dental Examiners, the National Association of Dental Faculties, the National Dental Association, the National Commissioner of Education, and, having 'a decent respect to the opinions of mankind,' to the Associated Press, the foreign and domestic dental journals, and the Fédération Dentaire Internationale.[41]

An editorial accompanying the report of the meeting in the *Dental Cosmos* clearly explained the reasons behind the establishment of the Universities' Association. It made equally clear the reasons for the appearance of a new division in the field of dental education. There were, at that time, according to the writer, three types of schools represented in the National Association of Dental Faculties, independent (or proprietary) colleges, dental departments of medical schools, and university-affiliated dental schools. This condition made the National Association of Dental Faculties inclusive, rather than exclusive. Standards were depressed to hold the poorer schools in line, but this more or less forced the better schools to reduce their requirements in order to compete for students. Hence the Universities' organization. The editorial continued:

> The movement is one which is in line with the general trend of higher education everywhere—that is, the centralizing of professional education within the institutions of higher learning, the universities of the world. . . . Under the centralized system of the universities the economic aspect of higher education finds its simplest solution, just as in commerce under a centralized system the world's business is most economically transacted.[42]

A year after the establishment of the new educational body, one of its founders, Dean J. G. Sharp of the University of California, elaborated on the objectionable features of the existing institutions of control of dental education. The arguments he advanced went to the heart of the existing problem. "It certainly commands our pity that an organization [the National Association of Dental Faculties] so worthily begun should falter in its progress, and that the real object for its existence, the protection of our people through high educational standards, should give way to the welfare of its members," he said. Sharp went on to show that the Faculties' society and the Examiners' organization were interrelated in such a way that neither had any great amount of control over the other.[43]

The two organizations thus criticized responded immediately. Their initial move looked toward cooperation in the face of the challenge of the university movement. Committees appointed by the two societies met at Old Point Comfort less than a month after the establishment of the Dental Faculties Association of American Universities. The chief product of this conclave was a decision to enlist the weight of the National Dental Association on their behalf. Accordingly, they invited the president of the National Dental Association to name a committee of five to take part in the organization of the Dental Educational Council of America at the annual session of the Association at Denver in 1910.

The Educational Council was formally established at that time, having as its object "the advancement of dental education and the unifying of the standards of the various national bodies of the dental profession." The Council gave equal representation to the National Association of Dental Faculties, the National Association of Dental Examiners, and the National Dental Association. The Dental Faculties Association of American Universities, however, was not recognized. The founders laid out an ambitious program for the new organization. Three standing committees divided the work of the Council among them, the Committee on Colleges, the Committee on Curriculum, and the Committee on Uniform Dental Legislation. The duties of the various committees were broad. The Colleges Committee was "to inspect the various colleges under their jurisdiction with a view of ascertaining the character of work done, and whether the needs of the community in which colleges exist are fully satisfied." The Committee on Curriculum had only to perfect a model curriculum, while the last group was to make a study of the existing dental laws of the various states, and present a report on the possibilities of more uniform laws.[44]

Ambition was not, seemingly, accompanied by energy. Little progress was made during the following year and a mid-year meeting in January, 1912, failed to attract a quorum. In the meantime, apathy became complicated by intransigence. The Educational Council's secretary told the Executive Council of the National Dental Association in 1912, "The sincerity of the desire of the National Association of Dental Examiners to cooperate effectively in the future education work of this Council is on trial, and the Dental Examiners should see to it that no unholy educational alliance between individual colleges and individual state dental boards to the detriment of dentistry shall be permitted to gain a foothold in this country." In near-despair, the report suggested that another year's trial should show whether the Educational Council could accomplish its work or whether some new method of organization would be needed. The alternative the secretary offered was a direct challenge to the National Dental Association. "Possibly it [a new Council on Education] should be controlled by the one body which has for its membership men belonging to all the organizations known to dentistry." [45]

This very qualification made it exceedingly difficult for the National Dental Association adequately and expeditiously to handle the problem. Many prominent and active members of the Association were associated with the proprietary dental schools. When Dean Sharp of the Universities society solicited the backing of the National Dental Association for his organization at the Denver meeting of 1910, the deep and bitter division with the Association showed forth fully. Sharp advanced a provocative suggestion. "I urge upon this association," he said, "that it take steps immediately to adopt a properly secured standardization of our educational institutions by demanding their control by standardized universities." This goad to the representatives of the independent schools climaxed a sweeping indictment of the existing system of education and certification:

The success of our schools, based upon financial competition and aggrandizement of the members of their faculties, the appointment of our boards of examiners because of their political rather than their educational attainments, an organization of our dental schools for the protection of its members, and our own indifference to it all, present a formidable barrier to our professional and educational progress, and expose our standards to the ridicule of foreign nations and to the scorn of the American people.

Sharp called upon the National Dental Association to assert its leadership of the profession and demand reform.[46]

Sharp's essay precipitated a furious discussion. The veteran educator and professional leader, B. Holly Smith of the independent Baltimore College of Dental Surgery, mounted a vigorous counterattack. "When the essayist, Dr. Sharp, was a mere man, he impressed me with many attractive personal qualities, but since he has become dean of the University of California he has assumed an aggressive tone, and in my judgment has done much to set back dental education in this country, to depreciate the American degree, and to bring into our very organization disunion and disloyalty." Smith issued a flat denial of Sharp's charges as they applied to the colleges and the faculties association. Other prominent men in the Association endorsed Smith's views.

A considerable part of the dissension revolved around the problem of raising standards of admission. Many dental leaders acknowledged the desirability of this course of action. A member of a state examining board declared he had "found that many of the candidates who came before our board—a prerequisite being the D.D.S. degree—had no idea of the use of the English language." But the elevation of entrance requirements meant a substantial sacrifice. C. R. E. Koch of Northwestern University's Dental School reported that raising their demands for two years' high school training to completion of the high school course had cut the entering class from one-hundred sixty-six to sixty-six. Such a drop was a severe financial blow even for the relatively well-endowed university-related schools, for a proprietary college it might well be disastrous. The internal problem of financial support was not the only consideration. In the face of the fact that the supply of trained dentists could not meet the rising demand for dental services, did the profession dare further diminish the numbers of students?

One critic of Sharp's paper denied the practicability of reliance on the National Dental Association. His remarks brought into sharp focus the critical situation confronting the Association. "To say that the power of regulation must be taken out of the hands of the Faculties association and the Examiners association and put into the hands of this association, and that this association shall instruct the people of this country and the United States government as to what is to be done, is a reductio ad absurdum," Koch declared. "Who has constituted this body a representative body? What has made it a representative body? You are trying to make it such, but certainly no fairminded man can claim that this body is today a more representative one than the body which comes from the appointive officers of the people, the examiners from all the various states."[47] Koch was right. Before it could hope to assert leadership over any aspect of the profession, the National Dental Association had first to effect an organization with a claim to the role.

Chapter XV   REORGANIZATION BEGUN

DEBATE CONCERNING the nature of the National Dental Association resumed with hardly a pause after the amalgamation of the American Dental Association and the Southern Dental Association. An editorial in the *Dental Digest* in 1899 epitomized the uncertainty among thoughtful dentists regarding the role of a national dental society. This editor considered that such an organization might perform legislative or scientific functions, or both. In the former aspect, the Association could set qualifications for entry into the profession. It could foster the formation of local and state societies. It could influence educational standards. In the eyes of the writer, the American Dental Association had performed these legislative tasks satisfactorily. The record of scientific activities seemed to him less creditable. There was some disagreement, the editor allowed, as to the reasons for this difficulty. Some critics blamed the plan of organization on which the American Dental Association had operated. Others held that the time of meetings inhibited scientific achievement. Another group attributed scientific shortcomings to "too much politics." Still another faction believed the sessions were "too commercial," the display of dental goods being considered detrimental to a gathering whose prime objective was scientific work. For whatever reasons, a substantial body of opinion agreed that the American Dental Association had

267

had no great success in furnishing scientific leadership to the profession. Yet, the *Digest's* editor went on, the National Dental Association was organized on very similar lines. He thought that some of the changes that had been made were likely to be detrimental.

The principal difficulty seemed to him to lie in the membership provisions of the constitution. The base was even narrower than that of the American Dental Association and that society, he reminded his readers, had often had difficulty mustering sufficient attendance to secure excursion rates from the railroads. An expanded membership was necessary to sustain the Association's claim to represent and legislate for the profession. But the *Digest's* editor stressed the intellectual function of the National Dental Association. "If we expect to maintain our claim of being a scientific profession," he concluded, the Association must have "a permanent membership of from two to three thousand and at least one thousand in attendance at annual meetings, taking an active part in its work, and contributing by their annual dues a sufficient fund to carry on the scientific work of this body."[1]

Administratively, the constitution of 1897 introduced no substantial change. The usual array of officers was aided by an Executive Committee that was charged with certain financial and management duties that could be performed best between conventions. The various sections of the Executive Committee were charged with the auditing of the books, with the examination of the credentials of delegates, and with the arrangements for the annual sessions. All other matters had to be brought before the business meeting at the annual convention. The system was time-consuming and distracting. It had occasioned complaint before the amalgamation and continued to be the object of attack afterwards.[2] The principal argument on behalf of this system was that to surrender the political functions was to abandon any pretense of a representative character for the Association.

On the other hand, the membership provisions of the new constitution clearly aimed to set up an organization representative of the profession. It recognized only state societies as eligible to name delegates to the national body.[3] This clause was not strictly adhered to, and may have been adopted in a fit of absent-mindedness, for other features of the document seemingly contradicted its intent. Nevertheless, the exponents of the plan hoped to establish a sort of hierarchy of dental associations from the local through the district to the state and at last to the national society. According to the constitution of 1897, each state society was entitled to one delegate for every ten members.[4] These clauses plainly envisioned a national political structure for dentistry analogous to that of the federal government. Other terms of the constitution tended to obscure this intention. The amalgamated organization, like its predecessors, was dominated by the permanent members, former delegates who had maintained membership in the national society by signing the constitution and paying dues annually. Only permanent members were entitled to hold office.[5]

This institution had its opponents in the profession. It tended to undermine the character of the Association as either a delegated society, speaking for the organizations sending delegates, or a body which represented the whole profession. Furthermore, the restriction of office-holding to the permanent members encouraged a preoccupation with politics. And it tended to retard the growth of the membership. James Truman, presiding at the final meeting of the American Dental Association, attacked permanent membership as a "poisonous element in associated effort."[6] The membership terms of the 1897 constitution appeared somewhat more restrictive than those of the parent organizations. They were obviously not calculated to foster an increased membership.

A major development in streamlining the administrative aspect of the National Dental Association was accomplished in 1899. The session at Niagara Falls acceded to the long-standing demand that the meetings devote more time to the scientific papers and discussions and less time to business matters. An Executive Council was created. In effect, the business of the Association that was not already being handled by the officers and Executive Committee was turned over to this new agency. All new questions not otherwise provided for were automatically referred to the Executive Council without debate. The reports of the Council before the general sessions of the Association were also not subject to debate. The body could only accept or reject the decisions of the Executive Council.[7]

At the same session, a revision of the membership provisions was advanced. According to the proposal, all "permanently organized dental societies" would be accorded representation. This was a move back to the system under which the American Dental Association had

operated. It was a temporary abandonment of the concept of the
national organization standing at the apex of a regular hierarchy of
lesser societies. At the same time, the reformers suggested a change
in the delegate ratio. Both changes were adopted at the ensuing meeting at Old Point Comfort, Virginia.[8] The amendments marked a re-
laxation of membership policy that seems to have been part of a
general movement in the direction of greater emphasis on the educational and scientific aspects of the Association's work.

The presidential administration of G. V. Black carried the trend
further. One of the general meetings under his leadership granted
privileges of the floor to all present.[9] In his annual address, Black
called for a "rigorous revision" of the constitution calculated to improve the operation of the scientific sessions of the annual meetings
and to establish the Association at the head of organized dentistry.
Black attacked the system of permanent membership. His review
of the attendance at the annual sessions disclosed considerable fluc-
tuation in the number of societies represented and hence of the
number of delegate members. On the other hand, the permanent
membership roster had grown steadily. Black observed, "From this
it would seem that the organization is rapidly losing its representative character and lapsing into a fixed organization controlled by its
permanent members exclusively." Black advocated severe limitations
on the permanent membership in an effort to reawaken the interest
of the state societies in the National. He had two other proposals to
vitalize the state organizations. First, he suggested that the corresponding secretary resume the former practice of presenting an annual report on the activities of the state organizations. Further, he
recommended sending the *Transactions* to members of the state societies, levying small additional dues to defray the costs.

After his criticisms of permanent membership and of relations with
the state societies, Black turned his attention to the vexatious and
exasperating delays resulting from the existing publication arrangement. Dr. Black then advanced to a series of recommendations concerning the administration of the society. He endorsed the Executive
Council. The business affairs of the Association should be "lodged
in the hands of a few, whose acts would be under the censorship of
the main body without debate." He urged greater rotation of the
officers except the secretaries and treasurer. Next, to enhance the

stature of the annual sessions and to put the National Dental Association in its rightful place at the head of the profession in the country, the great Illinois dentist advised confederation of the National with the national associations of dental faculties, dental examiners, and the Association for Dental Pedagogics. If all of these organizations met together at the same time, the annual meeting would truly be a convention of the dental profession.

Finally, Black addressed himself to a series of reforms of the scientific portion of the Association's work. He observed that the existing arrangement of sections led the members to devote the major portion of their time at the annual session to preparation of their report to the general meeting. As a consequence, many papers received inadequate attention. And time prevented the reading of many more. To meet the difficulty, Black proposed consolidation of all the sections into three and that these meet simultaneously under their own officers. These men would be selected on the same basis as the other officers. Black thought this arrangement would best satisfy the needs of the growing number of dentists with specialized interests. He closed by stressing the critical importance of improving the scientific performance of the Association. "The time is fast approaching when dentistry must make much greater advances along scientific lines and in the adaptation of these to its practice, or lose caste with the related professions, and we cannot allow it to do the latter," he warned.[10]

Black's suggestions provoked considerable discussion. The Committee on the President's Address was jolted. They decided that, while they approved the proposed reformation, the scheme should "lie over one year." In the meantime, the Committee suggested that copies be printed and mailed to each member of the Association. In a supplementary report, the Committee also recommended appointment of a special committee to encourage the activities of state and local societies.[11] Black again brought forward his proposals before the Executive Council at Niagara Falls in 1902. At that time he won appointment to a committee of three on revision of the constitution and by-laws. He spoke so convincingly that it was decided to implement as many as possible of his proposals by resolution pending formal adoption of the amendments for which there was a compulsory waiting period of one year.[12]

Only part of the Black revision was adopted in 1903. The scientific portion of the Association's work was entrusted to three sections. Provision was made for election of the chairmen and secretaries of the sections in the same way the other officers of the Association were chosen. The revised constitution called for regional rotation of membership in the Executive Committee, the Council, and of the section officers. Similarly, the terms of the members of the Executive Committee and Council were staggered. Black's proposals for reorganization of the Program Committee became the rule under the revision.[13] On the other hand, his suggestions regarding permanent membership were ignored and nothing was done about confederation with the other national dental societies. Relations with the state societies continued to be a matter for an annually appointed committee of the Association. Many circumstances conspired to hamper implementation of Black's reforms. Some of the changes could not be effected until 1904. At the brief business session in 1904, the rotation on the Executive Committee and the Council was deferred. Harvey J. Burkhart, long-time chairman of the Executive Council, announced a motion to repeal the Black constitution and to restore the "original" document in 1905. The election of section officers was entrusted by the general meeting to the Executive Council. The latter device became an annual practice.[14] In sum, the massive revision proposed by Dr. Black was finally reduced to no more than a consolidation of the sections into three, a reorganization of the Program Committee, and regional and temporal rotation in office of the members of the Executive Committee and Executive Council.

In the constitutional arena, the problems of membership policy overshadowed consideration of the problems of administration. Through the early years of the century there was unanimous agreement on the need to increase the length of the membership list. The Association was divided, however, on the manner in which this increase was to be achieved. One group held that the roster must be expanded to include the whole of the profession in the United States. Others demanded that the membership be restricted to members of duly constituted state and territorial societies. In the view of the latter, the objective of embracing the entire profession could only be achieved by building a strong foundation in the state organizations. Insistence that candidates for membership in the National Dental Association be members of a state society was one way to insure the cooperation of the state bodies in building up the national organization. For some years, no one managed to bring up any proposition that would reconcile the two aspirations. During the first decade of the century the two contentions run in a sort of counterpoint through the records of the Association. From 1899 through 1903, the tide seemed to be setting in favor of a broader membership policy. In the former year, the 1897 restriction of membership to delegates from state societies gave way to allow reception of delegates from all permanently organized dental societies. The annual meetings were widely advertised to the profession at large. In 1901, for example, the recording secretary sent circulars and copies of the program to three thousand "society members," although the paid-up membership at that time was only 355. At one of the general sessions, all those present were proffered the privileges of the floor.[15] The philosophy implicit in this gesture was expounded by President J. A. Libbey in 1902: "The National Dental Association is a delegate body representing the organized dental profession of this nation. Its membership is not merely the few who come as delegates and bear the burden of the work and expense, but every member of a state or local society which is represented." Dr. Libbey followed James Truman and G. V. Black in attacking permanent membership. "As the permanent membership increases [the Association] is losing its identity as a delegate body and assuming an individuality—merely a society—and as such its influence with the organized profession will decrease."[16]

The preoccupation with numbers continued during the presidency of L. G. Noel. In his annual address of 1903, Noel discussed the problem at length. According to the best estimates he could discover, Noel reported, the profession in the United States numbered about twenty-eight thousand. Of this number, somewhat more than one-third, about ten thousand, could be considered eligible for membership in the National Dental Association. The remainder comprised "the large number of advertising men and those who by unethical methods put themselves outside the ranks of the regular profession."

Some means had to be found to reach the legitimate practitioners who lingered beyond the fold of dental organization. "Our difficulty here lies in our inability to make tangible our acquisitions [from membership and attendance at the annual sessions]," he explained. "We must add to these invisible benefits something more apparent and better calculated to fix the attention of the rank and file of the fraternity." To this end, Noel proposed that the National Dental Association establish a fund for the relief of aged and ailing dentists. He thought that such a program might well include a life insurance feature as an inducement to membership. He also urged easing of the regulations governing the naming of delegates. Noel suggested that consideration be given to the granting of membership upon the mere payment of a fee and subscription to the constitution and by-laws. In an effort to overcome the effect of distance on participation in the activities of the Association, the speaker suggested establishing more branches. He proposed winter meetings, when the brain is more active, instead of summer when the sessions had to compete with the lure of vacations. More practically, Noel reminded his auditors of the success enjoyed by the official journals sponsored by the British Dental Association and the American Medical Association. Offer of a subscription to the official journal would serve as a further attraction of membership.[17]

On this last point, Noel's recommendations found a receptive audience. Sentiment had been running strongly against the existing practice of offering the *Transactions* to a commercial publisher to spare the Association the expense of publication. Each year, it seemed, the volume appeared later and later. The proceedings of 1900 were not mailed to the membership until July 31, 1901. After this experience, the endorsement of Noel's proposal concerning a journal hardly seems surprising. After hearing propositions from two publishers at the 1903 meeting, the matter was referred to a committee.[18]

The brief business meeting that constituted the annual session of 1904 broke the momentum of reform. Perhaps the change in sentiment had already begun, for, although the 1904 meeting was supposedly held solely for the purpose of election of officers, Dr. Burkhart also gave notice of a motion to repeal the Black constitution at the 1905 meeting. At the same time, the required notice of another amendment to again restrict the reception of delegates to those from

state societies was given.[19] The stage was set for the adoption of a
new course of action at the 1905 meeting.

Waldo E. Boardman's presidential address did not directly deal
with the constitution, but gave considerable attention to the membership question. His views ran counter to the prevailing ideas on the
subject. The National Dental Association numbered 603 in 1903, he
related, and counted but 645 in 1905. With an estimated 35,000 dentists in the United States, Boardman thought the roster should be
about ten times as large. He suggested the introduction of younger
men to positions of leadership as one means of increasing the numbers enrolled. More significantly, Boardman proposed further liberal-
izing of the membership clauses of the constitution in two ways:
First, he advocated repeal of the requirement of a dental or medical
degree as a prerequisite of membership. Second, he urged "making
[the National Dental Association] a representative body instead of
a delegated organization." The model Boardman had in mind was
the system of the British Dental Association, which accorded membership to all applicants on the recommendation of three members,
one of whom was personally acquainted with the candidate. Boardman's ideas won the partial endorsement of the Committee on the
President's Address. His proposal to drop insistence on the collegiate
degree was rejected. The session adopted, not Boardman's liberal
recommendation, but the amendment accepting delegates only from
state and territorial societies. At the same time, an echo of Black's
plan was heard. An amendment terminating permanent membership
when the member ceased to belong to his state or territorial society
was proposed, only to die without action at the next session.[20]

New voices were raised in 1905 on behalf of Association sponsorship of a journal. President Boardman declared that recent experience
had been of an "exceedingly unsatisfactory character." "Abolish the
present method of farming out the Transactions, and in place thereof
have a journal of our own modeled on the order of that of the British
Dental Association, or that of the American Medical Association," he
urged. B. Holly Smith echoed the sentiment on behalf of the Southern
Branch of the Association.[21] The Committee on a Journal, appointed in
1903, presented an elaborate statement advocating publication of
an independent journal. The Committee report added a stern warning: "The future of this organization as a leader in professional work

and ethics is imperiled. It is absolutely essential that it separate itself from all direct connection with commercial influences." [22]

Financial considerations tempered the urgency of the Committee's recommendations. The size of the membership, they found, was inadequate to support a new periodical. Accordingly, the Committee suggested that the National Dental Association take over an already-existing independent organ, the *International Dental Journal*. The stockholders offered to convey their magazine to the Association without cost, provided it was never turned over to a dental supply house. The Journal Committee claimed the *International Dental Journal* was self-supporting and might well become a source of revenue. Again caution prevailed. The Journal Committee was enlarged and in the meantime the existing publication arrangements were continued.[23] The relation of the journal question and the membership problem was clear. The Association did not have the membership to support an independent journal. Publication of a journal would attract new members. All in all, the 1905 meeting seemed to indicate a trend toward caution and conservatism in the face of the problems of the day.

Proponents of a generous membership policy did not give up. President Mark F. Finley, at the 1906 session in Atlanta, advised permitting all active members of state dental societies to become delegates to the National Dental Association. The Executive Council ignored Finley's suggestion and also rejected a proposal to restore representation to all regularly organized societies.[24] President A. H. Peck returned to the attack in the next year. His "Annual Address" reviewed the advantages of organized action. He endorsed Finley's scheme to admit all state society members to the National Dental Association rolls. His great appeal, however, stressed the importance of the will to build the Association.

In the last analysis, then, the burden is laid upon our own shoulders. Have we the desire and the capacity to make this Association such as shall carry irresistible appeal to every ethical dentist in this land? To do this it will be necessary for every man to ask himself, and answer for himself, what can I do to make the National Dental Association invaluable to my professional brethren? Having asked and answered this question, there remains a measureless and endless devotion to the best interests of this body. . . . The enlargement that we covet, the growth in numbers and influence so essential to the fullest success of our organization, are not beyond our realization. We can have them if we will.[25]

Peck's appeal set the tone of the meeting. The Committee on a Journal urged the importance of increasing the membership. They pointed out that offer of a subscription to an official journal supplied an added inducement to join the Association.[26] The afternoon meeting of Section II, devoted to "Operative Dentistry, Nomenclature, Literature, Dental Education, and Allied Subjects," spent the entire session on a paper concerning "The Functions of the State Dental Society." The speaker found the functions to be three, social, educational, and political. The latter, he insisted, was "the keystone of the dental arch." The reasons he advanced were severely practical. "In this day of money madness and of unbridled extravagance almost every modern business concern or corporation has among its employees men well schooled in political economy and civic government, whose work is to study proposed laws or amendments in order that they may adjust their affairs to meet changes in legislation." The speaker insisted that dentistry could do no less. He urged his auditors to become better informed concerning the operations of government and to take a more active part in political affairs. Great care must be exercised in the drafting of legislation, the speaker cautioned. But given a good bill, the lawmakers could be counted on to adopt it. "Our movement must be forward," he concluded. "Already we have done much, but we can do more. There is in man an eternal principle of progress which no power on earth can stay." [27]

The discussion of the paper brought out the first description of the Illinois plan in the proceedings of the National Dental Association. C. P. Pruyn of Chicago took the floor, announcing, "I would like to tell you something of our society." He boasted of the numbers enrolled under the Illinois system. Pruyn explained that district societies had been formed "with regard to the railroad facilities, so that men could get together very easily." "By joining a district society, a man becomes a member of the state society; one fee makes him a member of the state and local society, and gives him also the privilege of receiving the journal that publishes our proceedings,"

Pruyn reported. The Illinois organization also published a bulletin ten times a year in which the activities of the local societies were reported, he said. "We are now on the road to success, and hope that in time this plan will be carried out so successfully that membership in the state societies will entitle a man to membership in our national organization." Other commentators on the paper extolled the virtues of a strong and active state society and reported the spread of the Illinois plan to other state associations. The discussion indicated considerable interest in the possibilities of increasing influence with state legislatures through a vigorous state dental organization.[28]

These expressions favoring a reform of membership policy had been anticipated by the actions of the general session of the National Dental Association on the preceding afternoon. The Committee on the President's Address endorsed the Finley-Peck recommendations according membership to all members of state societies. The Committee likewise advised dropping the provision requiring a dental degree. The general session adopted the Committee report.[29] A three-year check in the movement to broaden the membership base of the National had been broken. The new policy, however, could not be put into effect until the following year.

Reorganization, especially as related to membership policy, remained in the forefront of attention at the Boston meeting in 1908. President William Carr presented a concise survey of the state of the profession in his annual address. He acknowledged the pressure to liberalize membership terms, but he scorned the threat of the founding of a new national society. "We have been accused of being a closed corporation," he said, while "some advocates of the new association have favored the open door and the indiscriminate admission of every legal practitioner who desires to become a member." He warned, "Such action would be dangerous in the extreme, as it would admit all licensed practitioners, many of whom, unfortunately, are not only unethical in regard to advertising their offices and in other ways, but who have procured their licenses by fraud." Carr suggested instead that the National Dental Association admit every member of a state society or of a district or local society entitled to representation in a state society. "In this way, every ethical and reputable practitioner who desired to do so could . . . become a member, the state societies being responsible for the ethical and

professional standing of the delegates presenting their certificates."
The increased membership, he thought, would make it possible to
support a journal. He spoke glowingly of the success of the *Journal
of the American Medical Association*. It was, he reported, a highly
regarded advertising medium because the American Medical Association checked the characteristics and claims of the products before
accepting the copy. He urged the establishment of a permanent committee to undertake the publication of an official journal for the National Dental Association.

The administrative problems of the Association also claimed Carr's
attention. He noted, "The so-called reformers are like the poor, they
are always with us." Carr declared he was weary of the "hue and cry
against politics and . . . that the association is ruled by a few." He
warmly defended "politics of a proper character" as a wholesome and
necessary part of every organization. In any case, he pointed out,
"No set of men can rule a live organization for a long time if they
are inefficient or corrupt . . . the remedy is in your own hands." Carr
recommended an amendment to the constitution that would require
the Executive Council, the principal target of the criticisms, to meet
publicly, organize, and name the committees for the coming year
before the close of each annual session. In conclusion, the president
expressed the hope "that in the near future we shall see a truly great
National Association—not a new organization raised on the ruins of
the old, but an association of natural growth, resulting from the
needed and healthy increase of a vigorous and effective society." [30]

Carr's address set off a series of reform proposals. Both the Maine
and the Massachusetts State Dental Society presented a series of
recommendations to the Executive Council. The Massachusetts suggestions echoed the pattern of Carr's address. They called for inauguration of "a representative journal," reorganization of the society, and
enlargement of the membership. They favored revising the fees
charged by the National Dental Association, if it was necessary to
accomplish these reforms. Basically, the Massachusetts Society advocated following the lines they attributed to the American Medical
Association so that "all members in good standing of state, district,
and county societies, and such other societies as may be determined
upon, [would] be eligible for membership in the National Dental
Association." [31]

Rodrigues Ottolengui, the volatile editor of *Items of Interest,* appeared before the Executive Council and offered a completely revised draft constitution and by-laws. Ottolengui declared that his revision followed the American Medical Association plan of organization as a model. It contemplated changes in both membership and administrative arrangements. Membership in the National Dental Association would "consist of such members of the Constituent Associations, and such members of the Army Dental Corps and of the Naval Dental Corps (when established), and such others as shall be elected in accordance with the By-Laws." Constituent societies Ottolengui defined as those state associations that were organized in conformity with the general plan of the National Dental Association and had declared their allegiance to it and agreed "to the formation and perpetuation of the House of Delegates." Ottolengui's plan allowed a five-year "interim constituent membership" while a state society effected its reorganization.

The new proposal eliminated both the Executive Committee and the Executive Council. It established in their stead the House of Delegates as the business body of the Association. The House would choose all general officers and trustees and transact all business of the Association, public, professional or scientific, not otherwise provided for. Members of the House of Delegates would be chosen by the constituent societies and by several other units of the profession. A nine-man Board of Trustees would "have charge of the property and of the financial affairs of the Association." Elected for three-year terms, the Board's composition rotated, three members being elected each year. The by-laws enjoined the Trustees to provide for and superintend publication of the *Journal of the National Dental Association.*

The terms of the Ottolengui constitution sought to eliminate politics from the considerations of the House of Delegates by making its members ineligible either for general office or for the Board of Trustees. The latter, however, were made non-voting members of the House of Delegates. As a further stabilizing feature, the proposed constitution called for one-year terms for the officers and the annual election of one-third of the Trustees for three-year terms.[32] Ottolengui's revision and the recommendations of the Massachusetts State Dental Society were not necessarily incompatible. They indicated the wide-spread concern in the profession with the languishing state of the national society. In accordance with the suggestion of President Carr's address, the Council named a new Committee on Revision of the Constitution and By-Laws. The various reorganization proposals were referred to the new Committee.[33]

The Boston meeting did not wait to take action on membership policy. It went beyond the position set down by the Minneapolis session and wrote an even more generous change into the constitution. After 1908, not only could any member of a state dental society be enrolled in the National Dental Association, but any member of a local or district society that was entitled to membership in the state society became eligible to be a delegate to the National Dental Association, and therefore a member, by sending a certificate from the state society and membership fee to the National Dental Association treasurer. At the instance of H. J. Burkhart of the Executive Council, the amendment became operative immediately.[34] This measure represented a compromise between the urge to enlist members wherever they might be found and the desire to preserve the ethical standards of the National Dental Association while entrusting enforcement of those standards to the state societies.

Reorganization became a lively topic of discussion among dentists everywhere. Ottolengui opened the pages of *Items of Interest* to dignified expressions of opinion on the problem. He addressed a circular letter to the members of the National and invited them to submit their views for publication in *Items*.[35]

The first response printed in the *Items* came from G. V. Black. The Chicagoan was dubious about Ottolengui's scheme. "I do not think anything in the form of a constitution will help matters in the National Dental Association," he wrote. "There are other things that must be remedied, and I doubt very much if the present body, as it meets and discusses matters, is the place to undertake the remedy." Black recalled his long observance of the "doings of the association." "It is a study of men that we want, more than of constitutions," he said. His own reformation, he sadly concluded, had been of no value whatever in correcting the errors that had crept into the Association.[36] What Black only hinted, other correspondents made more explicit. The complaints were of politics. "The injection of politics has been the ruin of our association; the wire-pulling begins the first day and lasts through the whole meeting," a university professor charged. "Those that attend the meeting in order to get some good out of it cannot, for the politicians and ward heelers will not keep still." A New York dentist explained, "Members of organizations are apt to become restless and dissatisfied when their voice and voting power on business matters are taken from them and vested in delegates and committees; and soon the rumors of politics and ring rule is heard [*sic*], which is usually the precursor of cliques, hard feeling, and dis-integration." [37] Arthur D. Black, son of the famous G. V. Black and leader of the Illinois reorganization movement, reported in similar vein. "It seems to be the general opinion that there will be no material progress in reorganization of the National association so long as the men who have controlled its affairs for the past ten years continue in office." Black denied that his observations were intended as criti-cism of the work of these men. On the contrary, he declared that recent sessions (since the reorganization of 1903) had been "the best in history." Black insisted, however, on the virtue of rotation in office. "Most of our people believe President Roosevelt did right in refusing to run again, and most dentists seem to think that there are enough good men in the profession to make a constant shift-ing . . . desirable." [38]

The charges of political domination of the National Dental Asso-ciation by an inner circle finally goaded Burkhart to reply. If there was any truth to the charges of "ring rule," they struck at Dr. Burk-hart as the ring leader. From the time of its establishment, Burkhart served as chairman of the Executive Council, the key position in the Association. Securely ensconced in charge of the most powerful agency of the National Dental Association, whose decisions were not subject to debate, Burkhart could guide the course of the society and watch presidents come and go with equanimity. An attack on the existing regime of the National Dental Association was an attack on Burkhart. On the whole, Arthur Black's judgment seems to have been accurate. The Association's meetings ran reasonably well. The chang-ing course of membership policy argues that it was run with con-siderable flexibility responsive to the general sentiment of the mem-bership. Ordinarily, Burkhart's practice was to ignore criticism and discussion outside the regular meetings of the Council. On this oc-casion, he was less reticent. The charges of autocratic rule of the

Association, he stated, were "maliciously and atrociously false." He proclaimed the Council to be made up of dedicated men who devoted long, weary hours to the onerous duties assigned them. The Council members remained in office solely because of the earnest solicitations of many members. Then Burkhart turned from defense to attack. "I have no hesitation in saying that much criticism of the National Association in years gone by has been largely due to personal disappointments, and the failure to carry out, or have prominence given to pet schemes." He minimized the prospects of any significant developments at the time. "There is no occasion . . . for any individual to get chesty, and insist that any particular plan is a cure-all for our ills. Neither is there any need of becoming personal, or flying into a passion because some may disagree with us."

Between the scolding passages, Burkhart's response considered the merits of some of the reform proposals. Unrestricted membership, he claimed, had been tried without appreciable effect on the enrollment. He acknowledged that there was always room for improvement in the administration of the business of the Association, but he insisted that the American Medical Association plan was unsuited to the needs of dentistry because of "the wide differences of local conditions." In sum, he argued that the National Dental Association membership was small for reasons other than those the reformers sought to correct. Dentists stayed away from meetings of the National because they could not spare the time or the money to attend, or because the meetings were too remote from their homes. Other national dental organizations attracted many potential members away from the National Dental Association. State and local activities held the loyalties and service of many more practitioners. "For these and other reasons it will be many years before there is an appreciable increase in membership in the National Association," Dr. Burkhart concluded.[39]

Other contributors to the discussion managed to keep their attention specifically on the problems confronting the profession. A considerable number endorsed Ottolengui's scheme, apparently because it was based on that of the American Medical Association. Arthur Black urged a special committee of the National Dental Association to lead in the reorganization of the state associations. He further advocated a requirement that members of the state societies join the National body. Ottolengui, too, perceived the significance of state developments. Noting that organizations had been implementing the Illinois plan for nearly five years, he predicted this would lead eventually to a reorganized national association.[40]

Ottolengui reviewed the controversy in his January, 1909, issue. On the whole, he felt the response had been good. He emphasized the importance of the spreading reorganization movement in the states (by the fall of 1909 there were nineteen states in various stages of the process). This situation led him to repeat his earlier prediction of its impact on the National. "If the present so-called National Dental Association is fatuous enough to try to cling to its antiquated methods, it must be prepared for the spectacle of a convention of the reorganized State societies, and the organization of an American dental association. Such an association would start with approximately 5,000 members." [41]

With the appointment of a Committee on Revision of the Constitution and the discussion precipitated by this development and by the discussion itself, as Ottolengui said, reorganization was now "fairly before the profession." [42] There was, however, a considerable distance to go.

Chapter XVI   MOVING FORWARD

IN ITS FINAL PHASES, the story of the reorganization of the National
Dental Association passed through three stages. During the first,
the principal obstacle to any change was the opposition of the ruling
clique, coupled with the inertia of the society, which itself constituted
a leading argument for reform. In the second stage the necessity of
obtaining the support of the state dental societies for any effective
reformation was emphasized. The final stage involved settlement
of matters of detail arising from the differences in the degree of
organization in the various states and from lingering suspicions and
resentments generated during the earlier reorganization proceedings.
Only during the first of these periods was there any profound difference of opinion regarding the basic premises of the new structure.
Running through the whole of the debate and serving as a carrier
of the basic theme of each stage was the old and recurring problem
of defining the function of a national professional organization. As
always, each aspect of professional function found its supporters.
Some argued on behalf of a scientific role, others for an educational
one, and still others insisted on stressing a political and legislative
objective for the Association.

The editorial views of the *Dental Cosmos*, perhaps the most important of the dental periodicals of the day, indicated the seriousness

285

of the demand for reform. "A total change of base seems necessary," editor E. C. Kirk declared. He reviewed all the legitimate aims of dental organization, the aspiration for uniform state dental legislation and reciprocity of licensure, the improvement of dental education, the hope of achieving commissioned status for dentists in the Army and Navy, the desire for an independent dental journal. "And yet, like a voice crying in the wilderness, the demand for these things is made in vain because we have no organization with sufficient inherent force to materialize these ideals." Pointing to the success of professional organization in medicine, to the contemporary developments in British medicine and dentistry, and to the spectacular achievements of reorganization in Illinois, Kirk endorsed Ottolengui's draft constitution in its main principles.[1] The lesson for the ruling clique of the National Dental Association should have been plain to read, yet developments at the Birmingham meeting in the spring of 1909 indicated that the dental leadership was insulated from such sentiments.

On the surface the annual session seemed serene. V. E. Turner's presidential address urged that a specific time for the launching of a journal be fixed. The campaign, he thought, had dragged along too long. To this point, the address had offered no surprises. Even Turner's consideration of the organizational problems of the Association seemed bland. Only his acknowledgment that the membership question constituted a most serious problem disturbed the relative tranquility of his address.[2]

The Committee on the President's Address reported promptly. Their recommendations and observations showed that the Executive Council and the profession were somewhat in advance of the president's views. Aside from endorsing many of Turner's suggestions, the Committee noted that the membership drive "already gives great promise of success, as twelve or fifteen states today indicate through their representatives or letters from their officers that they will join the National in a body." The estimate was overoptimistic to the edge of smugness. At Birmingham only twenty-two new members were added to the rolls. A year later over a hundred dentists presented credentials and were added to the list. Nearly another thirty presented credentials but failed to indicate a desire for permanent membership. Including the recruits added in 1910, the total membership numbered scarcely more than seven hundred. The geographical distribution of these accessions argues persuasively against attributing the increase to "twelve or fifteen" state societies enrolling *en masse*. Although the Committee on the President's Address took an unduly rosy view of the membership situation, they were clearly ahead of the president in contemplating the enlistment of state societies in a body. Similarly, the Committee proposed "a consecutive and consistent effort on the part of the officers and members of this association to establish a loyal relation between our National body and the various state dental associations throughout the country" through systematic correspondence and visitation.[3]

Part of the optimism of the Committee was grounded in the determination of the Executive Council to commence publication of an official journal of the Association on October 1, 1910. This decision rested on a very favorable reading of the report of the Committee on Journal. This Committee reported communicating with some 4,000 members of state societies who were not members of the National Dental Association. More than 400 had responded with conditional agreements to subscribe. Many of the 300 secretaries of state and local societies who were circularized also responded favorably. The Allied Dental Societies offered to merge their *Journal,* the successor to the *International Dental Journal,* with the National organ under certain conditions. To buttress the potential subscription list thus compiled, the Committee reported "private pledges of $400" and "the pledge of a public-spirited member of the profession to make good any deficiency."[4] Under such circumstances, the decision to begin publication was understandable.

In spite of the surface indications of serenity, the bitter divisions sundering the profession over the reorganization question threatened to break out at any moment. The customary brevity of the minutes served to conceal any outbursts during the official proceedings. But the practice of reporting the discussions of papers read in the section meetings shows the participants giving vent to some of the bitterness. The veteran educator and dental statesman, B. Holly Smith, in commenting on a paper, called up memories of the Boston meeting of 1908 where Ottolengui's draft constitution following the American Medical Association model had been offered. Smith complained, "A proposition was made for such a reorganization of the National Association as would exclude all possible continuance of our delightful affiliation with the Southern Branch of the National."[5]

Smith's comments provoked a retort from Emory A. Bryant. He, too, alleged grounds for dissatisfaction. He traced the difficulties, at least in his own case, back to 1904. "At St. Louis an amendment to the constitution was offered, which was adopted at Buffalo by a small majority vote, excluding members of local associations from becoming members of this association," he related. "When the error of this was demonstrated, this amendment was amended to take in all the members of state societies. This has not fulfilled expectations." He alluded grimly to the work of the Revision Committee since the Boston meeting of the previous year and directed a warning at Smith and his associates. "I say to those who are in control of our organization that if they will be considerate in their treatment of the younger members and not mix in local society squabbles, they will have no such antagonism as has permeated this organization for the past five years."[6]

Scattered through the discussions of other papers presented at the Birmingham meeting were indications of other cleavages splitting the fabric of the National Dental Association. There was, for example, the enduring division between advocates of a scientific and a practical orientation. One speaker lamented the deterioration of relations with medicine. The complainant elaborated his recital and at length concluded, "This association might easily have been a good second to the medical, if a broader and more active personal interest had been taken in society work by authors of dental works, contributors to dental journals, state examiners, and the faculties . . . of the numerous dental colleges of the country."[7]

Such signs of conflict within the profession had relatively little effect since they were not directly related to the movement for reorganization. Behind the smooth facade thrown up by the bald entries in the "Minutes of the Executive Council," the first stage of the battle of reorganization took place.

The Committee on Revision of the Constitution presented a number of amendments embodying, according to the official view, "a liberal plan of reorganization." The proposed membership clause seemed generous. It offered admission to the National Dental Association to members of "local" and "collateral" societies upon presentation of a certificate from the president and secretary of the society. A measure of control allowed the Executive Committee to "determine what constitutes a permanently organized local or collateral society." In addition, the suggested revision would permit state and territorial organizations to "elect to become, as a body, constituent members of this Association, and each member of such organization shall thereupon become a permanent member of this Association."

The new draft substituted a "House of Delegates" for the old Executive Council. The House was to consist of the president and secretary and fifteen others chosen equally from three geographic divisions, East, West, and South. The reports of the House of Delegates to the general meetings of the Association, like the reports of the Executive Council, would not be subject to debate. Nomination for national offices was to be by "informal ballot." Regional representatives to the House of Delegates were to be selected by regional caucuses meeting at the annual session of the Association.[8] Except for the token creation of a House of Delegates, the proposals of the Committee on Revision ignored the draft constitution submitted by Rodrigues Ottolengui at the Boston meeting. For the time being it seemed that the reform movement was checked.

The Executive Council apparently found the Committee's work to their liking. The amendments were on the verge of adoption when the spectators, led by H. A. Kelley of Portland, Maine, objected strenuously. Reluctantly, the Council decided merely to receive the report and ordered it printed and distributed to the membership. Early circulation of the proposed changes would, the official version said, "give ample opportunity to thoroughly understand same before final action is taken."[9] Defeat in this skirmish seems to have ended most of the active resistance of the ruling clique to substantial revision of the constitution. The debate in the dental press through the ensuing year thoroughly exposed the inadequacies of the Revision Committee's suggestions. Thereafter, except for B. Holly Smith's rearguard defense of the Southern Branch, Executive Council opposition to extensive reform was confined mainly to delaying tactics, which could legitimately be defended as insurance of fair play and calm deliberation.

Critics of the Revision Committee's suggestions handled the plan roughly. None was more severe than Rodrigues Ottolengui, editor of *Items of Interest* and author of the draft constitution submitted at the Boston meeting and referred to the Revision Committee. Ottolengui began his attack in his September issue. He resented the neglect of his draft proposal, but he concentrated his fire first on the new "House of Delegates." It was, he charged, "the same old 'Executive Council' in a new dress." He continued, "The new body, call it what you will, has the same old ambiguous powers granted it in the same old ungrammatical paragraph." Conceding that the increase in numbers provided in the revision might mark an improvement, he objected that their method of appointment was even worse than heretofore. With this comment, Ottolengui turned to a second aspect of the revision. He explained that the selection of Executive Council by "the good old ring-rule method of having 'the secretary cast one ballot,' etc., etc." at least had the merit of affording any member the constitutional right to object, "though no one ever did, probably because no one ever cared enough." In contrast, Ottolengui protested, the new House of Delegates was to be composed of five from each geographical division, and these were to be chosen by a caucus of those present from each division. He gibed, "Could anything be more entertaining?"[10]

The next month, Ottolengui launched a full-scale assault on all the proposed changes. He repeated his criticisms of the new House of Delegates and attacked every suggestion of the Revision Committee. From Ottolengui's review of the plan and from other comments in the dental press through the winter of 1909-1910, it was evident that the proposals of the Revision Committee, backed though they were by the governing faction of the National Dental Association, were destined to be rejected—and forgotten.[11]

The pressure for change continued unabated. J.P. Root wrote, "The National Dental Association must be reorganized, or else become a living corpse. There is only one way to reorganize, that is by having all State Dental Associations become constituent bodies, and to accomplish this, there should be compensating inducements offered, so that the dentist from a far Western State will feel he receives more than he pays for." Root's challenge to enlist the support of the state societies had commanded the attention of the Executive Council at the Birmingham meeting. The newly elected corresponding secretary, Homer C. Brown of Columbus, Ohio, had been instructed to direct his efforts to the end of winning the support of the state societies. The leading officers of the National Dental Association regarded the campaign as largely a token gesture. H. J. Burkhart, B. Holly Smith and Charles S. Butler, recording secretary for many years, all viewed the enterprise skeptically. "The principal thing now is to get busy with the various state societies," Burkhart told Brown in approving a draft of Brown's appeal. "My opinion is that very few of the societies will avail themselves of the offer of the National Association, but we can give them a chance to say no if they want to." [12]

Brown was optimistic. In his official statement that appeared in the dental press, he claimed that a number of state associations had already declared their desire to affiliate as a body with the National Dental Association. Brown was, however, ready to admit that no state had as yet effected direct affiliation with the National Dental Association. On the basis of a long-standing correspondence with Arthur D. Black regarding the reorganization of the Illinois society, Brown expected to secure an easy prize for the National Dental Association campaign. "Illinois will possibly be one of the easiest State Societies to co-operate with as well as one of the most influential ones owing to the active interest taken in dental matters there and the fact that the state is so thoroughly organized," he explained optimistically. [13]

By the early summer of 1909, almost before it had begun, Brown's campaign to enlist the state societies seemed doomed. He not only missed attending the Illinois meeting, but "overlooked" the date of the New York meeting as well. He sent an apologetic letter to C. S. Butler pointing out that the other officers of the National Dental Association had also been commissioned to labor at state society meetings on behalf of the National's cause. Butler's reply brought no comfort. "Our State Society referred the whole question of reorganization to a committee to report next year," Butler reported. "I think there will be no question about our Society coming in so long as the plan does not break up our present organization, but no scheme to change our present arrangement is likely to go through." [14] Ohio affiliation with the National, Brown well knew, could not be effected until the Ohio Society had altered its constitution.

With Ohio, New York, and Illinois unfavorably accounted for, Brown cast up his accounts in mid-June. "Kentucky and Nebraska have expressed themselves in favor of joining the National as a body, but they are the only ones that have been specific in this particular," he found. Almost a year later, on the eve of the Denver meeting, he reported to the president, "I have done about all I can with the State Societies, . . . but up to this writing have heard from but two or three and most of these do not seem to be what we might have hoped for."[15] Prospects for the official amendments did not seem promising as the time for the annual meeting of 1910 neared.

The ensuing session of the National Dental Association confronted a number of diversionary forces that may account for its disappointing record. The host city, Denver, in 1910 was in the throes of a lively political controversy that epitomized the appeals that enlisted so many Americans in progressive causes during these years. That B. Holly Smith, the staunch guardian of the established order in the National Dental Association, should speak sympathetically of the current political contest against monopoly illumines one aspect of the period that historians have always found hard to explain. Smith had been chosen to respond to the welcoming addresses of the dignitaries representing the host city and state. He said, "The entire country has had its eyes focused upon you while the struggle for supremacy was going on between the public service corporations and corrupt politics on the one side, and the people on the other. In the last engagement the people, led by that doughty little fighter, Judge Lindsay, seem to have had the advantage."[16]

If the fascination of politics did not detract from the interest in the dental sessions, the varied character of the assemblage itself added to the distractions. Over 1,200 persons connected directly or indirectly with the profession gathered for the 1910 meeting. Although the session may have been considered a success in terms of the size of the turnout, the accomplishments of the session were few. The very size of the assemblage may have contributed to the lack of achievement. Dentists accounted for about three-fourths of those registered, the balance being made up of dentists' wives and exhibitors of dental supplies and equipment. The nine hundred dentists in attendance exceeded the membership list, including those added to the rolls at Denver, by around two hundred names.[17] Even on the unlikely assumption that the whole permanent membership attended, it is evident that less than two-thirds of those present in Denver could participate in the decisions to be made there. Under the existing constitution, the deliberations of the Executive Council determined the policy of the Association. But even among the governing few, distractions were numerous.

The most difficult problems the ruling faction faced, however, arose in connection with the reorganization process. Thorpe's presidential address furnished the keynote for the meeting's disposition of the problem. The matter of the proposed revision of the constitution and by-laws had been under consideration for two years, he reminded his audience. "On account of the meager and unsatisfactory responses and evident disinclination on the part of the various state societies to accept the proposed plan of revision, it seems to me that it would be the part of wisdom to defer action for another year, and in the meantime invite all state societies to send representatives to a conference meeting to be called before the next annual session, and thereby endeavor to formulate changes and modifications which will receive the approval of the various state organizations and the profession generally." Thorpe also attacked Ottolengui's prediction that failure to reorganize according to the plan of the American Medical Association would eventuate in formation of a rival national organization.[18]

The Committee on the President's Address stood loyally behind Thorpe's views.[19] He and the Committee apparently shared two profound convictions. First, they believed the current political management of the National Dental Association should be continued in that role. Second, they held that the failure of the state societies to respond to the invitation to become members of the National indicated not that the reorganization proposals needed alteration but that the constituency they sought in the state societies needed further education regarding the advantages of affiliation with the National Dental Association.

The Executive Council adopted the same cautious attitude toward change. They heard "a long and full discussion" of the reorganization question then decided to continue the Committee on Revision for another year. Brown and Ottolengui were added to the ranks of the Committee. The enlarged group was instructed to call a conference of dental society officials to consider changes in the constitution of the National and report at the next annual meeting.[20] And so, the reorganization issue, which, as Thorpe had pointed out, had already been before the profession for two years, was continued for yet another year.

The interval between the Denver meeting and the Cleveland meeting of 1911 witnessed a variety of developments. The addition of Brown to the Committee on Revision apparently represented an effort to invigorate that rather lethargic body. The appointment of Ottolengui was calculated to allay the antagonism toward the official reorganization movement resulting from the manifest reluctance of the National Dental Association leadership to contemplate any broad alterations in the structure and procedures of the Association. As the affair worked itself out, Brown seems to have supplied most of the energy and Ottolengui the ideas and arguments that carried the movement forward in the ensuing period.

Most of the missionary activity among the state societies had to be deferred until the spring when a majority of them held their meetings. The nominal head of the Committee on Revision, J. D. Patterson, conceived the idea of holding the convention of society representatives on the eve of the Cleveland meeting of the National. Such a late conference would allow only a minimum of time in which to formulate the conference's conclusions for presentation before the annual session. Ottolengui had envisioned holding the conference during the Christmas holidays. Afterward the Committee would summarize the conference results and distribute them among the states for ratification. Although Patterson's scheme unquestionably imposed handicaps on the Committee and conferees, in the long run, it more or less forced the conference to use Ottolengui's draft of 1908 as the basis of discussion. The short time allotted for the meeting of society representatives virtually demanded some previously recognized point of reference for the discussion.[21]

Early in March, Ottolengui reminded Brown of the imminence of the state society meetings and the necessity for prompt action. At the same time, "in strictest confidence," the editor of the *Items* warned of difficulties looming in another quarter. He reported, "I have authentic information to the effect that if the National does not reorganize on broad enough lines to have plenty of money in the treasury, there will be an attempt to organize a National Association of Oral Hygiene." [22] Brown turned almost immediately to the preparation of a circular letter for distribution to the state societies. He sent copies of the draft to the members of the Revision Committee and the Committee on State and Local Societies. In his covering letter, Brown stressed the urgency of inaugurating an aggressive campaign among the state organizations.[23] From this point, although he continued to show deference to the established managers of the Association, Brown adopted a more decisive role in driving forward the movement to revitalize the National Dental Association.

Brown addressed the Southern Branch in Atlanta in April. He attributed the difficulties of the National Association to the renaissance among the state and local societies. These organizations had absorbed about all the time and energy of those interested in society work. Brown stressed, however, that these lesser organizations had imposed only a temporary handicap. "We should recognize the local society as the unit of both state and national organizations, and accept the opportunity presented through such preliminary work . . . thus taking advantage of the favorable conditions to adopt a new constitution and by-laws, which will make possible an equitable and representative National Association." [24]

The course of the discussion must have been an unpleasant surprise to the diplomatic recording secretary of the National Dental Association. The respected B. Holly Smith first opened fire. "I do not oppose anything Dr. Brown has said except that I think he has presented a phase of co-operative action which is absurd," Smith began. He acknowledged that amendment of the organic law of the Association was quite in order, if it was necessary. He admitted the desirability of winning the affiliation of the local and state societies. His concluding remarks, while somewhat bewildering, indicated the grounds for his discontent. "It seems strange to me that from an almost extraneous source, a source practically out of the influence of this great organization, there should come the movement toward turning it upside down," he said. "In the first plan brought forward, the Southern Branch, which was as much a component part of the National as the

American Dental Association, is practically wiped out and accorded no voice in national affairs." [25]

Brown was hurt and dismayed. Recounting the episode to B. L. Thorpe, Brown diffidently declined to write a report of the Southern meeting for Thorpe's *Dental Brief,* "since this was the first time I ever attended the Southern Branch, and besides, I might not give a report that would be agreeable to some." He related Smith's reactions and explained, "He had been having rather a good time and seemingly developed somewhat of a grouch that morning. He did not discuss the paper to any extent, but lambasted those who have been contending for a reorganization." In something of an understatement, Brown opined, "I believe we may have some opposition from some of the southern men, especially since Dr. Smith took the position that he did." [26]

J. D. Patterson, chairman of the National Dental Association Revision Committee, followed Smith on the rostrum to discuss Brown's paper and echoed Smith's sentiments. "I am not in favor of reorganizing and casting aside all the safeguards that were thrown around the American and the National Associations in times past, but, if necessary, and if the majority so decrees, I will acquiesce, and work with the majority." Another leading dentist, a former president of the National Dental Association, M. F. Finley of Washington, adopted a similar approach. [27]

Brown did not readily forget Smith's criticisms. He sent Ottolengui a reprint of his remarks before the Southern Association and added, "Some of the Southerners had a tendency to want to take a fall out of the reorganization proposition." Ottolengui replied, "I imagine the Southern Branch have an idea that we intend to do away with branches when we reorganize. Frankly, that is exactly what I think ought to be done, but it is not necessary." He admitted considerable impatience with the adherents of the Southern society. "I am a Southerner myself, but nevertheless, after the Spanish war, I had hoped that the spirit of the '61 Civil War was over. . . . There are always enough men still alive to hang onto these old sentimental ideas, instead of going into what makes for the general progress of science." [28]

In addition to conducting the negotiation and administration connected with the preparations for the annual meeting, Brown continued his efforts to secure a full attendance at the conference on reorganization that was to precede the annual meeting. He wrote to Otto U. King, secretary of the Indiana State Dental Association, giving information about the existing National Dental Association constitution and the Revision Committee proposals. Brown urged King to cooperate in an effort to see that Indiana was represented at the forthcoming conference. Brown corresponded with many others and sought to obtain the support of prominent leaders in the various states. When Charles S. Butler withdrew a paper on the subject from the program, Brown sent his regrets and solicited Butler's ideas for presentation at the meeting. Butler replied, disappointingly, "I am not looking for any radical changes." [29]

In spite of the pessimism expressed by men like Butler and Burkhart, and in spite of the antagonism to reorganization revealed by Smith and Patterson, Homer C. Brown's analysis of professional sentiment was vindicated. Representatives of twenty-four states gathered at the Hotel Hollenden in Cleveland on July 24. An overwhelming majority of the states represented adopted a resolution urging the National Dental Association to reorganize along the lines of the plan of the American Medical Association. The vote was twenty-two to one with one state absent at the time of the balloting.[30] President Edward S. Gaylord added his voice to the clamor for change. "For years we have struggled with a membership of less than one thousand, with a list of upward of thirty-five thousand to draw from," he said. "I know that I am voicing the minds of many when I appeal to the Committee on Revision to submit some plan at this meeting by which we may hope to largely increase our membership." [31] The agencies directly concerned, the Revision Committee and the Executive Council, tried to oblige.

The *Transactions* announce simply that the chairman of the Revision Committee made a verbal report. They do not indicate the course of discussions at the Hotel Hollenden conference nor do they reflect the nature of the deliberations of the Revision Committee in the preparation of its report. Fortunately, the editor of *Items of Interest* sat as a member of the Revision Committee. He subsequently reported the deliberations of the Committee for his readers. The dues question seemingly posed a considerable obstacle. The Committee on Revision knew approximately the income needed to sustain a journal. They estimated that this figure could be obtained by offering two-dollar dues to state societies that became constituents of the National Dental Association, provided the constituent organization guaranteed that two-thirds of its members would join the National Dental Association. Ottolengui added, "Of course, this guarantee of two-thirds may be reduced to one-half; or the guarantee may be omitted altogether, provided the State Societies, when applying for Constituent Society Membership, can at the same time offer to the National a membership large enough to make the reorganized association financially as prosperous as at present." As Ottolengui interpreted it, the guarantee asked of the state societies applying for constituent status became so flexible as to be no guarantee at all.

The Committee demonstrated its desire to accommodate the state societies in other ways. In fact, one compromise the Committee agreed upon went almost to the point of defeating the purpose of the reorganization. State societies, it decided, could become constituent members without revising their constitutions. The Revision Committee also acknowledged the appeal of the oral hygiene movement. The popular impact of meetings on oral hygiene thrown open to the public at Denver and again at Cleveland had been great. Consequently, the Committee added a new scientific section to be devoted to public oral hygiene. At one stroke the proposal sought to bind the popularity of the new vogue to the reorganization movement and, at the same time, to forestall the possibility of the founding of a new and rival society by the hygiene enthusiasts. To allay the antagonism among the southerners and to strengthen the supporters of reorganization in that quarter, the Committee provided specifically for the continuance of the Southern Branch under the new regime.[32]

In spite of the impressive support they seemed to have won among the state dental associations, the Revision Committee proposed that the reorganization proceed cautiously. Patterson, presenting the Committee report, offered a resolution that envisioned the drafting and distribution of a constitution in accordance with the recommendations of the conference as interpreted by the Committee. The draft should be "forwarded to the state societies with the request that such as desire shall make application for constituent membership at the next [1912] meeting, stating how many members they can guarantee." Then, Patterson's group suggested, "if properly supported by the state societies the Constitution and By-laws will be finally revised and adopted at the next meeting, the same to take effect at the meeting of

1913." The Executive Council and, subsequently, the general session of the membership adopted the recommendations of the Revision Committee.[33]

The process of reorganization had now reached a critical stage. Concessions had been made to conciliate the state societies on the one hand and the conservative leadership of the National Dental Association on the other. The great task yet facing the reformers was to maintain the unstable compromise for two full years. The situation was very precarious. The details of the new system remained to be worked out. When the generalities of the 1911 resolution on reorganization were made concrete, any of the factions concerned might become dissatisfied and upset the whole movement.

Resentments stirred up in arranging the Cleveland meeting smoldered. The profession seethed with dissensions both directly and indirectly related to reorganization and each one was intensified by personal antagonisms.

The Ohio State Dental Society served admirably as a bellwether for the profession. Ohio was usually the first of the state societies to hold its annual meeting after a meeting of the National Dental Association. Brown had been able to use the decisions of the Ohio association to foster support for the Cleveland conference in the preceding year. Now he succeeded in bringing Ohio into the van again. The resolution that Brown piloted through the Ohio State Dental Society provided that the constituent societies were to be "entitled to a proportionate representation in the House of Delegates when two-thirds of the membership . . . is officially reported to the National as members." Two clauses followed. The first endorsed the proposals of the Cleveland meeting. The second announced that the Ohio Society "officially expresses a desire to become affiliated with the National Dental Association and pledges at least two-thirds of its membership for a period of two years, beginning in 1913, in accordance with the aforesaid constitution." [34]

Among the other states the reorganization movement faced formidable problems. Ottolengui reported concerning New York:

The political clique which runs the New York State Dental Society have been moving heaven and earth to retain their grip on that body. It is a small and rather close corporation, which only accepts about sixteen new members per year, and these members have to be nominated by their local society. As there are 800 members now in the First District Dental Society, you can figure out about how old some of these men would be before they could get into the State Society, the First District being entitled to nominate about four members a year.[35]

Ottolengui's description revealed three problems, not one. First, it exemplified the institutional barriers to reorganization of the state societies and illustrated the institutional inertia that had to be overcome before alteration of a state society constitution could be effected. Secondly, Ottolengui's outline of the New York situation symbolized the regional power rivalries within the states. These were reproductions, on a smaller scale, of the sectional jealousies on the national scene. Finally, the editor's comments showed the personal differences that divided many a state into contending factions. Following the Ohio meeting, state society business took a recess until into the spring. In the meantime, other problems relating to the revision had to be dealt with.

Brown's handling of the routine administration of National Dental Association affairs was distracted, though apparently not diverted, by an extensive correspondence with Emory A. Bryant. Both correspondents were prolific letter-writers. Their exchanges ranged from contemporary political developments and the behavior of the economy through the congressional fortunes of National Dental Association-sponsored legislation to the personal feuds that rent the profession in Washington and had produced two local societies, both of which were recognized by the national organization. Brown, surveying the political situation from afar, observed, "I note by the papers that 'things' have been on the 'hum' in your city for a few days and I am of the opinion that it's going to be up to Ohio to furnish the next President by nominating two Ohio men and then it will be a good lively scrap." He continued, "As it stands today in Ohio our Governor [Harmon, a Democrat] can defeat our President [Taft] and I hardly see how things are going to change enough to shift the results, although it is possible for this to be done." Bryant retorted with assurance, "Well my dear boy, talking politically, I am afraid you are not in touch with the political current of the air around this burg in the past week, or you would not be so egotistical regarding Ohio's chance of having two candidates for the Presidency in 1912. Harmon has about as much show as a snow ball in h - - - for the Democratic nomination. That lies between Clark of Mo. and Wilson of N. J. and in my opinion Bryan will dictate which it is." Bryant was equally doubtful about Taft's prospects. "I would almost be willing to bet my old shoes it won't be Taft and if it is, that a democrat will be the next President." He added, "There are worse things than democrats laying around loose, and there are better than either to be had for the asking." [36] Bryant was evidently a shrewder political observer than Brown. Brown at length wearied of Bryant's constant diatribes against other Washington dentists and sought to terminate the correspondence— without success.

In the meantime, more pressing matters of Association business were going forward. The program for the coming annual meeting un- folded. Rumors filtered through the profession forecasting trouble for the reformers. Ottolengui wrote anxiously from New York, "Now I have from several sources received a persistent report to the effect that the 'plan of reorganization for the National won't be recognized when it comes out of the Committee's hands in Washington.' The intimation is that the resolution adopted at Cleveland will not be carried into effect." Ottolengui took comfort from the fact that he, Gaylord, and Brown constituted a majority of the Committee. "I can- not see how the Committee itself can be made to retract its position," he went on. "It is my belief that my personal enemies in Washington have a notion that because the National meets in Washington that they will be able to run things to suit themselves." [37]

After the turn of the year, word began to reach the secretary of the action of state dental societies on the proposed constitution. Arizona wrote "promising that the whole membership . . . will join the National Dental Association when that organization is reorganized on the 'Illi- nois plan.'" The District of Columbia society endorsed the reorgani- zation. In early April, news reached Brown that Rhode Island's associ- ation had "tentatively" endorsed the proposed revision. By mid-April, Brown could write optimistically to C. S. Butler, "Regarding the re- organization proposition, will say that most of the Societies seem to be more or less enthusiased [*sic*] in this matter and I believe that a very large majority of them will vote to become affiliated with the National in accordance with the constitution which was tentatively adopted at the Cleveland meeting." [38]

The campaign was not without its setbacks. "I regret very much that Missouri failed to 'come under the wire,'" Brown told Ottolengui. "Mrs. Thorpe was sick and B. L. was not able to attend this meeting. I had written to Patterson, Allen, Thorpe, and Dameron in my efforts to bring about a successful result in Missouri." Michigan's adherence was won—at a price. "It would have been impossible to get Michigan to vote to join us had they been obliged to make any guarantee of membership," Ottolengui reported. "I therefore had them vote simply to express their willingness to affiliate with the National, and they will immediately endeavor to enroll voluntary memberships in the National, so that by the time we meet the Secretary will be able to notify us how many men they can guarantee." Brown responded "You will recall that I wrote you that reports from Connecticut, Michigan, and Missouri were not any too encouraging, but I feel that we got a great deal more than a 'break-even.'" [39] The battle was still far from won. Some of the states with the largest societies had yet to be heard from. And Ottolengui's reading of his experience with the Michigan dentists foreshadowed two vexing problems.

The first problem was immediately reflected in other states. This had to do with the requirement that a society applying for constituent status in the National Dental Association must guarantee that two-thirds of its members would become members of the National. The second problem involved the guaranteed ratios of representation. Ottolengui declared, "I am not really sure what sort of guarantees have been given by states that have already voted to come in. I do know, however, that we could not get New York State with a guarantee." Dental leaders in other quarters were also finding this necessity a formidable obstacle. George E. Hunt of the Indiana State Dental Association noted, "I think we will have a thousand members when the coming meeting is over and to get six hundred and sixty-six of them to join the National would be quite a feat." [40] Arthur D. Black, on behalf of a committee of the Illinois Dental Society, explained, "A state society which has not been reorganized should have little difficulty to pledge two-thirds of its membership to join the National; it is quite a different proposition with a reorganized society having anywhere from 500 to 1700 members, many of whom know practically nothing of the National Association. We feel that there would be danger in such a pledge, in that it might cause a serious loss to our present membership if we should force two-thirds to join the National." The secretary of the Missouri State Dental Society attributed his organization's failure to act to similar considerations.[41]

To counteract the effects of the two-thirds clause in the draft constitution, Ottolengui penned an exhortatory editorial for his May issue. He observed that the two-thirds clause "has caused some confusion, and has engendered some hesitation. . . . The true status, therefore, may be explained to advantage." He reviewed the background of the clause. He reiterated the importance of financial solvency to the success of the reorganized society. Nevertheless, he added, "If any State Society should find it impossible to make such a promise [of two-thirds of its membership for the National Dental Association], it should, nevertheless, pass a resolution applying for Constituent Society membership." He pointed out that the National Dental Association resolution directing the Revision Committee did not stipulate two-thirds. This resolution asked only that the state society declare how many members it could guarantee. Furthermore, Ottolengui argued, the draft constitution distributed by the Revision Committee had not yet been adopted. Its provisions could be changed; they were not yet binding.[42] In spite of Ottolengui's efforts, the two-thirds clause, and even the request for a guarantee, continued to inhibit the adherence of some state dental associations.

At the time the *Items* editorial appeared, a number of important state societies had not yet met. Their actions would be significant in themselves and also for their influence on lesser societies. New York and Illinois were two such states.

The Empire State, although it boasted many nationally prominent dental leaders in its ranks, was handicapped by its constitution, which was set up in consideration of the traditional rivalry between the metropolis and the up-state region. Ottolengui appealed for Brown's aid. He sketched the New York situation briefly and concluded, "If you could be present and present this argument, it would be very potent as coming from a man outside the State." The secretary was unable to attend the New York meeting. Ottolengui and Gaylord dispatched a telegram reporting the New York action: "Impossible to

get guaranteed membership because of pending reorganization of
state society. Resolution passed endorsing reorganization of National
and pledging affiliation." From Burkhart came a fuller explanation.
"I objected to any limited joining of the National. Our State Society is
in no shape to go in and won't be for a year or two. Under the plan of
amendment of our by-laws, as proposed by me, we will next year take
in all our district members, and get money enough to pay our law com.
debts of several thousand dollars. Ottolengui wanted to hop right in,
but I told him it was better to go in right and stay, than have to withdraw on account of financial trouble. The thing is all right here any
time we move for it, but I'm not in favor of crippling a state society
by joining the National. It's better to go slow, and we are making safe
progress all the time." [43]

On the heels of the news of the decision in New York came word
of the Massachusetts society's action. Massachusetts followed the
precept of Ohio and announced its "desire to become affiliated,"
pledging two-thirds of its membership for two years. Connecticut and
then Vermont followed suit. Brown was carried away. "Personally,
am much gratified at the progress we seem to be making and from
present indications I can see no very good reason why this plan is not
going through practically unanimously," he exulted. "At least I feel
that we will have 35 or 40 States lined up for this, with the others in a
position to take definite action before this becomes effective in 1913."
The optimistic secretary had not lost all touch with reality. He expressed some foreboding about the position of the Illinois society.
"Numerically speaking, Illinois is the best society to secure," he explained. "Should they pledge two-thirds of their members it would
mean probably 1200 by the time this goes into effect, as they have
1700 members at present." [44] He did not see fit to add that Illinois'
leadership in the state reorganization movement had extended the
influence of that association beyond the borders of the state.

Because of the widespread influence of the Illinois State Dental
Society among the reorganized state dental associations of the Middle
West, news of the response of the Illinois organization to the reorganization occasioned considerable dismay among the workers for National Dental Association reorganization. The Illinois meeting had
reviewed the campaign for reorganization and found it had been without satisfactory results. It decided that the plan offered by the Re-

vision Committee was not a practical solution and proposed to call a conference of the reorganized state societies. The Illinois leadership insisted that "the majority of our Society sincerely desired to assist in the National reorganization as soon as a plan that they consider feasible of application to our Society can be worked out." Ottolengui at first thought that "it almost appeared that Illinois desired to start a rump convention." After receiving an explanatory letter from Arthur Black, however, the editor felt "much less agitated." Nevertheless, Ottolengui held up the last form of the June *Items of Interest* and penned a special editorial on "The Peculiar Attitude of the Illinois State Dental Society."[45] Ottolengui's reaction was mild compared to that of his colleague.

Homer Brown was deeply stirred. The Illinois difficulty stimulated him to some spectacular efforts which he recounted to his colleagues of the National Dental Association. His reception of the Illinois action was neither sympathetic nor calm. "True, the letter reads better than the resolution, but in my opinion neither are expressive of what is really intended," he said. The energetic Ohio dentist determined to forestall the machinations of the Illinois crowd. Brown announced, "Not that I am a supporter of the author of the expression 'my hat is in the ring' yet I am free to say that my headgear and entire wearing apparel may be so placed and I am going to use every possible effort to bring this reorganization question to a successful termination." Brown first heard of the Illinois action "from a prominent Illinois man," who said he had information which he did not wish to give by letter. A rapid fire exchange of letters and telegrams ensued as Brown and his would-be informant tried to arrange a mutually satisfactory rendezvous. Brown told his co-workers, "I had no idea this [meeting] was so urgent until I got a telegram just as I was getting on an interurban limited car to go to Springfield, as a number of us dentists had agreed to attend a dental meeting there. I road [sic] about three miles on this limited and figured that I'd get off when they were making a very abrupt turn at the outskirts of the city, which I did and by pressing into service a stranger and friend with automobiles I made my train and reached Indianapolis about midnight."[46]

As a result of this strategem, Brown not only augmented his knowledge of the Illinois situation, but was able to persuade the Indiana State Dental Association, meeting in Indianapolis, to endorse the Reorganization Committee's constitution, with a reduction of the guarantee to fifty per cent, and to adopt a resolution expressing their disapproval of the attitude taken by the Illinois Society. Brown also managed to do some negotiating with "a number of the Kentucky boys present." Later he sought to enlist the aid of President Melendy to help swing the Kentucky association in the right direction. He explained, "I feel that it is quite important that we use our best efforts to counteract this [Illinois] influence and believe if we can get some of the Societies meeting the next few days or weeks to pass a similar resolution to that passed by the Indiana Society that such action . . . may have considerable influence in checking the activities of the Illinois insurgents." Ottolengui agreed. "If we could get Pennsylvania to do the same as Indiana it would be a great help," he said.[47] At the same time, the *Items* editor began direct negotiations with Black.

Ottolengui forwarded proofs of his June editorial to the Illinois spokesman. He assured Black of his esteem and respect. He pleaded with Black, "Why not turn in and help reorganize the National in September?" He conceded that the Illinois group might be justified in seeking special consideration. "If you still think that Illinois and the other reorganized States should have a special voice in formulating the new plan, why not ask Dr. Patterson, the Chairman of our Committee, to call a meeting one or two days before the meeting of the National, and let us all meet together?" Black professed to be hurt by Ottolengui's charges. He vehemently denied any thought of sponsoring a rival association or of delaying reorganization of the National. "Our only object was to hasten, instead of delay, the national movement," he vowed. Both spokesmen spent considerable time endeavoring to clarify some incidental misunderstandings. The correspondence produced little else. Black insisted the Illinois action would not hamper or delay the national reorganization movement in any way. Ottolengui held to the opposite view. Ottolengui was unable to discover any basis for the Illinois action other than the objection to the two-thirds guarantee. This difficulty, the editor thought, had been obviated by his May editorial where he had explained that acceptance of the offer of constituent society membership was not contingent upon the guarantee. He begged the insurgents to meet with the Revision Committee at the Washington session. "For Illinois to attempt an entirely separate conference to do the work of a committee appointed by the National is certainly open to the interpretation of being disrespectful to that Committee," he reasoned. "It is commonly said now that Illinois is not willing to join the National Association unless Illinois itself does the reorganizing."[48] The exchange gained little for either participant.

While the National Dental Association reformers sought to frustrate or moderate the designs of the Illinois dentists and Arthur Black and his cohorts planned their conference of reorganized societies, the returns from other states continued to come in. Brown's endeavors to win Kentucky's backing went awry. His correspondent, President Melendy, told Brown that "things were in a bad shape there and that it was impossible to secure the passage of the Ohio resolution, but that he had been assured that they would pass a resolution expressing their sympathies." The Washington State Dental Society decided that it was too weak financially to accept the National Dental Association proposal. In South Dakota, the question was tabled. Brown's correspondent in Kansas, who signed himself "Old Shot," reported his state's decision to withhold affiliation. "They keep asking, 'In what way will it be a benefit to our society to belong to the National until we get the Journal?'" the writer explained. "Our society is made up of men from small country towns mostly and they think they must have some tangible evidence to show." From Iowa, too, came news of delay. In mid-June, North Dakota notified the secretary of the National Dental Association that its society was so weak and its membership so indifferent that no action was taken on the reorganization proposition and word came that Mississippi and Georgia societies subscribed to the reorganization "*provided* same is satisfactorily arranged at our Washington meeting."[49] The prospects of an overwhelming ratification of the proposed revision seemed more and more remote.

Neither Brown nor Ottolengui nor Arthur Black seemed quite willing to let matters take their course. Ottolengui, as a matter of fact, began to organize an informal conference among the interested men in advance of the meeting proposed by the Illinois Society. He wrote to Black, "This leads me to the thought that you might have the conference proposed by Illinois held in Chicago at that time, and I think if you would invite Dr. Patterson and the rest of our committee to be present with you, much would be done to advance the interests of

proper reorganization, and that is what we all want—is it not?"[50]
Ottolengui's projected conference did not materialize. He did, however, meet with Black and others in Chicago on Monday, July 1. One
of the Chicago negotiators telephoned Brown to summon him to join
the others toward the end of the week. Brown prepared for another
hasty trip.

When Brown arrived in Chicago the situation he confronted was
tense. Through the preceding weeks Brown's efforts to frustrate the
Illinois scheme had generated considerable resentment among the
Chicagoans. The tone of sweet reasonableness in Ottolengui's correspondence with Arthur Black had not mollified Black's feelings.
Black and his colleagues of the Illinois committee confronted the
National Dental Association workers with a long statement reciting
their grievances. This document reviewed the complaints already expressed in the Illinois resolutions establishing their committee. It
declared that the actions of Brown and Ottolengui were "absolutely
unwarranted and unjust." On this account, the document declared,
"it would be only fair to the Illinois Society" for Ottolengui to publish
an editorial doing justice to the Illinois position and for Brown to write
to the officers of the societies invited to the Illinois meeting expressing
his approval of the action of the Illinois Society. If the representatives
of the National refused to accede to these demands, the Illinois committee vowed to publish a full statement of the situation and forward
copies to all members of the National Dental Association and of the
reorganized state societies. The document, as it was presented to
Ottolengui and Brown, provided space for their signatures to indicate
their "hearty approval" of its contents. As Brown expressed it with
surprising moderation, "We were opposed to this proposition."[51]

Some eighteen dentists participated in the "long and earnest conference" that followed Brown's arrival in Chicago. Both sides aired
their grievances, but neither side made any substantial concessions of
principle. The representatives of the Revision Committee agreed,
however, to discontinue their efforts to prevent the meeting of the
reorganized states. Brown told his colleagues, "I do not believe they
expect to have a very large attendance from these re-organized Societies, but I have agreed to write several of those explaining recent
developments and advising if they feel sufficiently interested and can
send a representative . . . that we have no objection and it is possible

that this will work to the benefit of all." For their part, the Illinois contingent explicitly disavowed any intent to develop a rival national association. They agreed to present their recommendations through the official committee of the National Dental Association.[52]

On his return to Columbus, Brown set out to fulfill his side of the agreement. He wrote to the president of the Ohio State Dental Society asking him to dispatch a representative to the forthcoming Chicago conference. Next, Brown addressed a circular letter to leaders in other states recounting the recent developments. He informed his correspondents that the National Dental Association Committee's objection to the meeting of reorganized states had been waived. He encouraged attendance at the meeting. "If a goodly number of States are represented it may be possible that such strong recommendations may be presented to our Committee, that much good may come from this conference." [53]

Ottolengui went from Chicago to the annual meeting of the Wisconsin dental profession. He sent an exultant report to Brown. He had succeeded in winning "personal pledges to join the National" from "63 of the 75" present. The officers of the society thought they could raise the figure to around 250 by the time of the meeting of the National Dental Association in September. "I think I have discovered an important item in getting members," he went on. "I promised the Wisconsin men a certificate of membership which they could hang in their offices, and I told them this would aid their patients in distinguishing them from the quacks and men who take all they can get for nothing. I was loudly applauded and worked like a charm [sic]." Ottolengui outlined his understanding with Black. "He will abandon all argument for dollar dues and will have practically no important suggestions to make on Constitution and By-Laws," the editor announced triumphantly. He understood the Illinois conference would be principally concerned with methods of recruitment. Ottolengui concluded, "In other words, Illinois is now with us." Then he withdrew to his retreat at Brant Lake and set to work completing the long-deferred draft of by-laws to accompany the proposed constitution.[54]

Black, in the meantime, energetically resumed preparations for his meeting. The invitation list comprised a dozen states, all except Pennsylvania located in the Central Valley. Black's plans envisioned a morning session, an afternoon automobile tour of the Chicago park system, and dinner at the Chicago Yacht Club, followed by an evening session at which a report of the proceedings and recommendations of the conference would be adopted.[55]

On the eve of the conference, Brown summarized the progress of the reorganization movement to date. He listed twenty-two states and territories that had "voted to become components of the National." Although the summary was somewhat misleading (Kansas, for instance, was claimed despite its rejection of affiliation until foundation of a journal), it was not overoptimistic insofar as it implied that "the nucleus of a good National organization" seemed assured.[56] This may have served to forestall any effort at the Chicago conference to effect a substantial change in the Cleveland draft constitution.

The conference of reorganized state dental associations assembled in Chicago on July 20. After the furor that preceded it, the meeting itself, both in the numbers represented and in the recommendations it made, approached anticlimax. Twelve delegates from seven states attended. Illinois alone contributed four of the conferees. Ohio and Iowa each had two representatives; the other states, Michigan, Minnesota, Missouri, and Kansas, a single delegate apiece. Black told Ottolengui that Wisconsin and Nebraska had accepted the invitation but their delegates failed to appear.

Though few in numbers, the members labored earnestly. All told, the conference was in session for eight hours. Four general features of the reorganization problem were the subject of specific recommendations. The conference evolved a scheme for the proportional representation of the constituent societies according to the membership they enlisted in the National Dental Association. Under the same general head, the conference proposed that the votes to which a state was entitled might be divided among such delegates as actually attended. Secondly, the conference urged that delegates be made eligible to election as trustees. The meeting recommended that trustees be allowed to speak but not vote in the House of Delegates and that the Board of Trustees seek the prior consent of the House of Delegates for "the expenditure of any funds for other than current expenses." As its third proposal, to effect an increase in membership, the report of the conference stated, "It is the consensus of opinion of this gathering that dues of $1.00 per member will serve best." The fourth suggestion involved a series of measures to assist the state societies in convincing their members of the advantages of affiliation with the National Dental Association. These included the establishment of a monthly bulletin, which would be mailed to all members of the state societies; additional materials, which the secretaries of the state dental associations could send to their members; the recommendation that the state societies urge their components to discuss affiliation with the National as a special subject at their next meeting; and, finally, that the National Dental Association provide an annual membership certificate "suitable for framing." The recommendations of the conference of reorganized societies concluded with the declaration that, if the National adopted its suggestions, the states with which the conferees were familiar would join the National with at least as many members as the number set down after the name of each state, as follows: Ohio 600, Michigan 500, Wisconsin 300, Minnesota 300, Illinois 1,500, Iowa 700, Nebraska 200, Missouri 500, Kansas 200, Oklahoma 200, a total of 5,000.[57]

In private letters to Ottolengui and Brown following the conference, Black presented additional information regarding the proceedings of the meeting. He assured both men that the entire spirit of the meeting was such that the members of the Reorganization Committee could have no fault to find with it. He expressed confidence that, if the recommendations of the conference were adopted, the National would have a membership of not less than 10,000 within two years. Ottolengui's August editorial announced with satisfaction, "It is pleasant to report that all misunderstandings have been cleared up, and that Illinois will probably become a potent factor in building up a great national organization."[58] Most of the divisive issues had now been brought before the Revision Committee and the management of the National Dental Association.

Early in August, Brown was able to evaluate the reorganization situation with some confidence. To Burkhart he reported that twenty-one states and two territories had voted to become constituents of the National, but that some had taken more decided action than others. Brown claimed that "several other States give very encouraging reports of taking final action next year." For the current year, only West Virginia had still to be heard from. Within a month, West Virginia's dental society voted to become affiliated with the National guaranteeing that one-eighth of its membership would join the national body.

Brown was indefatigable in compiling his data—sometimes to the point of irritating his correspondents. W. G. Dalrymple of Ogden, Utah, reported his state's favorable decision in a brief note. He added, "Say Brown—for heaven's sake, make a record of this as it's at least the third time I've told you about it." [59] With the campaign virtually completed, only the final hurdle of the annual meeting itself remained to be surmounted.

At the Washington meeting, the effort at reorganization reached its climax. The passage of the change through the regular procedures of the Association seemed singularly undramatic. President Arthur R. Melendy announced, "I am credibly informed that twenty-five of the states have taken favorable action upon the [Cleveland] resolution and the Revision Committee may consider that they have sufficient support to warrant them in reporting the new constitution for your adoption." He gave the reform his blessing but issued a *caveat* regarding the financing of the new plan. A public meeting announced by Burkhart attracted a vocal crowd. Some of the objections raised by the debate seemed to require negotiation among a smaller group. Accordingly, a private conference between the Reorganization Committee and a number of state society officers met the following day. After a good deal of "back and filling," the reorganization plan as drafted by the Committee, with three important changes, was agreed to. One major point, upon which the state representatives insisted, reduced the dues to one dollar until the journal of the Association was established. The other changes demanded by the states can only be conjectured, for the *Transactions* and the dental press are silent on the subject. It seems safe to conclude that one of the alterations related to the service of the members of the Board of Trustees. The differences of opinion on this point have already been discussed. The constitution, as adopted, provided: "No member who has served one full term as a member of the Board of Trustees, shall be eligible for re-election on the board until a period of three years has elapsed, provided that this does not apply to ex-officio members of the board. (Resolved, That the present Council shall be members of the first Board of Trustees, and shall serve out their present terms, and they shall also be eligible for re-election for one full term of three years.)" This section clearly represented a compromise between the Black faction, who agitated to prohibit re-election, and the Reorganization Committee, who were dedicated to at least two full terms.[60]

The third change apparently had to do with the formula for proportional representation. In October, a month after the meeting, Brown discussed this matter with Burkhart. As the managing clique of the Association saw it, the problem was to prevent the domination of the National Dental Association by the enormous state societies of the middle west, led by the antagonistic Illinois organization. Brown advocated a steeply graduated formula for additional representatives. The section in the Washington constitution, however, provided for regular increases justifying additional delegates. The managing element of the National Dental Association was most anxious to avoid an open floor fight on the terms of the new document. Ottolengui suggested the private conference that has already been referred to. He explained to Arthur Black, "You know that an instrument as complex as this could be ruined by amendments made from the floor, by men who would only consider the clause under discussion, and not its general relation to the scheme as a whole." [61] In some fashion, at least an uneasy compromise was achieved.

The resultant document passed smoothly through the official channels of the annual meeting. In the Executive Council, J. D. Patterson, chairman of the Revision Committee, encountered little difficulty winning the acceptance of his report and a recommendation to the Association for adoption. Under the existing rules of procedure, the action of the general session was virtually automatic. On Thursday afternoon, September 12, 1912, the sixteenth annual meeting of the National Dental Association adopted the constitution and by-laws as prepared by the Revision Committee.

Two further steps remained to be taken. First, it was necessary to provide for the transition from the old plan to the new one. In the process it was necessary to appraise what they had done. Superficially, the first step seemed easy. On Friday the thirteenth, Dr. Patterson offered a resolution calling for a single meeting of the House of Delegates at the 1913 convention of the Association "for the election of officers, the appointment of committees, and such other business as may be necessary for placing the new constitution in operation, and the same members . . . shall serve as the house of Delegates at the session for 1914, and their terms of office shall begin thereat." The intricacies of accomplishing the transition, however, were already becoming evident. The Executive Council had already been obliged to consider the problem posed by the Maryland Dental Society, which had collected dues "with the understanding that the reorganization was to become effective" at the Washington meeting. The Council decided that societies that had decided to become affiliated and had increased and collected their dues with this action in view should be accorded the privilege of membership at this session of the Association.[62] A not-altogether-satisfactory expedient, this measure created only the first of the perplexities that had to be dealt with.

The problems of interpreting the new instrument can best be appreciated if the significant clauses are first described. The first article provided the name of the Association. The second announced the object. This was a new statement. It read, "The object of this association shall be to promote the art and science of dentistry." A second sentence elaborated revealingly on the means by which this aim was to be accomplished:

To achieve this [object] the association shall endeavor to unite the dental profession of the United States into one compact body, thus creating a power the units of which, working with a harmony of purpose, will foster fraternal relations and intercourse among dentists; safeguard the material interests of the profession; elevate the standards and improve the methods of dental education; secure the enactment and enforcement of just dental laws, while aiming at a unification of state dental statutes, and enlighten and direct public opinion in relation to oral hygiene, dental prophylaxis, and advanced scientific dental service."[63]

By contrast, the object enunciated in the Old Point Comfort constitution of 1897, declared its purpose "to cultivate the science and art of dentistry and all its collateral branches." It aimed "to elevate and sustain the professional character of dentists." Presumably by 1912 this latter objective had been attained. The later constitution enumerated a wider and more specific array of purposes. It seemingly assumed greater responsibilities than the Old Point Comfort constitution. But the 1912 charter only declared that the Association would endeavor to unite the dental profession. The consolidated or-

Relief Fund Seals of the American Dental Association

ganization, formed in 1897, vowed "collectively to represent and have cognizance of the common interests" of the profession, an evidently bolder stand.[64] Deeds, not words, best show the purposes of the Association, of course. Too much significance should not be read into an article that was virtually a preamble to the truly operative clauses of the constitution.

The 1912 constitution accomplished a revolution in the membership clause. Gone were distinctions between delegate and permanent members. All members of constituent societies (and, transitionally, such other individuals as might be elected) became members of the National Dental Association. This feature alone accomplished the overthrow of the domination of the Association by the permanent members. Furthermore, the large increase in membership necessitated some sort of representative system. This meant an inevitable dispersal of control of the Association affairs. The new constitution established "a business body known as the House of Delegates . . . , elected by the constituent societies." This group, according to Article

V, was directed to "elect the general officers . . . and a board of nine trustees, and . . . [to] transact all the business of the association, public, professional, or scientific, not otherwise provided for." In effect, the House of Delegates replaced the permanent membership in control of the affairs of the Association. The substitution of the Board of Trustees for the old Executive Council reduced the powers of that managing element, for the trustees only had charge of the property and of the financial affairs of the Association.[65]

The new governing instrument continued the existing division into three sections for the scientific deliberations of the society. Article VII explicitly provided for the continuance of the Southern Branch and allowed the House of Delegates to create such branch organizations as were deemed essential to the welfare of the National Dental Association and of the dental profession. Most of the other significant terms of the new constitution marked relatively little change from the existing order. An orthodox article set up the general officers of the Association. The former offices of recording and corresponding secretaries were now combined in the general secretary. The long-term significance of this change was concealed in part by the provision that this officer, like the others, was subject to annual election.[66]

One item showed a definite alteration in the proposals that had previously been made for the reform of the National Dental Association. This was the article relating to the constituent societies. It read, "State and territorial societies which have, or which hereafter may, become organized in conformity with the general plan of the National Dental Association, and which have declared their allegiance to said National Dental Association and which shall agree to the formation and perpetuation of the House of Delegates, shall be recognized as constituent societies."[67] Would-be constituent societies were now obliged to alter their organic law in accordance with the National Dental Association plan before they could become constituents. This necessity, added to other complications that became evident during the ensuing year, meant that completion of the reform of the National Dental Association could not be accomplished by 1913.

The adoption of the new constitution was greeted with delight in the dental press. The editor of the Dental Cosmos commented, "The need for reorganization has long been apparent. The plan under

H. C. Brown

R. Ottolengui

H. J. Burkhart

A. D. Black

F. O. Hetrick

E. S. Gaylord

Prominent Figures in the Reorganization of the Association

which our national body has been operated is a relic of the past that
long ago became obsolete as an effective scheme for conducting the
work of the National Association." Now, the writer went on, the
National Dental Association has not only been reorganized, "but
what is of greater importance, it is 're-nationalized.'" The *Dental
Brief* hailed the action as "the most important step taken in recent
years." Like the *Cosmos,* the *Brief* read greatest significance in the
membership clauses of the new instrument. Secondarily, dental
spokesmen acclaimed the prospects of an independent and official
journal. The *Monthly Bulletin,* published by the Illinois association,
related nationalization to "the publication of a broad gauge, independent dental journal. . . . Heretofore, most of our journals have
been more or less sectional in both principles espoused and in their
circulation." [68]

In Illinois, the official organ of the state dental society claimed
much credit for the reformation. Inspired by their accomplishments
at Washington, the Illinois leadership began at once to place their
state "in the forefront" in implementing the new plan. The Executive
Council held a special meeting in late September to outline the
procedure. Their objective was that Illinois should be the first to join
the reorganized National in a body. The Illinois Society informed its
members that National dues had been reduced from five dollars to
one dollar. For this annual fee, the member would receive a monthly
bulletin, a copy of the *Transactions,* and "a handsomely engraved
membership certificate." Finally, the Illinois Executive Council, to
minimize the cost to the individual member, "voted to ask each local
society to vote to send in to the Secretary of the State Society, $3.50
instead of $3.00, as heretofore, and the council will recommend that
the other 50 cents for the National be paid out of the State Society
treasury." Such strenuous appeals could not but yield results. Each
issue of the *Bulletin* proudly announced a "Roll of Honor" bearing
the names of component societies that had elected to support the
leadership in enlisting the entire state society membership in the
National Dental Association. [69]

Chapter XVII   REORGANIZATION ACCOMPLISHED

FOR HOMER C. BROWN, still the recording secretary of the National Dental Association, the transitional year began much as had former years. There were the usual details completing the business of the Washington meeting. There were the usual problems involved in establishing the committees for the coming year. But the autumn of 1912 was an unusually exciting season in the history of the United States. The din of political battle distracted the conduct of professional affairs, while Theodore Roosevelt marched at the head of his "Bull Moose" party. On election day, Homer Brown cast his ballot and went to his office to write to Burkhart. He reviewed the political situation and concluded that "things are going to have a general shaking up." He thought that Wilson and the Democrats would probably carry Ohio. Brown injected a canny note of caution, "All signs fail in dry weather and this is an ideal fall day, so we may all be surprised when the votes are counted." [1]

The presidential campaign constituted more than an incidental distraction. Frank O. Hetrick, incumbent president of the National Dental Association, was an ardent backer of Theodore Roosevelt. Brown found this ground for complaint. After the returns were in he confided to his friend, Thorpe, "He [Hetrick] has been so 'chucked full' of this 'Bull Moose' business that it has been hard for him to realize that he was President of the National and this has delayed some matters. . . . However, now that Teddy is relegated to the rear, at least for some long time I hope, it is possible that we will get down and get things cleared up in a short time."[2]

Brown himself had been far from idle. In addition to the ordinary routine of Association business, Brown sought to bring the Ohio State Dental Society into the van of the reorganization movement for the third year. He labored with the component organizations. He sought the aid of prominent dental leaders from outside the state, Thorpe, a former president of the National Dental Association, Hetrick, the incumbent, and Arthur Black. At its Cincinnati meeting in early December, the Society obligingly decided to join in a body. Brown also cooperated with the drive to secure funds for dental research. He had supported the scheme in the Executive Council. Now he helped in the selection of committee members and offered suggestions on both the procedure of the campaign and the problems to be investigated.[3] Far more than in previous years, the problems of the reorganization occupied the center of his attention from the beginning.

Much of the difficulty may be attributed solely to the tension generated by the rivalry between Brown and Arthur Black of the Illinois Society. Although the Washington meeting had presumably settled the differences among the reformers, Brown continued to view Black's activities warily. He tried to persuade Black to serve on the National's Committee on State and Local Societies and thus carry forward the work of reorganization. Brown explained his reasoning to Burkhart: "Explanatory, will say that I believe that we may get a better co-operation, by having some of these fellows work directly with us."[4] He could not conceal his disapproval of the Illinois dentist even in his ostensibly cordial communications. To some of his correspondents, Brown was more explicit in his disapproval of the Illinois campaign. To both Burkhart and Ottolengui, Brown complained that the Illinois package seemed to be "promising a great deal for one dollar."[5]

The element of personal antagonism in all of this is inescapable. Noting the energetic drive of the Illinois contingent to bring that state into line, Brown wrote to Ottolengui, "No doubt you have been impressed with the fact that they are not any too modest in assuming their part in this work." Ottolengui replied, "I quite agree with you that the Illinois people are taking considerable credit, but heaven knows, I don't care what they claim, if they only come in." Burkhart's response to a similar letter must have been more consoling. "I have known of his [Black's] modesty for some time," Burkhart said. "I am waiting for the proper time and place to puncture one or two of his bubbles. . . . It won't be too late next year if he and some others get too gay." [6] Brown's driving insistence on pushing through the reorganization against or over Black finally exhausted the patience of the genial Hetrick, who sought throughout to soothe ruffled sensibilities. At the same time, Black's determination to upset the ruling coterie of the National Dental Association strained many of his views and riled many of his correspondents. The clash of personalities served to heighten the difficulties inherent in the ambiguous arrangements that had been made for the transition from the old regime to the new.

A major dilemma involved the status of organizations that had agreed to enroll their entire membership in the National Dental Association at the Washington meeting. Were these societies, and those that took similar action prior to the Kansas City meeting of 1913, to be assessed dues under the new or the old constitution? The District of Columbia precipitated the issue by remitting dues for the 1913 meeting at the new rate of one dollar per capita. Brown wrote anxiously to Ottolengui who acknowledged the difficulty.[7] Arthur Black, too, had seen the problem. He told Brown, "There seems to me to be but one plan that will be satisfactory and will eliminate confusion, that is, for the dues of the National to be for the calendar year, and therefore to be due on January 1st." Black thought most of the reorganized state societies already had this arrangement and that minor adjustments could cover the situation of such states as Ohio, which held its meeting late in the year, as had already been done for states meeting in the spring. On this reasoning, Black announced, "We are, therefore, collecting now the dues for our local and state society and for the National for 1913." [8]

Black wrote optimistically of the acceptance of the new system among the large societies of the middle west. "It is practically certain that all of Missouri, Iowa and Indiana will join and there seems to be very little question but that all, or very nearly all, of the members of the other states of the central west will go in," he told Ottolengui.

Developments were coming too rapidly to suit the management of the Association. Brown set out to apply the brakes. He informed Black in December of the Ohio action in agreeing to join the National in a body. Then he exploded his bomb:

You understand that our dues to the National will commence with our next year's collection and in this there is just a little confusion since we meet at the close of the year. This is true with Arizona, D.C., and Md., and I will be very glad to have any suggestions that you may have to offer in connection with getting such discrepancies adjusted, that is, we will have to have a fixed period for paying dues and we will have to base our rating on the previous year, as I would seem to understand it. What is your advice about this?

Brown then administered a second stunning blow. "You understand that this next meeting is to be held under the old Constitution and By-Laws etc., but that the first House of Delegates is to meet on the third day and select place of meeting, elect officers, appoint committees, etc." [9]

The Chicago dentist did not at first appreciate the full significance of Brown's statements. To him, it seemed obvious that dues should be collected for the calendar year. This, he pointed out, was the procedure in Illinois. Similarly, the operation of the 1913 meeting under the old constitution came as a revelation to him. "Is it your understanding that there is to be but this single session of the House of Delegates next year?" he asked in some surprise. "I do not know exactly what action was taken to cover the point at the recent meeting, but it was my very definite understanding that the House of Delegates would have at least two sessions on two different days, in order that action might be taken to correct minor points in the By-Laws, in order to have them in better form." [10] Black's assurance gave Brown pause. In his uncertainty, he sought support from the other leaders of the National Dental Association. He encountered some disappointment. President Frank O. Hetrick proved dilatory in answering queries. Brown confided his grievance to Thorpe. A letter of December 27 had received no reply by January 7, he complained. [11] When Hetrick finally responded, his views brought little cheer to Brown. "You recently wrote that Arthur Black proposes to bring in 1700 members from Ill. at this year's meeting, but I cannot understand how this can be done under our arrangements," Brown declared. "If I am wrong in this, I hope to be straightened out. My understanding is that we must pay our dues for the 1913 meeting as heretofore, and if that is the case we cannot expect others on any different basis, except by action of the Association such as was done last year in order to meet a peculiar situation in Md." Under cover of this letter, Brown forwarded a draft of a long notice concerning the reorganization that he had prepared for insertion in the journals. "I feel that there is urgent need for something of this kind as some of our plans are not fully understood and am getting more or less inquiry from different sections," he explained.[12]

Brown's draft opened with an announcement of the adoption of the new constitution at the 1912 meeting. There followed a lengthy paraphrase of the document. Not until the third of the legal-size pages had been reached did Brown proclaim, "The 1913 meeting . . . will be under the provisions of the old Constitution. Annual dues, at $5.00 per member, will be collected as heretofore." Toward the end of the paragraph, the convening of the first House of Delegates was announced. Brown stated that it would be impossible for all the state societies to comply literally with all constitutional provisions for the first meeting of the House of Delegates, such as dues being paid prior to its representatives taking part in the business of the House. For that reason, it seemed best to him that the dues provision be waived at the first meeting, but that no constituent society should elect a greater number of delegates than that to which they anticipated their paid membership would entitle them. Before he closed, Brown also endorsed Black's proposal to make the calendar year the basis of dues assessments. Inasmuch as the first of the year had already passed, this suggestion seemingly precluded effective adherence of new constituents before 1914.[13] The position thus outlined could hardly have differed more from the interpretation upon which Black and the Illinois contingent had proceeded.

Brown underscored the differences in a letter forwarding a copy of the paper to Black. He called attention to the resolution adopted the last day of the Washington meeting. "This provides for one session of the House of Delegates . . . , but if there is other important business to be considered it no doubt would be possible to continue the meeting by recessing if not in any other way, but hardly believe such a procedure would be necessary." For the first time, Brown seems to have perceived a genuine difference in interpretation. "From re-reading your letter I am led to believe that you think this new arrangement becomes effective for the 1913 meeting, but this is not my understanding and it is quite important that some of these matters be straightened out," he said. Brown suggested the possibility of a conference in connection with a dinner honoring Truman W. Brophy in Chicago in late January.[14]

Black now appreciated the full effect of the official policy on the transition. In shocked dismay, he told Brown, "If it is a fact that a resolution was passed which provided that the dues for 1913 will be $5.00 and that the House of Delegates for 1913 will also be the House of Delegates for 1914, and such a resolution holds, then in my opinion the present movement for the reorganization of the National was killed at birth and we have spent much time and effort since then to line up several thousand state society members for nothing." He argued that the proposed arrangements, as interpreted by Brown, would delay reorganization. The enthusiastic new members could not join the National until 1914 and would "not be properly represented in the House of Delegates until 1915." Hopefully, Black added, "My personal view is that the resolution adopted does not justify your interpretation ... but exactly the opposite." He agreed that there should be a conference among the interested parties at the Chicago meetings.[15] In the meantime, he set to work preparing an elaborate counterstatement.

The first reaction coming from Black's typewriter sketched the origins of the misunderstanding. In his preliminary summary of the situation, Black tended to minimize the difficulty, saying that he thought constitutional difficulties could be circumvented if agreement was reached at the Kansas City meeting. Black's suggestion was that the Executive Committee of the National Dental Association tacitly admit that Ottolengui's resolution at Washington had been a mistake. The Committee should recommend that the reorganized societies continue the efforts they had begun. The Committee should also announce their intent to bring the objectionable resolution before the Association at the first general session. In the meantime, the secretary should be authorized to receive dues (presumably at one dollar) "conditionally ... giving the state societies the privilege of having the amounts paid returned on demand of any society, then the state societies may anticipate favorable action by the Association and proceed with their work for the reorganization movement."

Black then argued, somewhat tortuously, that the official program would leave control of Association affairs in the hands of the current limited membership until 1915, and, in the case of the Board of Trustees until 1918. Black proposed to overcome this problem by convening the House of Delegates, selected on the basis of one-dollar dues, at the outset of the 1913 meeting. The Executive Council and Executive Committee would report to the House until these older agencies had been superseded by a Board of Trustees. The three members of the Executive Committee, Black thought, might serve a one-year term as trustees and then be eligible to election to a full term. The balance of the retiring management could, of course, be chosen trustees for either two- or three-year terms by the House of Delegates.[16] In short, the Chicago organizer would be satisfied if the National Dental Association management abandoned its own arrangements for the transition and accepted his interpretation.

Black issued another circular to the representatives who had participated in the Chicago conference before the Washington meeting. In this document, he again explained the origins of the deepening misunderstanding that appeared to threaten the success of the reorganization. Black also interpreted the resolution concerning the transition to mean that the House of Delegates, as it would be constituted in 1913, would also be the House of Delegates in 1914. In other words, the societies affiliating with the National under the terms of the new constitution would not be represented in the House of Delegates until after 1914. Black contended that the clear will of the Association had been for the new plan to begin operation at the 1913 meeting.

Black closed this communication with a terse summary of the existing situation and a series of suggestions to the participants in the Chicago conference. "The questions at issue cannot be settled until we arrive in Kansas City," he observed. "An advance copy of a statement to be issued by the officers of the National requests all old members to remit $5.00 dues, and also requests all State Societies to vote to affiliate and to send in dues at $1.00 per member, the money to be held subject to the action taken at Kansas City. This statement also suggests that the first House shall be made up of one delegate from each state, regardless of its number of members." Black recommended that his colleagues comply with these suggestions. Encouragingly, he estimated that "at least four states will send dues to Kansas City covering their entire memberships, amounting to a little over three thousand members, and it is not unlikely that the number may yet exceed five thousand." [17]

Black's circular to the Chicago conferees goaded Brown into an extended rebuttal. Forwarding his effort to Hetrick, Brown complained, "This recent development is most unfortunate and the peculiar thing about it is, that I believe that every one can readily appreciate the impossibility of putting this plan into operation at once, with the exception of Black and possibly Volland of the Iowa society." [18]

In his rebuttal circular, Brown defended his course in the affair. He insisted that he spoke for the Reorganization Committee in his belief that to alter the arrangements already inaugurated "would seriously handicap at least three-fourths, if not more of our State Societies." He explained, "We take the position that no State Society can officially anticipate what action they may take until they meet and vote to become affiliated and then we assume that they must amend their Constitution and By-Laws to harmonize with the National and increase their dues in order to collect the National dues, and we are of the opinion that they could not collect such dues in time to transmit to the National for the 1913 meeting, even though there was provision made for them to come in at this particular time, but as above explained it has always been our understanding that the new conditions did not become effective until the close of the 1913 meeting." [19] Here Brown's discourse paused for breath, but he did not pause to consider that the answers to his objections had been effectively made in the procedure followed by Illinois and, as a matter of fact, in the actions he had induced the Ohio society to take.

As circular letters began to deluge dental leaders, feelings grew more intense. Black's resentment could hardly have been allayed by a letter he received from Ottolengui. "A good deal of what you say is perfectly sound, but quite some of it seems to me a little illogical," the *Items* editor confessed. "And now, my dear Dr. Black, I want to put a little proposition to you with all the courtesy in the world. Do you think it impossible that you may be wrong in this matter?" Otto-lengui argued plausibly that if the new system was to be in operation in Kansas City it had not been necessary to elect officers under the old constitution. "As last year's Council had charge of the Washington meeting, if the House of Delegates was intended to convene prior to the Kansas City meeting, please tell me why we elected a new Coun-cil." [20] Aside from his distortion of Black's position, Ottolengui's tone was hardly calculated to elicit a calm response from the Chicagoan.

Furthermore, Ottolengui entirely overlooked the fact that Illinois, and a number of other states as well, had been proceeding in the ex-pectation that the new constitution would be in force at Kansas City. These promoters had assured their members of membership in the National. Otto King of the Indiana State Dental Association told Black of his state's situation. "It will be a great mistake and an irre-parable thing for us in Indiana if the National does not organize in 1913. Our association has been canvassed and educated up to the point where we can harvest into the National a very large number, I believe two-thirds of our membership, but if we 'dilly dally' around for another year, the fire of enthusiasm will have died down and it will be a question as to what we can do." [21] S. C. A. Rubey, a prominent Missouri dentist, reported a similar situation in his state. "I have not seen the copy of the circular recently issued by Dr. Brown, but can see no process of logic whatever that would justify any attempt to defer the operation of the Agreement," he said. Rubey explained that he had been visiting district societies in Missouri assuring the dentists they could join the National on the basis of dollar dues. "I have written more than a thousand letters to dentists in the State, urging them to join their component society . . . telling non-members that member-ship in the District would carry with it membership in the National, and a great many . . . expect to attend the Kansas City meeting on the basis of my promise," Rubey claimed. "If this Agreement is now rescinded, I certainly see my finish in this State." Roscoe Volland placed Iowa in an even more extreme position. He told Black that the Reorganization Committee of the National was fully informed of the Iowa point of view. "My parting statement to both of these gentlemen was that if the Iowa Society could be assured that its delegates would be recognized and given full authority at the Kansas City meeting, and if our entire membership could participate in the meeting at

$1.00 dues, I was very positive that the entire membership of the Society could be voted in this year; otherwise, I was very sure that the matter would be dropped just where it is until the National finally made provisions which would stand." [22]

In Minnesota and Michigan conditions were somewhat more ambiguous. One Minnesota leader, F. J. Yerke, declared, "I should like to see things [in the National Dental Association] wholly different from what they have been in the past and from what they are likely to be in the future unless certain personal associations are dissolved, in other words, unless certain cliques are broken up." To this end, Yerke said he could "see nothing unfair or unreasonable in the resolution regarding the one-year House for 1913, in fact it seems the only thing to do in order to hurry the reorganization movement and give those who come in during 1913 a fair representation in 1914." Having thus seemingly placed himself in opposition to Black's views on procedure, Yerke swung back again to the Chicagoan's side. "Your resolutions would solve the difficulty but I fear they will be turned down, and in that event, we shall have no recourse other than the organization of a new association for those who are not in accord with the management of the one we have at present." [23] Brown, on the other hand, was receiving somewhat different intelligence from Minnesota. He had official notification that, due to state reorganization, Minnesota could offer only its "present 17 members and whatever additional members can be gathered individually." Brown's correspondent stated regretfully that his state had declined the opportunity to bring the entire membership into the National Dental Association "thus leaving Minnesota between the devil and the deep sea." [24]

Marcus L. Ward of the Michigan State Dental Society made a statement of the Michigan stand on the transition controversy that must have been a disappointment to Arthur Black. "To put the situation in a nutshell, we hold that the old order of things must prevail until we have complied with the new order of things in every detail, and this we cannot do until January First Nineteen Fourteen." Michigan, however, stood ready to assist in preparing for 1914, but would not complain if denied representation until it had fully met the conditions stipulated in the constitution. Black received similar word from G. C. Bowles of Detroit. Bowles endorsed Homer Brown's compromise proposals. He tried to convince Black that the changes could not be effected overnight. "I fear we will have to wait another year before your ideal of a paid-up membership of 7000 for the National will be realized. But doctor, we can afford to wait for such a consummation." [25]

Black began an ardent courtship of the Michigan leaders. He dispatched a long letter to Ward reiterating his views and rebutting what he understood the Reorganization Committee's arguments to be. "All we want . . . is a square deal and we certainly feel that we are not getting it," he declared. "In Illinois, we have had and still have but one object in view in this whole movement, namely: to see the National reorganized on a plan which will preclude the possibility of any clique of men ever gaining control. I am sure that I can speak for Illinois in saying that we seek neither office nor control." Ward remained unmoved. At last he grew impatient with Black's persistent pleas. "I have at hand yours of the 3rd," Ward wrote, "and will say that I have here also a communication protesting against creating a sentiment which will tend to band together a few States instead of doing that which will get together a great number of States, and it places the situation before me in a light which I feel justifies me in the stand that I have taken." Bowles, on the other hand, yielded to Black's persuasion. He estimated that Michigan could enlist some 350 to 400 members in time for the Kansas City meeting, if they would receive full membership privileges. He added cautiously that he would favor any plan that would assure the speedy and harmonious reorganization of the National and guarantee equal justice to all.[26] This concession from Bowles was, at best, a limited and ambiguous victory for Black.

Homer C. Brown, in the meantime, had also embarked upon a vigorous effort of his own. To all within range of his letters, Brown expounded and repeated his understanding of the reorganization difficulties. At the same time, he tried to refute the objections to the official policy raised by the Black coterie. Abandoning his proposal to waive dues, Brown now advocated admitting a single delegate from each constituent society for the first meeting of the House. This would, he reasoned, be strictly representative, especially if a large majority of the state societies voted to affiliate. He argued that few, if any, societies could collect dues before the 1913 meeting. He therefore proposed that, for purposes of organizing the first House, member-

ship for 1914 be anticipated by organizations that decided to affiliate
and that dues at $1.00, collected by associations before the 1913 ses-
sion, be accepted to cover membership until January 1, 1915. For the
further benefit of such organizations as collected $1.00 dues before
this sum could really support the full privileges of membership,
Brown again proposed to issue "Pledged Member" badges at the
Kansas City meeting. These badges would entitle the representative
to all privileges of membership except the *Transactions*. Brown declared that he was not wedded to any definite procedure, but that he
desired to be governed by the wishes of the majority. Accordingly, he
enclosed in both his general letters a series of questions designed to
elicit, from his correspondents, a consensus on a number of disputed
points.[27]

Brown also forwarded a draft of his queries to Arthur Black noting,
"I am extremely sorry any misunderstanding developed in connection
with this work and trust all points of difference may be readily adjusted." "Personally," he went on, "I expect to be guided by the answers to questions submitted and in this I trust whatever position it
is necessary to take will meet with the ultimate approval of all."
Brown offered to defer sending out his queries to the state society
leaders until Black had a chance to comment.[28]

Black telegraphed an immediate request that Brown suspend his
correspondence pending receipt of a detailed answer. When the letter
arrived, however, it merely reiterated Black's previous argument and
stressed again his conviction that a "square deal" was "impossible."[29]
While Brown may well have anticipated such a reaction from Black,
the replies from his other correspondents indicated widespread difference of opinion. In forwarding the material to Hetrick, Brown
hinted that he was dissatisfied with the president's position. Hetrick,
who had been endeavoring to placate the contending factions, replied
indignantly, "In the first place, let me say that my receiving a letter
from Dr. Black had no influence on my understanding of the reorganization matter at all." Hetrick suggested the possibility of two
classes of members at the 1913 conclave. He underscored his willingness to cooperate with the desires of the majority, however, and
vowed, "I will do all I can to get Black and the others satisfied." He
complained, "Now without any personal criticism whatever I want
to say it is a darn shame that this reorganization has had to drag along

to such a lengthy period. It should have been wound up and out of the way for some other progressive movement or movements." [30]

Brown's survey provoked an indignant answer from Mark F. Finley of the District of Columbia Society. His organization had already remitted dues for 1913 for its entire membership, "so that there is no question as to how the men in Washington feel about the matter of dues." Finley added, "We also feel that the Constitution goes into effect now although the old mode of conducting the meeting shall prevail at Kansas City owing to the necessity of Committees' preparing for the literary program for such meeting." He pointed out the source of much of the antagonism to the official procedure. "The resolution you now present for the first time so that any one outside of the Council can see it possibly would not have been passed had the full impact of it been understood at the time," he declared. "It was read but once in open meeting and then when there was considerable confusion." Brown's pained and defensive reply listed a series of places where the constitution might have been read. The objectionable resolution, he said, had appeared in the December issue of the *Dental Cosmos*.[31]

Finley's retort was fierce and bitter. He scolded Brown for passing on the rumor that the District of Columbia dues to the National had been paid from a surplus accumulated through fees collected from exhibitors of dental supplies at the Washington meeting. "Our dues are sufficient and were then sufficient to meet our obligations," he declared. "It is no one's business outside our membership and the exhibitors as to our handling of the exhibits at the time of the meeting of the National Dental Association in Washington, D. C." Brown ran for cover. He wrote a conciliatory letter to Finley and solicited the intercession of a friend in Washington to restore good relations.[32] Some of the other responses Brown received were equally disconcerting.

Burkhart answered Brown's questionnaire irritably. "Ottolengui told me of your seance in Chicago. I'd like to know who delegated so much authority to Black. The politics in the thing is what is responsible for these alleged misunderstandings." Burkhart announced his determination to carry on under the resolution of the Washington meeting. "This hair-splitting makes me tired, when I know what is back of the whole business," he growled. "Black may hear some plain things before he gets through. I've kept quiet and let things drift so as not to disturb the harmony of affairs, but he must not crowd too hard." Under the same cover Burkhart forwarded another letter, which he authorized Brown to use officially. This missive opened with a staunch defense of the actions of the management of the National Dental Association and a vigorous attack on its critics.·So far the contents must have been the occasion of some satisfaction to Homer C. Brown. But Burkhart then came out in favor of two classes of members for the 1913 meeting. He moved closer to Brown's position in advocating a House made up of a single delegate from each affiliated state "so that a combination of a few large States may not be able to control the Association."

B. Holly Smith wrote, "I am submerged by typewritten copy, for which you are partly responsible. I am greatly disturbed at the developments in the National situation. It seems to me that somebody is trying to make trouble, which I sincerely hope can be averted." Smith said he would answer Brown's queries after he had heard from some of his colleagues on the Council. He favored a conference to iron out the misunderstandings. "Correspondence is very unsatisfactory and categorical questions and answers do not always lead to the wiseest solution," he said.[33]

Hetrick continued his efforts to moderate Brown's attitude. He quoted with approval a letter he had received from Arthur Black. "'Where is the wisdom in keeping these [dollar-dues] men out with a lot of red tape?'" Hetrick declared, "I agree with him in this respect. We will land more of the Middle West States than we will in the course of 8 or 10 years if we don't." He urged that the deliberators try to forget personalities and work for an equitable solution to the difficulties. Brown remained unmoved by Hetrick's pleas. He denied on behalf of his colleagues the imputation that personalities impeded the progress of the work. Hetrick resorted to plain talk. "First, let me say that my reference to personalities was not intended for the council and reorganization committee, but was intended for you," he began. "If you don't like a man, you can't see any good in him." Hetrick added, "Now you know you do not particularly like either Black or Ottolengui, and they have a cordial dislike for each other and you, darn your old picture, are apt to view with disfavor either or both of their recommendations and if I have included the Council and Committee, cut it out and take it as a personal shot, for I do not even know what the rest think."

When Hetrick turned to consideration of the reorganization difficulties, he assumed an independent position. "I agree with Black in some things and disagree with all of you in some others," he said. "Now don't get up on your hind legs and howl that I am not working with you for that is what I am coming to," he went on. "If I don't write you as long a letter as you do me, you will think I am not giving you proper consideration." The president then turned to a consideration of "the whole bone of contention." In his analysis, this seemed to turn on the question of 1913 dues and the timing of the change-over from the old to the new constitution. In fairness to the officers elected at Washington, Hetrick insisted that the transition could not be accomplished earlier than the time settled at Washington. On this account, Hetrick reiterated his desire for two classes of members and endorsed the idea of "Pledged Member" badges to identify those joining under dollar-dues. The House of Delegates, he thought, should be constituted according to paid memberships. This would give the reorganized states a "slight advantage," but he considered that this would not be too objectionable to the other states.[34]

Burkhart, during March, had been working toward a compromise solution that would make it possible to clear matters up when the Association met for the 1913 session. He consulted with Ottolengui and Gaylord of the Reorganization Committee; he corresponded with Arthur Black. He concluded that the best arrangement would be to have two classes of members so far as dues were concerned and to admit one representative from each constituent society to the first House of Delegates. On April 14, Burkhart reported agreement with Ottolengui and Gaylord on a modification of his proposal and sought Brown's opinion before putting the matter up to Arthur Black. On the same day, Hetrick dispatched another earnest plea for his proposition. "Darn it all, I know that if you are going to stick strictly to the letter of the law, that you can't do some of the things at this meeting that I suggested, but I am reminded of the fellow who was put in jail for some minor offense. He sent for a lawyer who told him they could not put him in jail for that offense. He looked at the lawyer for a moment, kind of dazed, and then said, 'I guess that's so! But how in hell did I get in here then?' "[35]

Homer Brown nevertheless stuck to his guns. He took comfort in the fact that Black seemed to be moderating his position somewhat. In a letter of April 18, Black reiterated his views, but acknowledged, "We recognize that the officers of the National may think it best for that body not to meet our views, and if so, we will accept the situation."

Brown triumphantly informed Burkhart of this concession. At the same time, he argued strenuously against Hetrick's proposition for two classes of members. Brown suggested consulting a parliamentarian for a solution to the difficulties.[36]

Burkhart's patience was wearing thin. "This whole business is in a chaotic state and appears no nearer a solution than some months ago," he complained. He refused to entertain the idea of consulting a parliamentarian. He declined Brown's invitation to confer in Columbus with Black. "I might go to Cleveland," Burkhart said grudgingly, "but I don't want to spend the time." He added, "Perhaps the best thing in the end will be to put off the organization another year, and see if we can't get some proper definite understandable action in Kansas City, and formulate an up-to-date simple and satisfactory plan of procedure. We had better let matters rest than make a fall at the start." Black and Hetrick continued to maintain their stands. Brown turned to Ottolengui for support. He found the New York editor still antagonistic to equal representation of all states.[37] The situation may have looked disheartening to Homer Brown, but then came news of occurrences at the annual meeting of the Illinois State Dental Society that put a different face on matters.

The official report of the Illinois session presented an undramatic appearance. Brown's private informants gave a somewhat different picture. According to a "confidential letter," Brown told his friend Thorpe, Black had experienced a rebuff at the Illinois meeting. This news prompted Brown to undertake a special trip to Indiana's annual session. "I found Black in a different attitude . . . and we got a good deal nearer together on several points than we have ever been," Brown exulted. "I never have been willing to assume that he carried Illinois in his vest pocket, although many people have given him credit for having full control of affairs in his state. He banks very positively on the action of Missouri and Iowa." "Your Chicago friend thinks he owns Ills & Mo, but he dont, not by a darn sight," Thorpe replied. "I hear he is ambitious to be Secy of the NDA."[38]

Brown confided to Thorpe that he thought the news "might have some little significance with matters at Kansas City." "Not that I have any 'lightning rod' up, but you know I have had quite a scrap on my hands with some people in regard to this Re-organization work and have met with more or less opposition from Arthur Black," he explained. "The fact that Black met with defeat in Illinois, and that something like this has come our way might have a good influence in satisfactorily adjusting some of these differences." The next month was to reveal the accuracy of this prediction. News of Brown's appointment to the Ohio State Board of Health by Governor James M. Cox seems to have provided the impetus for a movement to name him to the presidency of the National Dental Association. So far as the reorganization movement was concerned, all parties involved seem to have adopted the policy announced by Burkhart. He declared, "I'm going to waste no more time over it till I get to Kansas City." [39]

On the day preceding the opening of the momentous Kansas City convention of the National Dental Association, the Executive Council, the Executive Committee, and "those interested in formulating the new rules" conducted the most important business transacted at Kansas City. It was at this conference that the major differences of opinion regarding the transition were finally composed. Only the results of the deliberations of this unofficial gathering are of record. The conferees agreed upon a series of resolutions to govern the transition. These were duly endorsed by the Executive Council at its first official meeting shortly before the annual session convened.

The settlement compromised the differences that had so agitated the leadership of the profession through the preceding winter and spring. The conferees decreed (and the Association in general session agreed) that the officers and Executive Council should manage the convention as they had in the past except that the Council should present its reports to the House of Delegates after it was organized instead of the general session as had previously been the case. The meeting decided that the first House of Delegates should consist of one delegate from "each state society which has voted to affiliate with this association." The resolutions provided for the first meeting of the House of Delegates on Wednesday, July 9. This provisional House was to choose the place of meeting and the officers and a full Board of Trustees, who would hold office for one year only. All of these decrees violated the letter of the constitution or of the Washington resolution governing the transition. The next item in the compromise therefore explicitly stipulated that the new constitution and by-laws "shall be in full force as applied to the 1914 meeting." Dues for 1913 were specifically declared to be five dollars covering membership "up to January 1, 1914." It was agreed that all members of affiliated societies should have all privileges of membership without payment of dues, except the right to receive the *Transactions* for 1913. As a final gesture, the Council scheduled a meeting for the afternoon at which it proposed to "clean up the business of the old association before the House of Delegates takes charge of the new." [40]

In this way, largely before the meeting actually opened and largely outside the constitutional framework of the Association, the passing of the old order and the inauguration of the new occurred. The proceedings of the several parts of the annual session, however, are not without interest. First, the regular proceedings served notice that the current challenges to the profession in the domains of research, education, philanthropy, and publication remained unanswered. Secondly, the deliberations of the House of Delegates indicated that the process of revision was not yet completed. And, finally, the actions of the new professional government showed the same old tendency to avoid, defer, or temporize when confronting divisive questions.

Hetrick in his presidential address confined himself largely to considerations other than the reorganization. Here his intervention was unnecessary. Hetrick recalled the Association to the three significant projects that had been held in abeyance during the reorganization controversy, the establishment of an independent official publication, the provision of relief for aged and indigent dentists, and the sponsorship of scientific research. He suggested the sale of life memberships as one means of accumulating funds to begin the publication of a journal. Whatever method was adopted, he declared, the project should be delayed no longer than the first of 1915. He rather perfunctorily commended the relief fund campaign, placing the major responsibility on the individual dentist to aid his colleagues in distress. With much more enthusiasm, Hetrick warmly advocated increased support for the drive to raise research funds. Hetrick concluded by calling attention to the two recent recognitions of dental prestige. The Association had sponsored the accumulation of dental equipment to fit out the expedition for the exploration of Crocker Land, sponsored by the American Museum of Natural History, the American Geographical Society and the University of Illinois. Participation in this endeavor, the president implied, placed the National Dental Association in the ranks of the sponsors of scientific advance. It likewise represented a signal recognition of the importance of dental care to the maintenance of health. Hetrick ended his discourse with an allusion to Brown's appointment to the Ohio State Board of Health. The Committee on the President's Address endorsed Hetrick's recommendations.[41]

Once the resolutions governing the transition had been adopted, there was little for the general sessions of the membership to do but listen to a series of papers and reports. The most significant of the latter was Weston A. Price's account of the drive for a Scientific Foundation Fund. Price summoned the dental profession to take its place "in line with all the great professions of the world" and join in the great crusade for better health conditions. A number of large laboratories had tendered free facilities for dental research, Price continued. What was needed was funds for the support of the workers. He pleaded for contributions to inaugurate the work and to show potential donors of large grants that the profession itself was dedicated to its scientific development. Price warned that if dentistry did not act, the medical profession would assume the work on dental disease. Price flung out a ringing challenge: "Do you want insignificant, unsatisfactory work done in a haphazard way in a few laboratories? No!—we all want a magnificent organization with a central institute, or with institutes in different parts of the country . . . so that the entire world will look to the dental profession for help, and will acknowledge it as having wrought the greatest single service for the emancipation of humanity from its various afflictions." [42] The general session, having surrendered its powers, could only listen and applaud.

The Executive Council received a variety of reports, but found little need for action. The Journal Committee, for example, repeated its performance of earlier years, reporting insufficient funds, which seemed unlikely to increase until the reorganization had been completed. The Committee asked to be continued with directions to report at the next meeting. The Executive Council endorsed the establishment of a committee to investigate the possibilities of the Association undertaking to insure its members against unjust malpractice suits. Other actions taken by the Council were similarly indecisive. Perhaps the most significant service performed by the Council was the preparation of a list of accredited state representatives to the first provisional House of Delegates.[43]

The slate of delegates included members from thirty-one states, the District of Columbia, and the U. S. Army Dental Corps. Two delegates were accepted from California and two from the District of Columbia, making a total of thirty-five voting members at the initial sessions of the new governing body of the National Dental Association. Hetrick and Brown participated in the deliberations as president and secretary. Burkhart took part in the debates also, presumably as chairman of the Executive Council prior to his election to the first Board of Trustees.

Most of the business at the first two meetings involved alterations in the constitution and by-laws. These amendments largely represented adjustments that the transitional period had already shown to be desirable. Two significant additions were made to the document. A series of amendments to the constitution and by-laws added a "State Society Officers' Section" to the three scientific sections provided for. Sponsored by Arthur Black, this new section furnished an agency through which the national association could foster the activities of the state organizations and, in turn, expand its own membership. Another major innovation erected within the National Dental Association a Scientific Foundation and Research Commission in accordance with the recommendations of Weston Price.

Arthur D. Black created a brief moment of drama by proposing a pair of amendments to the by-laws, relating to the election of officers and trustees. The principal feature of Black's proposal was to provide for nominations by means of informal balloting. Secondarily, the slate of three trustees chosen each year would be the three nominees receiving the highest number of votes after the nominating ballot. These suggestions occasioned considerable discussion before they were tabled. In spite of the rebuff, Black engineered the adoption of a resolution that would permit amendments to the constitution and by-laws to be introduced and acted on at the 1914 meeting without the necessity of obtaining unanimous consent. The measure constituted notice to the Association that the process of altering the constitution was not yet complete.[44]

The election of the first officers under the new regime produced the old charges of political maneuvering. Harvey Burkhart's brother, A. P., declared, "I saw more politics than ever before." Homer C. Brown was chosen president after his name was placed in nomination by the president of the Ohio State Dental Society, Weston A. Price. Brown wrote subsequently, "I was so busy and so taken back with the very high honor paid me by the Association that I may have neglected to personally thank you for your very generous words in presenting my name. I did not know what the plans were in reference to nominating me but it certainly could not have been better arranged for as President of the State Society you naturally could speak officially for Ohio."

Brown's election gave rise to rumors of a deal. A. P. Burkhart confided that he had aspired to the post of general secretary if Brown was giving it up, but "when too late I learned you had combined with Black," he added. "Of course Black, as you know, not only wanted to defeat you for Secy. but tried his best to kill you for the Presidency, but could not quite land the votes to carry out both plans." Brown coolly denied any bargain with Black for the presidency, and, indeed, it seems unlikely that any was necessary. The forces behind Brown's candidacy had been at work for some time. So far as can be ascertained, they were not at all friendly to Black.

The contest for the office of general secretary produced similar charges. Arthur Black nominated Otto U. King of Huntington, Indiana, a prominent worker in his state society, for the post. King was elected. A. P. Burkhart warned Brown, "The office of Secy. is mighty important and Black knows it, consequently he secured a man so I'm told whom he can control absolutely." Brown heard the same charge from Ottolengui. To both his correspondents he returned the same answer. "While it is true that Dr. Black presented Dr. King's name for General Secretary, I think it is also true that most every one understood that he wanted Dr. Volland for Secretary, and Dr. King knows this. He also knows that I had something to do with him being definitely decided upon and I have every reason to believe that we will work along in full accord." Evidently there was much political maneuvering, and somewhat more complicated than A. P. Burkhart's summary: "It is simply a shifty New York City trying to out-general Chicago." [45] The slate of trustees was headed by Harvey J. Burkhart. Apparently, the veteran administrator was not yet ready to lay aside the onerous duties of which he had complained before the meeting. The panel of officers selected by the first House of Delegates did not seem to indicate any radical change in the practices, control, or policies of the National Dental Association.

After the election of officers, Black again assumed the center of the stage in a move to encourage the president and general secretary to undertake publication of an official bulletin to be sent to the members of the Association. Homer Brown, not to be outdone, suggested that in order to stimulate affiliation of all societies, it would seem advisable to send this bulletin to the membership of every state dental society, regardless of whether or not they were component societies. After a further amendment placing the bulletin under the jurisdiction of the Publication Committee appointed by the Board of Trustees, the policy was adopted.[46]

One further note of drama appeared in a bitter controversy over the activities of the Legislative Committee during the preceding year. The precipitating factor seems to have been the enmity between Emory A. Bryant and the partisans of Williams Donnally, a feud that had smoldered among the dentists of Washington for some years.

The affair was, as Otto King later commented, "a disgraceful wrangle." [47] That it arose during the meetings of the first House of Delegates suggested that the new system of professional government had not ushered in a Utopia. Indeed, the Executive Council, as well as the successor bodies, had dodged the issue by seating delegates from both of the squabbling District of Columbia factions.

The Board of Trustees behaved mainly as a provisional or caretaker body. They decided to allow the general secretary fifty dollars per month for stenographic assistance, but deferred the determination of the salary of the general secretary until the next year.[48] The House of Delegates abdicated its right of ratifying committee nominations. The Board of Trustees delegated its responsibilities to an *Ad Interim* Committee. These gestures might have led to a reappearance of autocratic direction of the National Dental Association within the framework of the new system. The full dimensions of the change remained in doubt.

Through the ensuing year, there was little public discussion of the details of the new constitution. Most comments tended to praise the achievement in general terms. Those accounts that probed more deeply into the matter emphasized the provisions for a journal and the drives to raise funds for needy dentists and for research.[49] All three of these projects made substantial gains during the year. Otto U. King took hold of the bulletin proposal enthusiastically. His ideas for its development show that he considered the bulletin an embryonic journal. King arranged for short articles. "I wish we could get two or three of the best men (writers) in our profession to give us an article say 150 words [*sic*] on our duty to humanity in reference to the Oral Hygiene movement." He elaborated on the qualities he sought, "fellows who can give us good sledge hammer blows of argument, so that we may all be awakened to the important place we occupy relative to preventive medicine."

The major problem confronting King was the compilation of a mailing list. While waiting for the state secretaries to submit these lists, King observed that there was immediate need for communicating directly with the state officers. He considered issuing a special bulletin explaining the reorganization procedure. By late September, however, eight states had forwarded the names of some 4,000 practitioners. A week later the number of states had increased to ten and the names to more than 6,000. In mid-October, nearly 15,000 names were in the secretary's files. Preparations took another month, but at last all was in readiness. The first issue of the *Bulletin of the National Dental Association* was issued on Saturday, November 22, 1913. King wrote exultantly to Brown:

Here are some facts that will show you the magnitude of this first bulletin. It took fifty-four mail sacks and several boxes to contain them. It took a two-horse dray to haul them to the post office. . . . These bulletins in their envelopes, if piled in a stack, one on top of the other would reach a height of over a quarter of a mile. If corded up in a pile, it would have made a stack four feet high and over two hundred feet long. If placed end to end, they would have reached approximately three miles in length.

By the time the third issue was off the press, King was thinking in terms of "a colored cover of good, extra-heavy enameled paper. . . . I would like for us to so plan our bulletin and its general make-up, so that our aim shall be that we will gradually work it up to a magazine in appearance," he said.[50]

The Relief Committee commanded equally energetic response. Rodrigues Ottolengui suggested the issuance of a Christmas seal and the scheme was tried out so successfully that it earned about $3,500 for the Relief Fund. This modest drive inspired its establishment on an annual basis, the returns from which have steadily increased over the years.[51] The work of the Scientific Foundation and Research Commission moved forward appreciably during the year. Research workers were hired to assist three projects in the fall. At that time, pledges amounting to $17,000, about half the estimated annual needs, had been received. The second general session of the Association at Rochester heard reports from the directors of the projects financed by the funds of the Research Commission.[52]

None of these achievements can be attributed directly to the altered constitutional set-up. Additional changes in the organic structure of the National Dental Association were introduced at the Rochester meeting in 1914. After these amendments had been added to the constitution and by-laws, the modern Association had assumed its shape.

Homer C. Brown's presidential address at Rochester in 1914 reviewed the activities of his administration and advanced some suggestions as to the future course of the profession. Brown estimated that he had traveled 10,000 miles visiting the meetings of state dental societies on behalf of the National. In addition, he had dispatched night letter telegrams of official greeting to those organizations he had been unable to attend in person. He had likewise sought recruits for organized dentistry among recent graduates of dental colleges through correspondence addressed to the deans of the schools. He reported with pride that he had attended the meeting of the Southern Branch of the Association, held jointly with the Georgia State Dental Association. In an address before the two organizations, he advised the discontinuance of the Southern Branch. The Branch unanimously adopted his recommendation. After relating this negative accomplishment, President Brown devoted the remainder of his remarks to the broader problems facing the profession.

Foremost of these difficulties was the establishment of an official journal for the National Dental Association. The prospect of a subscription to the official journal had been a big selling point in the recruitment campaign of the preceding years. Still the management of the Association approached the step reluctantly because of the financial dangers involved. Brown seemingly shared these fears. He emphasized the necessity of increasing the annual dues to cover the added expense of publication. Conditional on that increase, he offered two alternative courses of action. The first contemplated an immediate increase of dues to $2.00 and the inauguration of the journal by the first of 1915. Brown feared the effects on the membership of an early increase in dues. Secondly, he thought it possible to continue issuance of the *Official Bulletin*. By further improvement of this medium, he believed a change of title and a switch to quarterly publication might be warranted. Such a procedure would avoid the criticism that would naturally follow an increase of dues for the second year, he explained. For the management of the journal, Brown recommended the establishment of a commission of fifteen members under the control of the Board of Trustees. He pointed out that the constitution charged the trustees with the responsibility of publication, but since the Board was a more or less changeable body due to the constitutional limitation to three-years' service, he thought a commission would serve the needs of continuity better.

Dr. Brown considered other perennial problems. He urged elevation of dental educational standards. He praised the Research Commission's work. He declared that the military status of dentists should be at least equivalent to that recently accorded the Veterinary Corps. Provided it could be undertaken without increase of dues beyond that necessitated by publication of an official journal, the president favored the Association offering to defend its members against unjust malpractice suits.

A final series of propositions related directly to the administration of the Association. Brown urged clarification of the ambiguous relationship with the National Mouth Hygiene Association. He proposed resolution of the difficulty posed by recognition of two societies from the District of Columbia and from California. In order to give the House of Delegates time for thorough study and thoughtful consideration of the President's Address, Brown suggested that it be printed and distributed in advance of its delivery. Brown's recommendations regarding the committee system were specifically of a practical character. He suggested amendment of the by-laws to allow continuance of committees for which there was a demonstrated need. He thought some committees might be consolidated. Brown advocated the creation of a general conference committee to cooperate with related organizations. Brown believed that the trustees should be exempt from the prohibition of election to general office of members of the House of Delegates. A final proposal envisioned creation of an office of president-elect. His experience of the past year, plus the example of the American Medical Association and a number of state medical organizations, argued the utility of providing a training period before the chief position in the society was assumed.[53]

The hastily-convened Committee on the President's Address echoed Brown's approval of the oral hygiene movement. The Committee proved more circumspect when dealing with matters of immediate import to the Association. The Committee report advised against undertaking publication of a journal in 1915. This recommendation reminded the House of Delegates that there would be no regular annual meeting in 1915, the Association having accepted an invitation to merge its session with an international congress at the Panama-Pacific Exposition in San Francisco. On this account, the Committee held it would not be advisable to increase dues for the coming year. The Committee referred most of the other suggestions in Brown's address to the appropriate committees of the Association.[54]

At the Rochester meeting in 1914, the busiest committee was undoubtedly the Committee on Amendments. To this group was sent Brown's proposal regarding committee changes and creation of the office of president-elect. Early in the session, Arthur D. Black, again representing the Illinois organization, submitted a series of amendments that were likewise referred to the Committee on Amendments. One of the proposals involved the establishment of geographic districts from which the trustees would be elected. On Black's motion, the Committee was also directed to present a tentative regional division of the country in connection with the action to be taken on the amendment.

The deliberations of the Committee on Amendments produced few surprises. Somewhat startling was the decision of the House of Delegates to reject an amendment giving to the delegates the power to accept new constituent societies. As a result, the trustees retained this authority. Other actions by the House on recommendations of the Committee more nearly followed the expected pattern. One amendment provided for dividing the delegation where a state or territory contained two constituent societies. The clause providing for branch societies was repealed. The nation was divided into nine Trustee Districts each to be represented by a trustee. Caucuses of the district's delegates nominated candidates for the office from their district. Brown's proposal for a president-elect was lost in the Committee.[55]

With the adoption of the 1914 amendments, the National Dental Association was launched on its modern career. The altered membership clauses opened the way to a vastly increased membership. Indeed, the Association could now realistically aspire to enrolling the great majority of the dentists of the country. Regional distribution of the trusteeships and representation in the House of Delegates based on state and territorial affiliations assured a truly national organization. The new structure in itself disposed of none of the perennial questions facing the profession, while the changed system of professional government and the tremendously enlarged membership imposed added responsibilities and created new perplexities.

1931–1943

1943–1956

1956 to date

Central Offices of the American Dental Association

PART THREE

Professional Organization in Contemporary America

THE REORGANIZATION of 1913 laid down the basic structure that still characterizes the American Dental Association. It furnished the means for meeting the major problems of professional organization as they were then understood. But in itself, the new constitution solved none of the problems of dentistry. As a matter of fact, the new structure soon raised a novel array of administrative problems. The enlarged membership challenged the Association to justify itself by an ever broadening variety of services to the members, by assuming leadership of the profession, and by representing dentistry before the public. The history of the Association since the reorganization encompasses the efforts to meet the perennial problems of the profession within the new framework and, in addition, the attempts to cope with new difficulties created both by the new form of organization and by changing conditions in the nation.

President Truman signing the Dental Research Act, June 24, 1948

NDA Research Institute, Cleveland
Association's first research laboratory

Division of Chemistry, Council on Dental Therapeutics

National Institute of Dental Research

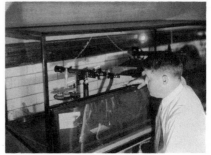

National Bureau of Standards

Sites of American Dental Association Research Activities

Chapter XVIII   THE ASSOCIATION AND ITS MEMBERS

ADOPTION of the new system of government provided the means for enrolling all ethical practitioners in the National Dental Association. The problem of accomplishing this end remained to be solved. Membership figures over the years indicate a fairly regular growth. Homer C. Brown, the Association's president in 1914, boasted that the National had more than 12,000 members. The boom years of the period of World War I brought new increases so that by 1920 some 25,000 dentists belonged to the Association. The rising membership curve faltered briefly during the post-war slump, but by 1925 the 30,000 mark had been attained. The Great Crash of 1929 wrought no immediate effects. Thirty-six thousand practitioners paid dues in 1930. During the early 1930's enrollment fell off somewhat, reaching a low of barely 30,000, less than half the profession, in 1933. Thereafter, the upward climb was resumed. Recovery of the 36,000 peak was accomplished by 1935. By the end of the decade the membership had soared to 46,000. The decade of World War II saw the addition of nearly 20,000 more dentists to the ranks of the Association. By that time, according to one estimate, about 85 per cent of the country's dental practitioners belonged to the Association. In 1955, the 75,000 mark was attained. Three years later, the administration claimed a further 15,000 members, making a total of some 90,000 dentists.[1]

Such numbers did not join the Association automatically. The generally upward tendency seems to have persuaded the national leadership to leave recruitment in the hands of the state organizations. The Association, however, was not entirely unconcerned. Beginning in 1926, it sponsored an annual conference of the officers of constituent societies at which mutual problems, including those of membership, might be discussed.[2] In 1927, President Henry L. Banzhaf tried to stimulate further interest on the part of the national organization. He recited the advantages accruing from a larger membership, and stressed the obvious fact that increased membership meant increased income, which, in turn, would permit improved services to the members.[3] In spite of Banzhaf's attempt to rouse interest in a program to build a larger roster of members, the American Dental Association continued, through the rest of the twenties, to rely on the efforts of the state organizations.[4] Not until the Depression began to make itself felt in the membership lists did the Association move to create a permanent program to attract members.

Robert T. Oliver, presiding over the annual session of 1931, urged the Board of Trustees to initiate a special membership drive to offset the losses due to depressed economic conditions. He was distressed by the declining numbers, especially since he felt that the Association needed the political and financial strength of an enlarged and growing membership to fight off any attempt to impose on the profession a system of panel or state dentistry.[5] In the following year, the first steps toward the modern membership program of the American Dental Association were taken. President Martin Dewey took up the subject in his address before the general meeting and in his report to the House of Delegates. With less than fifty per cent of the profession on the rolls of the organization, he declared, the Association's record was one that no business organization would have tolerated for a minute. He pointed out that the large number of practitioners unaffiliated with any society represented a menace to organized dentistry. In two states, Dewey reported, unorganized dentists had blocked legislation supported by dental societies. Like Banzhaf before him, Dewey concluded that "if the American Dental Association wishes to do the greatest good for the profession and the public, the Association must follow and develop some plan to make membership in the Association attractive to the non-members."[6]

The main proposal considered by the House of Delegates at the important 1932 meeting was submitted by A. R. Ross of the Indiana State Dental Association. This so-called Indiana Plan was an elaborately developed scheme for canvassing the profession. Since some of the features of the proposal have proved significant in the development of the Association's services to dentistry, in addition to its usefulness in stimulating membership, it is worth examining in some detail. The central feature of the plan recommended the establishment of a permanent Committee on Organization and Membership to administer a continuing drive for new members. This new standing committee would be assisted by an extension of the annual conference of state society officers to include the local, or component, societies. Both the committee and the conferences would make recommendations involving organizational changes to encourage more applications for membership. The chief incentive behind the membership drive would be an annual contest among the constituent societies.

The Indiana Plan suggested a number of expedients to assist in a thorough canvass of the profession. It proposed that each state society annually obtain a list of all licensed dentists from the secretary of the state board of dental examiners, so that every eligible dentist could be personally solicited to enroll in organized dentistry. The plan also urged cooperation with the dental colleges and the examiners' boards to bring in the new practitioners entering the profession each year. There would be a campaign among the senior dental students to secure from them a declaration of intention to join a dental society. The Indiana Plan also suggested substantial concessions in the matter of dues for the first year after the practitioner obtained his license. The plan was adopted, and an amendment to the constitution established a standing Committee on Organization and Membership, the duties of which were to develop and administer a program to augment the rolls of organized dentistry.[7]

The ensuing year witnessed considerable activity in the promotion of membership. The new Committee set energetically to work. President G. Walter Dittmar of the American Dental Association prepared an article on the plan and sent it to a number of the bulletins and journals of the state societies. *The Journal of the American Dental Association* itself summarized the proposal in its January, 1933, number. At its annual meeting, the American Association of Dental

Schools approved the membership plan and urged its member colleges to cooperate with the Committee.[8] The Indiana Plan had evidently stimulated interest. It remained to be seen whether it could be implemented.

The time of the annual session of the American Dental Association in 1933 was a busy one for the advocates of a vigorous recruitment campaign. The State Society Officers' Conference, meeting at the same time, recommended some changes in the plan as originally conceived by Ross and his Indiana colleagues. Ross, anticipating some of these alterations, prepared the way for their acceptance by the trustees and the House of Delegates.[9] Later in the session, Ross submitted a supplemental report showing widespread support for the general features of the plan. He reported that thirty-two of the thirty-five colleges in the American Association of Dental Schools had agreed to cooperate with the new system. Out of twenty-two constituent societies that had met since the scheme had been promulgated, Ross reported twenty-one endorsements of the plan. Finally, Ross announced, the National Association of Dental Examiners had approved the Indiana Plan at its annual session and had asked its members to cooperate.[10]

After some minor changes in the plan had been debated and approved, the first membership contest opened on March 1, 1934.[11] One feature of the new system proved particularly attractive. This related to the dental colleges as sources of new members. Homer C. Brown had perceived the possibilities in this approach during his term as president.[12] Now the idea was extended in an attempt to enroll dental students before graduation. The Indiana Plan proposed a junior membership for students recommended by the deans of their schools. At the 1933 session, the House of Delegates approved a recommendation that the proper committee draft amendments providing for junior membership in the American Dental Association.[13] From this proposal came a new category of membership, now called a Student Membership, that has grown to embrace a high proportion of the men enrolled in the nation's dental schools, more than 10,000 members in recent years.[14]

Since its establishment in 1932, the standing Committee on Organization and Membership, now called the Council on Membership, has undergone little essential change. The devices for attracting members have varied in emphasis through the years. But the truth stressed by Presidents Banzhaf, Oliver, and Dewey during the membership crisis of the late twenties and early thirties has been abundantly confirmed. Sundry booster techniques have been augmented by increased privileges and services offered to members. These two interrelated features of the Association since the reorganization of 1913, a growing roster of members and an expanding array of services for the membership, have between them produced much of the recent history of the American Dental Association.

Since 1913 there have been two major revisions of the constitution. The first, in 1922, resulted from the expansion of membership and services. The governing instrument of 1913 had been "outgrown" as the Association increased in size. Furthermore, legal difficulties complicated the publication of the *Journal* in Illinois under a corporation charter issued in the District of Columbia. President Thomas B. Hartzell recommended endorsement of the action of the reorganization committee in obtaining an Illinois charter. He proposed that the newly organized Illinois corporation take over the assets, liabilities, membership, officers, constitution and by-laws of the National Dental Association of the District of Columbia. Hartzell also suggested changing the name back to the original title, "The American Dental Association." He explained, "In going over the country from state to state I find the spirit of the great war bred in every man's soul that America should be first and all the time." The changes in the constitution and by-laws required by the need for a new legal business basis were minor. None effected any essential change in the society's ways of doing business.[15]

The revised constitution of 1922 served as the organic law of the Association for a quarter of a century. During that time, one or another provision was amended almost every year. Naturally, the true status of any given section became increasingly difficult to determine. Twice attempts were made to recodify and simplify the maze of amendments and standing resolutions. The first of these reforms began as a result of the recommendations of President Frank M. Casto in 1935. A special committee was appointed for the purpose and instructed to report to the next annual meeting.[16] Simultaneously, the Board of Trustees hired a firm of management consultants to survey the work of the American Dental Association "to better consolidate our organization and thus make it more efficient."[17] The consultants laid down two broad principles that should govern the operations of the Association. First, activities of purely professional interest, involving a minimum of administration, should be decentralized as far as possible. This policy would interest larger numbers of the membership in the activities of the Association and allow for the accommodation of individual and local differences. On the other hand, centralization was to be the key for the service activities of the Association. Such a policy would permit greater efficiency in supervision and correlation of these programs.[18] Also at the 1935 meeting, a committee of the Board of Trustees proposed several devices to enable the Board and officers to be informed better regarding current policy, standing resolutions, and precedents. Adoption of the various suggestions effected only a temporary solution to the difficulties.[19]

The second major attempt at revision of the organic law began with the establishment of a Standing Committee on Constitutional and Administrative By-Laws in 1942.[20] The House of Delegates directed this body to receive and consider proposed amendments. The next phase in the reform occurred in 1945 when the Board of Trustees appointed a special committee to draft a revision of the constitution and by-laws. The committee labored through the following spring and summer and presented an extensively revised instrument to the Board of Trustees at Miami in October, 1946.

Two full years' discussion and debate produced relatively few essential changes in the draft constitution submitted in 1946. By 1948, most of the controversial questions had been composed and the document passed through the processes of adoption smoothly. The constitution and bylaws of 1948 were an improved version of the institutions that had governed the Association since the great reform of 1913, and clarified and streamlined the power and procedural relationships in the operation of the Association.[21]

The American Dental Association, then as now, is governed by the House of Delegates, consisting of representatives from the constituent, or state and territorial, dental societies. Each constituent society is entitled to name delegates in proportion to the number of members enrolled. As the membership of the Association has increased, so has the size of the House of Delegates. In consequence, the House has often seemed too large for the efficient conduct of business. Through the years, sundry efforts have been made to reduce the membership of the House, all without success. The formula for representation today remains substantially the same as the formula in the constitution of 1913. The increasingly numerous House requires an increasingly elaborate organization.

The deliberations of so large a body present a challenge to the parliamentary skill of the presiding officer. Until the revision of 1948, the president of the Association served as chairman of the meetings of the House. To ease the burden on the president, a standing resolution of 1930 authorized the appointment of a speaker of the House. Efforts to write the office into the constitution and to persuade the president to take advantage of the enabling resolution were without effect until the debates over the 1948 revision. During these discussions, the New York state organization sponsored a successful movement for a speaker of the House. The speaker of the House of Delegates is now one of the five annually-elected officers of the Association.[22]

A number of reference committees, appointed from the delegates prior to each annual meeting, analyze the reports, resolutions, and other business that come before the House and advise the parent body regarding the action to be taken. Special committees are also appointed from the delegates from time to time. In addition to these committees, the Association's work features standing committees, designated councils. The number of councils has risen steadily from the original four provided in the constitution of 1913 to a peak of eighteen under the revised bylaws of 1948, from which it receded to seventeen in 1955. These councils furnish the House of Delegates with a continuing source of information and guidance on their subjects. In a way, the councils also represent a link among the membership, the House, and the Board of Trustees, since the councils' work often involves direct work with the membership, while that work is outlined, in general, by the House and carried out by council members nominated by the trustees.[23]

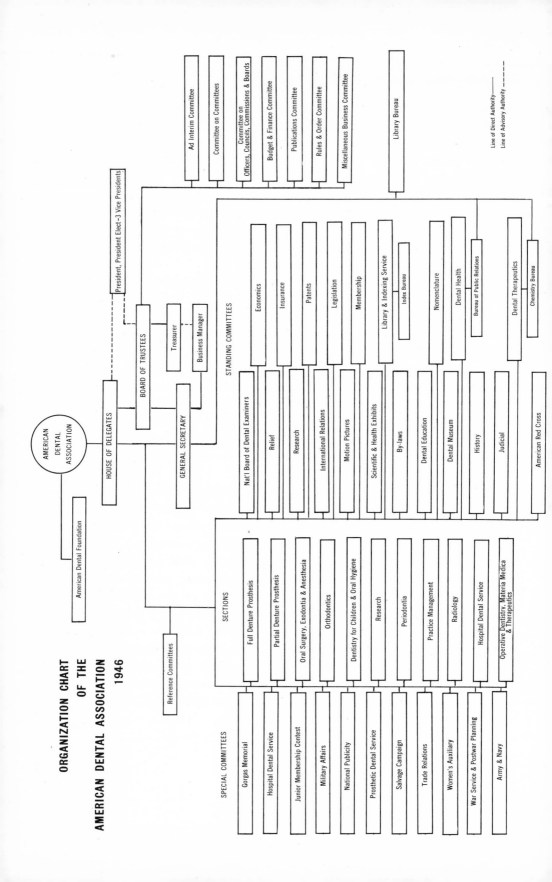

ORGANIZATION CHART
OF THE
AMERICAN DENTAL ASSOCIATION
1946

AMERICAN DENTAL ASSOCIATION

American Dental Foundation

HOUSE OF DELEGATES

Reference Committees

BOARD OF TRUSTEES

President, President Elect - 3 Vice Presidents

Treasurer

Business Manager

GENERAL SECRETARY

Ad Interim Committee

Committee on Committees

Committee on Officers, Councils, Commissions & Boards

Budget & Finance Committee

Publications Committee

Rules & Order Committee

Miscellaneous Business Committee

Library Bureau

Line of Direct Authority ———
Line of Advisory Authority ------

STANDING COMMITTEES

Nat'l Board of Dental Examiners
Economics
Relief
Insurance
Research
Patents
International Relations
Legislation
Motion Pictures
Membership
Scientific & Health Exhibits
Library & Indexing Service
Index Bureau
By-laws
Dental Education
Nomenclature
Dental Museum
Dental Health
History
Bureau of Public Relations
Judicial
Dental Therapeutics
Chemistry Bureau
American Red Cross

SECTIONS

Full Denture Prosthesis
Partial Denture Prosthesis
Oral Surgery, Exodontia & Anesthesia
Orthodontics
Dentistry for Children & Oral Hygiene
Research
Periodontia
Practice Management
Radiology
Hospital Dental Service
Operative Dentistry, Materia Medica & Therapeutics

SPECIAL COMMITTEES

Gorgas Memorial
Hospital Dental Service
Junior Membership Contest
Military Affairs
National Publicity
Prosthetic Dental Service
Salvage Campaign
Trade Relations
Women's Auxiliary
War Service & Postwar Planning
Army & Navy

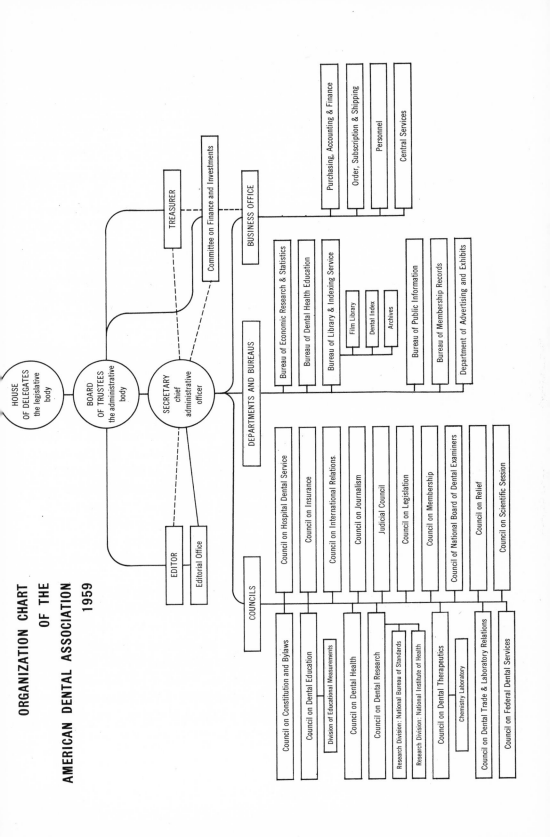

ORGANIZATION CHART
OF THE
AMERICAN DENTAL ASSOCIATION
1959

HOUSE OF DELEGATES
the legislative body

BOARD OF TRUSTEES
the administrative body

SECRETARY
chief administrative officer

TREASURER

Committee on Finance and Investments

EDITOR

Editorial Office

BUSINESS OFFICE

Purchasing, Accounting & Finance

Order, Subscription & Shipping

Personnel

Central Services

DEPARTMENTS AND BUREAUS

Bureau of Economic Research & Statistics

Bureau of Dental Health Education

Bureau of Library & Indexing Service

Film Library

Dental Index

Archives

Bureau of Public Information

Bureau of Membership Records

Department of Advertising and Exhibits

COUNCILS

Council on Hospital Dental Service

Council on Insurance

Council on International Relations

Council on Journalism

Judicial Council

Council on Legislation

Council on Membership

Council of National Board of Dental Examiners

Council on Relief

Council on Scientific Session

Council on Constitution and Bylaws

Council on Dental Education

Division of Educational Measurements

Council on Dental Health

Council on Dental Research

Research Division: National Bureau of Standards

Research Division: National Institute of Health

Council on Dental Therapeutics

Chemistry Laboratory

Council on Dental Trade & Laboratory Relations

Council on Federal Dental Services

The Board of Trustees is "the managing body of the Association." [24] Endowed with full power to conduct all business of the Association, the Board is subject only to the restrictions of the constitution and bylaws and the decisions of the House of Delegates. The Board is vested with broad powers of nomination and appointment in the selection of the sundry appointive officers of the Association, councilmen, and the chairmen of councils. Through the years the steady expansion of the Association's activities has induced repeated changes in the organization and functions of the Board of Trustees. Its numbers increased from nine to thirteen in 1928.[25] The Board meets throughout the annual sessions of the Association and at least two other times during the remainder of the year. In this way, as well as through the reports and advice of the councils and the work of the appointive officers, the Board maintains a close surveillance over the business of the Association.

With the passing years the appointive officers have come to conduct the great bulk of the work of the Association. The most important of these men is the secretary. Already a powerful official when the reorganization of 1913 took place, the secretary became a full-time employee of the Association in 1918. During the early years of the regime of Otto U. King, the secretary served also as editor of the *Journal* and the other publications of the Association. But the complexity of the duties assigned to the secretary made a division of the office necessary. King gave up the editorship in 1925 while retaining the post of business manager of the *Journal*.[26] The secretaryship was further subdivided when King was succeeded by H. B. Pinney in 1928. Thereafter, until the reorganization of 1948, the business manager became a separate office in the Association's burgeoning bureaucracy.[27]

Pinney served as secretary for nineteen years. On his retirement in December, 1946, he was succeeded by Harold Hillenbrand, who continues in that capacity. In 1948, the constitutional revision brought the business manager directly under the supervision of the secretary.[28] Although many of the duties formerly performed by the secretary have been assigned to other employees, these functionaries have ordinarily been placed under the supervision of the secretary. He is the "principal administrative officer of the Association," responsible "directly and solely" to the Board of Trustees. The secretary directs the operation of the Central Office and has over-all supervision of the branch office of the Association in Washington, D. C. He selects and discharges employees whose status is not otherwise provided for. The work of the councils, bureaus, and committees is carried out under his supervision.[29] The many services performed by the Association's Central Office have necessitated employment of increasing numbers. Otto U. King directed one full-time and occasional part-time workers. Secretary Hillenbrand administers a staff of 165 at this writing.

The other appointive offices have developed in a similar way. The editor serves directly under the Board of Trustees since he administers the publication of the *Journal,* which is constitutionally the responsibility of the trustees. The editor is likewise editor-in-chief of all official and specialty journals of the Association. Like the office of secretary, the editorship has been a singularly stable position. Only five men have held the office since its inception. Otto King functioned both as secretary and editor until 1925. C. N. Johnson, a noted dental educator and journalist, began a thirteen-year career as editor in that year. Johnson was succeeded by L. Pierce Anthony in 1938. Anthony's association with the *Journal* began when the *Dental Cosmos,* of which he had been editor for some years, was combined with the *Journal* in 1936. Harold Hillenbrand became editor on Anthony's retirement at the end of 1944. When Hillenbrand was appointed secretary of the American Dental Association in 1946, Lon W. Morrey, the present incumbent, moved into the editorial chair early in 1947.

The third major appointed officer, the treasurer, has enjoyed a similar long tenure. Each occupant had formerly been a president of the Association. Arthur R. Melendy, president in 1911-1912, served as treasurer from 1914 to 1928. Roscoe H. Volland moved into the treasurer's post on Melendy's death, which occurred shortly after Volland's presidential administration terminated. Volland retired in 1948. H. B. Washburn completed his term as president at that time and succeeded to Volland's post as treasurer. The growth of the resources of the Association has increased the responsibilities of the treasurer. The nature of the office is such that time has brought little essential change in its duties. Larger sums and a more elaborate variety of funds to be administered have increased the complexity of the position without changing its fundamental character.[30]

Some of the increased complexity of carrying on the business of the American Dental Association has resulted from the sheer increase in membership and resources. Much more of this development, however, is a consequence of the additional services to the membership the larger and wealthier organization can perform. At the organization of the Association in 1913, one of the primary services which it was expected to undertake was the publication of an official journal. The Association's first humble periodical, the quarterly *Official Bulletin,* became *The Journal of the National Dental Association,* also a quarterly, in January, 1915. In January, 1917, the *Journal* expanded from a quarterly to a monthly publication. Its lengthy subscription list soon placed the *Journal* in the forefront of dental periodical literature. Proprietary and independent magazines with long and respected careers behind them bowed before it. The venerable *Dental Register* succumbed in 1923. Even the *Dental Cosmos,* for so long the bellwether of dental journalism, finally merged with the *Journal* in 1936 and disappeared altogether in 1938.[31]

Occasionally the dedication of the *Journal* to technical and scientific subjects has suggested the establishment of another organ for the dissemination of professional and organization news. Two attempts have been made in this direction. During 1927, the *Dental News,* a quarterly, was distributed to the membership of the American Dental Association. Then, to avoid duplication and extra expense, the quarterly was merged with the *Journal.*[32] During World War II, a supplement, called *Midmonthly,* appeared. Devoted to information related to the war effort, *Midmonthly* was absorbed by the *Journal* and disappeared in 1946. At the same time, the *Journal* became a semi-monthly publication, an objective long-sought to reduce the bulk of the magazine and to increase its readership and advertising revenue. The semi-monthly schedule endured for only a year. The financial crisis of the late forties forced abandonment of the experiment, and monthly publication was resumed in 1948.[33]

The publishing services of the American Dental Association have not been confined to issuance of the *Journal.* The Association has sponsored the *Journal of Oral Surgery* since its inception in 1943. Originally a quarterly, the *Journal of Oral Surgery* now is distributed by subscription on a bi-monthly schedule. Beginning with the January, 1959, issue, its scope was enlarged and its name changed to the *Journal of Oral Surgery, Anesthesia and Hospital Dental Service*. In 1947 there was some discussion of the Association's undertaking the publication of additional specialty journals, but the financial difficulties of the time abruptly silenced the movement.[34]

A third periodical is published by the editorial offices of the American Dental Association. This is *Dental Abstracts*. For many years, the need of such a service was the subject of discussion in the profession. The number of dental periodicals issued in this country, and throughout the world, is too great for even the most energetic researcher to absorb, and is far beyond the reading capacity of the average practitioner. A privately-sponsored effort in 1939 to supply the need for an abstracting service failed after two issues. Two years later, the students and faculty of the Columbia University dental school took up the task. The Columbia project was highly selective in subject matter and in the journals it covered. Its career ended in 1950. After long study and discussion, the Board of Trustees of the Association finally authorized the editor to begin issuance of an abstract journal. Inaugurated in 1956, the monthly *Dental Abstracts* makes available to its subscribers a selection of significant articles from the world's dental literature.[35]

In addition to the publications issuing from the office of the editor and several council and bureau periodicals,[36] the Association publishes two reference tools of considerable importance to the profession. One of these is *Accepted Dental Remedies*, which disseminates to the profession general information concerning drugs used in medicine and specific information about those used in dentistry. The other is the *Index to Dental Literature*.

The first edition of *Accepted Dental Remedies* was published by the Council on Dental Therapeutics of the Association in 1934. It has since become an annual publication, the volume issued in 1958 being the twenty-third edition. This method of dealing with dental therapeutic preparations stands at the end of a long line of development extending back through the history of the profession. Just as one of the aims of the pioneer professional organization was to eliminate secrecy and to discourage misleading claims by practitioners, so has the organized profession sought to discourage the use of secret nostrums by the laity and by dentists. Similarly, dentists have shared the concern of pharmacists and physicians regarding the preparation, purity, safety, and dispensing of therapeutic agents. During the presidency of Mark F. Finley (1905-1906), the Association won representation in the National Pharmacopeial Convention.[37]

It was during those years that Harvey W. Wiley, veteran chief of the Bureau of Chemistry in the Department of Agriculture, succeeded in his long campaign for a federal food and drug law. The basic act was approved in 1906. While Wiley was deeply interested in eliminating patent medicine abuses, his irascibility and the large economic interests involved rendered the work of his Bureau of Chemistry highly controversial. Sundry attempts to mitigate the controversies through administrative channels hampered the work of the Bureau and failed to solve the problems facing the health professions. Indeed, one appeal to the Department of Agriculture for assistance in settling a dentifrice controversy received an outright rejection.[38]

The Bureau of Standards, founded in 1901, was still attempting as late as 1906 to discover the dimensions of its duties; it was not yet ready to undertake the definition of standards for dental products.[39] During World War I, the Bureau of Standards undertook a limited testing program establishing specifications to assist in the procurement of supplies for the dental services of the armed forces. This activity was no permanent solution to the profession's need for scientific guidance regarding dental remedies and materials. The Association had no regular relationship with the Bureau of Standards before 1928. Even then the principal concern of the Bureau of Standards' dental program was with dental materials. The problems relating to dental therapeutic agents remained unsolved.[40]

In 1922, the Association directed its standing Committee on United States Pharmacopeia and Formulary to investigate the purity of remedies and to publish its findings in the *Journal*. Since the Committee lacked facilities of its own to undertake the experiments, it was authorized to seek the assistance of government agencies or private institutes to carry them out. From time to time, the Research Commission was also urged to enter this field.[41] In 1928, the Association launched its own investigatory program, employing a chemist to conduct experiments under the direction of a special committee. Establishment of the Council on Dental Therapeutics in 1930 gave permanence to the scheme.[42]

The Council on Dental Therapeutics and the laboratory, designated the Bureau of Chemistry, found themselves in trouble virtually from the outset. Criticism came from the manufacturers whose products or advertising failed to meet the Association's standards. President Martin Dewey, who had sponsored foundation of the Council at the 1929 meeting, declared in his 1932 report that the operations of the Council and the Bureau of Chemistry were unnecessarily expensive and might be productive of legal trouble. The difficulty, as Dewey saw it, arose from the temptation of the Bureau to "go out of its way to criticize products and manufacturers of products when the criticism [had] no bearing on the scientific value of the report." The business manager, L. T. Claridge, reported in the same year that "due to the activities of the Council on Dental Therapeutics and the general business conditions there has been a considerable drop in advertising revenue."[43]

On the other hand, many members of the Association indicated their approval and support of the program. A movement to suspend the activities of the Council and the Bureau of Chemistry was forestalled. Numerous requests for publication of the Council's reports in book form eventuated in the appearance of the first edition of *Accepted Dental Remedies* in 1934.[44] Since that time, the function of the Council on Dental Therapeutics and its Bureau of Chemistry (changed to the Division of Chemistry in 1951) has become firmly established among the services of the Association.

Next to the *Journal*, the *Index to Dental Literature* claims the longest history among the publications of the Association. Around the turn of the century, Arthur D. Black began to devise a means of indexing that would give access to the voluminous periodical literature of dentistry. He announced his proposed system before the Institute of Dental Pedagogics in 1909. The Institute and interested private individuals set out to acquire funds for the publication of the *Index of the Periodical Dental Literature*. This did not prove to be an easy task. Black demonstrated the practicability of the system in 1914, when he published an index of the *Transactions* of the Illinois State Dental Society.[45] Nevertheless, a committee for the *Index* labored for more than a decade before it was able, in 1921, to bring out the first volume covering the dental literature for the years 1911–1915. Publication remained in the hands of the Dental Index Bureau, composed of representatives of interested societies, through the twenties. The Association early showed an interest in the *Index,* serving as one of the sponsors of the first volume. Beginning in 1925, the Association assumed major financial responsibility for the support of the *Index.* In 1930, a committee of the Association, headed by A. D. Black until his death in 1937, assumed direction of the work. After 1933, the volumes carried the American Dental Association copyright. Not until Black died did the Association move to assume the labors of compilation as well as administrative and financial responsibility for the *Index.* In 1939, the title of the publication was changed to the *Index to Dental Literature.* In 1950, the *Index* became a quarterly cumulative publication. The volume for 1952 contained materials from more than one hundred and fifty publications appearing in ten English-speaking countries. Its pages also included references to articles printed in English in periodicals published in Finland, Italy, Lebanon, Norway, Puerto Rico, Sweden, and Switzerland. The service thus brings a vast amount of information within reach of the interested researcher. The preparation and publication of the *Index* is now one activity of the Bureau of Library and Indexing Service of the American Dental Association.[46] The establishment of this agency, under the title of the Department of Literary Research, brought the Association into another field of service to its members, that of continuing education to help the practicing dentist keep abreast of the latest advances in dental art and science. Inauguration of the service was announced at the annual session of 1927. Initially, the Bureau offered to lend to members "package libraries," consisting of reprints of articles relating to particular subjects, books on dentistry and related subjects, and bibliographies.[47] The program won immediate approval of the membership. The services have steadily expanded so that motion pictures, film strips, slides, television and radio material may also be borrowed or rented from the Bureau. The passing years have added extensive reference service, and the responsibility for historical and archival material, nomenclature, and audio-visual guidance to the regular activities of the Bureau.

The American Dental Association has come to offer a variety of supports to the personal welfare of its members in addition to its contribution to their professional improvement. A program for assistance to aged and indigent dentists was another aspiration deferred while the profession struggled with problems of organization in the early years of the century. In the closing days of the reorganization movement, the Relief Fund program got underway. The committee for the Association, led by past presidents L. G. Noel and Edward S. Gaylord, sought individual contributions; they asked the state and local societies to increase their dues, setting aside the increase for relief purposes; they inaugurated the Christmas Seal drive. From these and other sources, the Relief Fund of the Association grew. By 1920, $52,-000 had been set aside for charitable purposes. In another five years, the total resources of the Relief Fund exceeded $128,000. This figure had almost been doubled by 1930. In spite of the Depression, the total amount continued to climb. In 1935, the Relief Fund boasted $358,-959.71. By the end of the decade, the figure was $446,718.71. Through the forties, contributions and returns from investments continued to mount. At mid-century, the Relief Fund approached two-thirds of a million dollars. The Fund continued to flourish. Investments alone yielded more than $50,000 in 1955. Receipts from the Fund campaign of 1957–1958 exceeded $120,000.[48]

As the sums available increased, procedures for administering and dispensing the money became more elaborate. The cooperation of the state and local societies was sought and finally demanded in rules adopted in 1924. The new regulations stipulated that no applicant should receive a grant "unless his or her state association [appropriated] an equal amount." Grants were divided into monthly allotments. In subsequent revisions of the program, the contribution asked of the state society was reduced to one-third of the total amount of the grant. Three years' membership became a principal requirement for eligibility. Requests for assistance had to be initiated and approved by the local and state societies, which also recommended the amount of the

grant. Grants were limited in duration to one year and in amount according to the period of time the recipient had been a member of the
Association.[49]

The program underwent a major revision in 1948. The most significant change came with the establishment of the American Dental
Association Relief Fund as a separate corporation for charitable purposes. This move made contributions to the Fund deductible for income tax purposes. The change encouraged increased contributions.
Membership in the Association was no longer a prerequisite for the
receipt of benefits. Policy regarding the contributions of local and
state societies to the grants has varied. At present the Relief Fund
matches the contributions of the local and state societies. This policy,
in effect, has frequently limited the size of the grants to the size of the
constituent's relief fund rather than to the need of the recipient. Although repeated pronouncements have declared that the Relief Fund
is not a pension or retirement system, many of the grants to elderly
recipients have been continued until death. The Council on Relief,
however, reviews every case each year.

Inevitably, discussion of changes in the program and of the rules
governing it have tended to emphasize the security of the Fund and
safeguarding it against unwarranted appeals for assistance. From
some members have come suggestions for broadening the program
to extend low-cost loans to practitioners suffering personal disasters
or to establish a retirement home for dentists. Others have argued that
campaigns for contributions are no longer necessary. Both tendencies
have been resisted, the first on the ground that the tax status of the
Fund might be jeopardized, and the second because the earnings from
the endowment, plus the reserve available for making grants, are not
yet large enough to meet the heavy drain that might be expected in a
general depression.[50]

The Association has endeavored in other ways to assist its members
in protecting themselves from the mischances that befall ordinary
mortals. Since 1929, the Association has sponsored a group life insurance program for its members. During its early phases the plan
was handled by a special committee, but in 1935 it was placed under
the control of a standing committee, now called the Council on Insurance. In 1952, the program was broadened to include health and
accident coverage.[51]

While endeavoring to expand group insurance benefits to its membership, the Association had difficulty deciding on a policy regarding the inclusion of dentists in any extension of federal Old Age and Survivors' Insurance to the self-employed. In 1948, the House of Delegates directed the Council on Legislation to advocate inclusion of dentists in the Old Age and Survivors' Insurance program.[52] The following year, the Council on Legislation reported that a bill extending coverage to the self-employed, with the exception of lawyers, physicians, and dentists, was currently before the Congress. The Council reported that it had not requested that dentists be included in the bill because the proposal was part of the Social Security system and the Council was then energetically opposing another facet of the system, compulsory health insurance, at the direction of the Association. The Council's statement added that both the American Medical Association and the American Bar Association had "actively opposed the inclusion of their professions in the bill."[53] The Reference Committee on Legislation, to which the Council's report naturally found its way, supported the action of the Council. The Committee reasoned that the proposed legislation "would tend to jeopardize the financial security of the country." Furthermore, the Committee argued, "the real security of the professionally self-employed lies within the individual and his contribution to the community rather than in any government-sponsored system of old age insurance." The House of Delegates rescinded the endorsement of the preceding year and directed the Council on Legislation to seek amendments eliminating dentists from coverage in the event the profession was covered by the bill.[54]

The official attitude evidently stirred some discontent among some of the rank and file, for in 1951 the Board of Trustees directed the Bureau of Public Information to prepare an explanation of the official policy for early dissemination among the membership.[55] Although two constituent societies appealed for a change in the policy, the House of Delegates remained unmoved until 1955. A 1952 effort by the Massachusetts State Dental Society to secure the neutrality of the Association on the question met defeat in the House of Delegates. Later, the Council on Legislation was directed to bring the Association's opposition to the attention of Congress, and the Council was instructed to look into the possibility of obtaining amendments in the event bills offered in Congress included dentistry in their coverage.[56] Representatives of the Association, testifying before congressional committees, argued that since most dentists continue to practice until they die, they could not benefit from OASI coverage. Association spokesmen pleaded for the right of dentists to choose their own retirement program, or none.[57]

The House of Delegates in 1955 retreated from its former firm opposition in the matter and approved the voluntary inclusion of dentists under the Old Age and Survivors' Insurance program of the Social Security Act. In August of the following year, an amendment to the federal legislation extended mandatory coverage under OASI to dentists.[58]

Legislative problems had vexed the Association long before the reorganization of 1913. The Council on Legislation is one of the oldest standing committees of the Association. Originally, national legislation constituted the main concern of the Committee. During the twenties, however, the Committee also kept the Association informed of state developments and recommended action that seemed appropriate.

In 1926, for example, a bill was proposed in the Colorado state legislature granting a license, upon payment of a nominal fee, to any dentist holding a license from any other state. The Committee chairman proposed that the American Dental Association extend help to the Colorado State Dental Society in trying to defeat the bill. As the profession rallied around, the Colorado dentists succeeded in defeating the bill.[59]

With the increasing membership and the increasing complexity of problems of professional concern, the Legislative Committee reached out for additional resources to permit it to perform additional services. In 1931, the Committee chairman proposed that his Committee draft a model state dental law to assist in obtaining more nearly uniform state legislation. The Reference Committee of the House of Delegates endorsed the suggestion and supplemented it with a recommendation for the establishment of a central agency to collect and act as a clearing house for information regarding state dental legislation and court decisions.[60]

Such proposals of reform triggered a series of revisions of the composition and duties of the Committee on Legislation that characterized its history during the following years. The agency that emerged from the changes had a much greater variety of functions and a far larger membership with which to work. The reformed Committee consisted of thirteen members, each selected from one of the Trustee districts. Each member was directed to appoint one deputy from each state in his district. These officials were to cooperate with state and local societies in matters pertaining to legislation and to keep the chairman and secretary informed of developments in their districts. A bureau, headed by a permanent secretary assigned by the trustees and located in the central offices of the Association, was established. The duties of the Committee in connection with state legislative matters were to advise, inform, and assist the constituent societies. It was to compile data relating to dental regulation and practice. The information accumulated by the Committee was to be disseminated through bulletins and the *Journal*. In pursuance of these duties, the Committee rallied support for the defense of state laws protecting the professional status of dentistry.[61] The manner in which the Committee functioned is well illustrated by the Semler case.

An advertising dentist, one Harry Semler, challenged the advertising restrictions in the Oregon state law. Defeated in the lower courts, Semler carried an appeal to the highest tribunal in the state. Rebuffed again, Semler appealed to the Supreme Court of the United States. Up to this point, the defense had been handled by the Oregon State Board of Dental Examiners and the state dental society. The final appeal taxed them beyond their resources. President Frank M. Casto of the American Dental Association and the Committee on Legislation mobilized the necessary financial assistance enabling the Oregon profession to win vindication of the state laws regulating dental practice. In the following year, some citizens of Oregon resorted to their constitutional right of initiative and began proceedings to introduce an amendment to the Oregon constitution that would allow any person to advertise providing the claims were true. Again the profession in Oregon and around the country rallied. And again the profession was vindicated.[62]

When occasion demanded it, the Committee has sought changes in the revenue code to take account of the particular needs and expenses of dental practice. To the same end, it has argued on behalf of special interpretations of the terms of the code for the benefit of dentists.[63] A related type of activity grew out of the use of gold as a dental material for fillings, restorations and appliances. In pursuit of the interest of the profession in this connection, the Committee was obliged to work for changes in excise tax regulations and in the regulations of the Treasury Department when the country abandoned the gold standard. The Committee on Legislation has also been concerned with the impact of tariff legislation on the dental profession.[64]

Another class of activity has dealt with the interests of individual dentists employed in government service. The Association has interested itself in the recruitment of dentists for the government, both in terms of numbers and quality, and it has been concerned with their proper recognition. Finally, the American Dental Association has tried to protect the independence of the practice of dentistry in the government service. This aspect of government dentistry has posed difficult problems, for dental work has been subordinated to the broader purposes of the agency in which the service was being performed. The dividing line between purely dental considerations and the broader ones of total agency policy has been exceedingly difficult to draw. In the period since the reorganization of 1913, the Association has repeatedly dealt with all of these aspects in connection with dentistry in a number of government agencies.[65] The most important of these have been the armed forces. The American Dental Association and dentistry in the Army may serve as an example of the way in which organized dentistry has handled the problems of dentistry in government service.

Legislation of the first World War established the framework within which subsequent developments had to be worked out. The Act of October 6, 1917, granted Army dental officers equality in rank and other privileges with officers of the Medical Corps. For the Navy and Marine Corps dentists this status of equality with medical officers was partially attained July 1, 1918. The same act established the proportion of one dental officer per thousand of the authorized strength of the Regular Army. This ratio, adopted also for the Navy, remained the basis for determining the size of the Dental Corps through most of the years of peace. Between wars, American policy has ordinarily tended toward drastic reductions in the size of the armed forces so as to limit federal expenses. The period of the twenties was no exception to this rule. As the armed forces were reduced, so, too, were the number of dentists in uniform.[66]

During the twenties, the Association devoted considerable effort to seeking an increase in the ratio of dentists to military personnel of one to five hundred. It also endeavored to raise the ceiling on the rank to which dental officers could rise. This effort was caused in part by the desire to enhance the prestige of dental officers, but also to secure rewards for length of service, and to furnish an incentive for dental officers to remain in uniform. A member of the Army Dental Corps, Colonel Robert T. Oliver, became president of the American Dental Association in 1930. Colonel Oliver had served as Chief of the Dental Section in the Office of the Surgeon General from 1919 to 1924. He had been one of the first group of dental officers to receive commissions under the Act of March 3, 1911.[67] When Oliver had completed his term as president of the Association, a movement was begun to obtain for him the first commission as a brigadier general to be awarded to a dentist. Coming, as it did, at a time when the congressional urge to economize was at a peak, the campaign seemed inauspicious to the Committee on Legislation. It was accordingly deferred until a more favorable moment. As a result, the distinction of becoming the first General of the U. S. Army Dental Corps fell to Colonel Leigh Cole Fairbank, who became a brigadier general in 1938.[68]

Similarly, agitation on the part of the Association for increases in the pay schedules of dental officers was wrecked on the shoals of economy in government expenditures during the twenties. The insistence on retrenchment, a favored device for combatting the Depression, threatened to bring an unwelcome change in the size of both the Army and the Navy Dental Corps, and menaced particularly the continued service of the reservists on active duty. Representatives of the American Dental Association worked to salvage the careers of these officers. Through most of the period between the wars, the Association struggled to maintain the ground that had been won in the earlier period. This largely defensive program on behalf of military dentists remained characteristic of the Association's efforts until the beginnings of the restoration of the country's defense establishment in the late thirties.[69]

The changing international picture prompted President C. Willard Camalier to recommend special Association action for preparedness in 1938. Dr. Camalier suggested the establishment of a special liaison committee representing dentists in the government services and the profession at large.[70] Early in the next year, the Director of the Dental Division in the Office of the Surgeon General asked the Association to form a committee on defense problems. After a second request from this source, the Committee on National Defense of the American Dental Association was established.[71] The Committee underwent a series of name changes and rapidly acquired new duties in the course of the succeeding months. On the eve of the annual meeting of 1940, the Surgeon General again asked the assistance of the Association. In effect, he requested that the Association assume the responsibility of managing the procurement of dental officers to serve the expanding armed forces, while maintaining the necessary minimum of dental care for the civilian population. The request was a high recognition of the place of the Association in the profession. It posed one of the greatest challenges the Association has had to face.

The Surgeon General's request outlined a tentative plan to be based on a survey of the profession to determine the distribution of dentists, the civilian needs for dental care, and the personal necessities and qualifications of the individual dentist. On the basis of the survey, which was to be conducted through the cooperation of the constituent and component societies of the Association, the local societies were to locate prospective volunteers for military service, who could be spared in their local community.

The Association accepted the responsibility gladly. At the annual session in 1940, the House of Delegates approved an appropriation of $25,000 to put the program into effect. To lay the groundwork for the system, the House also authorized the preparation of a questionnaire to be sent to all dentists in the United States whose addresses were known. The document was drafted and sent out by October, 1940.[72] Returns from the inquiry were disappointing and slow in coming in. Pending a full evaluation of the results of the survey, the chairman of the Preparedness Committee suggested an alteration in the strength of the Dental Reserve Corps in January, 1941. The Surgeon General approved of the idea, but the following month, when the Association proposed a specific increase in strength from five to eight thousand officers, the Surgeon General rejected the proposal. He pointed out that if the figure suggested proved larger than the needs of the service, officers not called to active duty would, in effect, have been granted an occupational deferment from a draft call. Deferments, the Surgeon General reasoned, were the prerogative of the Selective Service System and its local boards.

The Preparedness Committee convened in Chicago in the early spring of 1941. From its deliberations emerged the first estimates of the number of dentists that could be spared from civilian life without unnecessarily sacrificing the minimum needs of the community. The Committee estimated that there were about 21,000 dentists of draft age in the country. Of these, only about 6,700 were available according to criteria of the Selective Service System.[73]

This finding may have been cause for worry among the ranks of the Committee, but it seems unlikely that the Surgeon General was disturbed. At the end of April, only slightly more than one-third of the Dental Reserve officers were on active duty. Dental reserve officer procurement had been closed in the autumn of 1938 and two years later had been but slightly modified. Through the early stages of rearmament, the winter of 1940 to 1941, opportunities for reserve commissions for dental officers were severely restricted. There were not even vacancies for dentists inducted under the Selective Service System.[74] The Board of Trustees felt obliged to dispatch a resolution to the President of the United States stressing the importance of utilizing dentists in the profession for which they had been trained, whether they practiced as civilians or in uniform, and this position was strongly supported by the War Service Committee in testimony before the Senate Armed Services Committee and before the War Department itself.[75] These efforts had a salutary effect and provision was made for commissioning dental inductees in May, 1941; but, in October, the Surgeon General still pursued a cautious policy regarding dental reserve strength. Not long thereafter the Procurement and Assignment Service for Physicians, Dentists, and Veterinarians, was established in the War Manpower Commission by Executive Order of the President. It assumed the functions the American Dental Association had been performing in allocating the nation's dental strength.[76] The chairman of the Association's War Service Committee represented dentistry in the Procurement and Assignment Service. The Surgeon General stationed an officer in the central offices of the Association as a liaison man in May, 1942. Through this officer, the American Dental Association continued to contribute to dental officer procurement by assessing the professional and ethical qualifications of applicants for dental commissions.[77]

As best it could, the American Dental Association also sought to help the dentists after they had entered the service. These activities involved negotiations with the Office of the Surgeon General regarding the policies on rank and promotion and, for the first time, a serious attempt to win a clear-cut definition of the administrative position of post dental surgeons. As late as 1944 there were complaints about the Navy regulation making the medical officer on ship board senior to the dental officer. Both lines of endeavor were occasioned by real and fancied discriminations against dental officers in the armed forces.

Administrative difficulties plagued the military dental services throughout the period of World War II, partially because of the often-stated assumption that dentistry was a branch of medicine. As a result of this view, there were no clear-cut lines of authority separating the dental services from the medical in the armed forces. After considerable effort by the Association, the Army Dental Corps achieved limited independence under a Director with the rank of major general in the Surgeon General's office. The Navy Dental Corps was less favored. As late as 1944, that Corps was administered merely as a division of the Bureau of Medicine and Surgery with no lines of authority distinct from medical officers. The desired clarification was achieved by an act of December 28, 1945, proposed by the Association's Legislative Committee, placing the dental functions of the Bureau of Medicine and Surgery under an officer of the Dental Corps as its chief with the rank of rear admiral. Association efforts to persuade Congress to enact legislation to improve the organization and administration of the dental care programs in the Army and Air Force continued unavailing as the Association's centennial year began.

The representatives of the American Dental Association labored with some success in connection with rank and promotions. While spokesmen for dentistry received sympathetic consideration in Washington, the administrative and command status of dental officers in the field remained uncertain and frequently unsatisfactory. Too often, the Association heard complaints that dental officers were not being utilized in their proper professional capacity.[78]

The military's dental manpower policy continued to be perplexing. Against the advice of representatives of the Association and the American Association of Dental Schools, a Dental Army Specialized Training Program was instituted. Intended to assure an uninterrupted flow of new dental officers into the army, the program was abruptly terminated in 1944 when it appeared that the turnover of dental officers was much less than had been anticipated. It seemed that military needs for dentists had been satisfied. Difficulties began to appear with the end of hostilities in Europe, which reduced incentives to leave civilian life. The beginning of demobilization created pressure from dentists with longer service records and overseas service for release from active duty. At about the same time, the flow of new dental officers from the Dental ASTP died away with the graduation of the last class in the spring of 1945. Thereafter, the Association found itself in the middle of conflicting pressures—from the armed forces for assistance in keeping the servicemen adequately supplied with dental care, and from dental officers angrily demanding acceleration of their return to civilian life.

The Association began to assume a firm attitude toward the military through the months of 1945 in view of mounting protests from dental officers that separation procedures were lagging and that they were being held without being used for dental duties. The January, 1946, issue of the *Journal* carried a scathing editorial charging the services with mis- and non-use of their dental personnel and with failure to maintain the normal ratio of dentists to enlisted men. Late in the spring, while the shortage of dentists in the service persisted, medical officers with thirty months' service were declared eligible for release. Many dental officers, however, were still required to serve three years.[79] Not until the autumn of 1946 was the dental officer situation well enough in hand to permit belated acceleration of the release of officers who had not volunteered for extended service.

The Association learned well the lessons of World War II. Little change has been made in the fundamental policies toward the military, but the Association has insisted that the services and some federal agency, such as the Office of Defense Mobilization, maintain

boards of civilian dental advisors on procurement problems. The drive
to improve rank, administrative and command status of the dental
corps has continued through the Korean War period to the present.[80]

The Association has been extremely active in promoting the Career
Incentive program designed to keep dentists in the service and make
it more attractive for those desiring to volunteer.

The experiences of the World War II era shed light on another
aspect of the problems of dentists in government service. The question
arose repeatedly: For whom shall this service be performed? Here the
use of the armed forces as an example does not at first seem appropriate. It is obvious that dental officers of the armed forces are supposed to supply dental care to the servicemen. On the other hand,
dentists employed by the Public Health Service or the Veterans Administration have no such sharply delineated practice. As a matter of
fact, however, the military dentist has confronted similar problems
involving the dependents of service personnel. Furthermore, if the
objective of the profession is defined as the maintenance of the dental
health of the community, dentistry, in World War II and after, confronted the question in connection with the dental health of regis-
trants and inductees under the Selective Service System. The problem
during the World War II period was simply stated: Should inductees
with serious dental defects be rejected for military service, or re-
habilitated? If the latter alternative was chosen, the question remained whether the rehabilitation was to be accomplished before or
after the inductee entered the service. If the work was to be done
before induction, who was to pay for the work? Inability to reach a
satisfactory answer to the latter question has led the American Dental
Association to insist on rehabilitation after induction.[81] In a special
way, these questions and answers raised a perennial problem that has
perplexed the profession increasingly through its history. The profession is dedicated to maintaining the dental health of the community. How can the dental welfare of the entire community be
secured without lowering the standards of the profession?

Chapter XIX   THE ASSOCIATION AND THE PROFESSION

THE ENDEAVORS of the American Dental Association to assert leadership of the profession have been complicated by the fact that in some professional fields the Association has had to deal with other dental organizations with special interests. Conflicting and special interests within the profession further complicated the perplexing problems challenging effective leadership. The power of the American Dental Association in these special areas is limited. Policy is difficult to define since the Association embraces all interests. These considerations help account for the gradual and uncertain approach that has often characterized Association policy.

In the field of education, the evolution of the role of the Association has been erratic. The problems of professional education are manifold; the powers of the Association tenuous. The 1913 reorganization of the National Dental Association wrought little change in its relation to dental education. During the period following reorganization, the Association restricted its activities to recommendations and to participation in the work of the Dental Educational Council of America. The indecisiveness of the Association's policy is understandable when the composition of its active leadership is recalled. There was a sharp division between representatives or supporters of the surviving proprietary schools and advocates of the university-related colleges, a

377

split that existed prior to reorganization and that was unaffected by the change in the constitution.[1]

The principal agency in the making of dental educational policy continued to be the Dental Educational Council of America. The Council was independent of the National Dental Association, which had only equal representation with the National Association of Dental Faculties and the National Association of Dental Examiners. Other national educational societies in the dental field were unrepresented, as in the case of the Dental Faculties Association of American Universities, or were represented indirectly, as in the case of the National Institute of Dental Teachers.

Although its representative character remained uncertain, the Dental Educational Council of America grew in prestige during the period of the first World War. The Surgeon General of the Army consulted the Council on questions of dental education. The Council proceeded to exploit this recognition by expanding its functions. Prior to this time, the Council had confined itself to surveying dental education, inspecting dental schools, and advising on educational policy and curricula. To these activities, the Council now added the classification of dental colleges. It published the criteria on which the classification was based. It conducted inspections and published the results of its findings. Three categories were established, "A," "B," and "C." The latter rank indicated failure to meet the standards of the Council.[2]

Publication of a classification of dental schools awakened the university-related colleges of the Dental Faculties Association of American Universities to renewed interest in the Council. Negotiations between the two organizations began in 1918. The main point at issue lay in the antagonism of the Dental Faculties Association toward proprietary dental schools. On this point, the Council's position was ambiguous. It had proclaimed that the operation of a dental college for profit of any sort, direct or indirect, was undesirable. But in its classification of 1918, the Council accorded "A" and "B" ratings to several proprietary schools.[3] Successive and more stringent redefinitions of the Council's policy toward commercial dental schools did not produce corresponding action. At one point, the university-related colleges broke off negotiations. Discussions were soon resumed, however, and on January 23, 1922, three representatives of the Dental Faculties Association of American Universities were seated on the

Dental Educational Council of America.[4] The spokesmen of the university-related schools immediately launched an attack on the commercial colleges—to no avail.

The admission of the Dental Faculties Association produced an imbalance on the Council. With three delegates from the universities' organization, the dental schools now had eight representatives on the Council, while the examiners and the National Dental Association still had but five each. To preserve the equality of representation, the delegations from the practitioners' and the examiners' societies were increased by three each, swelling the ranks of the Council to twenty-four.[5]

Neither the direct influence of the Dental Faculties Association nor the enlarged membership of the Dental Educational Council endured for long. In the summer of 1922, the various societies of dental teachers and schools each appointed representatives to a conference. These delegates met in Omaha in January, 1923. From their deliberations emerged a new national organization concerned with the problems of dental education, the American Association of Dental Schools. The new organization declared itself "non-mandatory in authority," and "devoted mainly to the advancement of teaching." [6] The combination among the educational associations permitted a reduction in the size of the Dental Educational Council of America. In 1926 its numbers were reduced to eighteen with equal representation accorded to the national societies of educators, examiners, and practitioners.[7]

The establishment of the American Association of Dental Schools was the first of a series of related and nearly-simultaneous changes in dental education, creating a ferment in dental education that did not subside for more than a decade. When it was over many aspects of dental education had been radically altered. Instruction in proprietary schools had disappeared. The content, structure, and curriculum of dental education had all greatly changed. The policy-making agency for the training of dentists bore a vastly different relation to the national organizations of practitioners, educators, and examiners. Finally, a board for the construction and administration of a national uniform examination in the scientific and theoretical aspects of dentistry had begun to win support from state examining boards, thus establishing the rudiments of a feasible arrangement for interchange of licensing among the states.

The catalyst that did most to induce these many changes, although they were not all in the direction he advocated, was William J. Gies, a Columbia University biochemist. In 1920, Gies undertook a survey of dental education under the auspices of the Carnegie Foundation for the Advancement of Teaching. His findings were published under the title, *Dental Education in the United States and Canada*, in 1926.[8] Gies conceived his study so broadly that he considered most aspects of dentistry except those relating directly to practice itself. His approach was so thorough and so fresh that he found something significant to say on many topics within his broad subject. Although it seems probable that few dentists agreed fully with all of Gies's suggestions, he touched on so many different aspects of training and licensure that most practitioners found some points upon which they could enthusiastically agree with the author. Undoubtedly few dentists demurred at Gies's conclusion that "Dentistry is an important division of health service" that, "in the quality and efficiency of its service to the patient, should be made the full equivalent of an oral specialty of the practice of medicine." Gies coupled this declaration with a vindication of dentistry's independence from medicine on both historical and technical grounds. He went on to praise the "success with which dentists have brought dentistry to its present state of usefulness, appreciation, and opportunity, against persistent belittlement as 'merely a mechanical art,' and the strength of the evolution of its scope and function now plainly in progress, [that] indicate unmistakably that the leadership of the dental profession is advancing dentistry toward its full possibilities in health service." Gies then proceeded to sketch a program for dental education that would "effectually and economically" bring dentistry "to the full service equivalence of an oral specialty of medicine."[9] The dental profession hailed the Gies report.[10] But it often tended to ignore, when it did not oppose, carrying out all of his specific recommendations.

On one point, Gies and members of the profession were in accord. This was their agreement on the need to eliminate the commercial taint in dental education. The efforts of the members of the Dental Faculties Association of American Universities in this direction have already been recounted. In the conclusions of his report, Gies implicitly attacked the proprietary schools.[11] Elsewhere in his book, Gies made his condemnation of the profit-motivated colleges more explicit. In the opinion of one observer, the Gies report "spelled the doom of the proprietary dental school."[12] Nor was this the only contribution the Columbia biochemist made to the crusade against commercialism. Gies's initiative had been important in the formation of the American Association of Dental Schools.[13] This amalgamation of all national organizations dealing specifically with dental education removed the final obstacles to a full-scale assault on the proprietary colleges in the Dental Educational Council of America. The first move to drop from the "A" ranking all schools that lacked a university affiliation was beaten back. It was only a temporary defeat. The last proprietary schools disappeared from the "A" category in the classification of 1924 and the last one fell from "B" rating in 1926.[14]

Within the American Dental Association, there was opposition to one of Gies's recommendations. He advocated the continued independence of the Dental Educational Council of America as the agency for determination of educational policy. His argument was based on the example of the Council on Medical Education of the American Medical Association. He feared that dominance of the Council by the national organization of practitioners would open the way for the intrusion of commercial influences and would inhibit the Council's initiative.[15] The trend of sentiment in the Association ran counter to Gies's views in this respect. In 1925, for the first time, the Association combined its representation on the Dental Educational Council with the activities of its standing Committee on Education.[16] This was the first of a series of moves that reflected the increasing concern of the Association with the work of the independent Council.

Antagonism to the Dental Educational Council of America within the American Dental Association was covert rather than open at the outset. Then, in 1931, President Robert T. Oliver proposed to the House of Delegates that the status of the Dental Educational Council be drastically reduced. The Council, he charged, was far too large. Support of the Council was an unnecessary expense, Oliver declared, because it was merely trying to perform duties already assigned to the standing Committee on Education. The House of Delegates directed the trustees to reduce the membership of the Dental Educational Council to nine and its functions to "a sympathetic, advisory capacity, with no mandatory powers" except to consider colleges' applications for higher ratings.[17]

In 1932, Oliver's successor, Martin Dewey, renewed the attack. In his President's Address, Dewey challenged the value of the reforms favored by Gies's survey and the Dental Educational Council of America. Both had opposed private interests in dental education, he pointed out. They had favored university affiliation, and they had won out. Dewey continued, "After the existence of this state of affairs for a number of years, we find so far as economics is concerned, that the University Dental Schools are carrying on practices that the privately owned dental schools were unable to put into operation even in their most balmy [*sic*] days." The clinics of the university dental colleges levied higher fees, Dewey charged. The clinics were operated for profit in a manner "more flagrant" than done in the private schools. In effect, Dewey claimed, the university-related colleges were indulging in corporate dental practice. He pointed to controversies between the practitioners of New York and the Columbia University dental college, between the dentists of Memphis and the faculty of the dental school of the University of Tennessee, and between the Atlanta profession and the Atlanta Southern Dental School, as instances in support of his charge. "The majority" of dental colleges with university affiliations, he added, were "equally as guilty." [18]

In his annual report, Dewey advanced further complaints. He thought the Association's representation on the Council should be proportional to its membership in relation to the rolls of the other two participating societies. He recommended that the Association's standing Committee on Education take over the functions of the Council.[19]

Chairman Albert L. Midgley defended the Dental Educational Council of America. He pointed out that the profession had shown little interest in the Council until it began publishing its classification of dental schools. "Since that time, there has been more or less trouble for the Council in one way or another," Midgley said. He added that most of the controversies seemed to arise from "misinformation" and personalities, but insisted the differences were not "malicious." In the meetings of the trustees, Dewey returned to the attack. The organizations of examiners and educators should share the expense of the Council, he insisted. Subsequently, appearing as past-president, Dewey reported a conference with Morris Fishbein of the American Medical Association. The American Medical Association, Dewey noted, chose the entire membership of its Council on Medical Education. Dewey held that the American Dental Association should likewise name all members of the Dental Educational Council of America.[20] Dewey's proposals went further than the House of Delegates was willing to go. The campaign against the Council had reached a temporary peak. The 1932 session of the House of Delegates even rescinded the restrictive resolutions of the preceding year.[21]

Pressure from the Association on the Dental Educational Council continued. Although Dewey's successor, Walter Dittmar, did not add to the controversy, the standing Committee on Dental Education recommended that a study be undertaken and that conferences be held with other dental bodies to delineate the authority of the Council and determine how its efficiency might be improved.[22] In 1934, the Committee on Dental Education was reorganized. It was authorized to delegate clerical and other functions of the Dental Educational Council to an employee of the Association. The move clearly marked an increase in the Association's influence over the Dental Educational Council. At the same time, the Committee's duties were broadened to include nomenclature and dental history.[23]

In the following year, President Frank M. Casto, himself the dean of a dental school, proposed that the Association assume the functions of the Dental Educational Council and, in effect, supersede it. Casto recommended that the American Dental Association Committee on Dental Education be reorganized with five members. Three of these men would be elected by the House of Delegates as was customary with Association committees; the other two would be named by the National Association of Dental Examiners and the American Association of Dental Schools. The House of Delegates was not ready to go quite so far. It merely authorized yet another committee to survey dental education. The Dental Educational Council of America was not yet eliminated, but its end was in sight.[24]

The Committee to Study Dental Education, reporting in 1936, had little to suggest. It found that the profession had no confidence in the Dental Educational Council of America. The few concrete proposals the Committee made were rejected by the reference committee of the House of Delegates and by the House itself. The House of Delegates then proceeded to instruct the Board of Trustees to organize an educational council that would supersede the Dental Educational Council of America. The House resolutions envisioned a council numbering seven, three chosen by the American Dental Association and two each by the American Association of Dental Schools and the National Association of Dental Examiners. The examiners and educators were to submit nominees for these posts to the Board of Trustees who would then make up a slate for election by the House of Delegates. Other terms of the House scheme similarly asserted the intent of the American Dental Association to control the national agency for the determination of policy in the training of dentists. As evidence of that fact, the House recommended that the senior members of the delegations from the schools' and the examiners' societies retire.[25] The Dental Educational Council of America wound up its affairs at its 1936 meeting bringing to a close a turbulent twenty-seven-year career.[26]

For the next two years, the American Association of Dental Schools and the National Board of Dental Examiners struggled to preserve their roles in the establishment of educational policy, while the American Dental Association added further responsibilities to the duties of its Committee on Dental Education, now called the Council on Dental Education.[27] In resolutions directed to the Board of Trustees in 1937, the American Association of Dental Schools argued that the 1936 actions of the House contravened the American Dental Association constitution. The colleges' society reminded the practitioners' organization of the desirability of cooperation among the parties concerned. It outlined terms that it considered satisfactory as a basis for continuing cooperative efforts in dental education. The American Association of Dental Schools insisted that any proposal be ratified by the three interested agencies of the profession before it was put into effect.[28]

At length an agreement was reached and a new Council on Dental Education of the American Dental Association began its work in 1938. The new Council had much the same structure as that of its predecessor. It consisted of nine members, three from each of the national organizations of educators, examiners, and practitioners. The House of Delegates reserved the right of ratifying the members named by the other two bodies. The full expense of administering the program of the Council was assumed by the American Dental Association. At the 1938 meeting, the Association removed the auxiliary concerns of nomenclature, history and dental museum from the jurisdiction of the Council and created standing committees for these matters.[29]

In this reorganization of the Council on Dental Education, the Association found a compromise that seemingly satisfied the conflicting opinions regarding the proper agency for determining educational policy. Those who insisted that the national organization of the profession should control, conceded to the educators and examiners the right to equal representation of their own choice on the Council. But the Council was specifically described as "the agency of the American Dental Association in investigating conditions of dental education and associated subjects." The powers of the Council were limited to suggesting "means and methods" for improvement in the field of education to the House and the Trustees. In the 1948 revision of the constitution, the Council received, in addition to the responsibility of accrediting schools of dentistry and related subjects, the responsibility of approving "internships, residencies, and dental specialty boards." The bylaws provide that the classification shall be done "in accordance with requirements and standards approved by the House of Delegates." [30]

The American Dental Association, under its constitution and bylaws, controls the Council on Dental Education. Nevertheless, Harlan H. Horner, for many years secretary of the Council on Dental Education, has written that the Council "functions independently as an accrediting agency." He says that the Association has made no attempt "to influence or to restrain" the Council in its work, "except through duly appointed members." [31] The issue has never been really put to a test. The procedures of the Council have been such as to avoid stirring up controversy. And on one occasion where there was a clash over the independence of the Council, the outcome was not clear.

The Council on Dental Education held its organizational meeting in May, 1938. It suspended issuance of a classified list of dental schools such as the antecedent Dental Educational Council of America had made. There followed a period of study, discussion, and preparation. The Council issued a "Preliminary Statement," enunciating the principles by which it would be governed in April, 1939, but no secretary to the Council was appointed until 1940. [32] In January, 1941, the Council promulgated its *Requirements for Approval of Dental Schools.*

Neither the "Preliminary Statement" nor the *Requirements* necessitated any sweeping changes in the practices that the Dental Educational Council had advocated. The new Council was concerned with two main points. It desired greater emphasis on teaching dentistry as a university subject rather than as a mechanical and rote discipline. Secondly, it sought to increase the amount of time available to the student for independent study by limiting the hours spent in clinical work. The latter objective lent support to Martin Dewey's charges in 1932 that many of the university clinics were money-making rather than teaching operations. Beyond these general points, the *Requirements* stipulated maximum and minimum clock hours of instruction leading to the degree and listed the subjects that were to be taught without dictating the distribution of time among them. The Council took care to base its requirements on practices already widely accepted among the colleges. It allowed ample time to make the indicated adjustments before the inspection of the schools was to begin. The procedure was not calculated to create any substantial opposition. Other circumstances prolonged the interval before the inspections could begin.

The outbreak of the war and the inauguration of an accelerated program in the colleges intervened to delay the inspections. The preparation of the first list of accredited schools was finally ready for publication early in 1945. Then came a test of the independence of the Council. At its meeting in February of that year the Board of Trustees instructed the editor to withhold publication of the report on the ground that it had not received the approval of the House of Delegates and hence was "unofficial." The action was rescinded by a mail vote of the trustees in May, and the list was duly published in the June, 1945, issue of *The Journal of the American Dental Association*. Because of war-time restrictions on travel, the House of Delegates did not meet in 1945, but the Board of Trustees met in October. At that time, the Board heard the opinion of legal counsel that publication of "classifications of dental schools" was "a matter of policy," that should not be undertaken without the prior authorization of the House of Delegates. The attorneys did hold, however, that the Council on Dental Education was subject to the Board of Trustees only as provided in the bylaws. The opinion upheld the February action of the Board because the contents of the *Journal* are the responsibility of the Trustees.[33] The views of the Trustees were thus vindicated, but the Council's report was not unduly delayed. The question was not aired at the meeting of the House of Delegates in 1946. In the absence of any serious dissatisfaction with the work of the Council, the question of its independence within its own province remains open.

One of the major reasons for seeking relative uniformity of educational standards was to establish greater uniformity in the standards for admission to dental practice. The latter objective was desirable because it allowed greater freedom to the new dentist in selecting the location of his practice and because it eased the problems of the dentist who wanted to transfer his practice from one location to another. There is no need to labor the point that problems of education and licensure are closely related. It is a natural area of concern to the national organization of the profession.

In venturing into the field of dental licensure, the American Dental Association moved into an area fraught with conflict and charged with deep-seated emotion. Not all of the tension was of the Association's making. State suspicion of supra-state powers is of venerable standing in American history. Ever since the Civil War the trend toward nationalization has moved at an increasing tempo and the states have seen one after another of their prerogatives usurped or superseded by broader authorities, both private and public. The traditional tendency of state politicians to "view with alarm" any effort to create authorities larger than the state unit, or to impose policy from outside, was among the difficulties organized dentistry met in seeking a greater degree of uniformity in licensing procedure. Other obstacles, not entirely unique to dentistry, confronted the profession. Any setting of national standards tended to reduce the prestige of the administrators of the state programs. No official of a private or a public organization welcomes a diminution of his status. Thus when the Association sought to establish national standards for entry into the practice of dentistry, it encountered two "universal" sources of opposition at the outset.

There were problems enough in the nature of the profession and in its own history. In the beginning of the story of dentistry in the

United States, the individual dentist was free to travel and to practice where he chose. Access to the profession was unrestricted. As the more earnest practitioners sought to set up distinctions between the legitimate dentist and the unqualified and unscrupulous pretender, their first move was to found dental societies and their second was to seek legislative definitions of qualification. Early dental societies claimed special qualifications to advise the legislature in drafting the bills and to assist the executive in selecting the officials to administer the laws. Occasionally a state dental society received statutory rights to choose or nominate candidates for membership on the examining boards.

In this field of endeavor, the dental organizations could not clearly perceive the role they were performing. They represented, on the one hand, the interests of their constituency, the legitimate dentists. On the other hand, organized dentistry constituted the best source of information and advice the elected representatives of the community could find on the relation of dentistry to the common welfare. While, in an ideal sense, these two roles were, and are, identical, they often seemed to conflict. In consequence, the counsels of organized dentistry were, and are, frequently divided on questions involving the interests of dentistry and the common good.

Furthermore, the effort to grant the dentist some freedom of choice as to where he was to practice took place within the established framework of state legislation. By the end of the nineteenth century, most dental thinkers had abandoned any thought of federal dental licensure. Since there seemed little likelihood of early achievement of uniform dental standards throughout the nation, most efforts to afford mobility to dentists looked in the direction of reciprocity agreements. These were basically bilateral "treaties" between two states providing for the mutual acceptance of one another's licensing procedures. Of course, reciprocity had to have a basis in the statutes of the participants. These laws, however, merely set standards and left to the state examining board the determination of whether or not the regulations of a particular state met those standards. Now there were obviously serious obstacles to the extension of the system of reciprocity beyond certain limits. No state was likely to accept reciprocity with a state holding lower standards, since this would tend to undermine its own. The only way out seemed to be to wait upon the general elevation of standards throughout the country.[34]

The problem was the subject of frequent discussion in the meetings of the American Dental Association through the late nineteenth century but the discussions failed to produce a satisfactory solution. The examiners themselves organized a national society in 1883 to seek greater uniformity of standards. The National Association of Dental Examiners moved in two directions toward the improvement of the licensing situation. First, it tried to raise educational standards by agreeing to refuse to recognize degrees from colleges that failed to meet certain minimum specifications. Next, the National Association of Dental Examiners worked for greater uniformity in the licensing statutes. These representatives of the people of the states shared the concern of the educators and practitioners in matters of educational policy and the National Association of Dental Examiners cooperated in organizing the Dental Educational Council of America in 1909.[35] This effort at regularizing standards in the colleges was far in advance of any like achievement in licensing practices.

The medical profession had devised a partial solution to the problem. With the assistance of the Carnegie Foundation, the American Medical Association and the national organizations representing the medical schools and the state boards of medical examiners had organized a joint agency that devised and administered a standard national examination. A state board whose enabling statute permitted it to do so could accept a certificate of satisfactory accomplishment on the national examination in lieu of part or all of the state test. William J. Gies, in his report on dental education, suggested that reciprocity in dental licensing might be assisted in the same way, by instituting "an accessory system of uniform national examinations," exacting the highest standards. Gies thought the board that prepared the national examination might also draft requirements for qualification in dental specialties.[36]

Even before Gies published his report, he conveyed to the American Dental Association, in 1924, a strong hint from the Carnegie Foundation that it was prepared to underwrite a National Board of Dental Examiners. To get the Carnegie grant the national dental organizations that were concerned had to submit a formal request, accompanied by an outline of plans looking toward the accomplishment of the objectives. The Board of Trustees authorized the pres-

ident of the Association to appoint a committee of five to confer with
the other agencies regarding the suggestion. At the next annual
session, the House of Delegates endorsed the principle of a National
Board of Dental Examiners. The discussions continued through the
next two years. President Henry L. Banzhaf, in 1927, urged the
Association to seek the aid of the Carnegie Corporation in establishing
a National Board of Dental Examiners. The necessary amendments
to the constitution and by-laws could not be adopted until the following annual meeting.[37]

The proposition continued to excite discussion and debate through
the profession during the following year. The presidential address
of Roscoe H. Volland indicated that some of the aspects of the
proposal gave rise to argument. Volland pointed out that the establishment contemplated under Banzhaf's plan would have created a
"more or less independent organization, the majority of whose members would be selected by and acceptable to organizations other
than the American Dental Association." The statement implied a
strong desire to have the National Board under Association control.
Volland protested that he favored the idea of a National Board, but
he argued that much work had to be done to prepare the way for
it, mostly in the shape of state enabling laws. Furthermore, he declared that if the Association was to finance the new agency, it
should be "closely attached to and sanely controlled by" the parent
body. To assure "unreserved unanimity of purpose," he repeated, the
National Board should be "responsible and obligated to but one
organization." Volland presented a draft amendment embodying his
views.

After further discussion and debate, the annual session of 1928
passed the necessary amendments. The organic law establishing the
National Board of Dental Examiners followed the outline that had
already been the basis of discussion. Each of the three cooperating
societies was to be equally represented. The new by-laws provided,
however, that the Board of Trustees should nominate all members
for election by the House of Delegates. Two groups of the nominees
were to be selected from a choice of men named by the colleges' and
the examiners' organizations. In the event the trustees did not find
suitable candidates among the panel presented to them, they were
to ask the participating societies to supply more.[38]

The whole scheme very nearly failed because the cooperating agencies each desired to dominate the new organization or at least did not wish to allow it to be controlled by either of the others. The National Association of Dental Examiners warned the American Dental Association in 1929 that the proposed Board must offer equal representation to the participants and that each must have the privilege of naming its representatives. A compromise method of choosing the members of the National Board was adopted in 1930. This amendment seated the members elected by the American Association of Dental Schools and the National Association of Dental Examiners provided they were members of the American Dental Association.[39] This maneuvering for control of the National Board came simultaneously with the struggle over the Dental Educational Council of America. The whole period of the middle thirties was a time of strife over the control of the institutions of the profession.

The controversy over the National Board was sufficiently resolved to permit the holding of the first examinations in 1933.[40] But trouble was not far away. At the 1934 meeting of the National Association of Dental Examiners, one representative of a state examining body offered resolutions attacking the National Board. The resolutions asserted that the Board was "illegal and without authority in law." It was "neither feasible, practical, nor tending toward making our profession a higher ethical association." The program of the National Association of Dental Examiners, on the other hand, according to the resolutions, represented all those desirable qualities. This examiner therefore proposed that the examiners have nothing further to do with the national examination scheme. The resolutions were referred to a special committee for report at the next meeting.[41]

The 1935 convention of the examiners produced a lively debate on the merits of the uniform examination proposal. The special committee submitted a majority report that took a favorable view of the National Board of Dental Examiners. The committee found that the national examination scheme was "not foisted upon organized dentistry by any 'clap-trap' or under-cover methods for the purpose of exploitation; nor fostered by any group for ulterior motives." The report reminded the examiners that the National Board was not a creation of the National Association of Dental Examiners. Nothing the examiners did could stop, or even change, the plan of the National

Board of Dental Examiners. Nevertheless, the committee majority recommended that the Association of Examiners endorse the National Board and urge the state boards to seek amendments to their codes authorizing acceptance of the certificates of the National Board without making such acceptance mandatory. Echoing Gies's opinion, the committee concluded that the Board certification offered a better system than the bilateral reciprocity arrangements for achieving professional mobility while maintaining the protection of the public.[42]

The majority report provoked a violent dissent from one member. The critic assumed throughout his tirade that acceptance of the certification of the National Board was mandatory. He further assumed that the national uniform examination would determine qualification in all aspects of dentistry. This, he argued, would make it possible for an applicant passed by mistake to set up a practice in any state of the union.

The enemy of the uniform examinations claimed that the consequence of establishment of the system would be complete state interchange of licensing. "This will develop either 'fly by night' advertisers, or a class of floaters, and wondering [sic], irresponsible, low fee, 'journeyman dentists,' " he warned. He reiterated that the National Board was "illegal" because it had no statutory authority. If this menace was not eliminated, he foresaw the destruction of all the defenses of the profession erected in any of the states.

The practitioners' and the educators' organizations could not maintain the National Board without the support of the examiners, he continued. Thus, the threat could readily be eliminated by withdrawing the cooperation of the National Association of Dental Examiners. The critic turned next to a consideration of the argument that the national uniform examination scheme merited a trial. "A trial is all that Red Russia wanted! A trial is all that Mussolini wanted! That is all Hitler wanted—just A TRIAL!" In conclusion, the staunch defender of the status quo rose to a final flight of eloquence. "Cleopatra had her asp; Hamilton had his Aaron Burr; Caesar had his Brutus; and Christ, his Judas Iscariot. Dentistry has its National Board of Dental Examiners."[43]

The conflicting committee reports initiated a thorough debate that reviewed again the standard arguments already developed by the antagonists. Opponents of the national uniform examination system insisted that the National Board examined the wrong qualities. They pointed out that the tests merely explored the degree to which the student had absorbed the theoretical teachings of the schools. The state examiners' boards tried to determine the qualification of the candidate to practice. Furthermore, the opponents claimed, the Board certificates inhibited reciprocity and interchange of licensing. One debater explained that since the certificates had no legal standing, the states accepting them held standards inferior to those states with statutory regulations. There could be no reciprocity between these extremes.

The supporters of the innovation tirelessly, though fruitlessly, pointed out that the holder of a certificate still had to satisfy the requirements of the state where he sought a license. Others vainly sought to correct the charge that the National Board of Dental Examiners was illegal because it had not been established by law. Proponents of the uniform examination plan reminded the body that the scheme had been under discussion within the profession for a decade and under trial among the physicians for twice that time. The experience of the physicians had not produced the dire consequences the opponents anticipated. The proposal would work satisfactorily once a national standard curriculum had been agreed upon and uniform state laws adopted, other advocates said. With these objectives in sight, they reasoned, the National Board of Dental Examiners should have a chance to prove its merits. The innovators lost. The defenders of the states' control prevailed.[44] The National Board program had to limp along for five years without the participation of the examiners' organization.

The American Dental Association and the American Association of Dental Schools continued their support of the National Board of Dental Examiners in the face of the opposition of the examiners. By 1935, the Board reported eleven states had granted conditional acceptance to Board certificates. In that year 242 candidates were examined.[45] The National Association of Dental Examiners attacked the continued operation of the National Board without the participation of the examiners' society. This was contrary to the organization of the Board, they charged. Furthermore, the examiners claimed that the Board's publicity was misleading dental students. They demanded that the Board, and, implicitly, the Board of Trustees and the editor of the Association retract the statements of the purpose and progress of the Board's work.[46] The examiners' campaign had little effect. The Association by-laws outlining the duties of the Board of Dental Examiners were amended in 1937 to confine the examinations to dental theory, leaving practical tests to the several state boards.[47] Meanwhile, the Association continued to confer with representatives of the National Association of Dental Examiners in the hope of winning reaffiliation of the latter with the program of national uniform dental examinations.[48]

Reunion was finally achieved in 1941.[49] Since that time, the National Board of Dental Examiners has continued with no essential change. The states accepting the certificate of the National Board as a partial or complete substitute for the state administered written tests numbered twenty-four by 1950. In 1953, the American Dental Association began to administer this program directly from its central offices. More than 5,500 took the examinations in 1956, exceeding the estimates of the Council on National Board of Dental Examiners by 500. Some thirty-two states, one dependency, and three federal dental services now recognize the certificates of the Board.[50] In other words, after twenty-five years' experience, less than two-thirds of the states subscribe to the program. Yet for more than fifteen years, the major national dental organizations have been agreed on the objective of nation-wide tests. The still limited success of the program graphically illustrates the difficulties arising from the decentralized organization of the national professional societies.

Dental leadership has been tested by the problem of establishing standards of training and by the difficulties of achieving uniformity in licensing procedures. The fostering of advancement in the science and art of dentistry has posed a challenge equally great.

At the time of the reorganization of 1913, the dental profession was rent by the controversy over the Taggart patents on the process of casting precision gold inlays. The Dental Protective Association, upon which the profession had relied to defeat the crown patents, had negotiated an agreement with Taggart and offered to the profession membership in the Dental Protective Association and a license to use the Taggart methods in a single package. Aligned on the side of the Dental Protective Association were some of the most prominent and respected members of the profession, among them J. N. Crouse, beloved and honored for his leadership in the long fight against the tooth crown patents, R. Ottolengui, famed dental editor, and C. N. Johnson, educator and editor, a former president of the Illinois State Dental Society and, within a decade, to be successively president of the American Dental Association and editor of *The Journal of the American Dental Association.* Opposing the policy of the Dental Protective Association and battling the Taggart claims was an equally imposing array headed by Mark F. Finley, a former president of the National Dental Association.[51]

In Washington, in 1911, Taggart lost a suit on a minor aspect of his process. Not long thereafter, however, he brought a successful action in Chicago. The brutal demands with which Taggart's attorneys tried to follow up the victory galvanized the opposition to the patents. They organized the Dentists' Mutual Protective Alliance for the purpose of fighting the claims.

On the issue of the Taggart patents, the reorganized national association was in no better position to take a firm stand than its predecessor had been. Men prominent in Association affairs were to be found in both camps. As a matter of fact, after the reorganization, the pro-Taggart group seemingly held a somewhat stronger position in the National Dental Association. Homer C. Brown's successor as president was Don M. Gallie, one of the trustees of the Dental Protective Association, which was sponsoring the licensing arrangement with Taggart. The Dentists' Mutual Protective Alliance had to fight the patent claims without the explicit support of the National Dental Association.

A series of extraordinarily lucky breaks finally enabled the Alliance to overthrow the Taggart patents. By indefatigably running down every clue, the Alliance unearthed a Dr. B. F. Philbrook of Denison, Iowa, who claimed to have devised a process to cast inlays twenty years before Taggart announced his method. Dr. Philbrook's office records disclosed that during the middle nineties he had indeed produced several cast inlays for his patients. Some of Philbrook's colleagues recalled his having read a paper describing his technique before a small meeting of the county dental society. Fortuitously, the dusty shelves of the University of Iowa library yielded a copy of the paper. The chain of evidence was sufficient to defeat the Taggart claims.[52]

Having completed the task it had set out to accomplish, the Dentists' Mutual Protective Alliance lay dormant for over a decade. Then its directors decided to ask the American Dental Association to take over its functions. At length, an agreement was reached. The Alliance decided to disband and to turn over its assets, nearly $12,000 in bonds, to the Association as a contribution to the building fund. The Association, in exchange, established a standing Committee on Process Patents. The by-laws governing the committee expressly prohibited any compromise of a patent question. Thus the organic law of the American Dental Association protected the profession against any recurrence of the action of the Dental Protective Association. Satisfied with this safeguard, the Alliance dissolved. The bonds were delivered into the hands of the treasurer of the Association on December 21, 1931.[53]

In 1931, a standing Committee on Process Patents became a fixture of the activities of the Association. The first Committee was nominated jointly by a committee of the American Dental Association and the Dentists' Mutual Protective Alliance. The perennial chairman of the new Committee was M. D. K. Bremner, president of the defunct Alliance. The Committee flourished during the thirties. Bremner claimed that its existence inhibited would-be claimants of process patents. In any event, only one attempt was made to enforce a patent claim in the thirties. A Kansas City dentist asserted patent rights to a process for treating periodontal disease through the application of high frequency current. The Committee, on behalf of the Association, accomplished the defeat of the claim in 1939.

Thereafter the patent question seemed of less importance. In 1943, an amendment to the by-laws authorized the Association to take "whatever steps that might be necessary to acquire control or ownership of patents or copyrights useful in the practice of Dentistry." This ambiguous policy weakened the stand of the Association on the patent question. It was rescinded in the following year. During the early forties, the Committee received the additional duty of recommending to the Board and the House "individuals, living or dead, whose contributions to the advancement of dentistry deserve special recognition." This broadening of the duties of the Committee was in keeping with the apparent notion that the patent question had been settled. It was likewise consistent with the policy of granting appropriate recognition to innovators after they had made their contribution. The Committee on Process Patents, under the stern guidance of Dr. Bremner, maintained its aggressive posture until it was absorbed into the Council on Legislation in the constitutional revision of 1948.[54] In the absence of a significant test in recent years, it would be difficult to say whether the patent problem has at last been settled or has been merely swept under the rug.

The practice of encouraging progress by rewarding accomplishment has drawbacks. It does not aid the inventor or researcher at the time that he needs help, while he is developing his innovation. It does not guide the efforts of the research workers in the directions where improvement is most desirable. And it does not foster a sustained attack on the problems requiring solution. Repeated efforts have been made throughout the history of the profession to subsidize research work in progress.[55] Many enthusiasts waited impatiently for the reorganization process to be completed before inaugurating a drive to at last provide dentistry with continuing leadership and support in research to solve the many perplexing problems confronting dental science in the early twentieth century.

The constitutional revision of 1913 included provision for the establishment of the National Dental Association Scientific Foundation and Research Commission, which was authorized to solicit, receive, and disburse funds to be devoted to research. Vigorous activity by the contemporary leadership brought in funds sufficient to inaugurate the research program during the following year.[56] During 1915 the available funds had risen sufficiently to warrant a special drive for the purchase of a building to house the research activities of the Association. The Research Commission therefore incorporated the Research Institute of the National Dental Association, which purchased property in Cleveland and began operations in the following year.[57] The system seemed well started with the Institute undertaking a variety of projects and the House of Delegates authorizing the Commission to ask the constituent societies to raise their dues one dollar, the increase to be used to subsidize the Research Commission's work.[58]

During the War, the work at the Institute had to be severely curtailed because of the drafting of a large part of the technical staff. The Research Commission, however, continued its support of projects in other institutions. In 1919, the Commission decided to close the Institute and divert its funds entirely to grants-in-aid to dental schools and individuals. In 1920, the Institute building was leased to a group of physicians for use as a hospital and clinic; the equipment was sold, and the proceeds were placed in the research fund. This move roused some criticism among the profession. Subscriptions were slow coming in, many subscribers holding that the leasing of the Institute building abrogated their subscription agreement. The attempt of the national organization of the profession to conduct its own program of research had proved abortive.[59]

The Research Commission redoubled its efforts. It successfully sought additional funds from the Association. The annual dues were raised to four dollars in 1923 with the proviso that one-third of the income should go to research.[60] During the years between 1920 and 1933, the annual sums appropriated to the Research Commission amounted to about $25,000, about one-tenth of the income of the Association during that period.[61] The Commission also tried to stretch the funds it received. It sought to place the grants in institutions where the receiving school would make an equal or larger contribution to the cost of the project. The Commission endeavored to see that the assistance was given to worthwhile undertakings. In the case of applications that involved appraisal of the request it devised a system for processing them through a special committee of the National Research Council. After the first World War, the Council lost its intimate relation with the federal government agencies and became a sort of central bureau of the nation's scientific and engineering societies. Lacking funds of its own, the National Research Council functioned as the dispenser of money from the great Rockefeller and Carnegie foundations. The Council served also to coordinate research efforts around the country through its special committees based on the various scientific disciplines.[62] The American Dental Association did not benefit from the former aspect of the Council, but referral to the Research Council's committee helped prevent duplication of effort and furnished an outside judgment on the quality of the applications.[63]

Through the early twenties, the Association received no direct help from government agencies in the conduct of its research program. The work on dental materials, initiated during the war period in the National Bureau of Standards, was renewed in 1922 with the establishment of the Weinstein Laboratories Research Fellowship. Under a plan established by law, groups wishing to cooperate in the work of the Bureau of Standards may appoint research associates or establish fellowships at the Bureau. These workers are paid by the cooperating organizations, which also provide funds for the purchase of special equipment and materials. The Bureau furnishes standard equipment, laboratory and consultative facilities, supervises the work of the fellows and publishes the results. Louis J. Weinstein of Weinstein Laboratories was so impressed with the work on amalgams conducted by the Bureau during the war that he provided a fellowship for the continuance of the investigations of dental materials. The Weinstein precedent stimulated the American Dental Association Research Commission to begin negotiations with the Bureau in 1924 with an eye to the establishment of an American Dental Association fellowship program. Arrangements for an Association-sponsored fellowship were not completed until 1928. With this action, a new stage in the history of the Association's research activities began.[64]

The founding of a cooperative research program at the Bureau of Standards was a symptom of a change that had been agitated for some years rather than in itself a cause of reorientation in the Association's approach to dental investigations. In the beginning the Research Commission had envisioned work largely conducted by employees of the Association in the laboratories of the Institute in Cleveland. Through the twenties, the universities were the major source of research personnel. The American Dental Association did not pay the full salary of any researcher.

This early phase emphasized the biological and preventive aspects of dentistry. It aimed high. Frank O. Hetrick, chairman of the Commission for many years, wrote, "Research work should help to standardize our methods of procedure and prevention, as well as restorative practice. I mean by that to establish some universally recognized method, such as Dr. Black's method of cavity preparations,

now received by a great majority of our profession." [65] Problems under
investigation with American Dental Association assistance ranged
from the effects of malnutrition, through tuberculosis detection, to
the work of the Dental Index Bureau. The dispersal of efforts, the
dispersal of funds, and the emphasis on biological problems, many of
which still baffle science, contributed to a lack of accomplishment.
There were complaints that the research program had failed to yield
an adequate return for the money invested. In 1932, President Martin
Dewey summed up the discontent. "After considerable thought to
the progress of dentistry during the past few years, I am impressed
by the fact that there has been nothing outstanding so far as the
scientific side of dentistry is concerned," he declared. "It is true that
a large amount of money has been expended for research, but the
results . . . have done very little towards influencing the progress
of dentistry as a health measure or from a scientific standpoint." [66]

In response to the shifting tide of opinion in the profession, the
Association's research interests changed. The establishment of the
fellowship program in the Bureau of Standards marked the change
in all its aspects. Increasingly, American Dental Association research
funds were used to pay American Dental Association workers. The
list of recipients shrank as the Research Commission began to concentrate its expenditures. There was less disposition to make small
grants to the universities and an increasing exploitation of federal
facilities whose large resources and relative permanence permitted
carrying out long-range and continuing investigations. At the same
time, emphasis shifted from the biological and preventive aspects of
dentistry to dental materials and restorative measures, which seemed
to hold promise of more immediate and practical application to the
working dentist. The altered character of the profession's research
interests, coupled with the economic difficulties of the Depression
years, reduced expenditures for research to somewhat less than half
the average sums spent during the twenties. [67]

These new developments in the history of dental research coincided
with a change in the needs of research in dentistry. By the thirties,
some of the university dental schools had well-developed research
programs and no longer needed assistance from the Research Commission. In 1935, the Commission reported only three small grants,
none larger than $750, for purposes other than the support of the

fellowship at the Bureau of Standards.[68] The work in the universities was supplemented by the studies in the National Institute of Health, established as part of the Public Health Service in 1930. A dental division of the Service, anticipated for some years, was established the following year. At that time, the Surgeon General, Hugh S. Cumming, appointed five dental consultants to the Service. At a conference between representatives of the National Institute of Health and the dental consultants, held in January, 1932, a program of dental research was sketched. The problems selected for study in the government facilities at Bethesda, Maryland, indicated three fields that had no place in the reoriented program of the Research Commission. The conferees decided the dental studies of the National Institute of Health should concentrate on dental caries and dental infections, and continue its investigation of mottled enamel, the latter a dental phenomenon that had been mystifying dental scientists for years. The comment of the Research Commission on the potential role of the new agency reflects a new trend. "It is hoped that eventually this Bureau will conduct the major portion of our biological dental research. The same arguments can be used in support of the Bureau of Standards ultimately assuming the responsibilities of the investigation of dental materials. . . ."[69] While the tendency to place increasing reliance on federally supported projects has never gone so far, there can be no denying the growing role of governmental scientists in the investigation of health problems.

The new pattern of the research activities of the profession had scarcely been defined before it was questioned. Through the middle thirties, various dental spokesmen tried to restore the balance. C. T. Messner of the Dental Division of the Public Health Service and the American Dental Association Research Commission warned, "If the dental profession is to stand in the future on its ability and cleverness in repairing the loss of human structure due to disease, and if it does not make any concerted effort or sacrifice to discover the cause of dental disease, the future of the profession is not very bright." The Commission chairman, P. C. Lowery, lamented that the current work was "nearly all physical research." Biological investigations were also important, he noted. "To some members of our organization, it does not seem to be such important work. While in the field of physical research the solution of the problem is more rapidly accomplished and is to many of our members of more immediate value, to most of the members of the Research Commission, . . . both types of research are necessary and important." [70] Lowery, Messner, and their colleagues sparked a revival of interest in the biological aspects of dentistry during the late thirties. Their labors prepared the way for the establishment of the modern phase of the research activities of the American Dental Association.

The reformers of the late thirties awakened renewed interest in the problem of dental caries. The trend was signalized in 1936 by an appropriation for a special Advisory Committee on Dental Caries. The conception of the duties of the Committee was not clear. Apparently, it was expected to compile a definitive bibliography on the subject. In any event, the appropriation stipulated that three-fourths of the sum should be diverted to the International Association for Dental Research to assist in the publication of its journal. The scheme became more clear during the following years. The Committee began to collect summaries of current views on caries from authorities throughout the world. These statements the Advisory Committee compiled into a volume, *Dental Caries,* which was duly published in 1939. The book was, the Research Commission declared, "a new form of scientific literature." The Committee merely arranged the views presented by the authorities according to the alphabetical order of the author's name. The compilers made "no attempt . . . to evaluate the findings and conclusions . . . or to suggest which views may be regarded as most significant." "[The book's] contents are not subject to bias or accidental distortion by an abstractor or reviewer, nor to an editor's prejudgment, propaganda or censorship." The purpose, as the Commission's report noted, was "to promote" caries studies. The work was well received in the dental press. A second edition was published in 1941. The appearance of the book undoubtedly helped balance the research interests of the profession. [71]

In the meantime, the Research Commission had been agitating for the establishment of a dental fellowship at the National Institute of Health similar to that at the National Bureau of Standards. The objective was finally attained in 1941. The work at the National Institute of Health concentrated at the outset on a bacteriological approach to the periodontal diseases. Mapped on a long-term basis, the program outlined a fundamental attack on the problem that aimed first of all at establishing researches in the field on a sound foundation. Prior to the inauguration of the work at Bethesda, the whole subject had been shrouded in uncertainties.[72] The National Institutes of Health were likewise the center, through the thirties and forties, of the work of H. Trendley Dean and his colleagues that established the efficacy of fluoridation of water supplies as a caries-inhibiting measure. The onset of the second World War handicapped the work of the Research Commission somewhat, but it also fostered a broadening of the National Institute of Health program to investigate oral lesions.

Since 1946, the cooperation between the Association and the National Institutes of Health has expanded. The number of fellowships has been increased, and the Association has urged larger federal appropriations for dental research. The Council on Dental Research, the successor—since the 1948 revision of the constitution—of the Research Commission, now concentrates virtually all of its expenditures on the fellowship programs at the two federal agencies, the National Bureau of Standards and the National Institutes of Health. The sums devoted to the work at the Bureau of Standards are nearly twice as large as those for the National Institutes of Health. The testing of dental materials and the establishment of specifications for them has broadened through the years from the initial work on amalgam alloys to include casting materials, impression compounds, dental mercuries, gold wire alloys, dental cements, and denture base materials. The Bureau also worked for the improvement of dental instruments and equipment. The imbalance between the amounts devoted by the Association to the two programs does not indicate a like difference in emphasis, for the appropriation of federal funds for dental research within the Public Health Service has been growing to substantial proportions. A National Institute of Dental Research was founded as one of the National Institutes of Health in 1948. At that time the Association gave its support to a drive for the construction of a special building to house the National Institute of Dental Research. The campaign was a long one that finally won a substantial appropriation from Congress in 1958. Ground was broken and construction got underway in the Association's centennial year. A sum of $3,750,000 was spent by the National Institute in 1957–58 on dental research and the training of research personnel. The sum seems likely to increase in the years to come.[73]

The tremendous growth in research activities since the war with the Axis powers has resulted from a great outpouring of funds from various sources. The American Dental Association expenditures have increased proportionally. The burgeoning interest in research led to some confusion and duplication among the agencies of the Association concerned with research. In 1949, the House directed the Board of Trustees to form a special committee to study the research activities of the Association to eliminate conflicts and waste. The result of the survey was a redefinition of the duties of the Council on Dental Research. These, as the Council reported on them in 1952, placed renewed stress on the functions of the Council as a coordinating body and clearing house of information about the needs and opportunities in dental research. It is a measure of the importance of these new duties that in 1957, in the face of the greater expenditures on the fellowship program, between one-fifth and one-sixth of the Council's budget, around $25,000 out of $143,000, was allotted to the administrative aspects of the program.[74]

This change in the emphasis of the Council's functions, while not substantial in terms of the amount of money involved, is nevertheless indicative of a new turn in the Association's relation to the advancement of dental science. As other sources of funds for research have been developed (to an estimated $15 million in 1958), the American Dental Association's contributions proportionally declined. Although the Association's expenditures have increased more than ten-fold between 1930 and 1958, its share in the support of dental research is dwarfed by the huge sums derived from private and public sources. There has been a corresponding diminution of direct control of research by the Association. Other institutions now furnish the sinews with which to prosecute the war on dental diseases. Can the American Dental Association, as it embarks on its second century, supply the generalship?

Chapter XX   THE ASSOCIATION AND THE PUBLIC

THE PROBLEMS arising from the increased spending for research by public and private sources represented only one facet of the challenge confronting the American Dental Association. The role of the Association at the end of its first century was partly the result of its own seeking, partly thrust upon it; its difficulties were partly of its own making, partly the consequence of developments in American life. As spokesman for the profession, the Association aroused the nation to its dental needs. In so doing, it has encouraged demands for dental care that have exceeded the capacity of the profession to fulfill. This fact, in turn, has raised demands for increasing the amount of dental services available to the public. Faced with this insistent pressure, the leadership of organized dentistry has had to struggle to preserve the quality of dental care while endeavoring to increase the quantity of services available. At the same time, the Association has tried to vindicate the professional and scientific claims of dentistry upon the public while laboring to raise the social and professional level of its practitioners. The mediating position of the American Dental Association between the profession and the public has exposed it to countless conflicting strains and tensions. In some of its aspects, the history of this professional organization of dentists in recent times mirrors some

405

of the dilemmas perplexing American society in the twentieth century.

The reorganized Association of the period following the first World War inherited both a policy regarding its duty to the public and agencies to carry out the policy. The oral hygiene movement reached a peak as the National Dental Association wrestled with problems of reorganization. The oral hygiene program stressed public education in the importance of dental health and in the techniques of oral hygiene. The policy recognized the magnitude of the dental needs of the country. They were far beyond the capacity of the profession to service. Nevertheless, the profession aspired to supply dental care to all who needed it. The only practicable way of achieving some balance between needs and the resources for treatment placed high priority on preventive measures and the early and frequent examination and treatment of dental disorders, especially among children. The greatest success of this early oral hygiene movement was in the school program. The earliest endeavors to supply the dental needs of patients unable to pay for their care featured children's dentistry. The years before the first World War saw the endowment of children's dental clinics by philanthropists, such as the Forsyth brothers of Boston, and George Eastman of Rochester, N. Y. In many cases, facilities within the schools for the treatment of children were contributed by individuals. Occasionally, public funds were used for this purpose.[1]

During the years following the first World War, a standing committee of the Association, known as the Council on Mouth Hygiene and Public Instruction, continued the earlier efforts to spread the word on dental health. The increased numbers in the Association, plus the relative prosperity of the country and the maturity of the oral health movement, served to broaden and extend the program considerably. The Association in 1923 established a permanent bureau, which was to become the Bureau of Public Relations, for the purpose of preparing and disseminating materials for dental health education. In this process, the agencies of the Association cooperated with the growing number of state and local health departments, with departments of education, with the U. S. Public Health Service, with numerous voluntary health organizations, and with authors and publishers of textbooks on health. The Association encouraged dental health contests and observances. The dental health education program grew not only in bulk but in the scope of facilities upon which it drew to bring its message before the public. Slides and motion picture materials were developed, and in 1930 the resources of radio were added to the dental health education arsenal.[2]

Throughout the twenties, while the dental health education and related work among school children throve, the American Dental Association fought shy of smirching its program with any taint of commercialism. At the beginning of the decade, an offer of funds and cooperation from the Dental Welfare Foundation, formed by dental manufacturers and dealers for educational purposes, was rejected. A decade later, a brief trial of a plan for the dissemination of publicity regarding dentistry and dental care through the medium of paid advertisements in the press provoked much controversy and ultimate abandonment. A similar proposal submitted by the Dental Institute of America was debated from 1936 until its final rejection in 1939. The American Dental Association consistently relied on its own resources and those of educators and public health workers.[3]

In 1927, President Coolidge appointed a special Committee on the Costs of Medical Care, headed by Secretary of the Interior Ray Lyman Wilbur. The expense of this broad-gauge survey of the health service resources of the country was underwritten by private philanthropic foundations. The findings of this group and of related undertakings at about the same time furnished an early measure of the effectiveness of the work in dental health education. It was reported that the demand was less than the need for dental services. Dentists served only about twenty per cent of the population during the course of a year. Taken by itself, this might be regarded as a criticism of the efforts of the Committee on Dental Health Education. Further statistics, however, placed a different face on the matter. The surveys showed that the number of dentists had increased slightly faster than the population in the period since 1910, but that the demand for dental care had increased faster than the supply of dentists. The findings indicated that although the program of education had not been as effective as it might have been, yet it had perhaps been better than it needed to be.

One commentator pointed to an alarming feature of the situation. "The primary obligation of the profession is public service, and the profession cannot but view with concern—indeed with alarm—a situation in which an increasing number of our citizens are taught to recognize a dental need which they feel they cannot meet," he declared. "We have proceeded with programs of education which have transformed needs into latent demands without a due proportion of effort to make facilities available whereby those demands can be made effective in action." Homer C. Brown warned his colleagues that the profession must find a scheme to provide to the lower income groups the dental care "they have been educated to consider necessary for their well being."[4] The views thus expressed might well be taken as testimonials to the effectiveness of the Association's endeavors in dental health education.

More concrete expressions of confidence came directly from the House of Delegates. The popular impression regarding the excessive costs of medical and dental services had evoked a variety of proposals for state dentistry or insurance or panel practice. These schemes, some dental leaders held, constituted the "greatest menacing threat" the profession had ever faced. These attacks on existing modes of practice could best be combatted through an informed public opinion. A directive of the House of Delegates in 1933 charged the Bureau of Public Relations with this important task because of its long experience in dental health education.[5]

So the Association's agency for educating the public to recognize its dental needs acquired a new responsibility, that of presenting the views of the profession on the problem of dental care. During the thirties, the educational program continued to expand. New media of communication were exploited; the utilization of familiar ones intensified. As in the twenties, a variety of agencies supplemented the work of the Association in this field. A study of dental health literature, published in 1940, revealed that about one-fourth of the statements contained in the literature were fallacious, while about 44 per cent were controversial. The continued leadership of the Association in bringing about cooperation among the many bodies issuing materials on dental health and providing means of editing and verification was clearly needed and obviously required further extension. By 1938, sales of materials prepared by the Bureau of Public Relations yielded sufficient income to render the office virtually self-sustaining. In his report, the director, Lon W. Morrey, requested the employment of a publicity firm throughout the year. Morrey convincingly described the Association's need for carrying on a public relations and publicity program on a year-around basis rather than on an intermittent basis as the Association had been doing. The House of Delegates authorized the innovation.[6]

In the meantime, the passage of the Social Security Act of 1935 opened new possibilities for improving the dental health of the American public. The legislation obliged the Association to decide what program it should advocate. With virtual unanimity, the various agencies of the Association agreed that federal funds allocated to the states under the new law should be spent in part to further dental health education programs, both directly and through the founding of divisions of oral health in the state health departments. A continuation and expansion of dental health education became one feature of the participation by organized dentistry in plans for a national health program. This policy has been repeatedly confirmed since its inception.[7]

Studies of dental needs and knowledge of the American population over the past two decades afford some indication of the efficacy of the continuing and expanding efforts to spread the word of dental health. On the basis of a series of surveys during the fifties, it appeared that the proportion of the population served by the profession had grown markedly from the twenty per cent reported in the early thirties. According to a Gallup poll conducted in 1950, only four per cent of the adult population had never been to a dentist, although forty-seven per cent had not seen a dentist for two years or more. A narrower sample (confined to the inhabitants of Portland, Oregon) queried in 1955, showed that about two-thirds had a family dentist whom they visited for regular checkups. A 1954 survey by the Association's Bureau of Economic Research and Statistics indicated that about one-third of the male population and a somewhat smaller proportion of the females had not visited a dentist in more than two years.[8]

Dental health education cannot be given all the credit, or charged with the blame, that may attach to these returns. More people know the principles of good dental health practices than act on them.[9] This is borne out, for example, in the findings regarding the time for the child's first visit to the dentist. Two studies, about a decade apart, indicated that more than eighty per cent of the adult population know that dental care should begin before school age. About half of the respondents thought that the time of the first visit should be on completion of first dentition.[10] On the other hand, the Association's Family Dental Survey of 1953 found that three-fourths of the children under five years of age had never been to a dentist. Dental health education and dental public health enthusiasts might take some comfort from the fact that, in the age group from five to nine years, the number who had never visited a dentist dropped to about one-fourth.[11] At the same time, some misconceptions regarding oral conditions seemed stubbornly resistant to educational efforts. For example, a high proportion of respondents, around three-fourths, clung to the belief that pregnancy tends to induce caries in the mother.[12] The whole experience seemed to confirm the profession's faith in the usefulness and the necessity for continuing and broadening dental health education.

The profession recognized that educating the public to the value of dental health did not, in itself, end its responsibility. The public's need for dental care had to be determined and the means had to be found to accommodate those needs. Toward the end of the twenties, a number of events combined to create a considerable ferment in the social thinking of dentistry. In 1926, William J. Gies's report, *Dental Education in the United States and Canada,* challenged the profession to live up to the high ideals it expounded. In 1927, the Committee on the Costs of Medical Care began its investigations. The setting up of this Committee was only one of a number of government-sponsored and private studies of various aspects of American society during the twenties. One and all, they tended to bring many traditional American beliefs into question. Before the consequences of these developments had run their course, the Great Depression lent new urgency to examinations into the institutional basis of American life. The collapse of the economy also evoked a number of proposals for radical alterations in the economic relations of American society.[13]

The reactions of the dental profession to these developments were varied. The American Dental Association embraced the opportunity represented by the Committee on the Costs of Medical Care to expand knowledge of the dental needs of the population and of the economic aspects of dentistry. The motivation behind the action was a response to a variety of considerations. One was the perennial insistence on the analogy between medical and dental care. Wrote C. N. Johnson, "What concerns medicine in its relation to the public needs equally concerns dentistry." This argument reinforced the urgings of those practitioners inspired by the visions of dentistry proclaimed by William J. Gies. The idealistic motive was buttressed by practical considerations. There was increasing pressure for extending medical and dental care to a broader segment of the population. Large voluntary humanitarian organizations of laymen, such as the Red Cross and the parent-teacher associations across the country, raised insistent demands for increasing facilities for medical and dental treatment. They were joined by spokesmen of big business who wanted a healthier working force. Social philosophers, economists, sociologists, social workers, philanthropists, and statesmen advocated changes toward the same end. The editor of the Association's *Journal* admonished his readers, "We shall never meet the situation by following the tactics of the ostrich and hiding our heads in the sand whenever this subject is broached. . . . Our duties relate to the community as well as to the individual." Herbert E. Phillips, chairman of the Association's Committee on the Study of Dental Practice, reported widespread adoption in foreign countries of compulsory health insurance plans without the advice and against the opposition of the health professions. "In this country," he added, "the opportunity of having a hand in determining the direction of change is still before the professions." [14]

In the face of all this urging, organized dentistry moved cautiously. In 1928, the Board of Trustees appointed the American Dental Association's own Committee on the Costs of Dental Care. At the ensuing annual meeting, this Committee suggested the Association undertake two investigations, one of the income from dental practice, the other of capital expenditures in dentistry. The special Committee also urged that the Association offer to cooperate with the national Committee on the Costs of Medical Care in surveying "the incidence of dental disease, . . . the cost of dental service and the facilities at present for serving the public." Gradually, American Dental Association participation in the national survey increased. Association interest and cooperation flowered as recognition of the claims of the profession emerged both from the Committee on the Costs of Medical Care itself and from the establishment of a Dental Division in the Public Health Service. Simultaneously, the American Dental Association began to elaborate its own machinery for dealing with its social obligations.

Initially, the Association concentrated on laying a foundation of factual data upon which to build a structure of policy. Resolutions of the Chicago Dental Society, presented in 1930, set in train a movement to develop permanent machinery within the American Dental Association for this purpose. But not until 1934 did the discussion crystallize with the adoption of amendments creating a standing Committee on Dental Economics.[15] By that date it had already become necessary to consider announcement of a social policy.

The earliest returns from the examinations of the nation's dental needs revealed that, whereas the numbers of dentists had increased at a more rapid pace than the growth of the national population since the turn of the century, the distribution of dentists relative to population varied widely across the country. The proportion of dentists to population ranged from as many as one to 500 to as few as one to 4,000. Among the Negro population, the situation was even worse: The ratio was one dentist for every 8,500. For the nation as a whole, the figure was one to 1,900. There was evidently a serious shortage of dentists in some regions. At the same time, the researches indicated that there was less demand than there was need for dental care. The people were not keeping the dentists busy. One student reported that many people believed that dental treatment "costs more than they can afford." In common with many others at the time, this observer saw lower costs as the solution. This conclusion led to a wide variety of proposals that envisaged a greater or less degree of change in the traditional American form of private dental practice.[16]

The response of the profession to this challenge displayed a united front of opposition. There was less agreement as to why the proposals were bad. A private research organization polled more than 1,500 dentists for the Ritter Dental Manufacturing Company. The questions all related to only one variety of proposal, panel dentistry, but the responses may be taken as applicable to virtually all of the schemes then current. A large majority of the respondents, more than eighty-five per cent, opposed the plan on the ground that it would not attract the right kind of practitioners. These men claimed that the panel system, like government service, would attract only the unenterprising or the inefficient worker. Lacking any great economic incentive, the panel dentist's treatment might be perfunctory. At the same time, the replies from a smaller majority, but still representing about three-fourths of the sample population, opposed the panel practice idea as bad from "the public's point of view." About one-eighth of the answers to this query favored the scheme from the aspect of the common welfare. The interpreter of the returns explained that these answers meant the respondent merely felt that any care was better than none. Virtually all of the replies supported dental care for the needs of children.[17]

The Ritter survey of dental opinion found that economic considerations were somewhat less important than altruistic ones in determining the dentist's position on the question. Almost three-fourths of the replies thought the income of dentistry as a whole would decline if the panel plan was inaugurated. Less than two-thirds, however, anticipated a decline in their own income. The comments of dental speakers at the time place considerable stress on the prospects of economic loss to the individual practitioner. One debater, for example, attacked programs for dental care sponsored by insurance companies. "With this contract practice, insurance companies can come in and empty our offices of patients," he said. President Martin Dewey's address bristled with economic arguments coupled with an evident antipathy toward any other than private practice of dentistry. Dewey attributed the high costs of dental care to the high costs of dental education. He thought that educational standards could be maintained while costs were reduced. Dewey declared that university dental clinics represented "an entering wedge" encouraging the tendency toward practice of medicine and dentistry by agencies of the state and federal governments. Noting the opposition of the American Medical Association to this trend, Dewey insisted that the American Dental Association should cooperate to the end that those who could afford to pay, who constituted, he thought, a majority of the patients of the clinics, should not receive free care. Dewey's predecessor, Robert T. Oliver, summed up the argument of the profession. The various suggestions "would destroy our splendid American method of conducting, individually, a free and independent practice of dentistry in a manner befitting Americans." [18]

Along with arguments against the schemes to diminish private practice, the dental statesmen pronounced some of the principles that should underlie a satisfactory program. It should be "conservative and constructive," and preserve the traditions and ideals of the profession. The "personal relationship" between dentist and patient should be maintained. The social program of dentistry during the twenties had been based on education and care for children. These were not questioned. Any extension of that social program evidently would have to be confined to those unable to pay for the servicing of their dental needs.[19]

Expressions such as these anticipated the terms of the first formal restatement of the Association's social program, which was adopted in 1934. The American Dental Association reiterated its insistence that action be founded on a knowledge of the facts. In 1933, the House of Delegates established a special Committee on Dental Health Survey to cooperate with the United States Public Health Service in a large-scale investigation of the dental needs of children. The survey also studied the dental activities in state and local health, education, and welfare departments. In cooperation with the Public Health Service, it was expected to develop a dental health program for state health and education departments. The House enjoined all the machinery of organized dentistry to support the survey by publicizing it in the journals and assisting the work in every way possible. This effort was the largest coordinated investigation that had yet been made. Almost one-and-a-half million children between the ages of six and fourteen, living in twenty-six states, were examined.[20]

The annual meeting of 1934, held at St. Paul, adopted two statements that elaborated the formal social program of the American Dental Association. The principles set down at that time have endured. It was assumed as fundamental that any plan would give due consideration to the cost to the tax-paying citizen who would have to foot the bill. Next, the program showed concern to vindicate the status of the profession. Representatives of dentistry should participate in all conferences considering national health problems. The profession itself should prepare a plan to provide for the dental care of indigents and children. The next broad category of principles governing any acceptable proposal sought to preserve the integrity of the practice of dentistry. Hence, the House insisted that professional men should control the administration of treatment. All licensed dentists should be eligible to participate in the program. Freedom of choice for both patient and dentist should be protected. The patients should be free to take advantage of the services; they should have the right to choose the dentist who was to perform the treatment. Practitioners, on the other hand, should retain the right to refuse to care for any given patient.

A further series of principles, derived from the broader pronouncements, described suitable administrative features of a satisfactory plan. Decentralization, or flexibility and adaptability to local conditions, was stressed. A further resolution, adopted at the St. Paul meeting, stipulated that treatment of the indigent should be confined to the minimum care essential to the preservation of health. This was defined to include prophylaxis, fillings of amalgam or cement only, and the alleviation of pain and treatment of acute infections. The program should emphasize dental health education and preventive measures.

The health features of the Social Security Act of 1935 provided for the expenditure of funds in aid of state and local health work. The measure necessitated the interpretation of the Association's principles in the light of a specific bill. The annual session of 1935 was equal to the challenge. It decided to concentrate on securing the establishment of oral health divisions in state health departments. The Association also determined to request the inclusion of questions on dental conditions in any health surveys conducted by the Public Health Service. The 1935 New Orleans meeting not only upheld the principles adopted in the preceding year, it also extended them. The House of Delegates requested the Public Health Service to utilize funds appropriated under the Social Security Act for research on the two great scientific problems of dentistry, caries and periodontal diseases.[21]

The 1935 meeting of the American Dental Association also laid down an official policy relating to various proposals for insurance, credit, or deferred payment plans for dental care. The Board of Trustees declared its firm opposition to any form of compulsory health insurance whether administered by the federal, state, or local government, or by an industrial organization. Such schemes led to "regimentation and lay control" of practice, induced a lowering of standards of quality, and impeded scientific progress. The House of Delegates supported this view. President Frank M. Casto summoned the delegates to a "continuous campaign of publicity" against compulsory health insurance proposals. He warned that the fight would be a hard one. Compulsory health insurance, Casto said, enjoyed the backing of "influential organizations and wealthy foundations." Its proponents had ample funds and "a high-powered and high-priced publicity agent." The Association, Casto proclaimed, must publicize the "baneful results" of compulsory health insurance plans. The campaign must be well-planned and executed, Casto warned, for the people, at whom it was aimed, were influenced only by matters affecting "their personal well-being." Even then, he continued, the message would require "frequent repetition." [22]

The New Orleans meeting heard a report from the Committee on Dental Economics urging the Association to concentrate on prevention and on devising low-cost plans for low-income groups. "Obviously," the report noted, no proposal could be applicable to the nation as a whole; the nature of the problem demanded schemes tailored or adaptable to local conditions. The 1935 session also approved plans for two income groups, the unemployed and children, and employed people with limited incomes. The first proposal called for the establishment of a Federal Dental Health Work Relief Project for Children, that would at once aid needy dentists and supply preventive and adequate dental care for children. The other recommendation suggested a deferred payment plan for dental care. The details of this scheme were left to be worked out after further study of two such programs, one in Washington, D. C., the other in St. Louis. Both the St. Louis plan and the Washington plan involved a central referral agency that would direct patients to dental and medical facilities according to their ability to pay. Deferred payments were arranged and collected through the central bureau. A number of similar plans were operated briefly during the middle thirties. All eventually died out from the indifference of the participants. The significance of the episode lay in its demonstration of the Association's determination to be sure of its ground before adopting any proposition to supply low-cost or credit care, or care on the basis of insurance principles.[23]

In 1938, the American Dental Association adopted a restatement, embodied in eight principles, of its policies on the dental aspects of a national health program. Although this statement became the basis from which subsequent versions of Association policy evolved, it differed little from the principles of 1934. The Eight Principles clearly reaffirmed the Association's determination to have a voice in the development of national health programs and to maintain professional control over the "quality and methods of any service to be rendered." The Association again insisted that the program should be flexible and adaptable to local conditions. It again described the dental features of a satisfactory health program, with stress as before on prevention and education. Care would be provided for expectant mothers and for children, plus the minimum treatment essential for the health and rehabilitation of indigent adults. One new feature introduced in the Eight Principles demanded exclusion of nonprofessional, profit-seeking agencies from participation in the program. Provision for research was again omitted.[24]

The National Health Program Committee brought in another version of the plan, including specific administrative details, in 1939. This report envisioned expenditures for research as well as for education. It called for care for the dentally indigent—only enough for adults to maintain health and employability. The provision of care for the indigent became the subject of some disagreement at this session in Milwaukee. The Public Health Committee pronounced such treatment the "joint responsibility of local government and allied professions." The reference committee, with the House of Delegates supporting them, retorted that "indigent care is a local problem and not a responsibility of the dental profession."[25]

New survey techniques, developed in the survey of Hagerstown, Maryland, in 1938, yielded new understanding of the dental needs of the American population. Not long thereafter, the outbreak of war in Europe led to the passage of America's first peacetime conscription law. The dental deficiencies among the inductees vividly underscored the conditions disclosed by the Hagerstown survey. These findings suggested again the great unfilled need for dental care. On the heels of these discoveries came the crisis in dental manpower created by the increasing demands for dental officers to care for the growing numbers of American citizens in the armed forces. The situation illuminated a somewhat neglected aspect of the nation's dental health problems, the availability of dentists to meet the dental needs of the public.[26]

The main direction of the profession's thinking about dental health problems continued to follow the principles already embraced. The National Health Program Committee proposed a "Caries Control Program" in 1942. It featured four familiar measures, education, early and frequent examination and treatment, better nutrition, and better practices of mouth hygiene. The Committee attributed the high incidence of dental caries to the absence of the foregoing elements, but also acknowledged that lack of funds helped explain lack of adequate care. The Association voiced its antagonism to the Wagner-Murray-Dingell Health Bill of 1943. The House of Delegates passed resolutions opposing the legislation and referring again to the Eight Principles of 1938. This determination to gain or maintain recognition of the claims of dentistry as a health service appeared again in the decision of the Board of Trustees to cooperate in the National Physical Fitness Program and to join the National Council on Rehabilitation "so that dentistry may be included in a national plan 'to study, encourage and advise upon development of rehabilitation programs on federal, state and community levels.'"

At the Chicago mid-winter meeting in 1944, representatives of a number of Association committees and bureaus concerned with health programs drafted a new statement of Association policy, which the House of Delegates adopted. This document reduced the essentials of the Eight Principles to four: (1) research concentrating on ways to prevent and control dental caries, (2) dental health education, (3) dental care available to all regardless of location or income, and (4) participation by organized dentistry in all conferences on health problems. The statement on dental care stipulated that its basis should be prevention and control concentrating on child care and the relief of pain and infection in adults. Responsibility for providing care, the new policy asserted, rested primarily with the individual, next with the family, and then the community. If the community could not support a program for care, it might look to the state for assistance and, if necessary, to the federal government; but in all cases, the community should determine the method by which the treatment was dispensed.

The most significant difference between the 1944 declaration and the Eight Principles was the elevation of research to a position of prominence from which it has not since been shaken. By midwinter of 1945, an Association-sponsored bill calling for federal aid to dental research was before Congress. Bills assisting dental health education and dental care programs were almost ready for submission. Federal expenditures in these fields were not new, but, in the past, the funds had come from general appropriations for health research, education, and care programs. The Association now campaigned for money specifically dedicated to dental purposes.[27]

An extensive discussion of all aspects of the dental health and care question occupied the latter years of the second World War. Special committees of the Association's Council on Dental Health, established in 1942, (a union of the standing committees on National Health Program and Public Health), continued the prewar investigations of the various low-income and insurance schemes for extending the capacity to pay for dental care. In 1944, the Low-Income Committee reported that a loan or installment plan seemed to offer the best prospects of a satisfactory solution, while the Methods of Payment Committee declared that some form of prepayment looked most promising. The studies of both lines of attack continued as organized dentistry sought a definitive answer to the problem.[28]

New surveys of dental practice and dental care revived the question of the supply of dentists. The returns showed a persistence of the uneven distribution of dentists, first strikingly revealed in the studies of the Committee on the Costs of Medical Care published in 1932. Refinement of the statistics and additional correlations plainly linked economic status with dental need—the lower the income the greater the need for dental care. Even allowing for economic and geographical disparities, Lon W. Morrey of the Association's Bureau of Public Relations observed, "there is no disputing the fact . . . that dentistry is seriously undermanned." [29]

An economist, Melvin L. Dollar, presented an illuminating analysis of the situation in 1945. Dollar distinguished two varieties of need for dental care. The first he called "the prevalence of need," meaning the total dental deficiency of the population at any given time. The second he named "the incidence of need," meaning the deficiencies that occurred within a given period. These two categories required corresponding types of care; the former, Dollar termed "initial," the latter, "maintenance" treatment. He pointed out that the ideal approach to the problem would be to handle the incidence of need through maintenance care. He estimated that the annual cost of such a program would be in the neighborhood of a billion dollars. This course of action, however, would not satisfy the prevalence of dental needs. The initial cost of treating the prevalent needs and bringing the nation's dental needs to a maintenance basis would be five times as great as the annual cost of maintenance care, about ten times the sum spent on dentistry in 1940. Furthermore, Dollar pointed out, the available dental personnel limited the services in any one year to no more than five to six hundred million dollars. In other words, dentistry was capable of treating hardly more than half of the dental deficiencies accruing during any one year.[30]

The dilemma demanded an explanation and a solution. There was wide agreement on the origins of the difficulty. The proportion of dentists to population had remained substantially the same through the decade of the thirties and, consequently, the numbers of dentists had failed to keep pace with the increasing demand for dental care. Two factors were commonly advanced to explain this. The Depression had caused a decline in the rate of growth of the profession. The lengthening of the curriculum in the dental colleges, which occurred during the thirties, had operated in the same direction. More refined and sophisticated surveys of need probably exaggerated the predicament. Undoubtedly, the extension of dental practice into the hospital and industrial fields as well as in government agencies tended to have the same effect. Furthermore, it was noted that the cost of dental education nearly equalled that of medicine while dentistry lacked the "appeal and glamour" of medical practice. One commentator explained, "The average young man or woman looks upon the practice of dentistry as a relatively unpleasant occupation, because of the traditional tendency to associate the dentist with pain."[31] The growing pressure from some quarters for some form of government health insurance, thus increasing the number of potential patients, further complicated the picture. Against this confused background the American Dental Association, in the years after the second World War, sought to define a policy at once satisfying the needs of the public and protecting the interest of the dental profession.

The first postwar years set the tone of the actions that came later. There were two preoccupations: resistance to compulsory health insurance, and extending the benefits of dental care to more of the American population. Even before the end of the fighting, President C. Raymond Wells promised the profession that the Association would maintain "eternal vigilance to the end that private practice shall be preserved and that sufficient extension of dental service will be made for the benefit of low income groups and the legally dentally indigent." Wells and his fellow dental leaders had reason to apprehend the adoption of compulsory health insurance legislation at the time. The American Dental Association Committee on Legislation kept close watch on these developments. Some dentists, however, charged that the profession as a whole was not sufficiently alert to the dangers confronting it. In his report to the Board of Trustees in February, 1946, President Walter H. Scherer criticized dentistry for its tendency to "let things ride." He excoriated the "semi-complacent medical and dental professions, too proud to protest, too overworked and overburdened with war responsibilities to give adequate consideration to basic problems." Compulsory health insurance, Scherer warned, was a real danger. "This legislation is a threat to the American way of life. Our states' rights, our personal freedom, the sacred human relationship that has always existed between professional men and their patients, is being threatened."

Leroy M. S. Miner, a former president of the Association, worried about the impression dental opposition to compulsory health insurance might have on Congress and the public. "It seems to me that it is important that the American Dental Association be in a position so that no member of Congress, no member of the public can say that the American Dental Association is anti-social. We are opposing compulsory health insurance, but that does not mean that we are not in favor of doing something for the dental health of the American people, and we are showing our interest in social progress by being instrumental in introducing a bill into Congress which will provide that care through Federal support by this grant-in-aid system."[32] Even though the attempt to pass a compulsory health insurance bill failed in the mid-forties and subsequent proposals did not succeed, the American Dental Association consistently advanced and extended its efforts to solve the dilemma of American dental health on its own terms.

The activities of the Association have been in keeping with the principles first enunciated in 1934 and since clarified and refined. Hence, the Association has sought to expand research in various aspects of dental science. Dental health education has been strengthened and intensified. These endeavors have prospered through an ever-increasing flow of federal funds. The problem of making dental care available to all has proved the most difficult of solution. The principle of decentralization of administration remains the cardinal feature in providing care for the dentally indigent. The basis for realizing this principle has existed since 1935 when the Social Security Act was adopted. The Association has exerted much effort in trying to implement its views. To this end, it has sought specific federal appropriations for dental health programs. Thus far, this campaign has had only limited success. Dental programs in state departments of health have ordinarily been dependent on securing funds from generalized appropriations.[33]

Constructing an administrative basis for a dental health program along the lines of the American Dental Association's principles has proved easier. By 1956, all but one state included dental programs as part of their state health activities. In addition, three territories and the District of Columbia operated dental health units. Most of the expenditures for dental purposes, however, were drawn from Maternal and Child Health funds. This meant that the dental program in many states was administratively subordinate. The Association cooperated with its constituent societies in attempts to win division status for dentistry in state health departments. Similarly, the Association promoted the founding of dental health councils within the various levels of organized dentistry, from the national through the state to the local society, in order to have representation of the profession at each level of government health activities. In 1949, there were only about 1,300 full-time local health units. No figures were available on the number of local dental health programs, but they were undoubtedly far fewer than the number of local health units. While there have been some improvements since that time, there are still far too few. This condition can be attributed directly to lack of funds. If current legislative efforts of the Association eventually win specific appropriations for dental programs, a beginning will have been made toward a solution to this aspect of the difficulty.[34]

The Association has not only sought government assistance in bringing dental health to a broader segment of the population, but it has worked for the expansion of other facilities for dental care. The Association has long been interested in providing dental services in hospitals and other health centers. As early as 1922, a special committee recommended action to encourage establishment of hospital dental services. The duty was assigned to the standing Committee on Education where it apparently languished. Not until 1944 did the Council on Dental Education establish a Committee on Hospital Dental Service. The preparation of standards began. The first Association-approved requirements were published in 1946. The 1948 constitution provided for a Council on Hospital Dental Service, which in the centennial year continued to direct the program in spite of some efforts to reassign its duties to the Council on Dental Education.[35]

Inclusion of dental services in industry-sponsored and union-sponsored health programs has a shorter history. The Committee on Dental Economics first recommended minimum standards in 1940 and won approval of a revised statement from the House of Delegates in 1941. This aspect of dental practice, too, has shown development since its recognition by the Association. The policy of the American Dental Association toward industrial dental programs was established to maintain what it considered the essentials of professional dentistry —preservation of as many features as possible of private practice; development of specific programs only in consultation with representatives of the local dental profession; the limitation of services to examination, recording, referral, education, and emergency care; and administration of the program by a dentist in coordination with other health services.[36]

Although the provision of dental care through various institutional means, both governmental and private, is now a recognized aspect of American dentistry, it still accounts for only a small portion of the care administered. In 1952, there were only 540 dentists employed in public health departments of the federal, state, and local government. The 1956 survey of the profession found only 1.2 per cent of the respondents employed in salaried positions other than as teachers or in the office of another dentist. Slightly more than 10 per cent of the respondents acknowledged a combination of types of employment. The figures show a decline from the returns of the 1953 survey, which reported nearly 2 per cent in salaried employment with 12 per cent combining various sources of income. President C. Raymond Wells predicted in 1944 that one-third of the profession would eventually be found in salaried positions. His prophecy is not moving very rapidly toward fulfillment.[37]

A number of reasons may be advanced to explain the apparent miscarriage of Wells's forecast. Undoubtedly the Association's insistence on preservation of all possible features of traditional practice under the new arrangements for care has tended to minimize the number of dentists whose incomes derive from salaried posts in institutional programs. Furthermore, once the decentralization of care of the dentally indigent had been established as a fundamental element of governmental intervention, the efforts of the Association committees concerned with dental health turned to improving the ways in which the costs of dental care could be met. Since the forties, the Council on Dental Health has sponsored continuing study and experimentation in both prepayment and postpayment methods of defraying dental expenses. Its publications have outlined standards of acceptability for both varieties. Beyond the statement of general principles that should govern such programs and recommendations on the mechanics of administering them, the American Dental Association has avoided pronouncing any given plan as most suitable. This caution is in accordance with its determination to avoid any "hasty plunge into ill conceived plans or programs arising through political incentive and operated at a federal level." The policy is also consistent with the Association's position that all programs for dental care are ultimately the responsibility of the local community and the local profession. The relative prosperity of the nation in the years since the second World War has likewise tended to mitigate somewhat the pressure to extend dental care among low income groups.[38]

Although a rising national income has tended to minimize the concern for reducing the costs of dental care, it has brought more sharply into focus the shortage of dentists. In 1950, Harold J. Noyes noted, "Certain representatives of the public and the federal government have laid great stress on the need for increased personnel and have been most articulate in the demand for the training of more dentists." Suggestions from outside the profession emphasized two possibilities: Reduction in the length of the standard dental curriculum and delegation of some treatment procedures to auxiliary personnel. The

growing complexity of dental treatment and the increasing importance of the basic sciences and preventive measures make the former
alternative impractical. Leaders in dental education have favored
expansion of dental college capacity and the full utilization of existing facilities. On the other hand, they have been reluctant to develop
large new training capacity rapidly because the demand for dental
care, as studies over the past twenty years have repeatedly demonstrated, is keyed closely to economic conditions. An obvious check
on the precipitate expansion of the dental colleges has been a shortage of dentists qualified to man the instructional staffs. The number
of students in the country's dental schools is increasing. Enrollment
reached a peak during the second World War of around 9,000, then
fell away in the first years following the war. By 1950, however, the
war-time peak had been exceeded by nearly 3,000. The figure at
present exceeds 13,000.[39] Furthermore, the *1956 Survey of Dental
Practice* seemed to indicate that there had been an improvement in
the supply of dental services available. The interpreter based his conclusion on a small decline in the average number of days' wait for an
appointment between 1952 and 1955 and an increase during the same
period in the number of dentists stating they desired more patients.[40]

An increase in the numbers of dentists cannot alone account for the
growth in the amount of care available. The American dentist has
also relied increasingly on the use of auxiliary personnel. The experience of maintaining civilian dental practice under the war-time acute
shortage of dentists accelerated a trend that had been underway since
the beginning of the century. The Committee on the Costs of Medical
Care found that forty-one per cent of dentists employed at least one
full-time assistant in 1929. By 1943, the figure had risen to more than
fifty per cent. The *1950 Survey of the Dental Profession* indicated that
nearly two-thirds of all dentists had one or more full-time employees
on their payrolls. Five years later the percentage had risen to more
than seventy-five. The total number of auxiliary personnel exceeded
the number of dentists in private practice. The explanation of the
trend is simple. The use of auxiliary personnel noticeably increased
the number of patients who could be treated. The addition of a single
assistant meant that the dentist could handle one-third more patients.
If the assistant was augmented by the addition of a second dental
chair to the office equipment, the increase exceeded fifty per cent.

The type of help upon which the dentist could draw also influenced his patient load. One study found that a dental office, equipped with two chairs and served by a dentist with the help of an assistant, a hygienist, and a technician, could handle over two hundred per cent more patients than the one-man, one-chair office. On the basis of the 1950 Survey, Lon W. Morrey penned an editorial, "Dentistry Demonstrates Its Ability to Meet a Major Portion of the Increasing Demand for Its Services." [41]

The gain from the use of auxiliary personnel has not been without its drawbacks and embarrassments. The chief reliance for help in the office is the dental assistant. J. Ben Robinson, dental educator and a past president of the American Dental Association, has written, "Indeed there is reason to believe that the tremendous growth in the number and efficiency of dental office assistants has greatly increased the productivity of the dental office in 1950 as compared to its capacity for service in 1900." The assistant began to appear in dentists' offices with increasing frequency after the turn of the century. Her duties are general and differ from office to office. The assistant often serves both as business manager of the practice and helps at the chair in the operating room as well. Until recent years, aside from ordinary commercial education, there was no formal training for the assistant before beginning service in the dentist's office. She was trained on the job and for the job by her employer. Since 1951, the Association's Council on Dental Education has taken an increasing interest in formal training for assistants. In 1957, the Council sponsored a workshop on the problem. As the Association's centennial year began, the Council, in cooperation with the American Dental Assistants Association, was working toward the development of acceptable educational standards for submission to the House of Delegates. [42] The increasing concern of the Association with the qualities of the assistants has coincided with the rapidly increasing importance of these auxiliaries of the profession. The number of assistants rose from 45,000 in 1952 to 62,000 in 1955. During the same period, their mean annual salary increased from $1,788 to $2,421. [43]

Among dental auxiliary personnel, the hygienists constitute a much smaller group than the assistants. The occupation of the hygienist had its origins in the oral hygiene movement in the early years of the century. To augment the services available to school children, oral hygiene pioneers conceived the idea of training personnel to perform the operations of cleaning and polishing the teeth and to inculcate the principles of mouth hygiene, nutrition, and good health practices. By 1916, three states had amended dental practice laws to require the licensing of hygienists. The American Dental Association formally approved licensing hygienists in 1916. In 1922, the House of Delegates approved a model bill for this purpose. By 1925, the national organization of hygienists boasted fourteen state constituent societies. Twenty-six states had adopted licensing statutes. President Roscoe H. Volland, in 1928, suggested a meeting of "a group of people" to work toward a uniform course for dental hygienists. The Board of Trustees approved the idea. Nonetheless, the Association did not take formal action regarding the training of dental hygienists for another twenty years. In part this delay can be accounted for by the relatively slow growth in the numbers of hygienists since the twenties.

By 1951 hygienists were licensed to practice in all states, the District of Columbia, Alaska and Hawaii. However, only about four per cent of the nation's dentists employ hygienists. These account for two-thirds of all hygienists. Another 26 per cent are employed in schools. The balance are to be found mainly in federal employment and in hospital and industrial clinics. In view of the fact that the dental hygienist was originally expected to conduct routine examinations, prophylaxis, and dental health education in the schools, the apparent trend toward employment in private offices suggests a change in the hygienist's role. The first conception of the duties of the hygienist placed greatest emphasis on her educational work in the schools, although she was authorized to perform certain limited cleansing operations in the patient's mouth. It is apparent that there is now greater stress on what may be termed her operative functions. It is precisely on this point that the dental profession has encountered difficulty with its hygienist auxiliaries. To stretch dental manpower further, the delegation of some dental procedures or the assignment of some types of patients to auxiliary personnel has been suggested. The hygienist seems the most likely prospect, for the hygienist alone among the dental auxiliaries is licensed to perform certain operations inside the mouth. Recognizing the potential of the hygienist, the House of Delegates, in 1947, approved "Requirements for the Accrediting of a School of Dental Hygienists," prepared by the Council on Dental Education.

But the effort to augment the responsibilities of the hygienist in some quarters went too far to suit the Association. In 1949, the Massachusetts legislature passed a bill authorizing hygienists to perform additional dental operations in the mouths of children. The House of Delegates of the Association attacked the move. Training for such procedures cannot be accomplished with less expenditure of time and effort than is required to educate a dentist, the House proclaimed. The Association and the appropriate state society should have been consulted, another resolution of 1949 declared. The American Dental Association, the resolution explained, desired a voice in determining such steps for the purpose of protecting public health and welfare. In 1950, the House urged constituent societies to foster expansion of facilities for the training of hygienists according to the standards laid down by the Council on Dental Education. At the same time, the Board of Trustees declined to take further action in connection with the Massachusetts hygienist statute on the grounds that the state dental society had refused to move against the law. The Association's insistence on local and state society participation in such matters leaves the possibility of an expanded role for the hygienist open, although a prominent dentist has said that dentistry would be "irrevocably injured" by an invasion of dental practice by hygienists.[44]

A numerically lesser group among the auxiliaries in the dental offices of the land is the dental laboratory technician. This occupation, too, is largely a twentieth century development. Originally, the technician worked directly under the supervision and control of the dentist in his laboratory connected with his office. Most dentists at that time fashioned their own restorative and orthodontic devices. Only the busier dentists found themselves obliged to employ full-time technicians to assist in this part of the practice. As demands for more time in the operating room increased, some of the more skilled laboratory technicians opened independent laboratories to serve the needs of several dentists.

This aspect of dentistry has grown to major proportions since the first World War. In 1920, when it is estimated that the nation spent $400 million for dental care, the laboratory industry received estimated payments of $18 million. Ten years later, payments to laboratories amounted to around $35 million, while the nation's dental bill came to only $463 million. The laboratories received 50 of the $419 million paid for dental care in 1940. By 1950, Americans spent $991 million on dental care, of which $130 million was the laboratory bill. A 1956 survey showed a gross income to dentistry of $1,600 million and payments to commercial laboratories of one-tenth that sum. Information regarding the number of laboratory workers is less reliable, but it, too, stresses the importance of the commercial laboratory. In 1941, it was estimated that there were 15,000 dental laboratory technicians. Ten years later, their number approached 20,000. In addition, some 3,300 technicians worked in dentists' offices. The latter figure has been slowly declining. The 1953 survey of dental practice reported 3,000 and that for 1956, 2,900. The trend seems to be to divert more and more of the construction of prosthetic devices to the commercial laboratory.[45]

Through the twenties and thirties, while the proportions of the laboratory industry were still obscure, the American Dental Association remained relatively indifferent to developments within the craft. The House of Delegates, in 1927, approved President Banzhaf's suggestion of a committee to study the possibility of registration of laboratories meeting standards set by state boards of dental examiners, but nothing came of the proposal. In 1933, opposition was expressed to establishment under the National Recovery Administration of a national uniform code of prices for laboratories, but the Association took no official action. Around the time of the outbreak of the second World War, in 1939 and in 1941, the American Dental Association registered its disapproval of the licensing or certification of technicians and laboratories because there were no agreed-upon standards for education or training within the laboratory craft.[46]

During the war years, the large number of technicians trained in the armed forces and the increased resort to the aid of auxiliary personnel in civilian practice gave new importance to the relations of the profession with the commercial laboratories. Through its Council on Legislation, the Association finally obtained passage, in 1942, of the Traynor bill prohibiting traffic in dentures by mail-order laboratories, which undertook to fit dentures in the patient's mouth on the basis of impressions made by the patient himself and mailed to the laboratory. The Supreme Court upheld the legislation in 1946. President C. Raymond Wells, in 1944, recommended establishment of a standing committee to develop and maintain relations between the Association and the laboratory industry. This committee, Wells suggested, should also work out standards for accreditation of laboratories and cooperate with state and local societies toward regularizing relations with the industry. Wells's proposal was finally implemented in 1946. The agency became the Association's Council on Dental Trade and Laboratory Relations in 1949.[47]

Pending establishment of a permanent committee for dealing with the problem of the technicians and laboratories, a special committee labored in this field. At the end of the war, in October, 1945, this committee's first report precipitated the discussion of the appropriate methods for handling the question of relations with the laboratories. The committee proposed decentralization to the state level. It urged appointment of state dental society committees on the matter wherever corresponding laboratory organizations existed. The committee asserted that the laboratories were part of dentistry, but not a part of the profession; therefore, it believed that the laboratories should be controlled through the state dental practice acts. The Board of Trustees, on the other hand, thought a solution other than licensure should be found.[48]

In the following year, the second controversial issue relating to the technician and laboratory question came to the fore. The question of education of the technician assumed added importance at this juncture because of the opening of numerous schools offering to train veterans to be dental technicians under the G.I. bill. In question was not only the commercial character of many of these schools, but also the level at which the instruction should be given. In 1946, the House of Delegates agreed that training should not be limited to dental schools, "because of the present trend of vocational training at high school level." In the following year, however, the House pronounced a condemnation of proprietary schools for technicians "as not meeting standards designed to advance the welfare" of the student "or his potential service to the dental profession." The House held that training of dental laboratory technicians should take place "under the auspices" of accredited dental schools. Pending establishment of such a system, the House favored training technicians on the job.[49]

The House of Delegates, in 1947, adopted a statement of policy acknowledging dental technicians and laboratories "as essential adjuncts of the dental profession but in no sense as independent agencies capable of rendering a health service to the public." In the face of a strong movement in Connecticut toward licensing technicians, the House also reiterated its opposition to licensure or registration, while leaving the ultimate decision to "the good judgement of the dental societies in the individual states." This stand was restated in succeeding years.

In 1947, the Association stated that it would entertain "official relations only with a truly democratic national laboratory organization," which had a structure like that of the American Dental Association, "whose governing power arises from the state level." Two years later, the House of Delegates withdrew to a position that would "permit achievement of unity within the laboratory craft at the national level to rest with the interested groups of the craft." The Council on Dental Education submitted "Requirements for the Accreditation of a School for the Training of Dental Laboratory Technicians," in 1948, that won the acceptance of the House of Delegates.[50] With this step, the question of relations between dentistry and the technicians and laboratories reached a provisional, and temporary, settlement.

Leading dentists continued to hold a gloomy view of the trend toward placing greater reliance on the technician and the growing importance of the commercial laboratory. J. Ben Robinson thought the only solution was to re-establish the laboratory that used to be part of every dentist's office and bring the technician back under the constant and direct supervision of the dentist. "In no other way," he wrote, "can a truly scientific health service be provided the patient and in no other way can the profession hope to retain control over this type of oral health care for the public."[51]

When the Federal Trade Commission, in 1955, promulgated trade practice rules for the commercial dental laboratory industry, the rules contained some expressions that seemed to imply independent status for the industry. The American Dental Association complained. The Commission granted a hearing and, after several representatives of the Association offered arguments, revised the rules to take into account some of the profession's objections. The revision was promulgated in 1957. This incident reflects the determination of the American Dental Association to oppose any recognition of the laboratory industry, or of technicians, that implies, or seems to imply, that the industry is capable of performing any direct dental service for the public. The National Association of Dental Laboratories adheres to this view, too. Its bylaws prohibit members from serving the public directly.[52]

In cooperation with the National Association of Dental Laboratories, the American Dental Association's Council on Dental Education worked out a new program for the training of technicians that replaced the original "Requirements," which never enjoyed substantial support from the industry, from schools, or from potential technicians. The new "Requirements," approved in 1957, provided for an academic year of training in the scientific principles and technical skills of the craft as well as orientation in the ideals of service to the public through the dental profession. A second full calendar year would be devoted to practical study and experience, commonly "on-the-job" in an approved dental laboratory. Accompanying the educational program was a plan for developing a system of certification of dental technicians, recognizing five different classifications of skill and specialization. The National Association of Dental Laboratories in 1948 proposed to form a Certification Board to administer examinations for certification "under rules and regulations" of its own devising that would meet with the approval of the American Dental Association's Council on Dental Education. It was hoped that this would serve to forestall the drive for licensure and registration.[53]

The American Dental Association, in the meantime, conducted an educational campaign in its own ranks to remind its members of their obligations regarding the improper delegation of dental services to auxiliaries. Two issues of the Association's Information Bulletin were dedicated to the subject. The Council on Dental Trade and Laboratory Relations also reprinted the "Program for Maintaining Proper and Effective Relations between the Dental Profession and the Dental Trade and Laboratory Groups," which was adopted by the House of Delegates in 1954. The Association favored safeguarding the profession's responsibility by emphasizing the provision of the Principles of Ethics forbidding delegation of services. The American Dental Association held that the Principles of Ethics should have the sanction, in this regard, of the state dental practice statutes. Relations between the dentist and the laboratory should also be delineated by the dental practice laws of the states.[54] Whether as a consequence of the educational efforts of the Association, or of greater expenditures on other varieties of dental care, the proportion of the nation's dental bill that went to commercial dental laboratories declined from about fourteen per cent in 1950 to ten per cent in 1955.[55]

The Association's experience in augmenting the supply of dental care through the use of auxiliaries has apparently vindicated the judgment of Lon W. Morrey in 1945. Morrey suggested at that time that an increase in the numbers of dental assistants and hygienists while maintaining the existing level of technicians, offered the best possibilities for expanding the quantity of treatment services available.[56]

As the American Dental Association approached the beginning of its second century, dental leaders optimistically hoped that new methods of defraying the costs of dental care, the gradual expansion of the capacity of dental colleges, and the increasing utilization of auxiliary personnel would ease the imbalance among the three factors of the dental health ratio, the need, the demand, and the availability of dental care. One recent development in the field of science promised to bring the factors still closer to equivalence. It is now known that the incidence of dental caries among children is drastically reduced when fluorides have been added to their drinking water. This effect is particularly striking if the fluoridated water is consumed during the years when the permanent teeth are developing. This discovery may in time reduce the need for dental care to manageable proportions. The American Dental Association has long proclaimed its devotion to preventive measures in the interest of dental health. The discovery of the effects of fluoridation provided a major breakthrough, the first, in the prevention of a major dental disease.

From the beginning the American Dental Association has been connected with the investigations that led to this momentous advance. In the early years of the century, a young dentist of Colorado Springs, Frederick S. McKay, began trying to rouse his colleagues to seek the cause of the yellowish or brown stain that discolored the teeth of many of his patients. In some instances, the disfigurement extended to a pitting of the enamel surfaces of the teeth. Single-handed, McKay stimulated sufficient interest to raise the problem from a local curiosity to the status of a challenge worthy of dentistry's best investigators. By the time the National Dental Association organized its Scientific Foundation and Research Commission in 1913, the problem of mottled enamel had assumed proportions that justified extending one of the first grants to McKay.[57] Weston A. Price, long-time leader of the Association Research Commission and then the Association's representative to the National Research Council, reminded the House of Delegates, in 1925, of the interest of the Commission in the mottling problem and informed them of his efforts to win support within the National Research Council for a new and broad-scale approach.[58]

The first break in the problem came in 1931 with the identification of fluorine in drinking water as the discoloring agent. The discovery was made through minute analyses of water supplies from areas where the mottling was endemic, and, almost simultaneously, by producing the lesion in experimental animals by giving them drinking water containing fluorides. Neither the American Dental Association nor the U. S. Public Health Service was directly involved in the discovery. Neither had been able to muster the funds or the interest to aid in the latter stages of the experimental assault on the problem. However, the establishment of the National Institute of Health in 1930 and the assignment there, in 1931, of H. Trendley Dean soon made the Public Health Service a key agency in the continuing investigation of dental fluorosis. The American Dental Association, on the motion of J. Ben Robinson, in 1933, adopted resolutions urging the use of National Recovery Act funds to assist communities with endemic dental fluorosis in changing their water supply.[59]

The linkage between fluorosis and the amount of tooth decay had been frequently noticed, but never scientifically demonstrated. Through the thirties, the indefatigable surveys of H. Trendley Dean at length produced sufficient evidence to warrant his calling for an exhaustive chemical and epidemiological investigation of the possibility of controlling caries through fluoridating water supplies. Dean voiced his challenge in 1938 and immediately began to prepare a study. By 1942, a survey of twenty-one cities by Dean and his colleagues firmly established that one part per million of fluorine in the water supply resulted in a marked decline in the incidence of caries without producing the objectionable mottling. The next step, after determining the safety of fluoridation, was to try fluoridation under controlled conditions. Experiments began in Grand Rapids, Michigan, Newburgh, New York and Brantford, Ontario, in 1944. In the meantime, however, popular agitation threatened to force a precipitate adoption of fluoridation before the scientists had been fully satisfied of either its safety or its efficacy.[60]

The American Dental Association maintained a cautious attitude toward the discovery. An editorial, published in the October, 1944, issue of the *Journal*, opined that the "potentialities for harm far outweigh the good." Early in 1945, as the Grand Rapids study began, the Research Commission informed the Board of Trustees that it was "not yet ready to assume the responsibility of advocating the addition of fluorides to drinking water." The Commission carefully added, "Further experiments now in progress may prove to be of great value to coming generations." The Commission saw "no good reason" to oppose community fluoridation programs, as experiments, but did not want to put the Association behind the policy of general fluoridation.[61]

While the Public Health Service and the American Dental Association awaited the results of the Grand Rapids and Newburgh experiments, another method of using fluorides gained favor. Experiments begun in 1941 indicated that sodium fluoride, applied to the surfaces of the teeth several times during childhood and adolescence, produced significant reductions in the incidence of decay. In 1946, the Council on Dental Therapeutics of the Association reported extending grants for research on the efficacy of topical fluoride treatments. Two years later, Congress granted funds to the U.S. Public Health Service for further studies of this method of preventing tooth decay.[62]

In the meantime, popular pressure threatened to force a definitive policy statement from the Association and the Public Health Service. Early returns from the experimental programs seemed to show spectacular success, although the studies were designed to cover a period ranging from ten to fifteen years. In 1949, the Board of Trustees instructed the Council on Legislation not to oppose appropriations for a Public Health Service experimental program on a basis of grants-in-aid to states.

In the next year, resistance to endorsement of fluoridation on the part of the American Dental Association broke down. In June, 1950, the U.S. Public Health Service announced its approval of community fluoridation programs. The secretaries of the Councils on Dental Health and Dental Therapeutics of the American Dental Association polled their members and received favorable reactions. An August editorial in *The Journal of the American Dental Association* cited the narrowing gap between the immediate fluoridationists and those favoring a cautious approach and the action of the Public Health Service as conditions clearing the way for the Association to recommend fluoridation. At its November, 1950, annual meeting, the House of Delegates passed a resolution recommending fluoridation of community water supplies when approved by the local dental society.[63]

Since adoption of a favorable policy toward fluoridation, the Association has promoted the new preventive measure within the limits of its principles. The American Dental Association supplies information to parties interested in community fluoridation programs. It refuses, however, to intervene in local campaigns in keeping with its policy of placing responsibility for local problems in the hands of the local profession. The Association has even defined the most suitable role for the local dental societies as that of advising and consulting with community representatives rather than assuming active leadership in a drive to add fluorides to the local water supply.[64]

Widespread adoption of a program for fluoridating community water supplies may indeed, as the Research Commission speculated in 1945, "prove of great value to coming generations." It may even help the American Dental Association and the dental profession meet the challenge of Harlan H. Horner and make dentistry's second century as remarkable for advances in the prevention of dental disease as its first was for progress in restorative measures. The American Dental Association has developed machinery for meeting the many problems it confronts on the threshold of its second century. Whether the solutions will prove equal to the issues they face awaits the verdict of history.

PRESIDING OFFICERS

OF THE

AMERICAN DENTAL ASSOCIATION

DURING ITS

FIRST ONE HUNDRED YEARS

W. W. Allport
1859-60

W. H. Atkinson
1860-62

G. Watt
1862-63

W. H. Allen
1863-64

J. H. McQuillen
1864-65

C. W. Spalding
1865-66

C. P. Fitch
1866-67

A. Lawrence
1867-68

J. Taft
1868-69

H. Judd
1869-70

W. H. Morgan
1870-71

G. H. Cushing
1871-72

P. G. C. Hunt
1872-73

T. L. Buckingham
1873-74

M. S. Dean
1874-75

A. L. Northrop
1875-76

G. W. Keely
1876-77

F. H. Rehwinkel
1877-78

H. J. McKellops
1878-79

L. D. Shepard
1879-80

C. N. Peirce
1880-81

H. A. Smith
1881-82

W. H. Goddard
1882-83

E. T. Darby
1883-84

Presidents of the American Dental Association 1859 to 1884

J. N. Crouse
1884-85

W. C. Barrett
1885-86

W. W. Allport
1886-87

F. Abbott
1887-88

C. R. Butler
1888-89

M. W. Foster
1889-90

A. W. Harlan
1890-91

W. W. Walker
1891-92

J. D. Patterson
1892-94

J. Y. Crawford
1894-96

J. Truman
1896-97

T. Fillebrown
1897-98

H. J. Burkhart
1898-99

B. H. Smith
1899-1900

G. V. Black
1900-01

J. A. Libbey
1901-02

L. G. Noel
1902-03

C. C. Chittenden
1903-04

W. E. Boardman
1904-05

M. F. Finley
1905-06

A. H. Peck
1906-07

W. Carr
1907-08

V. E. Turner
1908-09

B. L. Thorpe
1909-10

Presidents of the American Dental Association 1884 to 1910

E. S. Gaylord
1910-11

A. R. Melendy
1911-12

F. O. Hetrick
1912-13

H. C. Brown
1913-14

D. M. Gallie
1914-15

T. P. Hinman
1915-16

L. L. Barber
1916-17

W. H. G. Logan
1917-18

C. V. Vignes
1918-19

J. V. Conzett
1919-20

H. E. Friesell
1920-21

T. B. Hartzell
1921-22

J. P. Buckley
1922-23

W. A. Giffen
1923-24

C. N. Johnson
1924-25

S. W. Foster
1925-26

H. L. Banzhaf
1926-27

R. H. Volland
1927-28

P. R. Howe
1928-29

R. B. Bogle
1929-30

R. T. Oliver
1930-31

M. Dewey
1931-32

G. W. Dittmar
1932-33

A. C. Wherry
1933-34

Presidents of the American Dental Association 1910 to 1934

F. M. Casto
1934-35

G. B. Winter
1935-36

L. M. S. Miner
1936-37

C. W. Camalier
1937-38

M. L. Ward
1938-39

A. H. Merritt
1939-40

W. H. Robinson
1940-41

O. A. Oliver
1941-42

J. B. Robinson
1942-43

C. R. Wells
1943-44

W. H. Scherer
1944-46

S. V. Mead
1946-47

H. B. Washburn
1947-48

C. E. Minges
1948-49

P. E. Adams
1949-50

H. W. Oppice
1950-51

L. M. Ennis
1951-52

O. W. Brandhorst
1952-53

L. M. FitzGerald
1953-54

D. F. Lynch
1954-55

B. C. Kingsbury
1955-56

H. Lyons
1956-57

W. R. Alstadt
1957-58

P. T. Phillips
1958-59

Presidents of the American Dental Association 1934 to 1959

REFERENCES

Note: Conventional abbreviations have been used throughout in citing dental periodicals: *J* for *Journal, D* for *Dental,* and *R* for *Review.* Frequent citation of the *American Journal of Dental Science* suggested adoption of a special abbreviation, *AmJDSc.* Other abbreviations are self-explanatory.

CHAPTER I

1. The statistics are from U.S. Department of Commerce, Bureau of the Census, *Historical Statistics of the United States, 1789–1945* (Washington: Government Printing Office, 1949), p. 25, ser. B, col. 2; and George R. Taylor, *The Transportation Revolution, 1815–1860,* Vol. IV of *The Economic History of the United States,* ed. by Henry David, *et al.* (9 vols.; New York: Rinehart and Co., Inc., 1945–), 388.

2. U.S. Department of Commerce, Census Bureau, *Historical Statistics,* p. 27, ser. B, cols. 48 and 54; James Taylor, "Valedictory Address," *DRegister,* VIII (Apr., 1855), 200, 203.

3. U.S. Department of Commerce, Census Bureau, *Sixteenth Census Reports: Population,* vol. II, pt. 1.

4. U.S. Department of Commerce, Census Bureau, *Historical Statistics,* p. 63, ser. D, col. 6.

5. Solyman Brown, "Remarks on Professional Morality," *AmJDSc,* I (Aug., 1839), 2; James Taylor, "Valedictory Address," *DRegister,* VIII (Apr., 1855), 203; John B. McMaster, *A History of the People of the United States, from the Revolution to the Civil War* (New York: D. Appleton and Co., 1923), VII, 206.

6. Chapin A. Harris, "Observations on the Qualifications Necessary to a Practitioner of Dental Surgery," *AmJDSc,* I (Sept., 1839), 56, quoting Dr. Bell in the *Eclectic Journal of Medicine;* Charles O. Cone, "Report on Practical Dentistry," *AmJDSc,* IX (Oct., 1848), 5; *New York Mirror,* XII (Mar. 14, 1835), 295, quoted in L. Parmly Brown, "New Light on Dental History," *DCosmos,* LXII (Aug., 1920), 938.

7. John C. McCabe, "Thoughts on the Abuse of Dental Practice," *AmJDSc,* I (July, 1840), 134; Solyman Brown, "Remarks on Professional Morality," *ibid.* (Aug., 1839), 7.

8. This whole affair is movingly described in James E. Dexter, *A History of Dental and Oral Science in America,* sponsored by the American Academy of Dental Science (Philadelphia: S.S. White Co., 1876), 63n and 64. On medical developments, see Richard H. Shryock, *The Development of Modern Medicine: An Interpretation of the Social and Scientific Factors Involved* (New York: Alfred A. Knopf, 1947), 270.

9. On the New York society, see *U.S. Medical and Surgical J,* I (Mar., 1835), 311–312, quoted in L. Parmly Brown, "New Light," *DCosmos,* LXII (Aug., 1920), 937; J. Ben Robinson, "The Foundations of Organized Dentistry," *Proceedings of the Dental Centenary Celebration,* ed. by George M. Anderson (Baltimore: Dental Centenary Committee of the Maryland State Dental Society, 1940), 1014–1015; and Bernard W. Weinberger, "The Origin of Organized Dentistry," *Bulletin of the DSociety of the State of New York,* V (Nov., 1937), reprint pp. 12–13. The statement regarding the New York organization's absorption in the American Society rests on the testimony of Eleazar Parmly, who was intimately involved in the affairs of both organizations. See his "Ad-

dress Delivered before the American Society of Dental Surgeons," *AmJDSc*, VI (Sept., 1845), 3–4. A communication from the Dental Association of Western New York to *AmJDSc* refers to itself as auxiliary to the New York society. See "Doings of Dentists' Convention," *AmJDSc*, I (Aug., 1839), 17.

10. Solyman Brown, "Remarks on Professional Morality," *AmJDSc*, I (Aug., 1839), 3. On the prevalence of quackery, see any of the contemporary dental literature or the newspapers of the day, e.g., "Latest Humbug [mesmerism]," "Quack Dentist [dentifrices and steam]," and "Introduction of Steam to the Practice of Dentistry," *DRegister*, II (Jan., July, Apr., 1849), 100–102, 161–164, 156.

11. Shearjashub Spooner, *An Essay on the Art of the Manufacture of Mineral, Porcelain, or Incorruptible Teeth* (New York: Collins, Keese and Co., 1838), 12, quoted by J. Ben Robinson, "Foundations," *Proceedings of the Dental Centenary Celebration*, 1009.

12. Eleazar Parmly, Elisha Baker, and Solyman Brown, "Address of the Publishing Committee to their Professional Brethren throughout the United States of America," *AmJDSc*, I (June, 1839), 7.

13. Bernard W. Weinberger, "Origin of Organized Dentistry," *Bulletin of DSociety of the State of New York*, V (Nov., 1937), reprint pp. 18–19; J. Ben Robinson, "Foundations," *Proceedings of the Dental Centenary Celebration*, 1024–1025 and n.

14. Eleazar Parmly, *et al.*, "Address of the Publishing Committee," *AmJDSc*, I (June, 1839), 6–7.

15. Enoch Noyes, Baltimore, to Drs. Parmly and Harris, June 12, 1839, *AmJDSc*, I (Aug., 1839), 18–19. The prospects for the future, including a discussion of the subscription list, are assessed in "Of Our Next Volume," *ibid.* (Jan. and Feb., 1841), 197. On the irregularity of the issues in the first volume, see Enoch Noyes, "For the American Journal of Dental Science," *ibid.* (July, 1840), 129; J. Ben Robinson, "Foundations," *Proceedings of the Dental Centenary Celebration*, 1027; James A. Taylor, *History of Dentistry: A Practical Treatise for the Use of Dental Students and Practitioners* (Philadelphia: Lea and Febiger, 1922), 167–168; and L. Parmly Brown, "New Light," *DCosmos*, LXII (Aug., 1920), 936n. The latter source lists the dates on which the issues of Volume I appeared.

16. "Doings of Dentists' Convention," *AmJDSc*, I (Aug., 1839), 17; "National Dentists' Society," *ibid.* (Aug. and Sept., 1840), 170. On the difficulties attending publication of the first volume, see L. Parmly Brown, "New Light," *DCosmos*, LXII (Aug., 1920), 936n; and J. Ben Robinson, "Foundations," *Proceedings of the Dental Centenary Celebration*, 1027. Robinson accepts the statements of the editors that the irregularity of issue resulted only in part from financial problems. The editors, he says, also found that other duties interfered with the timely publication of the *Journal*.

17. "Extracts from the Transactions of the Second Annual Meeting of the American Society of Dental Surgeons," *AmJDSc*, II (Sept., 1841), 135–136. On the other early dental journals, see William Bebb, "A Bibliography of Dental Journals Published in the United States and Canada," *JNDA*, VI (Mar., 1919), 255–261. Bebb lists several other magazines published during these years of which little seems to be known.

18. "The American Journal of Dental Science," *Maryland Medical and Surgical Journal*, I (1839–1840), 110–111; Chapin A. Harris, "Observations on the Qualifications Necessary to a Practitioner of Dental Surgery," *AmJDSc*, I (Sept., 1839), 56. For the former reference, I am obliged to Dr. George B. Denton, Research Associate of the American Dental Association and Editor of the *Bulletin of the History of Dentistry*.

19. J. Ben Robinson, "Foundations," *Proceedings of the Dental Centenary Celebration*, 1010–1013.

20. Thomas E. Bond, Jr., "Obituary Notice of Prof. Horace H. Hayden, being a Valedictory Address to the Graduating Class of the Baltimore College of Dental Surgery," *AmJDSc*, IV (June, 1844), 221–230. See also the excellent biographical sketch by J. Ben Robinson, "Foundations," *Proceedings of the Dental Centenary Celebration*, 1016–1017. Hayden's bibliography is listed in Chapin A. Harris, *A Dictionary of Dental Science, Biography, Bibliography, and Medical Terminology* (Philadelphia; Lindsay and Blakiston, 1849), 359–361. Beyond these items, Harris's entry on Hayden contains little of value. The reasons for this are discussed by J. Ben Robinson, *op. cit.*, 1017.

21. J. Ben Robinson, "Foundations," *Proceedings of the Dental Centenary Celebration*, 1016; Van Wyck Brooks, *The World of Washington Irving* (New York: E. P. Dutton and Co., Inc., 1944), 212–215.

22. Eleazar Parmly, "Introductory Address," *AmJDSc*, III (Sept., 1842), 3. This document is valuable because of the large amount of autobiographical material it contains. See also Chapin A. Harris, *A Dictionary of Dental Science*, 578–579; J. Ben Robinson, "Foundations," *Proceedings of the Dental Centenary Celebration*, 1018; Bernard W. Weinberger, "Origin," *Bulletin of the DSociety of the State of New York*, reprint pp. 10–13.

23. James Taylor, "Life and Character of Chapin A. Harris," *DRegister*, XV (Feb., 1861), 79–90; J. Ben Robinson, "Foundations," *Proceedings of the Dental Centenary Celebration*, 1019–1021; James A. Taylor, *History of Dentistry*, 82. Van B. Dalton, *The Genesis of Dental Education in the United States* (Cincinnati: The Author, 1946), 52 and *passim*, contains much of value and interest, not only on the early life of Harris and his contemporaries, but also on the early history of organized dentistry.

24. J. Ben Robinson, "Foundations," *Proceedings of the Dental Centenary Celebration*, 1025.

25. Chapin A. Harris, "Introductory Address," *AmJDSc*, I (Jan. and Feb., 1841), 210; C. A. Harris, "Extract from a Letter from Dr. Harris to the New York Editor," *ibid.*, 217.

26. Joseph H. Foster, "Address Delivered before the Society of the Alumni of the Baltimore College," *AmJDSc*, IX (Apr., 1849), 297–298; "An Imposter," *ibid.*, X (Jan., 1850), 140–141.

27. "Progress of Dental Science," *DNews Letter*, V (July, 1852), 399; Editorial, *NY DRecorder*, X (Sept., 1856), 216; Elisha Townsend, "Address before the American Society of Dental Surgeons," *DRegister*, VIII (July, 1855), 247; James A. Taylor, *History of Dentistry*, 159–160.

28. Chapin A. Harris, "Introductory Address," *AmJDSc*, I (Jan. and Feb., 1841), 208; John C. McCabe, "Thoughts on the Abuse of Dental Practice," *ibid.* (July, 1840), 134–135.

29. Shearjashub Spooner, *Guide to Sound Teeth*, 111, quoted in J. Ben Robinson, "Foundations," *Proceedings of the Dental Centenary Celebration*, 1009; Eleazar Parmly, "Address Delivered before the American Society of Dental Surgeons," *AmJDSc*, VI (Sept., 1845), 9; Chapin A. Harris, "Observations on the Qualifications," *ibid.*, I (Sept., 1839), 57.

30. Syracuse Editor [Amos Westcott], "General Items Suggested by a Review of the Minutes of the Last Meeting," *AmJDSc*, VI (Sept., 1845), 67–68.

31. "Letter from Dr. C. J. Clark," *AmJDSc*, III (June, 1843), 277–278; Editorial, "Practice of Dental Surgery in Alabama," *ibid.*, 291–292.

32. The first quotation is derived from Richard H. Shryock, *Development of Modern Medicine*, 261–262; the next is from *Boston Medical and Surgical Journal* for Oct. 28, 1840, quoted with approval in *AmJDSc*, I (Jan. and Feb., 1841), 243. For dental

comment in the same vein, see "Extracts from the Dental Periodicals," *DNews Letter*, X (Jan., 1857), 142–143; "Lambeth Police Court," *DCosmos*, I (Nov., 1859), 205; J. H. Foster, "Address before the Society of the Alumni," *AmJDSc*, IX (Apr., 1849), 281.

33. Joseph H. Foster, "Address Delivered before the Society of Alumni," *AmJDSc*, IX (Apr., 1849), 281. Shattuck is quoted in Dirk J. Struik, *Yankee Science in the Making* (Boston: Little, Brown and Co., 1948), 235. See also James W. Hurst, *The Growth of American Law: The Law Makers* (Boston: Little, Brown and Co., 1950), 277; Thomas N. Bonner, *Medicine in Chicago 1850–1950: A Chapter in the Social and Scientific Development of a City* (Madison, Wis.: American History Research Center, 1957), 206; Richard H. Shryock, *Development of Modern Medicine*, 262; Carl R. Fish, *Rise of the Common Man*, Vol. VI of *A History of American Life*, ed. by A. M. Schlesinger and D. R. Fox (New York: Macmillan Co., 1935), 53–55.

34. Solyman Brown, "Remarks on Professional Morality," *AmJDSc*, I (June, 1839), 7; Chapin A. Harris, "Address . . . at the Opening of the Fourth Annual Meeting," *ibid.*, IV (Sept., 1843), 4–5.

35. See Dirk J. Struik, *Yankee Science*, 199, 232; Carl R. Fish, *Rise of the Common Man*, 48–49; Thomas N. Bonner, *Medicine in Chicago*, 70.

36. Eleazar Parmly, "Address . . . before the American Society," *AmJDSc*, VI (Sept., 1845), 3–4; Elisha Townsend and Joseph H. Foster, "Report of Committee on Propriety of Rescinding the Amalgam Pledge," *ibid.*, 2d ser., I (Oct., 1850), 66–67.

37. "National Dentists' Society," *AmJDSc*, I (Aug. and Sept., 1840), 157–170.

CHAPTER II

1. "National Dentists' Society," *AmJDSc*, I (Aug., 1840), 159–167.

2. "National Dentists' Society," *AmJDSc*, I (Aug., 1840), 168; "Seventh Annual Meeting of the American Society of Dental Surgeons," *ibid.*, VII (Sept., 1846), 94, 95; "Proceedings of the Seventh Annual Meeting," *Stockton's DIntelligencer*, II (Oct., 1846), 223.

3. "National Dentists' Society," *AmJDSc*, I (Aug., 1840), 159–167.

4. "New York Dental Recorder," *DRegister*, II (Oct., 1848), 48–49. On transportation developments and difficulties, see George R. Taylor, *The Transportation Revolution 1815–1860: The Economic History of the United States*, IV, ed. by Henry David *et. al.* (New York: Rinehart and Co., Inc., 1951), *passim*, especially chs. i–xiii; and John B. McMaster, *A History of the People of the United States from the Revolution to the Civil War*, VII (New York: D. Appleton and Co., 1923), 207.

5. "American Society of Dental Surgeons," *DRegister*, VIII (Oct., 1854), 9–11; "Meeting of the American Society," *DNews Letter*, VIII (Oct., 1854), 33–36; Charles Bonsall, "Proceedings of the American Society," *DRegister*, VII (Jan., 1854), 92–93; Enoch Noyes, "To the Editors," *AmJDSc*, I (July, 1840), 129; Edward Taylor, "To the Editors," *DRegister*, I (July, 1848), 193; "Apologetic," *ibid.*, X (Mar., 1857), 271; "Peculiarities of the Post Office Department," *ibid.*, XI (Mar., 1858), 355.

6. The following is a list of convention sites: 1840, New York; 1841, Philadelphia; 1842, Boston; 1843, Baltimore; 1844, New York; 1845, New York; 1846, New York; 1847, Saratoga Springs; 1848, Saratoga Springs; 1849, deferred to 1850, Baltimore; 1850, Saratoga Springs; 1851, Philadelphia; 1852, Newport, R. I.; 1853, West Point; 1854, postponed to 1855, Cincinnati; 1855, Philadelphia; 1856, New York, dissolved.

7. James Taylor, "Valedictory Address to the Graduating Class," *DRegister*, VIII (Apr., 1855), 202; G. Y. Shirley, "To the Editors," *AmJDSc*, X (July, 1850), 289; Editor's note, *New York DRecorder*, II (Jan., 1848), 80; and "The First Number of the Register," *DRegister*, I (Oct., 1847), 51–52.

8. "Multiplication of Dentists in the West," *AmJDSc*, 2d ser., IV (Oct., 1853), 176–177; James Taylor, "Valedictory Address," *DRegister*, VIII (Apr., 1855), 202; John C. McCabe, "Thoughts on the Abuse of Dental Practice," *AmJDSc*, I (July, 1840), 134. See also Carl R. Fish, *The Rise of the Common Man, 1830–1850: A History of American Life*, VI, ed. by Dixon R. Fox and Arthur M. Schlesinger (New York: Macmillan Co., 1927), 3.

9. James Taylor, "Valedictory Address," *DRegister*, VIII (Apr., 1855), 204; "Mississippi Valley Association of Dental Surgeons," *AmJDSc*, V (Sept., 1844), 78–79; "Proceedings of a Convention of Professional Dentists," *ibid.*, 112–119; "The First Number of the Register," *DRegister*, I (Oct., 1847), 51–52; Editor's note, *New York DRecorder*, II (Jan., 1848), 80.

10. "Letter from the St. Louis Editor," *DRegister*, I (Jan., 1848), 57–63; James Taylor, "On Filling Teeth, Address Delivered before the Mississippi Valley Association," *DNews Letter*, IV (July, 1851) 149; Editor's note following "Dr. Slack's Communication," *DRegister*, I (Oct., 1847), 23–24; "Enquirer," "My Last Amalgam Filling," *ibid.*, IV (Apr., 1851), 118.

11. "R. R. Kellog, (from New York) Surgeon Dentist," *DRegister*, I (Oct., 1847), 50–51.

12. "A Travelling Dentist," *DNews Letter*, VII (Jan., 1854), 106.

13. "Meeting of the American Society of Dental Surgeons," *DNews Letter*, VIII (Oct., 1854), 33–36; Amos Westcott, "General Items Suggested by a Review of the Minutes of the Last Meeting," *AmJDSc*, VI (Sept., 1845), 68–69.

14. Carl R. Fish, *The Rise of the Common Man*, 28–29.

15. "Mississippi Valley Association," *DRegister*, VIII (July, 1855), 235–238; "Twelfth Annual Meeting of the Mississippi Valley Association," *ibid.*, IX (Apr., 1856), 242.

16. "Multiplication of Dentists in the West," *AmJDSc*, 2d ser., IV (Oct., 1853), 176–177.

17. Elisha Townsend, "Dr. Townsend's Address," *DNews Letter*, VIII (July, 1855), 236; "Fifteenth Annual Meeting," *DRegister*, VIII (July, 1855), 239.

18. "American Society," *DRegister*, VIII (Oct., 1854), 10; "Miscellaneous Notices: August, 1849," *AmJDSc*, IX (July, 1849), 373; Dirk Struik, *Yankee Science in the Making* (Boston: Little, Brown and Co., 1948), 229–231.

19. "American Society," *DRegister*, VIII (Oct., 1854), 10.

20. Among many secondary accounts, see Louis C. Hunter, *Steamboats on the Western Rivers, An Economic History* (Harvard University, *Studies in Economic History*; Cambridge: Harvard University Press, 1949), especially pp. 484 and 503–504; Robert R. Russel, "A Revaluation of the Period before the Civil War: Railroads," *Mississippi Valley Historical Review*, XV (Dec., 1928), *passim*; Frederick J. Turner, *The United States 1830–1850: The Nation and its Sections* (New York: Henry Holt and Co., 1935), 314–315.

21. Merle Curti, *The Growth of American Thought* (New York: Harper and Brothers, Publishers, 1943), 338–343. See also *ibid.*, 268–271.

22. Thomas E. Bond, "Valedictory Address," *AmJDSc*, I (Aug.–Sept., 1841), 249–251, 254, and *passim*. This whole essay contains many provocative insights once Bond's thorny rhetoric has been penetrated. See also Merle Curti, *Growth of American Thought*, 336.

23. See Merle Curti, *Growth of American Thought*, 322–324, 333–335.

24. "Dental Exhibitions," *DRegister*, VII (Jan., 1854), 96; J. H. McQuillen, "Individual and Associated Effort," *DCosmos*, I (Aug., 1859), 23.

25. J. H. McQuillen, "Individual and Associated Effort," *DCosmos*, I (Aug., 1859), 23.

26. "Dentists as Inventors," *New York DJ*, II (July, 1859), 139–142; Carl R. Fish, *Rise of the Common Man*, 105, 237–238; John B. McMaster, *History of the People*, VII, 99; R. H. Shryock, *Development of Modern Medicine* (New York: Alfred A. Knopf, 1948), 175–176; Dirk Struik, *Yankee Science*, viii, 221, 340–341; Merle Curti, *Growth of American Thought*, 322–324, 333–335.

27. R. H. Shryock, *Development of Modern Medicine*, 119; C. O. Cone, "Report on Practical Dentistry," *AmJDSc*, IX (Oct., 1848), 19; "Magendie's Opinion of Homeopathy," *Stockton's DIntelligencer*, III (Nov., 1846), 13–16; "Professional Health," *DRegister*, XIII (Dec., 1859), 253–256.

28. "Another Screw Loose," *DRegister*, XIII (Feb., 1860), 353. See also "Dentists as Inventors," *New York DJ*, II (July, 1859), 139–142.

29. Elisha Townsend, "Address before the American Society," *DRegister*, VIII (July, 1855), 246.

30. Chapin A. Harris, "Address at the Opening of the Fourth Annual Session," *AmJDSc*, IV (Sept., 1843), 4. See also Thomas N. Bonner, *Medicine in Chicago: 1850–1950* (Madison, Wis.: American History Research Center, 1957), 70.

CHAPTER III

1. Solyman Brown, "Address," *AmJDSc*, I (June, 1839), 10; Chapin A. Harris, "Observations on the Qualifications Necessary to a Practitioner of Dental Surgery," *ibid.* (Sept., 1839), 49, 50–51, 52.

2. C. O. Cone, "Report on Practical Dentistry," *AmJDSc*, IX (Oct., 1848), 5–6, 9–10; Joseph H. Foster, "Address Delivered before the Society of the Alumni of the Baltimore College," *ibid.* (Apr., 1849), 298.

3. "Extracts from the Transactions of the Second Annual Meeting of the American Society of Dental Surgeons," *AmJDSc*, II (Sept., 1841), 135–136; "Eleventh Annual Meeting of the American Society," *AmJDSc*, 2d ser., I (Oct., 1850), 92–93.

4. H. Crane, "Letter to Dr. Taylor," *DRegister*, I (Oct., 1847), 45–46.

5. S. Brown, "Information Concerning the American Society," *AmJDSc*, I (Jan. and Feb., 1841), 191–193; "Notice," *ibid.*, 196.

6. C. O. Cone, "Report on Practical Dentistry," *AmJDSc*, IX (Oct., 1848), 4–5; Editorial, *ibid.*, II (Sept., 1841), 159.

7. "Sixth Annual Meeting," *Stockton's DIntelligencer*, II (Nov., 1845), 15; "Dental Hygiene," *AmJDSc*, V (Mar., 1845), 244–245; "Tenth Annual Meeting," *ibid.*, X (Apr., 1850), 211; "Eleventh Annual Meeting," *ibid.*, 2d ser., I (Oct., 1850), 93, 95–96; "Twelfth Annual Meeting of the American Society," *DNews Letter*, V (Oct., 1851), 174.

8. For an example of the commissioned address, see Thomas E. Bond, Jr., "Dissertation on the Morbid Sympathy between the Mouth and Other Parts of the Body," *AmJDSc*, IV (Sept., 1843), 23–31. C. O. Cone commented, "[The address] just referred to showed plainly the anxiety of the association to extend the knowledge of general pathology in the profession." "Report on Practical Dentistry," *ibid.*, IX (Oct., 1848), 10.

9. "Seventh Annual Meeting of the American Society," *AmJDSc*, VII (Sept., 1846), 100; "Proceedings of the Seventh Annual Meeting," *Stockton's DIntelligencer*,

II (Oct., 1846), 228–229; "Eighth Annual Meeting," *AmJDSc,* VIII (Oct., 1847), 98–99; "American Society," *Stockton's DIntelligencer,* III (Aug., 1847), 192; "Ninth Annual Meeting," *AmJDSc,* IX (Oct., 1848), 146.

10. Charles Bonsall, "Proceedings of the American Society," *DRegister,* VII (Jan., 1854), 91; W. G. Adair, "The Tabular Sheet and Dr. Chapin A. Harris," *JAm.College of Dentists,* XVIII (Sept., 1951), 150–157.

11. "Eighth Annual Meeting," *AmJDSc,* VIII (Oct., 1847), 98–99; "American Society of Dental Surgeons," *Stockton's DIntelligencer,* III (Aug., 1847), 192.

12. C. O. Cone, "Report of Practical Dentistry," *AmJDSc,* IX (Oct., 1848), 3–82.

13. "Sixth Annual Meeting," *AmJDSc,* VI (Sept., 1845), 78.

14. *Ibid.,* 79; "Eighth Annual Meeting," *ibid.,* VIII (Oct., 1847), 105.

15. Edward Taylor, "Review of the Proceedings of the American Society for 1847," *DRegister,* I (Jan., 1848), 102–103.

16. "Eighth Annual Meeting," *AmJDSc,* VIII (Oct., 1847), 101.

17. A. Hill and Samuel G. Blackman, "Circular to Members of the Dental Profession," *DNews Letter,* I (Apr., 1848), 28–30; "Ninth Annual Meeting," *AmJDSc,* IX (Oct., 1848), 146–147; "American Society of Dental Surgeons," *New York DRecorder,* III (Feb., 1849), 116, 119.

18. "Letter from W. H. Elliott," *AmJDSc,* X (Jan., 1850), 78–79. See also on Hullihen's behalf, C. O. Cone, "Dental Ethics and the Compound Screw Forceps," *ibid.,* 79–99.

19. J. R. McCurdy, "Report of the Proceedings of the Fourteenth Annual Meeting of the American Society," *DNews Letter,* VII (Oct., 1853), 40–41; Charles Bonsall, "Proceedings of the American Society," *DRegister,* VII (Jan., 1854), 90–91.

20. "National Dentists' Society," *AmJDSc,* I (Aug., 1840), 160; "Sixth Annual Meeting of the American Society," *ibid.,* IV (Sept., 1845), 84.

21. "Seventh Annual Meeting," *AmJDSc,* VII (Sept., 1846), 101; "Review of the Proceedings of the Last Meeting," *ibid.,* 105; C. O. Cone, "Report on Practical Dentistry," *ibid.,* IX (Oct., 1848), 15–16.

22. "Eighth Annual Meeting of the American Society," *AmJDSc,* VIII (Oct., 1847), 105; C. O. Cone, "Report on Practical Dentistry," *ibid.* (Oct., 1848), 4–5; Joseph H. Foster, "Address Delivered before the Society of the Alumni," *ibid.,* IX (Apr., 1849), 284.

23. "Sixth Annual Meeting of the American Society," *AmJDSc,* VI (Sept., 1845), 82; "Advertisement," *Stockton's DIntelligencer,* II (Nov., 1845), 19–20.

24. "Meeting of the American Society," *AmJDSc,* 2d ser., IV (Oct., 1853), 60–61; Charles Bonsall, "Proceedings of the American Society," *DRegister,* VII (Jan., 1854), 91.

25. John C. McCabe, "Extract from a Letter to the Baltimore Editor," *AmJDSc,* IV (Dec., 1843), 89; Elisha Townsend and Joseph H. Foster, "Report of the Committee on the Propriety of Rescinding the Amalgam Pledge," *AmJDSc,* 2d ser., I (Oct., 1850), 66.

26. "National Dentists' Society," *AmJDSc,* I (Aug. and Sept., 1840), 167; Joseph H. Foster, "Address Delivered before the Society of the Alumni of the Baltimore College," *ibid.,* IX (Apr., 1849), 290-291.

27. The controversy is reviewed in *AmJDSc,* II (Dec., 1841), 209–210. On Gardette's brief connection with the American Society of Dental Surgeons, see "National Dentists' Society," *ibid.,* I (Aug. and Sept., 1840), 157, 167.

28. Solyman Brown, "Important Announcement," *AmJDSc*, I (Jan. and Feb., 1841), 189.

29. Solyman Brown, "Information Concerning the American Society of Dental Surgeons," *AmJDSc*, I (Jan. and Feb., 1841), 196.

30. Joseph H. Foster, "Address Delivered before the Society of the Alumni of the Baltimore College," *AmJDSc*, IX (Apr., 1849), 296.

31. The relevant portions of the organic law are Constitution, Art. VI, sec. 1; and By-Laws, Art. I, sec. 10. See "National Dentists' Society," *AmJDSc*, I (Aug. and Sept., 1840), 160, 165.

32. Eleazar Parmly, "Introductory Address," *AmJDSc*, III (Sept., 1842), 7; "American Society," *ibid.*, 71–72; "American Society," *ibid.*, IV (Sept., 1843), 70.

33. Joseph H. Foster, "Address Delivered before . . . the Alumni," *AmJDSc*, IX (Apr., 1849), 287; "Constitution and By-Laws of the American Society," *ibid.*, V (Sept., 1844), 66–67; "American Society of Dental Surgeons," *ibid.*, 74; "Sixth Annual Meeting," *Stockton's DIntelligencer*, II (Nov., 1845), 16; C. O. Cone, "Report on Practical Dentistry," *AmJDSc*, IX (Oct., 1848), 10–11.

34. "Seventh Annual Meeting of the American Society of Dental Surgeons," *AmJDSc*, VII (Sept., 1846), 94–98, 101; "Proceedings of the Seventh Annual Meeting," *Stockton's DIntelligencer*, II (Oct., 1846), 222–223, 229. For an apology and explanation of the Society's action, see "Review of the Proceedings of the Last Meeting," *AmJDSc*, VII (Sept., 1846), 102–103.

35. J. H. Foster, "Address Delivered before the . . . Alumni," *AmJDSc*, IX (Apr., 1849), 284. Hayden is quoted in Charles Bonsall, "Address before the Mississippi Valley Association of Dental Surgeons," *DRegister*, VII (Apr., 1854), 197.

36. J. H. Foster, "Address Delivered before the . . . Alumni," *AmJDSc*, IX (Apr., 1849), 283.

37. Statistics on the number of dentists in these early days are highly unreliable. Not until 1850 was there an official census enumeration of the profession, and this included not only those who were qualified but those who thought they were. Chapin A. Harris estimated "about twelve hundred" dentists in the United States in 1841, of whom, he thought, perhaps one sixth were qualified. ("Introductory Lecture at the Opening of the First Session," *AmJDSc*, I [Jan. and Feb., 1841], 199.) The editor of the *American Journal* estimated "some fifteen or eighteen hundred dentists" in 1846. ("Enlargement of the Journal and Library of Dental Science," *AmJDSc*, VII [Sept., 1846], 107.) Two years later, a bolder figure of twenty-five hundred was proposed. ("Dental Intelligencer," *New York DRecorder*, II [Apr., 1848], 139.) "We have twenty-five or twenty-six hundred practitioners of dental surgery," the *Journal's* editor guessed in 1851. "But it must at the same time be confessed, that a large majority of those who call themselves dentists have not a single qualification entitling them to the Appellation." ("Progress of Dental Surgery," *AmJDSc*, 2d ser., I [Jan., 1851], 222.) The census of 1850 reported 2,923 dentists. (Elisha Townsend, "Dr. Townsend's Address," *DNews Letter*, VIII [July, 1855], 237.)

CHAPTER IV

1. J. Ben Robinson, "Foundations of Organized Dentistry," *Proceedings of the Dental Centenary* (Baltimore: Dental Centenary Committee of the Maryland State Dental Society, 1940), George M. Anderson, ed., 1015; L. Parmly Brown, "New Light on Dental History," *DCosmos*, LXII (Aug., 1920), 936–958; Bernard W. Weinberger, "The Origin of Organized Dentistry," *Bulletin of the DSociety of the State of New York*, V (Nov., 1937), reprint pp. 1–40; Solyman Brown, "Remarks on Professional Morality," *AmJDSc*, I (Sept., 1839), 3; James Taylor, "Editorials," *DRegister*, I (July, 1848), 220. See also Charles C. Allen, "For the Dental Recorder," *New York DRecorder*, I (Feb., 1847), 61.

2. Joseph H. Foster, "Address Delivered before the Society of the Alumni," *AmJDSc,* IX (Apr., 1849), 285; "Letter from J. H. Foster, New York, to the American Society," *AmJDSc,* II (Sept., 1840), 130.

3. John C. McCabe, "Extract from a Letter to the Baltimore Editor," *AmJDSc,* IV (Dec., 1843), 89. Eleazar Parmly, Elisha Baker, Solyman Brown, "Address of the Publishing Committee," *AmJDSc,* I (June, 1839), 3; "Report of the Proceedings of the Pennsylvania Society of Dental Surgeons," *New York DRecorder,* I (Mar., 1847), 82–83.

4. "The Examination of the Several Materials now in Use for Filling Teeth," *New York DRecorder,* I (Nov., 1846), 33; James Taylor, "On Filling Teeth, An Address Delivered before the Mississippi Valley Association," *DNews Letter,* IV (July, 1851), 148–149.

5. Richard H. Shryock, *American Medical Research Past and Present* (New York: The Commonwealth Fund, 1947), 31; Richard Harrison Shryock, *The Development of Modern Medicine: An Interpretation of the Social and Scientific Factors Involved* (New York: Alfred A. Knopf, 1947), 119; Edward Taylor, "Address," *DRegister,* I (Oct., 1847), 6; "Proceedings of the Seventh Annual Meeting of the American Society," *Stockton's DIntelligencer,* II (Oct., 1846), 228.

6. C. O. Cone, "Report on Practical Dentistry," *AmJDSc,* IX (Oct., 1848), 19–20; J. H. McQuillen, "Dental Journals," *DCosmos,* I (Jan., 1860), 308–310; E. Taylor, "Address," *DRegister,* I (Oct., 1847), 6.

7. C. O. Cone, "Report on Practical Dentistry," *AmJDSc,* IX (Oct., 1848), 18–20.

8. *Ibid.,* 20.

9. See above, Ch. iii, 53–54; John S. Clark, "Paper Read before the New Orleans Academy of Sciences," *AmJDSc,* 2d ser., IX (Apr., 1859), 178–188; and *ibid.* (Oct., 1859), 504–520; "American Dental Review for February," *DNews Letter,* XII (Apr., 1859), 223–234; J. Richardson, "Dental Nomenclature," *American DReview,* I (Nov., 1858), 145–146; "Nomenclature," Ed. note, *ibid.,* 188–189; "Professional Health," *DRegister,* XIII (Dec., 1859), 253–256; and George S. Fouke, "Nomenclature of Dental Caries," *DRegister,* XIII (Mar., 1860), 448–450.

10. See R. H. Shryock, *American Medical Research,* 31–35; R. H. Shryock, *Development of Modern Medicine,* 270.

11. A. Clar, "Letter to the Editors," *AmJDSc,* I (Dec., 1839), 93–94.

12. Enoch Noyes, "Letter to the Editors," *AmJDSc,* I (July, 1840), 129–130, 132.

13. Charles C. Allen, "For the Dental Recorder," *New York DRecorder,* I (Feb., 1847), 61–62.

14. "Mineral Paste," *Stockton's DIntelligencer,* II (May, 1846), 134–135, reprinting a clipping from the *New York Tribune.*

15. "Extracts from the Transactions of the Second Annual Meeting of the American Society," *AmJDSc,* II (Sept., 1841), 136; Joseph H. Foster, "Letter to the American Society of Dental Surgeons," *ibid.,* 130–131.

16. "American Society of Dental Surgeons," *AmJDSc,* IV (Sept., 1843), 70.

17. "American Society of Dental Surgeons," *AmJDSc,* V (Sept., 1844), 76.

18. "Sixth Annual Meeting of the American Society," *Stockton's DIntelligencer,* II (Nov., 1845), 13; "Sixth Annual Meeting of the American Society," *AmJDSc,* VI (Sept., 1845), 75.

19. *Ibid.,* 14–16.

20. *Ibid.,* 16–17.

21. *Ibid.,* 15.

22. [Amos Westcott?] "General Items Suggested by a Review of the Minutes of the Last Meeting," *AmJDSc*, VI (Sept., 1845), 62–63; Charles C. Allen, "For the Dental Recorder," *New York DRecorder*, I (Feb., 1847), 6.

23. "Seventh Annual Meeting of the American Society," *AmJDSc*, VII (Sept., 1846), 91–93, 98; A. Westcott, "Review of the Proceedings of the Last Meeting," *AmJDSc*, VII (Sept., 1846), 104; "Proceedings of the Seventh Annual Meeting of the American Society," *Stockton's DIntelligencer*, II (Oct., 1846), 221–227; "Proceedings of the American Society," *New York DRecorder*, I (Sept., 1846), 10.

24. "Eighth Annual Meeting of the American Society," *AmJDSc*, VIII (Oct., 1847), 97, 98.

25. "Eighth Annual Meeting of the American Society," *AmJDSc*, VIII (Oct., 1847), 99, 104, and 105; Charles C. Allen, "The American Society of Dental Surgeons and the Dental Register of the West," *DRegister*, I (July, 1848), 192.

26. "Eighth Annual Meeting of the American Society," *AmJDSc*, VIII (Oct., 1847), 99. The first was the case of George Hawes. See also *ibid.*, 100, 102–103, 104, and 105. The latter two pages each record Keep's resignation.

27. *Ibid.*, 101–102.

28. *Ibid.*, 99–100, 103, and 104.

29. *Ibid.*, 105; "Dr. C. S. Brewster of Paris," *Stockton's DIntelligencer*, II (July, 1846), 173; "Tomes on Caries of the Teeth," *New York DRecorder*, II (Jan., 1848), 61–64.

30. J. S. Ware, "Prospectus," *New York DRecorder*, I (Sept., 1846), 1; James A. Taylor, *History of Dentistry: A Practical Treatise for the Use of Dental Students and Practitioners* (Philadelphia: Lea and Febiger, 1922), 168, 177; "Eighth Annual Meeting of the American Society," *AmJDSc*, VIII (Oct., 1847), 104.

31. B. B. Brown, "Comments on the Action of the American Society," *DRegister*, I (Apr., 1848), 134–135.

32. "Eighth Annual Meeting of the American Society," *AmJDSc*, VIII (Oct., 1847), 97, lists twenty-three members present when the meeting convened. "Expelled Member," *New York DRecorder*, II (Mar., 1848), 102, gives the number as twenty-eight, but insists that no more than thirteen members were actually present when the action was taken against the pro-amalgam members. The report of proceedings in *AmJDSc*, indicates that some members arrived after the session was first called to order. Edward Taylor, "Review of the Proceedings of the American Society," *DRegister*, I (Jan., 1848), 93, states that there were "about thirty" in attendance. "The attendance was not large, at no time numbering more than thirty members." (The American Society of Dental Surgeons," *New York DRecorder*, II [Nov., 1847], 33.) Amos Westcott's report in 1846 accounted for one hundred thirty-four members. One new member was added to the rolls in 1846, while three who categorically refused to sign the protest and pledge of 1845 were presumably dropped from the list. This would make the total membership at the beginning of the 1847 meeting one hundred thirty-two.

33. "Expelled Member," *New York DRecorder*, II (Mar., 1848), 102. See also Charles C. Allen, "The American Society of Dental Surgeons and the Dental Register," *DRegister*, I (July, 1848), 191–192: "Here then the matter rested until the meeting of the Society in 1847, when owing to the absence of the lukewarm, and the presence of a few dough faces, the Vandals again had it all their own way, by a majority of one."

34. B. B. Brown, "Comments on the Action of the American Society," *DRegister*, I (Apr., 1848), 139–140, quoting from a personal letter to Chapin A. Harris.

35. "Mineral Paste," *Stockton's DIntelligencer*, II (May, 1846), 137.

36. E. Taylor, "Review of the Proceedings of the American Society," *DRegister*, I (Jan., 1848), 98; Letter to B. B. Brown, Oct. 30, 1845, quoted in B. B. Brown,

"Comments on the Action of the American Society," *DRegister*, I (Apr., 1848), 137–138.

37. The citation above, n. 35, contains material that had appeared in the *New York Tribune*. "The Amalgam Controversy in New York," *Stockton's DIntelligencer*, III (July, 1847), 161–176, reproduces letters from the *Tribune* and the *New York Express* of June 5, 1847. *Ibid.*, III (Aug., 1847), 193–196, has material from the *Express* again; "Killed by Bad Dentistry," *New York DRecorder*, I (June, 1847), 117; "Death Supposed to have Resulted from a Bad Filling in a Tooth," *Stockton's DIntelligencer*, III (June, 1847), 145; Elisha Baker, "Letter from Dr. Baker," *New York DRecorder*, II (Mar., 1848), 107–110; "The Amalgam Controversy," *ibid.* (Oct., 1847); A. C. Castle, "Parmly vs. Amalgam," *ibid.*, II (Mar., 1848), 105–107; E. Parmly, "Letter from Eleazar Parmly," *ibid.* (Jan., 1848), 65–67. The impossibility of dealing reasonably with Parmly on the amalgam question is fully exhibited in his "Communication," *New York DRecorder*, I (July, 1847), 129: "When my friends or the public want further testimony than the handwriting of Mr. Ames himself, as to the effects of swallowing amalgam, I will, at any sacrifice of time, labor, or expense, endeavor to furnish it. When my enemies, false accusers, and slanderers want it, they may seek it where it can be found."

38. "The Amalgam Controversy," *New York DRecorder*, II (Oct., 1847), 17.

39. "Dental Surgeon," "Letter to Editors," *New York DRecorder*, II (Oct., 1847), 1–2; Editorial Comment on Letter from "A Dental Surgeon," *ibid.*, 3; "Society of Dental Surgeons of the State of New York," *ibid.*, (Dec., 1847), 56–59.

40. "New York Society of Dental Surgeons," *New York DRecorder*, IX (Jan., 1855), 21–22, reports the disbandment of this organization.

41. "Ninth Annual Meeting of the American Society," *AmJDSc*, IX (Oct., 1848), 143–145; "American Society of Dental Surgeons," *New York DRecorder*, III (Feb., 1849), 117. The resignations came from Lewis Roper, C. C. Allen, C. S. Rowell, and John W. [should be George?] Hawes. Allen, Rowell, and Hawes were on the list of delinquents in "Eighth Annual Meeting," *AmJDSc*, VIII (Oct., 1847), 97.

42. "Miscellaneous Notices: August, 1849," *AmJDSc*, IX (July, 1849), 373.

43. Editorial notes, *DNews Letter*, III (Apr., 1850), 69; "Tenth Annual Meeting of the American Society," *AmJDSc*, X (Apr., 1850), 209, 210. Townsend's speech was widely reproduced in the dental press. See "Remarks on the Propriety of Rescinding the Amalgam Pledge," *DNews Letter*, IV (Apr., 1851), 65–71.

44. *Ibid.*, 67–70.

45. *Ibid.*, 70–71; "Tenth Annual Meeting of the American Society," *AmJDSc*, X (Apr., 1850), 210; "Eleventh Annual Meeting of the American Society," *AmJDSc*, 2d ser., I (Oct., 1850), 91.

46. The rationalization of the Society is quoted from "American Society of Dental Surgeons," *AmJDSc*, 2d ser., I (Oct., 1850), 100. For Rich's resignation, see "Eleventh Annual Meeting," *ibid.*, 92. The relationship between the action of the Society and Rich's withdrawal is unmistakable.

CHAPTER V

1. "Sixth Annual Meeting of the American Society of Dental Surgeons," *AmJDSc*, VI (Sept., 1845), 82; "Seventh Annual Meeting of the American Society," *ibid.*, VII (Sept., 1846), 101; "Proceedings of the Seventh Annual Meeting," *Stockton's DIntelligencer* [II] (Oct., 1846), 229 (This journal carried no volume numbers at this time); "Eighth Annual Meeting," *AmJDSc*, VIII (Oct., 1847), 104; "American Society of Dental Surgeons," *New York DRecorder*, III (Feb., 1849), 118; "Tenth Annual Meeting of the American Society," *AmJDSc*, X (Apr., 1850), 209–210; and "American

Society of Dental Surgeons," *DRegister*, III (July, 1850), 192–195. Regarding the postponement, see the official announcement in "Miscellaneous Notices: August, 1849," *AmJDSc*, IX (July, 1849), 373.

2. "Eleventh Annual Meeting," *AmJDSc*, 2d ser., I (Oct., 1850), 92–93; J. H. Mc-Quillen, "Plans that have been Tried," *DCosmos*, I (Nov., 1859), 192; "American Society of Dental Surgeons," *New York DRecorder*, III (Feb. 1849), 118; "American Society of Dental Surgeons," *Stockton's DIntelligencer*, (Aug., 1847), p. 192; Amos Westcott, "General Items Suggested by a Review of the Minutes of the Last Meeting," *AmJDSc*, VI (Sept., 1845), 61–62; C. O. Cone, "Report on Practical Dentistry," *ibid.*, IX (Oct., 1848), 13.

3. "American Society of Dental Surgeons," *DRegister*, III (July, 1850), 195; "Eleventh Annual Meeting of the American Society," *AmJDSc*, 2d ser., I (Oct., 1850), 94; "American Society of Dental Surgeons," *ibid.*, II (Oct., 1851), 158; "Proceedings of the Twelfth Annual Meeting," *DNews Letter*, VI (Oct., 1851), 174; "American Society of Dental Surgeons," *AmJDSc*, 2d ser., III (Oct., 1852), 158, 160; "Meeting of the American Society . . . , West Point, August 2, 1853," *ibid.*, IV (Oct., 1853), 60; and J. R. McCurdy, "Report of the Proceedings of the Fourteenth Annual Meeting," *DNews Letter*, VII (Oct., 1853), 40.

4. Thus far I have been unable to locate a copy of this constitution. One significant provision, however, has come to light. According to one paraphrased account, the fee for admission to membership was "increased to twenty-five dollars." "The American Society of Dental Surgeons," *DRegister*, VII (Jan., 1854), 152. The reasoning that prompted this amendment may be reflected in the anonymous article, "Dental Societies," *AmJDSc*, 2d ser., X (Jan., 1860), 52–53: "It would be ridiculous to apply the [membership] test of scientific reputation or proficiency, and we have only the tests of morals and money left for our present needs. There can be no doubt that considerable fees will keep out a large class of persons who are not of the least use and who, under the present order of things, are exceedingly troublesome."

5. "The Fifteenth Annual Meeting," *DNews Letter*, VIII (July, 1855), 233–234; and "Fifteenth Annual Meeting," *DRegister*, VII (July, 1855), 239.

6. Elisha Townsend, "Dr. Townsend's Address," *DNews Letter*, VIII (July, 1855), 241.

7. "Eighth Annual Meeting of the American Society," *AmJDSc*, VII (June, 1847), 396; and "Twelfth Annual Meeting of the American Society," *ibid.*, 2d ser., I (July, 1851), 564. See also above, Ch. iv, pp. 82–83, and the sources there cited.

8. Ed. note, *New York DRecorder*, II (Oct., 1847), 3; "Tomes, 'On Caries of the Teeth,' " *ibid.* (Jan., 1848), 64; and C. O. Cone, "Report on Practical Dentistry," *AmJDSc*, IX (Oct., 1848), 11.

9. Henry J. Brown, "Voluntary Associations and Professional Reform," *DRegister*, II (Jan., 1849), 62–65.

10. "The American Dental Convention: What Use Is It," *New York DJ*, IV (July, 1861), 239–240.

11. C. O. Cone, "Report on Practical Dentistry," *AmJDSc*, IX (Oct., 1848), 13. See also "Eighth Annual Meeting of the American Society," *ibid.*, VII (June, 1847), 396; "American Society of Dental Surgeons," *New York DRecorder*, III (Feb., 1849), 118; Charles C. Allen, "For the Dental Recorder," *ibid.*, I (Feb., 1847), 65; and "American Society of Dental Surgeons," *Stockton's DIntelligencer*, III (Aug., 1847), 192.

12. "Seventh Annual Meeting of the American Society," *AmJDSc*, VIII (Sept., 1847), 94; and C. O. Cone, "Report on Practical Dentistry," *ibid.*, IX (Oct., 1848), 5, 9–10.

13. "National Dentists' Society," *AmJDSc*, I (Aug. and Sept., 1840), 166.

14. Chapin A. Harris, "Address . . . at the Opening of the Fourth Annual Meeting," *AmJDSc*, IV (Sept., 1843), 18–19.

15. Amos Westcott, "General Items Suggested by a Review of the Minutes of the Last Meeting," *AmJDSc*, VI (Sept., 1845), 68–69. See also Joseph H. Foster, "Address Delivered before the Society of the Alumni of the Baltimore College," *ibid.*, IX (Apr., 1849), 281–282. Foster blamed many of the failures of local societies on "want of sufficient material of a proper character to form a solid fabric; and to the introduction as a substitute, of such as could not assimilate with, or be consistently united in, the building of a strong and substantial edifice."

16. "American Society of Dental Surgeons," *AmJDSc*, V (Sept., 1844), 77; and C. O. Cone, "Report on Practical Dentistry," *ibid.*, IX (Oct., 1848), 11.

17. "Mississippi Valley Association of Dental Surgeons," *AmJDSc*, V (Sept., 1844), 78–79; and "Proceedings of a Convention of Professional Dentists," *ibid.* (Dec., 1844), 112–119. See also James Taylor, "Valedictory Address to the Graduating Class," *DRegister*, VIII (Apr., 1855), 204.

18. On the Virginia Society, see Van B. Dalton, *The Genesis of Dental Education in the United States* (Cincinnati: [The Author], 1946), 52; and James E. Dexter, *A History of Dental and Oral Surgery in America* (Philadelphia: Samuel S. White, 1876), 151–152. The meetings of this society are recorded with fair regularity in the early volumes of the *American Journal*. Dalton states, "This society lived only four or five years." It may well have become more or less inactive by that time. See "A Brief Review of Dental Associations," *DRegister*, XII (July, 1859), 445. The Committee on Dental Progress of the Mississippi Valley Association failed to include the Virginia Society in its list of 1858. "Report on Dental Progress," *DRegister*, XI (Mar., 1858), 283.

19. "Convention of Dentists," *AmJDSc*, VI (Dec., 1845), 183–184; "Pennsylvania Association of Dental Surgeons," *Stockton's DIntelligencer*, II (Dec., 1845), 33; and "Report of the Proceedings of a Convention of Dental Surgeons," *ibid.* (Jan., 1846), 45–48.

20. "A Society of Dental Surgeons," *New York DRecorder*, II (Nov., 1847), 40; "Society of Dental Surgeons of the State of New York," *ibid.* (Dec., 1847), 56–59; and James E. Dexter, *A History of Dental Science*, 153–154.

21. "Dental Associations," *DNews Letter*, VI (Mar., 1853), 183. See also "Report on Dental Progress to the Mississippi Valley Association," *DRegister*, XI (Mar., 1858), 283: "In something more than twelve months, no less than seven dental associations have sprung into a healthful and vigorous existence. We have the 'Western Dental Society,' organized in April, 1856; the 'North Carolina Dental Society,' in October, 1856; the 'St. Louis Dental Society,' in December, 1856; the 'Pennsylvania Central Society of Dental Surgeons,' in May, 1857; 'South Jersey Dental Association,' July, 1857; the 'Dental Convention of Northern Ohio,' in November, 1857; and the 'New York Dental Society,' in December, 1857. There are now in the United States, as far as the committee are advised by published reports, ten dental societies, including, with those just mentioned, the 'American Dental Convention,' 'the Pennsylvania Association,' and the 'Mississippi Valley Association.'"

22. "The American Society of Dental Surgeons," *DNews Letter*, V (July, 1851), 138; "Proceedings of the Twelfth Annual Meeting of the American Society," *ibid.* (Oct., 1851), 174.

23. Charles Bonsall, "Proceedings of the American Society," *DRegister*, VII (Jan., 1854), 90; and J. R. McCurdy, "Report of the Proceedings of the Fourteenth Annual Meeting," *DNews Letter*, VII (Oct., 1853), 40.

24. "Eleventh Annual Meeting of the American Society," *AmJDSc*, 2d ser., I (Oct., 1850), 95; "Proceedings of the Twelfth Annual Meeting," *DNews Letter*, V

(Oct., 1851), 213; "American Society of Dental Surgeons," *AmJDSc*, 2d ser., III (Oct., 1852), 158–160; "Meeting of the American Society . . . , West Point, August 2, 1853," *ibid.*, IV (Oct., 1853), 62; and J. R. McCurdy, "Report of the Proceedings of the Fourteenth Annual Meeting of the American Society," *DNews Letter*, VII (Oct., 1853), 43.

25. "American Society of Dental Surgeons," *AmJDSc*, 2d ser., II (Oct., 1851), 160–162; and "Proceedings of the Twelfth Annual Meeting," *DNews Letter*, V (Oct., 1851), 201–204.

26. "American Society of Dental Surgeons," *AmJDSc*, 2d ser., II (Oct., 1851), 162; and "Proceedings of the Twelfth Annual Meeting," *DNews Letter*, V (Oct., 1851), 201.

27. J. R. McCurdy, "Report of the Proceedings of the Fourteenth Annual Meeting," *DNews Letter*, VII (Oct., 1853), 40; Charles Bonsall, "Proceedings of the American Society," *DRegister*, VII (Jan., 1854), 90; "Fifteenth Annual Meeting," *ibid.*, VIII (July, 1855), 238; "The Fifteenth Annual Meeting," *DNews Letter*, VIII (July, 1855), 232; and "The Fifteenth Annual Meeting," *AmJDSc*, 2d ser., V (Oct., 1855), 643–647.

28. Elisha Townsend, "Dr. Townsend's Address," *DNews Letter*, VIII (July, 1855), 238–252, *passim.*

29. "Fifteenth Annual Meeting," *DRegister*, VIII (July, 1855), 239; and "Fifteenth Annual Meeting," *DNews Letter*, VIII (July, 1855), 233–234. The call is printed "Call for a Dental Convention," *DRegister*, VIII (July, 1855), 355. For the proceedings, see "American Society of Dental Surgeons and American Dental Convention," *DRegister*, IX (Oct., 1855), 77–78; and "Proceedings of the American Society," *DNews Letter*, IX (Oct., 1855), 1–2.

30. "Proceedings of the American Societies," *DRegister*, X (Oct., 1856), 37–38; "Second Annual Meeting of the American Dental Convention," *ibid.*, 82; and "Surgeon Dentist," "The Dental Convention," *New York DRecorder*, IX (Sept., 1855), 210–211.

31. "Our Profession," *DNews Letter*, XI (Apr., 1858), 188; "Twelfth Annual Meeting of the Mississippi Valley Association," *DRegister*, IX (Apr., 1856), 242; "American Society of Dental Surgeons," *ibid.* (June, 1856), 447.

32. J. H. McQuillen, "Plans that have been Tried," *DCosmos*, I (Nov., 1859), 192–193.

33. "A Brief Review of Dental Associations," *DRegister*, XII (July, 1859), 442–443, credited to the *American Journal of Dental Science.*

34. "Dental Associations," *DNews Letter*, VI (Mar., 1853), 183; and "General Items Suggested by a Review of the Minutes of the Last Meeting," *AmJDSc*, VI (Sept., 1845), 62.

35. Henry J. Brown, "Voluntary Associations and Professional Reform," *DRegister*, II (Jan., 1849), 63.

36. Amos Lawrence, "President's Address," *Trans.ADA* (1868), 11.

37. "General Items Suggested by a Review of the Minutes of the Last Meeting," *AmJDSc*, VI (Sept., 1845), 61–62.

CHAPTER VI

1. Elisha Townsend, "Address," *DNews Letter*, VIII (July, 1855), 242; and "The Fifteenth Annual Meeting of the American Society," *ibid.*, 233.

2. See "Call for a Dental Convention," *DNews Letter*, VIII (July, 1855), 268; and *DRegister*, VIII (July, 1855), 354–355. Both sources list the signers of the call.

3. "Dental Convention," *DNews Letter,* VIII (July, 1855), 253.

4. No reporter claimed accuracy for the number supposed to have attended. Two sources state that "about one hundred" dentists attended the meeting: "Editorial," *New York DRecorder,* IX (Aug., 1855), 190; and "Report of the Proceedings for the Permanent Organization of the 'American Dental Convention,'" *Forcep,* I (Sept., 1855), 51. The latter, however, lists only eighty-one signers of the articles of association. (*Ibid.,* 71.) This figure agrees with the number of signers listed in "American Society of Dental Surgeons and American Dental Convention," *DRegister,* IX (Oct., 1855), 79; and "Report of the Organization and Proceedings of the First Meeting of the American Dental Convention," *DNews Letter,* IX (Oct., 1855), 2.

5. "Editorial," *New York DRecorder,* IX (Aug., 1855), 189; "American Society of Dental Surgeons and American Dental Convention," *DRegister,* IX (Oct., 1855), 80; and "Report of the Proceedings," *Forcep,* I (Oct., 1855), 51; "Report of the Organization and Proceedings of the First Meeting of the American Dental Convention," *DNews Letter,* IX (Oct., 1855), 4–5; and "Report of the Organization of the American Dental Convention," *AmJDSc,* 2d ser., V (Oct., 1855), 546–574.

6. "American Society of Dental Surgeons and American Dental Convention," *DRegister,* IX (Oct., 1855), 80–81. See also the accounts cited in the preceding notes.

7. "Report of the Proceedings," *Forcep,* I (Sept., 1855), 72.

8. See the sources cited in n6 above.

9. An historian of this period, discussing the fate of the many voluntary organizations seeking one or another humanitarian reform during this era, has decided that the most successful and enduring of these movements were those with a sound foundation in *local units.* See Carl R. Fish, *The Rise of the Common Man, 1830–1850. A History of American Life,* VI, ed. by Arthur M. Schlesinger and Dixon R. Fox (New York: Macmillan Co., 1927). While Fish does not treat of the scientific foundations originating at the time, the experience of the American Society of Dental Surgeons and the American Dental Convention seems to indicate that dentistry was moving in this direction as well. This development was completed with the organization of the American Dental Association.

10. "American Society of Dental Surgeons and American Dental Convention," *DRegister,* IX (Oct., 1855), 103; *ibid.,* 110–111.

11. "American Dental Convention," *DNews Letter,* IX (Oct., 1855), 58; Editorial, *New York DRecorder,* IX (Aug., 1855), 189.

12. Editorial, *New York DRecorder,* IX (Aug., 1855), 189–190; "Report of the Proceedings for the Permanent Organization," *Forcep,* I (Sept., 1855), 71–72.

13. "The American Dental Convention," *DRegister,* IX (June, 1856), 447; "The American Dental Convention," *AmJDSc,* 2d ser., VI (July, 1856), 476; "American Dental Convention," *DNews Letter,* IX (July, 1856), 274; Editorial, *New York DRecorder,* X (July, 1856), 165.

14. Editorial, *New York DRecorder,* X (June, 1856), 143.

15. "The Approaching Meeting of the Dental Convention," *DNews Letter,* IX (July, 1856), 300. This communication was received, the editor apologized, "too late to occupy its proper place in the Journal, which from its importance, we regret."

16. Again, precision as to numbers is impossible. The estimates range from one-hundred and eighty-six whose names the Secretary secured, through two hundred and twenty-five to "about 350." See "American Dental Convention," *AmJDSc,* 2d ser., VI (Oct., 1856), 633; and "Second Annual Meeting of the American Dental Convention," *DRegister,* X (Oct., 1856), 108.

17. "Report of the Organization and Proceedings of the First Meeting," *DNews Letter,* IX (Oct., 1855), 4. The clause in question is Art. III.

18. "Second Annual Meeting of the American Dental Convention," *DRegister*, X (Oct., 1856), 68–71; "Our Present Issue and The American Dental Convention," *DNews Letter*, X (Oct., 1856), 95.

19. "Second Annual Meeting of the American Dental Convention," *DNews Letter*, X (Oct., 1856), 130; and "Second Annual Meeting," *Forcep*, I ([Dec. ?] 1856), 167.

20. "Second Annual Meeting," Forcep, I ([Dec. ?] 1856), 167.

21. Elisha Townsend, "Essay upon Professional Fees," *DRegister*, X (Dec., 1856), 169–179; "Second Annual Meeting," *DRegister*, X (Oct., 1856), 122, 130–131; "Second Annual Meeting," *Forcep*, I ([Dec. ?] 1856), 167.

22. Buckeye, pseudo., "Random Thoughts," *DRegister*, X (Dec., 1856), 192, 194–195.

23. "American Dental Convention," *AmJDSc*, 2d ser., VII (Oct., 1857), 595; "American Dental Convention," *DNews Letter*, XI (Oct., 1857), 1–70; "American Dental Convention," *AmJDSc*, 2d ser., VII (Oct., 1857), 465–549; "American Dental Convention," *DRegister*, XI (Sept., 1857), 28–104.

24. "American Dental Convention," *DRegister*, XI (Sept., 1857), 35–36.

25. "Third Annual Meeting of the American Dental Convention," *DRegister*, XI (Dec., 1857), 145; "American Dental Convention," *ibid.*, XI (Sept., 1857), 31–32; "American Dental Convention," *AmJDSc*, 2d ser., VIII (Apr., 1858), 289.

26. "American Dental Convention," *DRegister*, XI (Sept., 1857), 31–34. On the John Allen episode, see Ch. iii. Later in the session, the Convention apparently appointed a committee to consider Dr. Weiber's gold. The committee report found the substance similar to a type of gold tried and rejected in this country some six years previously. Nevertheless, the committee recommended that the good doctor receive an honorary degree. A critic was moved to gibe: "A mass meeting, without a charter, without even a constitution, is recommended to confer an honorary degree, in acknowledgment of a specimen of gold, of no use and six years behind the times; and it agrees to do it. . . . In plain Anglo-Saxon, all this is very funny." See "Third Annual Meeting of the American Dental Convention," *DRegister*, XI (Dec., 1857), 155–156.

27. *Ibid.*, 34.

28. *Ibid.*, 70.

29. J. Richardson, "Dental Nomenclature," *AmDR*, I (Nov., 1848), 145–146. Among other examples, see "Nomenclature," *ibid.*, 188–189.

30. "American Dental Convention," *DRegister*, XI (Sept., 1857), 87–88; "The American Dental Convention," *DCosmos*, I (Aug., 1859), 87; and "Report of the Annual Meeting of the American Dental Convention," *New York DJ*, II (Oct., 1859), 240–241.

31. "American Dental Convention," *DRegister*, XI (Sept., 1857), 90–95, 101.

32. "Fund for the Promotion of Dental Science," *DRegister*, XI (Oct., 1857), 113; A. J. Volck, "The Dental Convention," *AmJDSc*, 2d ser., VIII (Apr., 1858), 242.

33. "Fund for the Promotion of Dental Science," *DRegister*, XI (Oct., 1857), 114; *ibid.* (Dec., 1857), 230.

34. "North Carolina State Dental Society," *DNews Letter*, XI (Jan., 1858), 93.

35. "Fund for the Promotion of Dental Science," *DRegister*, XI (Dec., 1857), 229; and "American Dental Convention—Fourth Annual Session," *DRegister*, XII (Sept., 1857), 69.

36. "Third Annual Meeting of the American Dental Convention," *DRegister*, XI (Dec., 1857), 145; and A. J. Volck, "The Dental Convention," *AmJDSc*, 2d ser., VIII (Apr., 1858), 241–242. See, e.g., "American Dental Convention," *ibid.*, 289.

37. "American Dental Convention," *AmJDSc*, 2d ser., VIII (Apr., 1858), 290.

38. "Proceedings of the American Dental Convention—Fourth Annual Session," *AmJDSc*, 2d̃ ser., VIII (Oct., 1858), 477–502; "American Dental Convention—Fourth Annual Session," *DRegister*, XII (Sept., 1858), 61–104; "American Dental Convention —Fourth Annual Session," *DNews Letter*, XII (Oct., 1858), 1–34; S. S. White, "American Dental Convention," *ibid.*, 52.

39. "American Dental Convention—Fourth Annual Session," *DRegister*, XII (Sept., 1858), 66, 67, 69; "Minutes of the Third Regular Meeting of the Western Dental Society," *ibid.*, X (June, 1857), 423; "American Dental Convention—Fourth Annual Session," *DNews Letter*, XII (Oct., 1858), 6; and "The Employment of Dentists in the Army," *DRegister*, XII (July, 1859), 450–452 (copied from *DNews Letter*).

40. S. S. White, "American Dental Convention," *DNews Letter*, XII (Oct., 1858), 52. See also "American Dental Convention," *American DReview*, I (Aug., 1858), 123.

41. "American Dental Convention," *DRegister*, XII (Sept., 1858), 123.

CHAPTER VII

1. Junius, pseudo., [J. H. McQuillen], "Basis of a National Dental Association," *DNews Letter*, XII (Apr., 1859), 184–186.

2. "Proceedings of the Pennsylvania Association of Dental Surgeons," *DNews Letter*, XII (July, 1859), 273–274.

3. "Call for a National Association on a Representative Basis," *DNews Letter*, XII (July, 1859), 272; and "A Call," *DRegister*, XII (June, 1859), 452–453.

4. "Cincinnati Association of Dental Surgeons," *DRegister*, XII (June, 1859), 381–384.

5. "T" and "W" were undoubtedly Jonathan Taft and George Watt, respectively, who shared the editorship of the *Register*.

6. "Calls," *DRegister*, XII (June, 1859), 456; "The Meeting at Niagara," *ibid.*, XIII (July, 1859), 48–49; "Mississippi Valley Association," *ibid.*, XII (June, 1859), 454; "Ohio Dental College Association," *ibid.*; "Delegates of the Mississippi Valley Association," *ibid.*, XIII (July, 1859), 27; and "Delegates of the Ohio Dental College Association," *ibid.*, 28.

7. "Proceedings of the Pennsylvania Association of Dental Surgeons," *DNews Letter*, XII (July, 1859), 274; "Proceedings of Societies," *DRegister*, XIII (Feb., 1860), 360.

8. Compare the delegates in attendance listed in *Trans. ADA* (1859–1860) 5–6, with those elected by the various societies. "Proceedings of the Pennsylvania Association of Dental Surgeons," *DNews Letter*, XII (July, 1859), 274 (four out of eight attended); "Delegates of the Mississippi Valley Association," *DRegister*, XIII (July, 1859), 27 (two of seven); and "Delegates of the Ohio Dental College Association," *ibid.*, 28 (seven of eleven).

9. For the proceedings, see *Trans.ADA* (1859–1860), 5–8; "Proceedings of Societies," *DRegister*, XIII (Sept., 1859), 120–123; and "The National Delegate Convention," *DCosmos*, I (Aug., 1859), 73–79. See also the brief editorial note, "American Dental Association," *AmJDSc*, 2d ser., IX (Oct., 1859), 592.

10. An editorial concerning the meeting was entitled, "The Formation of a National Society," *DRegister*, XIII (Sept., 1859), 147–148. On the other hand, an editorial, "American Dental Association," *AmJDSc*, 2d ser., IX (Oct., 1859), 592–593, announced the subjects of essays to be read "at the first meeting" in Washington.

11. J. H. McQuillen, W. M. Wright, and J. Richardson, "National Society: Report of the Committee on Constitution," *DRegister*, XIII (Oct., 1859), 175–180. The report is captioned "Plan of Organization," in the proceedings, "The National Delegate Con-

vention," *DCosmos*, I (Sept., 1859), 74–78; Junius, "Basis of a National Dental Association," *DNews Letter*, XII (Apr., 1859), 185–186; J. Foster Flagg, "Dental Conventions," *ibid.*, XI (July, 1858), 279; "Association," *ibid.*, XII (July, 1859), 280.

12. "Cincinnati Association of Dental Surgeons," *DRegister*, XII (June, 1859), 382–383; J. G. Hamill, "Basis of a National Dental Association," *ibid.*, 372.

13. "W.," Editorial, "The Meeting at Niagara," *DRegister*, XIII (July, 1859), 48–49; Ed. note, *New York DJ*, II (July, 1859), 182–183; Editorial, [J.D.W.], "The American Dental Association," *DCosmos*, I (Oct., 1859), 139; Junius, "Basis of a National Dental Association," *DNews Letter*, XII (Apr., 1859), 186; J. G. Hamill, "Basis of a National Dental Association," *DRegister*, XII (June, 1859), 373.

14. "Cincinnati Association of Dental Surgeons," *DRegister*, XII (June, 1859), 382.

15. Junius, "Basis of a National Dental Association," *DNews Letter*, XII (Apr., 1859), 186.

16. "Correspondence," *American DReview*, III (May, 1860), 87.

17. Junius, "Basis of a National Dental Association," *DNews Letter*, XII (Apr., 1859), 186; "O.U.C.," "Correspondence," *American DReview*, III (May, 1860), 87; "Mississippi Valley Association," *DRegister*, XII (June, 1859), 454; "Ohio Dental College Association," *ibid.*, XIII (July, 1859), 27; and "Delegates of the Ohio Dental College Association," *ibid.*, 28.

18. "American Dental Association," *DCosmos*, I (Jan., 1860), 320; "O.U.C.," "Letter to the Editors," *DRegister*, XIII (Aug., 1859), 92–94; Editorial [J.H.McQ.], "National Dental Convention," *DCosmos*, I (June, 1860), 590–591.

19. Editorial [J.D.W.], "The American Dental Association," *DCosmos*, I (Oct., 1859), 138.

20. Editorial [J.H.McQ.], "National Dental Convention," *DCosmos*, I (June, 1860), 590. See, among many examples in the current dental press, "St. Louis," "American Dental Association," *DCosmos*, I (Jan., 1860), 320; "O.U.C.," "Correspondence," *American DReview*, III (May, 1860), 87.

21. Junius, "Basis of a National Dental Association," *DNews Letter*, XII (Apr., 1859), 186.

22. "Cincinnati Association of Dental Surgeons," *DRegister*, XII (June, 1859), 382–383, and 384.

23. Editorial, "A National Society," *DRegister*, XIII (Aug., 1859), 96.

24. Junius, "Basis of a National Dental Association," *DNews Letter*, XII (Apr., 1859), 184; J. Foster Flagg, "Dental Conventions," *DNews Letter*, XI (July, 1858), 278–279; Editorial, "A National Society," *DRegister*, XIII (Aug., 1859), 95.

25. "Dental Societies," *AmJDSc*, 2d ser., X (Jan., 1860), 48–49, 56; "Cincinnati Association of Dental Surgeons," *DRegister*, XII (June, 1859), 383–384; J. G. Hamill, "Basis of a National Dental Association," *ibid.*, 372–373.

26. J. H. McQuillen, "Convention of Delegates," *DCosmos*, I (Aug., 1859), 92–93. For a similar opinion, see Editorial, "A National Society," *DRegister*, XIII (Aug., 1859), 48–49.

27. Representative examples are to be seen in J. Foster Flagg, "Dental Conventions," *DNews Letter*, XI (July, 1858), 278–279; Junius, "Basis of a National Dental Association," *ibid.*, XII (Apr., 1859), 184; "Dental Societies," *AmJDSc*, 2d ser., X (Jan., 1860), 48–49; "Associations," *DNews Letter*, XII (July, 1859), 280; J. H. McQuillen, "National Dental Convention," *DCosmos*, I (June, 1860), 590–591.

28. Bourbon, pseudo., "A Suggestion," *DRegister*, XIII (July, 1859), 31; "E.T.," "American Dental Association," *ibid.* (May, 1860), 623. M. Blondin was a famous daredevil of the time. Among other feats, he walked a cable stretched across the gorge of the Niagara River near the site of the present International Bridge.

29. J. H. McQuillen, "Individual and Associated Effort," *DCosmos*, I (Aug., 1859), 25.

30. Editorial [J.D.W.], "Associations," *DNews Letter*, XII (July, 1859), 280–281. "A Delegate National Convention," *American DReview*, II (May, 1859), 95–96; and "Cincinnati Association of Dental Surgeons," *DRegister*, XII (June, 1859), 382–383. "W.," Editorial, "The Meeting at Niagara," *ibid.*, XIII (July, 1859), 48–49.

31. "W.," Editorial, "The Meeting at Niagara," *DRegister*, XIII (July, 1859), 48–49; J. G. Hamill, "Basis of a National Association," *ibid.*, XII (June, 1859), 373; Editor's note, *New York DJ*, II (July, 1859), 183.

32. "The National Dental Association," *New York DJ*, III (July, 1860), 202; "New York State Dental Convention," *ibid.*, II (July, 1859), 185–186; and "Minutes of the New York State Dental Convention," *ibid.* (Oct., 1859), 244–247; "W.," Editorial, "The American Dental Convention," *DRegister*, XVI (Dec., 1862), 567–568; "Minutes and Proceedings of the Kentucky State Dental Association," *ibid.*, XIII (May, 1860), 652–656; and "Kentucky State Dental Association," *DCosmos*, I (June, 1860), 584–585; "Northern Ohio Dental Association," *ibid.*, 585–586; "Another Local Society," *DRegister*, XIII (Dec., 1859), 294; "Georgia Dental Society," *AmJDSc*, 2d ser., IX (Oct., 1859), 593; J. H. McQuillen, "National Dental Convention," *DCosmos*, I (June, 1860), 590; George T. Barker, "Pennsylvania Association of Dental Surgeons," *ibid.* (May, 1860), 522.

33. J. H. McQuillen, W. M. Wright, and J. Richardson, "National Society: Report of the Committee on Constitution," *DRegister*, XIII (Oct., 1859), 175–180; and "The National Delegate Convention," *DCosmos*, I (Sept., 1859), 74–78.

34. Junius, "Basis of a National Dental Association," *DNews Letter*, XII (Apr., 1859), 186.

35. *Proceedings of the National Medical Conventions, Held in New York, May, 1846, and in Philadelphia, May, 1847* (Philadelphia; [Printed for the American Medical Association] T. K. and P. G. Collins, Printers, 1847), 9–10, 17, and *passim*.

36. *Ibid.*, 56–57. See also Morris Fishbein, *A History of the American Medical Association 1847 to 1947* (Philadelphia and London: W. B. Saunders [1947]), 32, 33. *Proceedings of the National Medical Conventions*, 56–57. A proposition to limit membership to delegates alone was considered in 1848 but failed of adoption. See *Transactions of the American Medical Association*, I (1848), 40–41. As a matter of fact, the conventions had considered an elective and self-perpetuating membership policy, but rejected the idea. See *Proceedings of the National Medical Conventions*, 42, and *Trans. AMA*, XII (1859), 631–633.

37. Junius, "Basis of a National Dental Association." *DNews Letter*, XII (Apr., 1859), 186; "Reviewer," "A Review of the Proceedings of the Dental Association," *Cincinnati DLamp*, II (No. 1, 1866), 4–5; "O.U.C.," "Correspondence," *American DReview*, III (May, 1860), 87; "Pennsylvania Association of Dental Surgeons," *DCosmos*, IV (May, 1863), 539–540.

38. *Trans.AMA*, XII (1859), 631–633; *Trans. ADA* (1859–60), 14.

39. "American Dental Convention (Letter to the Eds.)," *DRegister*, XIII (May, 1860), 623; G. T. Barker, "American Dental Association," *DCosmos*, I (July, 1860), 621.

40. "Has [the Convention] taken any step by which the cause of science may expect to be advanced?" the editor demanded. See "Dental Societies," *AmJDSc*, 2d ser., X (Jan., 1860), 56. See also Editorial, "A National Society," *DRegister*, XIII (Aug., 1859), 96.

41. Sections 4–7 of Article VI of the Constitution. See Report of the Committee on Constitution, cited n33 above, and *Trans.ADA* (1860), 15–16.

42. Editorial, "The National Convention," *Vulcanite*, I (Aug., 1860), 72; Editorial, "The American Dental Association," *ibid.* (Nov., 1860), 128.

CHAPTER VIII

1. *Southern DExaminer,* I (Jan., 1861), 152.

2. "To the Dental Profession," *Southern DExaminer,* I (Apr., 1861), 186–187. See also Editorial, "Dental Societies," *ibid.,* I (Apr., 1861), 189; "American Dental Convention," *New York DJ,* IV (July, 1861), 128–129.

3. "Postponement," *DRegister,* IV (Apr., 1862), 383–384. The American Medical Association also deferred its session, according to this report. The notice incorrectly states that the Convention had postponed its meeting. The official announcement of the A.D.A. deferment is in "Postponement," *ibid.* (July, 1861), 429–430.

4. "American Dental Convention," *New York DJ,* IV (July, 1861), 128–129.

5. "Proceedings of the Seventh Annual Meeting of the American Dental Convention," *Vulcanite,* II (Aug., 1861), 45–46.

6. "Proceedings of the American Dental Association," *DCosmos,* IV (Sept., 1862), 66; *Trans.ADA* (1862), *passim.*

7. Editorial, "The American Dental Convention," *New York DJ,* V (Sept., 1862), 113.

8. Lincoln announced his decision to publish the Emancipation Proclamation at a cabinet meeting, September 12, 1862. The Convention's War Meeting was on August 6.

9. "Enthusiastic War Meeting," *New York DJ,* V (Sept., 1862), 110–112; "Enthusiastic War Meeting Held by the American Dental Convention, at Trenton Falls, N. Y., August 6, 1862," *DCosmos,* IV (Sept., 1862), 98–101, an account attributed to the *Utica Herald.*

10. The reference was to Lee's campaign into Maryland. "Publisher's Notice," *DCosmos,* IV (Oct., 1862), 151.

11. "T.," Editorial, "Dentists in the Army," *DRegister,* XV (July, 1861), 430–431. W. B. Roberts, "Remarks on Dentistry in the Army," *ibid.* (Sept., 1861), 525–528, an article copied from the *American Medical Times;* "T.," Editorial, "Influence of Camp Life upon the Teeth," *ibid.* (July, 1861), 413–415; George T. Barker, "American Dental Convention," *DCosmos,* III (Sept., 1861), 84, 85.

12. *Trans.ADA* (1862), 5; William H. Allen, "Retiring Address," *ibid.* (1864), 19.

13. "Proceedings of the Eighth Annual Meeting of the American Dental Convention," *New York DJ,* V (Sept., 1862), 86–87.

14. "Report of the Proceedings of the Ninth Annual Session of the American Dental Convention," *DQuarterly,* II (Sept., 1863), 72–73; "Proceedings of the American Dental Convention," *DCosmos,* V (Sept., 1863), 98; "The American Dental Association," *DQuarterly,* II (Sept., 1863), 98.

15. "Minutes," *Trans.Southern DA* (1870), 10–11; "American Dental Association," *DCosmos,* VII (Oct., 1865), 144.

16. "American Dental Association," *DCosmos,* VI (Sept., 1864), 71.

17. "Minutes," *Trans.Southern DA* (1870), 10–11; John R. Lewis, "Exemptions from Military Service On Account of Loss of Teeth," *Trans.ADA* (1865), 164–165.

18. "American Dental Association," *DCosmos,* VI (Sept., 1864), 69–72; "The American Dental Association," *DQuarterly,* III (Sept., 1864), 64–65.

19. "Susquehanna Dental Association," *DCosmos,* V (July, 1864), 676; "T.," Editorial, "Influence of the Times upon the Dental Profession," *DRegister,* XVIII (April, 1864), 192; John F. Johnston, "The American Dental Association," *DCosmos,* IV (June, 1863), 597.

20. Editorial "United States Revenue Tax," *DCosmos,* IV (Apr., 1863), 472–473.

21. "T.," Editorial, "With Us Again," *DRegister*, XVII (Dec., 1863), 546–547.

22. "Proceedings of the Seventh Annual Meeting of the American Dental Convention," *Vulcanite*, II (Aug., 1861), 45–46; "American Dental Association," *DCosmos*, VII (Oct., 1865) 144; "Transactions of the American Dental Association, Sixth Annual Session," *DCosmos*, VIII (Oct., 1866), 148.

23. S. B. Palmer, "Advantages of Associated Labor," *DCosmos*, V (Aug., 1863), 9.

24. George H. Cushing, "Address [on Dental Education]," *DRegister*, XX (Apr., 1866), 164; S. B. Palmer, "Advantages of Associated Labor," *DCosmos*, V (Aug., 1863), 8.

25. *Trans.ADA* (1865), 175–176, 182–183.

26. *Ibid.*, 176; "American Dental Association," *DCosmos*, VII (Sept., 1865), 84.

27. T. L. Buckingham, "Animal Tissues," *Trans.ADA* (1865), 55.

28. "American Dental Convention," *DCosmos*, XV (Oct., 1873), 530.

29. *Trans.ADA* (1865), 190, 194; "American Dental Association," *DCosmos*, VII (Sept., 1865), 91–92.

30. *Trans.ADA* (1865), 192–193; "American Dental Association," *DCosmos*, VII (Sept., 1865), 91–92.

31. "Proceedings of the Odontographic Society of Pennsylvania," *DCosmos*, IX (Sept., 1867), 201n.

32. *Trans.ADA* (1865), 192–193; "American Dental Association," *DCosmos*, VII (Sept., 1865), 91–92.

33. See, e.g., "Correspondence," *DCosmos*, IX (Sept., 1867), 152.

34. Draper was well-known to the intellectual world for works of history of political philosophy. His *History of the Intellectual Development of Europe* (New York: Harper and Brothers, 1863) appeared during the Civil War and was followed at the war's close by *Thoughts on the Future Civil Policy of the United States* (New York: Harper and Brothers, 1865). Not long thereafter Draper published a *History of the American Civil War* (3 vols., New York: Harper and Brothers, 1867–1870) which fixed his place as a leading intellectual figure of the era. On Draper's role in American intellectual life see Merle Curti, *The Growth of American Democratic Thought* (New York: Harper and Brothers, 1943), 473–474. On Draper's history of the war, see Howard K. Beale, "What Historians Have Said about the Causes of the Civil War," *Theory and Practice in Historical Study*, ed. by Merle Curti (Social Science Research Council, Bulletin 54, 1946), 56, 63. Donald Fleming, *John William Draper and the Religion of Science* (Philadelphia: University of Pennsylvania Press [for the American Historical Association], 1950), presents the most comprehensive study of Draper's role in American intellectual life, as well as his scientific achievements. See the discussion of the nature of blood fibrin in "Odontographic Society of Pennsylvania," *DCosmos*, X (Jan., 1868), 26–31.

35. On Liebig's importance in American science, see Dirk Struik, *Yankee Science in the Making* (Boston: Little, Brown and Co., 1948), 342–344, 349; A. Hunter Dupree, *Science in the Federal Government: A History of Policy and Activities to 1940* (Cambridge: Belknap Press of Harvard University Press, 1957), 111–112. For an early dental appreciation of Liebig, see Elijah Slack, "Introductory Lecture," *DRegister*, I (Apr., 1848), 120. Slack proclaimed that Liebig had "demonstrated the chemical laws of vegetable and animal nature, and placed them upon an immovable basis." See also "Dr. Slack's Communication," *ibid.* (Oct., 1847), 18–19. On the role of Liebig in the history of biology, see Charles Singer, *A History of Biology: A General Introduction to the Study of Living Things* (rev. ed.; New York: Henry Schuman, 1950), 374. For a discussion of the relations between the history of biology and the development of caries etiology, see Frederick S. McKay, "Historical Review of the Major Episodes in the Attainment of

the Scientific Concept in Operative Dentistry," *JADA*, XXI (Mar., 1934), 417–420; and Frederick B. Noyes, "Dental Caries: A Review of the Development of the Century," *ibid.*, XX (Dec., 1933), 2122.

36. See, e.g., "Discussions," *Trans.ADA* (1864), 100–102; Charles Singer, *A History of Biology*, (rev. ed.; New York: Henry Schuman, 1950), 340–341, 347, 349, 480; and W. C. Dampier-Whetham, *A History of Science* (3d ed.; New York: The Macmillan Co., 1943), 279.

37. See, e.g., "American Dental Association," *DCosmos*, VI (Sept., 1864), 74, 77, 79, and *passim; Trans. ADA* (1864), 96–102, *passim;* and *ibid.* (1868), 131–132.

38. B. F. Winder, "Deterioration of the Teeth," *Trans. of the American Dental Convention* (1875), 312–313; Julius Chesebrough, "Ratios of Dental Caries," *Trans. ADA* (1864), 54–65.

39. "Proceedings of the Odontographic Society of Pennsylvania," *DCosmos*, IX (Nov., 1867), 201; Harrison Allen, "The Jaw of Moulin Quignon," *ibid.*, 169–180.

40. "Gleanings from the Proceedings of the Society of Dental Surgeons of the City of New York," *DCosmos*, IV (May, 1863), 524.

41. "Proceedings of the Odontographic Society of Pennsylvania," *DCosmos* IV (July, 1863), 65; "Transactions of the American Dental Association," *DCosmos*, IX (Sept., 1867), 80; *Trans.ADA* (1865), 181.

42. *Trans. of the American Dental Convention*, (1875), 275.

43. "W.," Editorial, "The American Medical Association," *DRegister*, XXI (June, 1867), 279.

44. "T.," Editorial, "Does the Dental Profession Progress?" *DRegister*, XVII (Dec., 1863), 518.

45. *Trans.ADA* (1873), 200.

46. Editorial, "The American Dental Convention," *DRegister*, XIX (Aug., 1865), 348.

47. "American Dental Association," *DCosmos*, VI (Sept., 1864), 92.

48. "American Dental Association," *DCosmos*, XIII (Sept., 1871), 462.

49. "Pittsburg Dental Association," *DCosmos*, V (Aug., 1863), 30–31; "Brooklyn Dental Society," *ibid.*, XIII (Jan., 1871), 22; "Discussions of the Society of Dental Surgeons of the City of New York," *ibid.*, X (Feb., 1868), 87.

CHAPTER IX

1. Jonathan Taft, "Dental Education," *DRegister*, XVIII (Apr., 1864), 150–151. See also "T.," Editorial, "American Dental Association," *DRegister*, XXIII (Sept., 1869), 400.

2. "Minutes of the Missouri State Dental Association," *DRegister*, XX (May, 1866), 232.

3. "Constitution and By-Laws of the Central States Dental Association," *DRegister*, XX (July, 1866), 301–302, 303.

4. "Proceedings of Societies," *DRegister*, XX (Mar., 1866), 135, 136, 138.

5. "Minutes," *Trans.Southern DA* (1869), 12–13.

6. *Trans.ADA* (1864), 17; James E. Dexter, *A History of Dental and Oral Science in America* (Philadelphia: Samuel S. White, 1876), 257.

7. "American Dental Association," *DCosmos*, VI (Sept., 1864), 68; J. H. McQuillen, "American Dental Association," *DCosmos*, V (Sept., 1863), 115.

8. C. W. Spalding, "Report of the Committee on Dental Education," *Trans.ADA* (1867), 49.

9. *Trans.ADA* (1866), 242; *ibid.* (1867), 15.

10. See, e.g., C. W. Spalding, "Report of the Committee on Dental Education," *Trans.ADA* (1867), 50; James Taylor, "Report of the Committee on Dental Education," *ibid.* (1865), 143–144.

11. "Transactions of the American Dental Association, Sixth Annual Session," *DCosmos*, VIII (Oct., 1866), 140; "Proceedings of the Odontographic Society of Pennsylvania," *ibid.* (June, 1867), 592.

12. James Taylor, "Report of the Committee on Dental Education," *Trans.ADA* (1865), 144; C. W. Spalding, "Report of the Committee on Dental Education," *Trans.ADA* (1867), 51–52, 53.

13. *Trans.ADA* (1867), 48.

14. *Trans.ADA* (1867), 8.

15. *Trans.ADA* (1867), 13; Dexter, *A History of Dental and Oral Science in America*, 195–196.

16. J.H.McQ., Editorial, "Association of the Colleges of Dentistry," *DCosmos*, VIII (Dec., 1866), 258; "Association of the Colleges of Dentistry," *DRegister*, XXI (Jan., 1867), 29–33; and "Transactions of the A.D.A., Sixth Annual Meeting," *DCosmos*, VIII (Oct., 1866), 140.

17. "Association of the Colleges of Dentistry," *DRegister*, XXI (Jan., 1867), 29–30; J.H.McQ., Editorial, "Association of the Colleges of Dentistry," *DCosmos*, VIII (Dec., 1866), 258–259. The purpose of the Association, the founders agreed, was to standardize the various elements of dental education so far as it was feasible to do this. The brief constitution provided for conferences among the representatives of the schools as the means to bring this about. The main concern of the document was to provide the mechanics by which agreement could be reached. The "individual members of the Association present at the meetings" were empowerd to decide "all ordinary questions." "The determination of any question of importance," however, fell to the colleges, "each College being entitled to but one vote." Ties were to be broken by balloting among the faculties. "Association of the Colleges of Dentistry," *DRegister*, XXI (Jan., 1867), 31.

18. *Ibid.*, 32.

19. "The Association of the Colleges of Dentistry," *DCosmos*, VIII (May, 1867), 540–542. The proceedings are also reported in "The Association of Colleges of Dentistry," *AmJDSc*, 3d ser., I (May, 1867), 35–39.

20. "The Association of the Colleges of Dentistry," *DCosmos*, VIII (May, 1867), 540–541.

21. T. L. Buckingham, "Dental Education," *DTimes*, V (July, 1867), 23.

22. "The Association of the Colleges of Dentistry," *DCosmos*, VIII (May, 1867), 541.

23. Jonathan Taft, Editorial, "The Association of the Colleges of Dentistry," *DRegister*, XXI (Apr., 1867), 188.

24. Editorial, "Association of Dental Colleges," *AmJDSc*, 3d ser., I (May, 1867), 49; "Proceedings of the Odontographic Society of Pennsylvania," *DCosmos*, VIII (June, 1867), 592.

25. "Unknown," "Quarterly Notes," *DTimes*, V (July, 1867), 17–20; "Index," "Diplomas," *ibid.*, 16; T. L. Buckingham, "Dental Education," *ibid.*, 25–26.

26. J. Taft, Editorial, "The Association of the Colleges of Dentistry," *DRegister*, XXI (Apr., 1867), 188.

27. *Trans.ADA* (1860), 16.

28. Editorial, "Dental Education," *DRegister*, XVIII (Apr., 1864), 151.

29. C. W. Spalding, "Report of the Committee on Dental Education," *Trans.ADA* (1867), 50.

30. M. S. Dean, "Report on Dental Education," *Trans.ADA* (1869), 72–74.

31. *Trans.ADA* (1879), 14.

32. J. H. McQuillen, Editorial, "Dental Education," *DCosmos*, I (July, 1860), 650; H. A. Smith, "Annual Address," *Trans.ADA* (1882), 41.

33. "American Dental Association," *DCosmos*, XVI (Dec., 1874), 660; *Trans.ADA* (1864), 17.

34. "Transactions of the A.D.A., Sixth Annual Session," *DCosmos*, VIII (Oct., 1866), 140; *Trans.ADA* (1866), 242.

35. *Trans.ADA* (1867), 15.

36. "American Dental Association," *DCosmos*, XVI (Dec., 1874), 662.

37. *Trans.ADA* (1874), 24; "American Dental Association," *DCosmos*, XVI (Dec., 1874), 662; and "The American Dental Association, Fifteenth Annual Session," *AmJDSc*, 3d ser., IX (Oct., 1875), 261.

38. Quoted in "American Dental Association," *DCosmos*, XVI (Dec., 1874), 662.

39. *Trans.ADA* (1875), 14; "The American Dental Association—Fifteenth Annual Session," *DCosmos*, XVII (Sept., 1875), 481; and "The American Dental Association—Fifteenth Annual Session," *AmJDSc*, 3d ser., IX (Oct., 1875), 261.

40. "Proceedings of Societies [11th Annual Meeting of the Michigan Dental Association]," *DRegister*, XX (Mar., 1866), 138; and "Constitution and By-Laws of the Central States Association," *ibid.* (July, 1866), 301–302.

41. "To remove diseased structure and replace it with gold, to remove diseased organs and replace them with porcelain, is the work which demands nine-tenths of the dentist's time; success in which gives him his reputation. You may call the one operative dentistry and the other mechanical dentistry, if you choose; but each consists in a series of operations, and both are purely mechanical manipulations of material, by means of instruments; both, also, are acts of replacement. I think it, therefore, more exact and descriptive to subdivide the peculiar work of dentistry into structural and organic prosthesis." "Professor" Austin as quoted in "Is Dentistry a Liberal Profession?" *DCosmos*, XVI (Sept., 1874), 501. This quotation helps justify the definitions proposed and at the same time indicates the difficulty of drawing a line between these two aspects of the profession.

42. J. A. Robinson, "Aristocracy of Professions," *DRegister*, XXXVI (Sept., 1882), 422; John Allen, "Report of the Committee on Mechanical Dentistry," *Trans.ADA* (1869), 62.

43. C. N. Hudson, "Process Patent Litigation," *JADA*, LVIII (June, 1959), 162.

44. "American Dental Convention—22nd Annual Session," *DCosmos*, XVIII (Nov., 1876), 601. P. G. C. Hunt declared, "The profession is to blame for the low state to which mechanical dentistry has fallen, because they submit to the popular demand. Why do we not say that because patients want teeth extracted we must extract them? It is our duty to educate patients, and not allow them to dictate. If we are united, we can place mechanical dentistry on the same plane as ourselves." (*Ibid.*, 604.)

45. L. G. Noel, "Dental Education," *DCosmos*, XVIII (Jan., 1876), 26; Truman W. Brophy, "Dental Education," *Trans.ADA* (1881), 173.

46. Abstract of an address of "Professor" Austin before the American Academy of Dental Science, "Is Dentistry a Liberal Profession?" *DCosmos,* XVI (Sept., 1874), 501; Editorial, "The Future of Dentistry," *DCosmos,* XIV (Nov., 1872), 610–611; "Southern Dental Association," *DCosmos,* XVI (Sept., 1874), 477.

47. "A Fundamental Requisite," *DCosmos,* XVII (Mar., 1875), 151–153.

48. C. N. Hudson, "Process Patent Litigation," *JADA,* LVIII (June, 1959), 162.

49. J. A. Robinson, "Aristocracy of Professions," *DRegister,* XXXVI (Sept., 1882), 422.

50. William H. Atkinson, "Relations of Medicine and Dentistry," *DCosmos,* VI (May, 1865), 533; Truman W. Brophy, "Dental Education," *Trans.ADA* (1881), 173–174.

51. "Seventh Annual Session of the ADA," *AmJDSc,* 3d ser., I (Sept., 1867), 253.

52. "Report of Some of the Proceedings of the American Medical Association," *DRegister,* XXV (June, 1881), 252–254; William H. Atkinson, "Union of Medicine and Dentistry," *Trans. ADA* (1881), 164; C. N. Peirce, "Annual Address," *ibid.,* 41.

53. Truman W. Brophy, "Dental Education," *Trans.ADA* (1881), 173–174; William H. Atkinson, "Union of Medicine and Dentistry," *ibid.,* 164; See also W. H. Atkinson, "Relations of Medicine and Dentistry," *DCosmos,* V (May, 1865), 533.

54. N. S. Davis, "Address," *Trans.ADA* (1865), 116–120; Daniel Brainerd, "Specialties and Specialists in Medicine," *ibid.,* 75.

55. See, e.g., the remarks of James Taylor in "A Synopsis of Remarks and Discussions of the American Dental Association," *Trans.ADA* (1867), 100; "Transactions of the A.D.A.," *DCosmos,* IX (Sept., 1867), 75; William H. Atkinson, "Relations of Medicine and Dentistry," *ibid.,* VI (May, 1865), 533.

56. C. W. Spalding, "Report of the Committee on Dental Education," *Trans.ADA* (1867), 52; James Taylor, "Report of the Committee on Dental Education," *ibid.* (1865), 144.

57. "Southern Dental Association," *DCosmos,* XVI (Nov., 1874), 582. See the abstract, "Is Dentistry a Liberal Profession?" *ibid.* (Sept., 1874), 501; "Southern Dental Association," *ibid.,* 477–478; "Periscope," "Special Degrees," *ibid.,* XVII (Jan., 1875), 29; Editorial, "Dentists and Doctors," *ibid.,* XVI (July, 1874), 379; W. C. Horne, "Phases of Professional Development," *ibid.,* XVIII (Sept., 1876), 451–452.

58. Joseph Richardson, "A Suggestion," *DCosmos,* II (May, 1861), 535–538.

59. "The American Academy of Dental Sciences," *DCosmos,* XVIII (Nov., 1876), 612; *Trans.ADA* (1877), 25–27; "American Dental Association," *DCosmos,* XX (Jan., 1878), 32–39; "American Dental Association–18th Annual Meeting," *ibid.* (Nov., 1878), 614–619; *Trans.ADA* (1878), 24.

60. W. W. Allport, "Response to the Toast 'Dentistry and Dental Education–Its Past, Present, and Future as Related to Medicine,'" *DRegister,* XXXV (May, 1881), 192–193.

61. "Changes," *DRegister,* XXXVI (June, 1882), 312, reports this development, involving a move by F. J. S. Gorgas and James H. Harris.

62. J. A. Robinson, "Aristocracy of Professions," *DRegister,* XXXVI (Sept., 1882), 420.

63. George Watt, Editorial, "Convention of Medical Teachers," *DRegister,* XXI (June, 1867), 278–279.

64. W. C. Horne, "Phases of Professional Development," *DCosmos,* XVIII (Sept., 1876), 451; "The Committee on American Medical Colleges," *DRegister,* XXXV (Oct., 1881), 430–431.

65. C. N. Peirce, "Annual Address," *Trans.ADA* (1881), 41–42.

66. Robert Arthur, "Dental Education," *DCosmos,* XVIII (Feb., 1876), 69.

67. *Trans.ADA* (1883), 22.

68. H. A. Smith, "Annual Address," *Trans.ADA* (1882), 41.

69. "Southern Dental Association," *AmJDSc,* 3d ser., VII (Sept., 1873), 210–211; "Southern Dental Association," *DCosmos,* XVI (Nov., 1874), 581.

70. J. N. Crouse, "Dental Education," *Trans.ADA* (1882), 139: "State legislation, deciding what practitioners have a right to practice in the respective States, has become quite general."

71. "Legislative Action Relative to the Practice of Dentistry," *DCosmos,* VIII (June, 1867), 604.

72. The speaker was Dr. C. S. Smith of Springfield. See "Joint Session of the Mississippi Valley and Missouri State Dental Associations," *DCosmos,* XVI (May, 1874), 263.

73. Truman W. Brophy, "Dental Education," *Trans.ADA* (1881), 169–176; "American Dental Association—21st Annual Session," *DCosmos,* XXIV (Feb., 1882), 90–97; J. H. McQuillen, Editorial, "Legislative Action Relative to the Practice of Dentistry," *ibid.,* VIII (July, 1867), 660–661; and *ibid.* (June, 1867), 603–605; "Joint Session of the Mississippi Valley and Missouri State Dental Associations," *ibid.,* XVI (May, 1874), 263.

74. See, e.g., the provisions of the laws quoted or paraphrased in the following: J. H. McQuillen, Editorial, "Legislative Action Relative to the Practice of Dentistry," *DCosmos,* VIII (June, 1867), 603–605; and *ibid.* (July, 1867), 660–661 (proposed Kentucky law); "Proceedings of the Central States Dental Association," *DRegister,* XX (June, 1866), 255 (Taft's description of the proposed Ohio statute); Editorial, "A Bill to Regulate the Practice of Dentistry [in Ohio]," *ibid.* (July, 1866), 324–328 (the bill is quoted pp. 327–328). The May, 1881, issue of the *Dental Register* (vol. XXXV) contains a great deal of material on legislation relating to medical as well as dental practice. The Alabama act of Feb. 5, 1881, is quoted pp. 213ff. See also legislation cited in the notes below.

75. Editorial, "Passage of the Dental Bill," *DRegister,* XXII (Apr., 1868), 176–177. For New York, see New York State Dental Society, *DCosmos,* XI (April, 1869), 192; for Pennsylvania, see Editorial, "An Act to Regulate the Practice of Dentistry in the State of Pennsylvania," *ibid.,* XVIII (June, 1876), 324–326; for Georgia, see "Georgia State Dental Society," *ibid.* (Apr., 1875), 204; and *ibid.,* XVIII (Nov., 1876), 615.

76. J. N. Crouse, "Dental Education," *Trans.ADA* (1882), 139.

77. *Trans.ADA* (1882), 140, and *passim.*

78. Editorial, "Why Not," *DRegister,* XXXVI (Aug., 1882), 414.

79. J. N. Crouse, "Dental Education," *Trans.ADA* (1882), 143, discussion by Jonathan Taft.

80. *Trans. ADA* (1882), 28.

81. C. N. Peirce, "Dental Education," *Trans.ADA* (1883), 83–84, 88–89.

82. *Trans.ADA* (1883), 22.

CHAPTER X

1. See, e.g., "Report of the Proceedings of the Ninth Annual Session of the American Dental Convention," *D Quarterly,* II (Sept., 1863), 67 (Jonathan Taft, William H. Atkinson, C. N. Peirce, and A. C. Hawes, all prominent A.D.A. men, were elected officers of the Convention); "Twentieth Annual Meeting, 1874," *Trans.ADC,* 190 (Jonathan

Taft addressed the Convention. He said he "was proud that [the Convention] still carried the standard of American dentistry high in the van of professional science."); "American Dental Convention-Twenty-Second Annual Meeting," *DCosmos*, XVIII (Oct. 1876), 534 (T. L. Buckingham, speaking in a similar vein); William H. Atkinson, "President's Address," *Proceedings of the American Dental Convention, the Southern Dental Association, and the Dental Association of Maryland and the District of Columbia* (1877), 8; and *ibid.*, 102–103 (Taft was chosen president to succeed Atkinson).

2. See "Transactions of the American Dental Convention," *DCosmos*, VIII (Nov., 1866), 193; and J. G. Ambler, "Congratulatory Greeting [at Long Branch, 1875]," *Trans. ADC*, 291; "Minutes of Proceedings of the 14th Annual Meeting of the American Dental Convention," *DCosmos*, X (Aug., 1868), 412.

3. "Transactions of American Dental Convention," *DCosmos*, VIII (Nov., 1866), 203; *Trans.ADA* (1866), 223–224; and *ibid.* (1867), 6–7; *ibid.* (1868), 2.

4. *Trans.ADA* (1868), 4, 5–6; and "American Dental Association," *DCosmos*, X (Sept., 1868), 458–459.

5. "American Dental Association," *DCosmos*, X (Sept., 1868), 461–462; *Trans. ADA* (1868), 18–20.

6. Editorial, J. H. McQuillen, "American Dental Association," *DCosmos*, X (Sept., 1868), 451–454.

7. J. G. Ambler, "Address of Welcome," *Trans.ADA* (1869), 24, 31; Editorial, J. H. McQuillen, "American Dental Association," *DCosmos*, XI (Sept., 1869), 471–480.

8. "American Dental Convention, 15th Annual Meeting," *DCosmos*, XII (Jan., 1870), 37; "American Dental Convention," *ibid.*, XVI (Oct., 1874), 533; J. G. Ambler, "Address [1871]," *Trans.ADC*, 49.

9. "Transactions . . . , Long Branch, 1875," *Trans.ADC*, 273.

10. William H. Atkinson [President's Address], *Proceedings of the American Dental Convention, the Southern Dental Association, and the Dental Association of Maryland and the District of Columbia* (1877), 8.

11. *Trans.ADA* (1875), 18.

12. *Trans.ADA* (1877), 17, 21; W. H. Atkinson [President's Address], *Proceedings of the American Dental Convention, the Southern Dental Association, and the Dental Association of Maryland and the District of Columbia*, (1877), 9.

13. *Ibid.* 103; "American Dental Association," *DCosmos*, XX (June, 1878), 344; "American Dental Convention," *loc.cit.*; Southern Dental Association," *ibid.* (July 1878), 393; "American Dental Convention," *DCosmos*, XX (Nov., 1878), 622.

14. H. J. McKellops, "President's Address," *Trans.ADA* (1879), 27.

15. *Trans.ADA* (1879), 16–18; *Trans.ADA* (1880), 15–16.

16. "Transactions . . . 1874," *Trans.ADC*, 190; "American Dental Convention," *DCosmos*, XVI (Nov., 1874), 596.

17. "Recent Dental Conventions," *AmJDSc*, 3d ser., XIV (Aug., 1880), 185, copying an account in the *Medical Record;* "American Dental Convention," *DCosmos*, XXII (Sept., 1880), 497; *ibid.*, XXIV (May, 1882), 260 (the call); *ibid.*, XXIV (Dec., 1882), 660.

18. "Obituary: Demise of the American Dental Convention," *Herald of Dentistry*, III (Oct., 1883), 6–8.

19. E.G.B. to the Ed., *DRegister*, XXXVI (May, 1882), 250.

20. "American Dental Association," *DCosmos*, XVIII (Feb., 1876), 91. These figures are not to be taken as absolutely accurate, but as indicative of an order of

magnitude. Jonathan Taft reported eighty societies in 1870. See also "American Dental Association," *ibid.*, XII (Oct., 1870), 529; E. T. Darby, "Annual Address," *Trans.ADA* (1884), 48; C. N. Peirce, "Report on Education, Literature, and Nomenclature," *ibid.* (1890), 55–56. In 1891, the same section reported "at least one hundred and three . . . , divided as follows: National, 4; interstate, 7; State, 41; district, county, and local, 22; city, 29." See Louis Ottofy, Report of Section II, *ibid.* (1891), 183.

21. Editor's note, *Herald of Dentistry*, II (Jan., 1883), 8.

22. "New Jersey State Dental Society," *DCosmos*, XXII (Oct., 1880), 550–551; Discussion on Anatomy, Histology, and Microscopy, *Trans.ADA* (1886), 128; Editorial, "Notes on the Transactions of the New York State Dental Society," *Herald of Dentistry*, III (July, 1883), 2.

23. Charles R. E. Koch, *History of Dental Surgery* (Chicago: National Art Publishing Co., 1909), 472.

24. See above n 20.

25. "Dental Colleges," *DCosmos*, XVII (Aug., 1875), 431–432 (from *Missouri DJ*); and "American Academy of Dental Science," *ibid.*, XXIV (Nov., 1882), 599–600.

26. "American Academy of Dental Science," *DCosmos*, XVIII (Feb., 1876), 96; "American Academy of Dental Science," *ibid.* (Nov., 1876), 612; American Academy of Dental Science, *A History of Dental and Oral Science in America* [James E. Dexter, comp.] (Philadelphia: Samuel S. White; 1876). This enterprise should not be confused with a contemporary project that the profession did not welcome, probably because biographies in the proposed volume could be purchased. See Editorial, "A History of American Dentistry," *ibid.*, XVI (May, 1874), 268–269; John B. Rich *et al.*, "To the Editor," *ibid.* (June, 1874), 332–333; Atlantic Publishing Company, by A. C. Rogers, president, to the Editor, *ibid.*, 331–332.

27. "American Academy of Dental Science," *DCosmos*, XVIII (Nov., 1876), 612; "American Academy of Dental Science," *ibid.*, XXIV (Nov., 1882), 599–600.

28. Editorial, "The Late Meeting at Long Branch," *AmJDSc*, 3d ser., IX (Sept., 1875), 231–232; "The American Dental Convention," *DCosmos*, VII (Apr., 1867), 479, 481; "American Academy of Dental Surgery," *ibid.*, XVII (July, 1875), 319–320; "American Academy of Dental Surgery," *AmJDSc*, 3d ser., IX (Dec., 1875), 339.

29. "New York Odontological Society" *DCosmos*, XVII (May, 1875), 236; W. C. Horne, "Phases of Professional Development," *ibid.*, XVIII (Aug., and Sept., 1876), 408–409, 451–453.

30. Editorial, "Important Notice," *AmJDSc*, 3d ser., XIV (June, 1880), 93; Editorial, "A National Dental Association," *DCosmos*, XXII (June, 1880), 317; "Call for a Mass Convention of the Dentists of the United States to Organize a National Dental Association," *AmJDSc*, 3d ser., XIV (July, 1880), 131–132; "Recent Dental Conventions," *ibid.* (Aug., 1880), 185 (copied from the *Medical Record*); *Trans.ADA* (1880), 15–16; "The National Dental Association," *Herald of Dentistry*, I (Jan., 1882), 30.

31. "The National Dental Association," *Herald of Dentistry*, I (Jan., 1882), 3; "Recent Dental Conventions," *AmJDSc*, 3d ser., XIV (Aug., 1880), 185; "National Dental Association of the United States of America," *DRegister*, XXXVI (July, 1882), 351; "National Dental Association of the U.S.A.," *DCosmos*, XXIV (Aug., 1882), 486.

32. Arthur M. Schlesinger, *The Rise of the City, 1878–1898: A History of American Life*, X, ed. by Dixon R. Fox and A. M. Schlesinger (New York: The Macmillan Co., 1933), 288–289, 221n. See also Thomas N. Bonner, *Medicine in Chicago 1850–1950* (Madison, Wis.: The American History Research Center, 1957), 77, 183; C. N.

Peirce, "Report on Education, Literature, and Nomenclature," *Trans.ADA* (1890), 56; L. B. Noel, "Dental Education," *DCosmos,* XVIII (Jan., 1876), 24, 78.

33. Richard H. Shryock, *American Medical Research, Past and Present* (New York: The Commonwealth Fund, 1947), 65–66; T. N. Bonner, *Medicine in Chicago,* 77.

34. A. M. Schlesinger, *The Rise of the City,* 216. See also "Bogus Diplomas," *DCosmos,* XVIII (Dec., 1876), 667 (copied from *Medical News and Library*).

35. See the preamble and resolutions to this effect in *Trans.ADA* (1879), 21; See also the Editorial by W. C. Barrett in *DPractitioner and Advertiser,* XXVIII (Apr., 1897), 105–106, and A. M. Schlesinger, *Rise of the City,* 216.

36. W. W. Allport, "Annual Address," *Trans.ADA* (1887), 48.

37. James W. Hurst, *The Growth of American Law: The Law Makers* (Boston: Little, Brown and Co., 1950), 278, 286–291.

38. See an abstract of the address, "Is Dentistry a Liberal Profession?" *DCosmos,* XVI (Sept., 1874), 502; W. W. Allport, "Annual Address," *Trans.ADA* (1887), 39.

39. *Trans.ADA* (1888), 23; R. H. Shryock, *American Medical Research,* 66.

40. This was one of the regular arguments for attending dental meetings. For a typical editorial on behalf of dental meetings, see "The Annual Meetings," *Western DJ,* II (Apr., 1888), 180–182. See also Editorial, "Recent Conventions," *International DJ,* XVI (Oct., 1895), 645.

41. Editorial, "American Dental Association," *Herald of Dentistry,* IV (Oct., 1884), 3.

42. Editorial, "Recent Conventions," *International DJ,* XVI (Oct., 1895) 645.

43. *Trans.ADA* (1872), 19–20, describes the beginning of the planning for the centennial occasion. See also *Trans. ADA* (1876), *passim.* "Southern Dental Association," *International DJ,* XVI (Oct., 1895), 654, prints the call for the meeting in Atlanta.

44. Editorial, "American Dental Association," *Herald of Dentistry,* IV (Oct., 1884), 2.

45. W. H. Trueman, "Meeting of the American Association of Dental Surgeons [*sic* (ADA)]," *Items of Interest,* IV (Dec., 1882), 179.

46. "American Dental Association—20th Annual Session," *DCosmos,* XXII (Oct., and Dec., 1880), 547, 661–662.

47. "Southern Dental Association," *AmJDSc,* 3d ser., VII (Sept., 1873), 208.

48. *Trans.ADA* (1886), 31.

49. *Trans.ADA* (1885), 29, 32, 36.

50. In the depths of the depression following the Panic of 1873, the A.D.A. considered resolutions noting that dentists had been forced to reduce their fees while a large majority of the standard articles used by the profession continued to sell at about war prices. The exponent of the resolutions held that the dentists were within their rights "to demand of manufacturers of and dealers in dental goods such reductions in their prices as will more nearly correspond with the depressed financial condition of the times." The Association tabled the resolutions. *Trans.ADA* (1879), 15; J. W. Hurst, *Growth of American Law,* 260–261.

51. "Minutes," *Trans.Southern DA* (1870), 28, 31–32, describes some of the activities of the "Colton Dental Association." The "Howland Dental Association" used untrained operators and lost a suit for malpractice. "Liabilities of Dentists," *Items of Interest,* IV (May, 1882), 76.

52. The S. S. White Dental Manufacturing Co. [Harry C. Keane], *A Century of Service to Dentistry: 1844–1944* (Philadelphia: The S. S. White Dental Manufacturing

Co., 1944), 11–12; "Monopoly," *Herald of Dentistry,* II (Apr., 1883), 2; "Dental Dealers' Convention," *DCosmos,* XXIV (Mar., 1882), 154; American Dental Trade Association, "To the Dental Profession," *DRegister,* XXXVI (July, 1882), 345; "Dental Dealers' Convention," *Herald of Dentistry,* I (Apr., 1882), 11.

53. American Dental Trade Association, "To the Dental Profession," *DRegister,* XXXVI (July, 1882), 348–350; American Dental Trade Association, "A Card to the Dental Profession," *DCosmos,* XXIV (July, 1882), 388–392. The manufacturers also presented their case before dental meetings. See "Proceedings of the Eighteenth Annual Meeting of the Illinois State Dental Society," *DRegister,* XXXVI (July, 1882), 344.

54. "Monopoly," *Herald of Dentistry,* II (Apr., 1882), 1–2.

55. B. H. Catching, "Is the Average Dentist of Today a Specialist in Medicine?" *Trans.ADA* (1888), 49.

56. "Fair Play *vs.* Monopoly," *Items of Interest,* IV (July, 1882), 100.

57. *Trans.ADA* (1885), 32.

58. Louis Jack, "The Necessity for Independent Dental Journalism," *Trans.ADA* (1889), 112–114; Discussion, *ibid.,* 117, 118–119.

59. *Trans. ADA* (1890), 21–23, 27, 37.

60. *Trans.ADA* (1889), 17; Editorial, "Recent Conventions," *International DJ,* XVI (Oct., 1895), 643–644.

61. *Trans.ADA* (1873), 16–17; "Southern Dental Association," *AmJDSc,* 3d ser., (Sept., 1873), 196.

62. J. B. Patrick, "Progress of Dental Surgery in the United States," *AmJDSc,* 3d ser., XIV (Nov., 1880), 310–311.

63. E. T. Darby, "Annual Address," *Trans.ADA* (1884), 48–49.

64. W. H. Atkinson, "Union of Medicine and Dentistry," *Trans.ADA* (1881), 168.

65. A. H. Thompson, "The Question of Utility in Dental Education," *DCosmos,* XXIV (June, 1882), 299–302.

CHAPTER XI

1. William C. Dampier-Whetham, *A History of Science and its Relations with Philosophy and Religion* (3d ed., rev. and enl.; New York: Macmillan, 1943), 294–303; Richard H. Shryock, *American Medical Research Past and Present* (New York: The Commonwealth Fund, 1947), 47–48; Richard Hofstadter, *Social Darwinism in American Thought* (rev. ed.; Boston: The Beacon Press, 1955), *passim;* Ralph H. Gabriel, *The Course of American Democratic Thought: An Intellectual History Since 1815* (New York: The Ronald Press, 1940), pt. iii. For typical reactions among dentists, see I. J. Wetherbee, "Nature and Her Voices *Versus* Darwin [1873]," *Trans.ADC,* 140–145; "Southern Dental Association," *AmJDSc,* 3d ser., VII (Sept., 1873), 205. In the latter a paper, "Darwinism *vs.* Six Year Molars," is summarized as follows: "[The author] strongly refuted the doctrine of Darwin that man had its origin in a fish, which had progressed to a frog, to a monkey, to a man, &c. It was as impossible, he said, for a frog to be changed into a monkey as it was to change a mosquito into an elephant or a dog into a horse." See also "Specialties," *DCosmos,* XVI (July 1874), 392; A. H. Thompson, "Dental Education as a Science," *ibid.,* XXII (Apr. 1880), 175.

2. A. H. Thompson, "The Dentition of the Felidae," Discussion, *Trans.ADA* (1891), 111–112. The discussion of this paper also shows how well the dentists shared the differences of the rest of the scientific community and mirrored the attitudes of American society toward the Darwinian controversy. "Does Professor Pierce really mean

to say that we are descended from the monkey?" demanded one outraged commentator. *Ibid.*, 116–117, 120, 122; W. C. Dampier-Whetham, *A History of Science*, 294–303; George G. Simpson, *The Meaning of Evolution; A Study of the History of Life and of its Significance for Man* (New Haven: Yale University Press, 1950), 266–272.

3. "Recent Dental Conventions," *AmJDSc*, 3d ser., XIV (Aug., 1880), 185; *Trans.ADA* (1882), 26, 27.

4. W. C. Barrett, "An Examination of the Condition of the Teeth of Certain Pre-Historic American Races," *Independent Practitioner*, IV (Oct., 1883), 513–521; Editorial, "The American Dental Association," *Herald of Dentistry*, III (Oct., 1883), 4; *Trans.ADA* (1889), 23, 92–94; H. A. Smith, "Report of Sec. VI on Physiology and Etiology," *ibid.* (1890), 137–138; *ibid.* (1891), 35–36; *ibid.* (1892), 177–190; *ibid.* (1894), 158–187; *ibid.* (1896), 5; *ibid.* (1897), 8.

5. Editorial, "What Others Say," *AmJDSc*, 3d ser., XIV (Sept., 1880), 234–235; R. H. Shryock, *American Medical Research*, 5–6, 31, 55, 151, and *passim*; Thomas N. Bonner, *Medicine in Chicago 1850–1950* (Madison, Wis.: The American History Research Center, 1957), 33–35.

6. See dental comments to this effect in "Scientific Theories and Processes," *DCosmos*, XVI (May, 1874), 270; Discussion on Materia Medica and Therapeutics [by Dr. Ingersoll], *Trans.ADA* (1888), 160; W. C. Barrett, "A Plea for Conservatism," *ibid.* (1891), 138–139.

7. T. N. Bonner, *Medicine in Chicago*, 31–32; R. H. Shryock, *American Medical Research*, 54.

8. "Scientific Theories and Processes," *DCosmos*, XIV (May, 1874), 270; "Claims of Medicine to be Regarded as a Science," *ibid.*, XVI (Mar., 1874), 144.

9. C. E. Francis, "Conservatism in Dental Practice," *DCosmos*, XVI (Apr., 1874), 183; W. C. Barrett, "A Plea for Conservatism," *Trans.ADA* (1891), 138.

10. W. H. Morgan, quoted in "American Dental Association," *AmJDSc*, 3d ser., VII (Oct., 1873), 249.

11. R. H. Shryock, *American Medical Research*, 5–6, 53; T. N. Bonner, *Medicine in Chicago*, 33–35.

12. "Southern Dental Association," *AmJDSc*, 3d ser., VII (Sept., 1873), 199–200.

13. T. Leber and J. B. Rottenstein, *Investigations on Caries of the Teeth*, trans. by T. H. Chandler (Philadelphia: Lindsay and Blakiston, 1873); Greene Vardiman Black, "Some Points in the Natural History of Caries of the Teeth and the Value of Fillings for its Arrest," *AmJDSc*, 3d ser., XIV (Nov., 1880), 289–308. See also (with due allowances for filial exaggeration) Carl E. and Bessie M. Black, *From Pioneer to Scientist: The Life Story of Greene Vardiman Black, "Father of Modern Dentistry," and His Son Arthur Davenport Black, Late Dean of Northwestern University Dental School* (Saint Paul, Minn.: Bruce Publishing Co., 1940), 178–181. The Appendix gives a chronological list (although it is neither complete nor completely accurate) of Black's writings. It is revealing to observe the development of Black's interests over the years in this way.

14. Arthur S. Underwood and W. T. Milles, "An Investigation into the Effects of Organisms upon the Teeth and Alveolar Portions of the Jaws," *Trans. International Medical Congress*, 7th Sess. (1881), III, 523; Gerald J. Cox, "Oral Environment and Dental Caries," in Guttorm Toverud, *et. al.*, *A Survey of the Literature of Dental Caries*, Publication 225 (Washington, D. C.: National Academy of Science-National Research Council, 1952), 248–253, for a summary of Miller's contributions. The bibliography at the end of the volume lists Miller's publications in chronological order.

15. See the brief summary of these developments in N. S. Hoff, "Operative Dentistry," *Trans.ADA* (1891), 218.

16. See the review of these innovations in Frank Abbott, "Annual Address," *Trans.ADA* (1888), 35–45.

17. See, e.g., William H. Atkinson's extravagant criticism in "New Jersey State Dental Society," *DCosmos*, XXII (Oct., 1880), 550–551.

18. James Truman, "Annual Address," *Trans.ADA* (1897), 37; T. N. Bonner, *Medicine in Chicago*, 32.

19. Alveolar abscess and "Riggs Disease," or pyorrhea alveolaris, were two prominent examples of this type. See "American Dental Association," *Herald of Dentistry*, IV (Oct., 1884), 2: "Riggs must have gotten his disease cured, or else like the thief its reputation became so bad it changed its name. We didn't hear anything about 'Riggs disease,' but the whole session was spent in a discussion upon the same conditions, but they had rebaptized it, and hereafter poor Riggs will be let alone and 'Pyorrhea Alveolaris,' blushingly goes to the head (Query, is she male or female, and, if so, why?) Pyorrhea is a daisy subject to talk about if you would listen to Harlan."

20. William H. Morgan, "Discussion on President Catching's Address," *Trans.ADA* (1888), 53.

21. The following are representative rather than exhaustive (or definitive) citations on these developments: Louis Jack, "A New Electro-Magnetic Mallet," *DCosmos*, XVI (July, 1874), 348–354. This is a useful article because it describes the works of Green and Bonwill as well as Jack's own improvement. On the electric oven, see *Trans.ADA* (1895), 24; *ibid.* (1896), 17–18. On the dental engine, see *Trans.ADA* (1876), 597; Charles E. Francis, "Conservatism in Dental Practice," *DCosmos*, XVI (Apr., 1874), 182.

22. See, e.g., Flagg's statement, "Amalgam is the best plastic filling known," in "American Dental Association, 15th Annual Session," *DCosmos*, XVII (Nov., 1875), 592; Charles E. Francis, " 'The New Departure,' " *ibid.*, XX (Feb., 1878), 94–96. In politics, the term was applied to the Democratic politicians who sought " 'reconciliation by acceptance' " of the results of the Civil War and the Reconstruction measures during Grant's first administration. See Paul H. Buck, *The Road to Reunion: 1865–1900* (Boston: Little, Brown and Co., 1937), 89ff. For the opposition to amalgam see "American Dental Association," *DCosmos*, XX (Jan., 1878), 30. See also the report of an American Dental Association committee, headed by A. W. Harlan, who reported in 1876 that "The investigations of Profs. Hitchcock, Bogue, and Chase, though presenting clearly some things not heretofore definitely known, were, however, far from proving that this substance [amalgam] was even the best of the baser materials in use." Harlan proceeded to offer a "refutation" of the New Departure arguments "premising that we must, until some better preventive treatment is discovered, rely mainly on gold, and that therefore the subject is and will continue to be of vital importance," in "American Dental Association," *DCosmos*, XVIII (Nov., 1876), 598–599.

23. "American Dental Convention," *DCosmos*, XV (Oct., 1870), 532.

24. "New York Odontological Society," *DCosmos*, XVII (May, 1875), 237. The findings of the papers are summarized, *DCosmos*, XVII (May, 1875), 237–249. One of the papers, E. A. Bogue, "The Physical Properties and Physiological Action of Dental Amalgams," appeared in *DCosmos*, XVII (Mar., 1875), 118–134. For Flagg's comments, see "American Dental Association," *DCosmos*, XVII (Nov., 1875), 592.

25. See, e.g., "Gleanings from the Discussions of the District Dental Society of the First Judicial District of the State of New York," *DCosmos*, XVI (Oct., 1874), 552; Greene V. Black, "Relative Merits of Certain Materials for Filling Teeth," *Trans. Ill. State D Society* (1877), 51.

26. "Test Tubes for Amalgam," *Herald of Dentistry,* I (Sept., 1881), 8.

27. James R. Taylor, *A History of Dentistry for Students and Practitioners* (Philadelphia: Lea and Febiger, 1922), 128. A dentist by the name of George H. Weagant, of Cornwall, Ontario, described the preparation of a copper amalgam to Greene V. Black in 1882. See also Greene V. Black, "How to Make and Use Copper Amalgam," *DReview,* I.

28. G. V. Black, "An Investigation of the Physical Characters of the Human Teeth in Relation to their Diseases, and to Practical Dental Operations, together with the Physical Characters of Filling-Materials," *DCosmos,* XXXVII (1895), 353, 469, 553, 637, 737.

29. See, e.g., "Association of the Alumni of the Pennsylvania College," *DCosmos,* XVI (May, 1874), 239, 241; *Trans.ADA* (1882), 21.

30. *Trans.ADA* (1866), 242.

31. "Dr. Horne called the Attention of the Association to the utility of Dr. Barnum's application of pure sheet rubber for isolating a tooth from moisture during the operation of plugging. This consists in puncturing or cutting a small hole in a piece of rubber, three or four inches square, this to be forced over and around the tooth, with the edges turned upward to the gum; if the teeth are near together, other holes must be made so as to include the teeth on either side of the one to be filled. By this means the plug will be kept dry during an operation of several hours." "American Dental Association," *DCosmos,* VII (Oct., 1865), 140.

32. *Trans.ADA* (1870), 26–27; "American Dental Association," *DCosmos,* XII (Oct., 1870), 532.

33. *Trans.ADA* (1871), 18–19; "American Dental Association," *DCosmos,* XIII (Nov., 1871), 575; *Trans.ADA* (1873), 22–23. For examples of rewards consisting of "thanks," see "Minutes of the . . . 14th Annual Meeting of the American Dental Convention," *DCosmos,* X (Aug., 1868), 415; *Trans.ADA* (1869), 15, 22; "American Dental Association," *DCosmos,* XXII (Nov., 1880), 611. For medals, see Jonathan Taft, "Report of the Committee on Societies," *Trans.ADA* (1864), 92, concerning the Odontographic Society of Pennsylvania: "They have, within the last year, given a gold medal for a valuable invention and improvement." The nature of the innovation is not mentioned. See also report of a medal awarded by the California State Dental Association to Dr. Barnum in *Trans.ADA* (1873), 19. Where a monetary award was to be made by someone else, the Association favored it. In 1872 the society adopted resolutions affirming Horace Wells's claim to priority in the discovery of nitrous oxide anesthesia. The resolutions also acknowledged the neglected obligation of the medical and dental professions to "give some substantial evidence of their appreciation." Accordingly, the efforts to collect a "Wells National Testimonial Fund" were approved, other dental associations were urged to cooperate in the drive, and "every individual member of the profession" was reminded of "the importance of doing all in his power to make this, not only a credit to his profession and a substantial gift to the family of Horace Wells, but an honor to the memory of one of the greatest of the world's benefactors." *Trans.ADA* (1872), 21–22; Jonathan Taft, "Report of Committee on Societies," *ibid.,* (1864), 89–90; "Minutes of the 22nd Annual Meeting of the Mississippi Valley Association," *DRegister,* XX (July, 1866), 314.

34. *Trans.ADA* (1867), 20–21; "Transactions of the American Dental Association," *DCosmos,* IX (Oct., 1867), 130; *Trans.ADA* (1887), 30.

35. H. A. Smith, "Annual Address," *Trans.ADA* (1882), 39–40; *ibid.,* 22–23; *ibid.* (1883), 20–21; "The American Dental Association," *Herald of Dentistry,* III (Oct., 1883), 4.

36. *Trans.ADA* (1883), 20–21, 26; *ibid.* (1887), 29.

37. A. Hunter Dupree, *Science in the Federal Government: A History of Policies and Activities to 1940* (Cambridge, Mass.: The Belknap Press of Harvard University Press, 1957), Chs. viii–xiii; R. H. Shryock, *American Medical Research,* 42–44.

38. R. H. Shryock, *American Medical Research,* 43–44.

39. See, e.g., *Trans.ADA* (1871), 17; *ibid.* (1887), 32.

40. "The National Dental Association," *Herald of Dentistry,* I (Jan., 1882), 3; "Recent Dental Conventions," *AmJDSc,* 3d ser., XIV (Aug., 1880), 185; C. N. Peirce, "Report on Dental Education, Literature, and Nomenclature," *Trans.ADA* (1890), 51–52; Louis Ottofy, "Report on Dental Education, Literature, Etc.," *ibid.* (1888), 230.

41. Williams Donnally, "An Opportunity for a Great National Museum," *Trans.ADA* (1895), 18, 145, 148; *ibid.* (1896), 9–11.

42. *Trans.ADA* (1897), 19.

43. R. H. Shryock, *American Medical Research,* 47–48, 49, 107 and sources there cited; James Truman, "Annual Address," *Trans.ADA* (1897), 46; "Report of Special Committee on President's Address," *ibid.,* 48.

44. *Trans.ADA* (1885), 23–24, 27–28.

45. W. C. Barrett, "Annual Address," *Trans.ADA* (1886); C. N. Peirce, "Annual Address," *ibid.* (1881), 42.

46. *Trans.ADA* (1878), 15.

47. *Trans.ADA* (1877), 17; *ibid.* (1878), 15, 16–17; E. T. Darby, "Annual Address," *ibid.* (1884), 53.

48. See, e.g., *Trans.ADA* (1881), 14; J. D. Patterson, "Annual Address," *ibid.* (1893–1894), 35–37; *ibid.* (1895), 25; Editorial, "Purpose of the American Dental Association," *DDigest,* I (July, 1895), 443; James Truman, "Annual Address," *Trans.ADA* (1897), 44.

49. W. C. Barrett, "Annual Address," *Trans.ADA* (1886), 37; *ibid.* (1875), 22. The earlier proposal had not been adopted.

50. C. N. Peirce, "Annual Address," *Trans.ADA* (1881), 42–43; W. C. Barrett, "Annual Address," *ibid.* (1886), 36; Editorial, "Dental Societies in America," *Independent Practitioner,* VIII (Feb., 1887), 106. In the 1870's, a reviewer commented on the proceedings of the societies: "It is a great relief to find the tendency of thought toward matters of a practical nature. We miss, with great satisfaction, the threadbare discussions on hackneyed subjects, in which theory supplanted fact, and ignorance knowledge." "Bibliographical," *DCosmos,* XVIII (Apr., 1876), 210. One man's theory, of course, was often another man's science.

51. James Truman, "Annual Address," *Trans.ADA* (1897), 44.

52. *Trans.ADA* (1892), 25; *ibid.* (1893–1894), 20–21; *ibid.* (1895), 25–26.

53. Editorial, "Are Our Dental Organizations Satisfactory?" *Odontographic Journal,* XV (Apr., 1894), 51; J. D. Patterson, "Annual Address," *Trans.ADA* (1893–1894), 35.

54. See, e.g., "T. J." to the Editor, "The American Dental Association," *Odontographic J,* X (Oct., 1889), 164; "Loriga" to Editor, "The American Dental Association and Her Future," *DReview,* IV (May, 1890), 341; Thomas Fillebrown, "Union of the American and Southern Dental Association," *DCosmos,* XXXIX (Apr., 1897), 318; *Trans.ADA* (1889), 27; "Separation of the National Associations," *International DJ,* XVII (Dec., 1896), 830–832.

55. See, e.g., *Trans.ADA* (1884), 40, for an episode on which such charges were based. See also W. C. Barrett, "Annual Address," *ibid.* (1886), 37; E. H. Allen, "Opinions of Illinois Dentists Regarding Dental Societies," *Trans. Ill. St. D Society* (1897),

especially 56–57; Editorial, "The National Dental Association: What Shall be Its Character?" *DDigest*, V (Jan., 1899), 66–67.

56. "T. J." to the Editor, "The American Dental Association," *Odontographic J*, X (Oct., 1889), 161; W. C. Barrett, "Annual Address," *Trans.ADA* (1886), 37: "We have had too much of business brought before the society and have too earnestly and long debated parliamentary law and questions of order."

CHAPTER XII

1. "T. J." to the Editor, "The American Dental Association," *Odontographic J*, X (Oct., 1889), 163; "Loriga" to the Editor, "American Dental Association and Her Future," *DReview*, IV (May, 1890), 341–342.

2. Editorial, "Politics in Dental Association," *International DJ*, XVI (Feb., 1895), 124–125; and e.g., Editorial, "Critics of the American Dental Association," *Western DJ*, IV (Sept., 1890), 430; Editorial, "Criticism of the American Dental Association," *DReview*, IV (Dec., 1890), 1001–1003; "The National Association," *Western DJ*, X (Dec., 1896), 555–557 (Editorial copied from *DDigest*). Two presidents-elect of the American Dental Association during this period felt constrained to deny that they had sought the office. See W. C. Barrett in *Trans.ADA* (1885), 34; James Truman in *Trans.ADA* (1896), 23.

3. On these questions, see Editorial, "Recent Conventions," *International DJ*, XVI (Oct., 1895), 642; the report of James K. Knight's paper, "The Relation of Dental Societies to the Profession," in "Massachusetts Dental Society," *Archives of Dentistry*, VII (Feb., 1890), 75; "Are Our Dental Organizations Satisfactory?" *Odontographic J*, XV (Apr., 1894), 52–53; Editorial, "The American Dental Association and Reorganization," *International DJ*, XVIII (July, 1897), 468–469.

4. *Trans.ADA* (1891), 21–23. The committee had been appointed as a result of a resolution adopted at the preceding session. *Trans.ADA* (1890), 28; B. Holly Smith, "Value of Annual Gatherings," *DCosmos*, XXXVI (Sept., 1894), 716–717. This was Smith's presidential address before the Southern Dental Association. Its contents and recommendations are discussed, *ibid.* (Nov., 1894), 916–918.

5. C. N. Peirce, "Report on Education, Literature, and Nomenclature," *Trans.ADA* (1890), 55–56. Peirce found that between three thousand and thirty-five hundred dentists belonged to one or more societies. His figures for the American Dental Association add up to one hundred and seventy-five.

6. W. C. Barrett, "Whither Are We Drifting?" *Trans.ADA* (1895), 75–76; C. N. Peirce, "Report on Education . . . ," *ibid.* (1890), 56; Editorial, "The National Dental Association—What Shall Be Its Character?" *DDigest*, V (Jan., 1899), 66.

7. "Are Our Dental Organizations Satisfactory?" *Odontographic J*, XV (Apr., 1894), 52. See also B. Holly Smith, "Need of a National Dental Organization," Discussion by Rodrigues Ottolengui, *DCosmos*, XXXIX (Sept., 1897), 774; B. H. Teague, "Dental Associations and the Meeting of the Southern," *Southern DJ*, VI (June, 1887), 224; Editorial, "Two National Associations—Should They Combine?" *Southern DJ and Luminary*, XIII (Oct., 1894), 430; Editorial, "A National Dental Association," *DPractitioner and Advertiser*, XXV (Oct., 1894), 216.

8. See, e.g., Editorial, "Critics of the American Dental Association," *Western DJ*, IV (Sept., 1890), 430; W. W. H. Thackston, "Combination or Consolidation," *Southern DJ and Luminary*, XIV (Oct., 1895), 395–396; Thomas Fillebrown, "Union of the American and the Southern Dental Association," *DCosmos*, XXXIX (Apr., 1897) 317, also printed in *DDigest*, III (Mar., 1897), 138–142; *International DJ*, XVIII (Apr., 1897), 236–240; Editorial, "The American Dental Association and Reorganization," *ibid.* XVIII (July, 1897), 468–469; B. H. Smith, "Need of a National Dental Organiza-

tion," *DCosmos*, XXXIX (Aug., 1897), 616. See also James W. Hurst, *The Growth of American Law: The Law Makers* (Boston: Little, Brown and Co., 1950), 279–280.

9. B. H. Catching, "Consolidation of the Two Associations," *DDigest*, III (June, 1897), 344–345; B. H. Smith, "Need of a National Dental Organization," Discussion by William Jarvie, *DCosmos*, XXXVIV (Sept., 1897), 773; "Bibliographical," *DCosmos*, XVIII (Apr., 1876), 211.

10. Arthur M. Schlesinger, *The Rise of the City. A History of American Life*, ed. by Dixon R. Fox and A. M. Schlesinger, vol. 10 (New York: The Macmillan Co., 1944), 364, 419; Thomas A. Bailey, *Diplomatic History of the American People* (New York: F. S. Crofts, 1941), 435, 446, 455, 464.

11. *Trans.ADA* (1872), 29; "American Dental Association," *DCosmos*, XVIII (Feb., 1876), 91: *Trans.ADA* (1876), 13; "American Dental Association," *DCosmos*, XVIII (Sept., 1876), 476.

12. *Trans.ADA* (1885), 32; Louis Ottofy, "Dental Education, Literature, Etc.," *ibid.* (1887), 70–71; *ibid.* (1888), 20; *ibid.* (1889), 21, 22; *ibid.* (1890), 17–19; *ibid.* (1892), 25.

13. See "A Compromise but not a Retreat," *DCosmos*, XXIX (Mar., 1887), 160–163; "Loriga" to the Editor, "The American Dental Association and Her Future," *DReview*, IV (May, 1890), 341; "Are Our Dental Organizations Satisfactory?" *Odontographic J*, XV (Apr., 1894), 52–53. See also W. C. Barrett, "At Old Point Comfort," *DPractitioner and Advertiser*, XXVIII (Oct., 1897), 196.

14. See, e.g., "American Dental Convention," *DCosmos*, XVI (Nov., 1874), 583–584; "Gratuitous Dentistry in the Schools of Paris," *ibid.* XXIV (Jan., 1882), 44; *Trans.ADA* (1886), 23–25, 32; Louis Ottofy, "Dental Education, Literature, and Nomenclature," *ibid.* (1887), 59; *ibid.* (1888), 23; *ibid.* (1889), 21; *ibid.* (1876), 13, 15; "American Dental Association," *DCosmos*, XVIII (Sept., 1876), 476; Greene V. Black, "The Herbst Method of Filling with Gold," *Ohio St. J DScience*, V (Mar., 1884), 66–73.

15. The "Periscope" of the *Dental Cosmos*, XVIII (1876), *passim*, is particularly rich in quotations from British publications. Apparently the British profession was undergoing a considerable renaissance at this time. See A. M. Carr-Saunders and T. B. Wilson, *The Professions*, 109–113. On the language difficulties of American dentists, see "Bibliographical," *DCosmos*, XVIII (Apr., 1876), 211; Carl E. and Bessie M. Black, *From Pioneer to Scientist: The Life Story of Greene Vardiman Black "Father of Modern Dentistry" and His Son Arthur Davenport Black Late Dean of Northwestern University Dental School* (St. Paul, Minn.: Bruce Publishing Co., 1940), 145 and *passim*. On "official" journals, see "Transactions of the Ohio State Dental Society," *DCosmos*, XVIII (May, 1876), 266–267.

16. W. W. H. Thackston, "Combination and Consolidation," *Southern DJ and Luminary*, XIV (Oct., 1895), 398; "In the Year 2000," *Odontographic J*, X (Jan., 1890), 244–245, reprinted from the *Medical Record;* see also "Bibliographical," *DCosmos*, XVIII (Apr., 1876), 211, where an extreme example of nationalistic pride is quoted; "Loriga" to the Editor, "American Dental Association and Her Future," *DReview*, IV (May, 1890), 341–342.

17. *Trans.ADA* (1877), 23; *ibid.* (1882), 19–20. Atkinson's reports may be found in the Transactions.

18. Richard H. Shryock, *American Medical Research Past and Present* (New York: The Commonwealth Fund, 1947), 44; Louis Ottofy, "Dental Education, Literature, and Nomenclature," *Trans.ADA* (1887), 70–71; *ibid.* (1890), 33; C. N. Peirce, "Report on Education, Literature, and Nomenclature," *ibid.*, 57; Editorial, "Recent Conventions," *International DJ*, XVI (Oct., 1895), 642.

19. For expressions of friendship, see *Trans.ADA* (1865), 121, 127; "Minutes," *Trans. Southern DA* (1870), 36; *ibid.* (1883), 25; W. W. H. Thackston, "Combination and Consolidation," *Southern DJ and Luminary*, XIV (Oct., 1895), 395–398; Editorial, "Southern Dental Association," *AmJDSc*, 3d ser., IX (Feb., 1876), 471. On the Southern's reception of members from all parts of the country, see also "The National Dental Association," *Herald of Dentistry*, I (Jan., 1882), 3. For the various signs of mutual appreciation, see George H. Perine, "Army and Navy Dental Appointments," *DCosmos*, XXIV (Jan., 1882), 56; E. T. Darby, "Annual Address," *Trans.ADA* (1884), 48; B. H. Catching, "Discussion of President Catching's Address," *ibid.* (1888), 63; J. Y. Crawford, "Annual Address," *ibid.* (1896), 30 (Crawford was a Georgian); Crawford's successor, the president-elect, was James Truman of New York. Truman's remarks are quoted from *ibid.*, 23.

20. "Southern Dental Association," *DCosmos*, XX (July, 1878), 393; "American Dental Association," and "American Dental Convention," *ibid.* (June, 1878), 344; H. J. McKellops, "President's Address," *Trans.ADA* (1879), 27. The American Dental Association appointed a committee in accordance with McKellop's suggestions. *Ibid.*, 16–17.

21. "Southern Dental Association," *DCosmos*, XXII (Sept., 1880), 500; H. J. McKellops, "President's Address," *Trans.ADA* (1879), 27; *ibid.* (1880), 15–16; *ibid.* (1883), 25; E. T. Darby, "Annual Address," *ibid.* (1884), 52.

22. *Trans.ADA* (1886), 33; *ibid.* (1897), 17–22, 28; "Southern Dental Association, Old Point Comfort, Va.," *Southern DJ*, VI (Oct., 1887), 403–404.

23. *Trans.ADA* (1888), 17–18, 22, 33; B. H. Catching, "Is the Average Dentist of Today a Specialist in Medicine?" *ibid.* (1888), 46–51. The discussion is recorded, *ibid.*, 51–63.

24. *Trans.ADA* (1888), 283–284.

25. Editorial, "A National Dental Association," *DPractitioner and Advertiser*, XXV (Oct., 1894), 215; Editorial, "Two National Associations—Should They Combine?" *Southern DJ and Luminary*, XIII (Oct., 1894), 430; Editorial, "Southern Dental Association," *AmJDSc*, 3d ser., IX (Feb., 1876), 471; "Southern Dental Association," *DCosmos*, XXIV (Aug., 1882), 487.

26. See, e.g., W. W. Allport, "Response to the Toast, 'Dentistry and Dental Education—Its Past, Present, and Future as Related to Medicine,'" *DRegister*, XXXV (May, 1881), 193.

27. C. N. Peirce, "Report on Education, Literature, and Nomenclature," *Trans.ADA* (1890), 56. See also, Thomas Fillebrown, "Union of the American and Southern Dental Association," *DCosmos*, XXXIX (Apr., 1897), 316: "The American has continued too much an Eastern institution. . . ." See also A. W. Harlan, "Presidential Address," *Trans.ADA* (1891), 60–61; "The National Dental Association," *Herald of Dentistry*, I (Jan., 1882), 3; "Are Our Dental Organizations Satisfactory?" *Odontographic J*, XV (Apr., 1894), 52; James Truman's remarks in *Trans.ADA* (1897), 29; and B. Holly Smith, "Need of a National Dental Organization," *DCosmos*, XXXIX (Aug., 1897), 616.

28. B. H. Teague, "Dental Associations and the Meeting of the Southern," *Southern DJ*, VI (June, 1887), 224; Editorial, "Two National Associations—Should They Combine?" *Southern DJ and Luminary*, XIII (Oct., 1894), 429; Editorial, "Union of the Southern and the American," *Texas DJ*, XII (Oct., 1894), 117–118; B. Holly Smith, "Need of a National Dental Organization," Discussion by W. W. Walker, *DCosmos*, XXXIX (Sept., 1897), 771.

29. W. W. H. Thackston, "Combination or Consolidation," *Southern DJ and Luminary*, XIV (Oct., 1895), 395–399. A brief summary of Thackston's harangue is W. W. H. Thackston, "Against Union," *Western DJ*, X (Feb., 1896), 91.

30. A. W. Harlan, "Presidential Address," *Trans.ADA* (1891), 60–61. See also Editorial, "Two National Associations—Should They Combine?" *Southern DJ and*

Luminary, XIII (Oct., 1894), 430; B. H. Catching, "Consolidation of the Two Associations," *DDigest*, III (June, 1897), 344–345. This article appeared originally in *International DJ*, XVIII (May, 1897), 314–315. See also "Report of the Special Committee on the President's Address," *Trans.ADA* (1891), 47–57. For the later proposal, see A. H. Thompson, "A Plan for a National Dental Association Divided into Four Coordinate District Branches," *AmJDSc*, 3d ser., XXX (Dec., 1896), 354–357. The same essay was printed in *Western DJ*, X (July, 1896), 294–299. For an extended favorable editorial comment on the scheme, see *International DJ*, XVII (Oct., 1896), 674–677. See also *Trans.ADA* (1893–1894), 25: "Dr. H. A. Smith moved that, in view of the fact that a committee has been appointed to confer with a like committee from the Southern Association looking toward a union of the two bodies in one National Association, the consideration of the revision of the Constitution be postponed till that committee has reported." This marked the end of fundamental constitutional reform until after union with the Southern in 1897.

31. B. Holly Smith, "Need of a National Dental Organization," *DCosmos*, XXXIX (Aug., 1897), 616.

32. *Trans.ADA* (1890), 17–19, 28; *ibid.* (1893–1894), 12.

33. *Trans.ADA* (1893), 24, 25.

34. J. Y. Crawford, "Annual Address," *Trans.ADA* (1895), 37. A committee was appointed. *Ibid.*, 25, 29, 30.

35. *Trans.ADA* (1896), 19, 23; J. Y. Crawford, "Annual Address," *ibid.*, 30.

36. Thomas Fillebrown, "Union of the American and Southern Dental Association," *DCosmos*, XXXIX (Apr., 1897), 317–319, also printed in *DDigest*, III (Mar., 1897), 138–142; *International DJ*, XVIII (Apr., 1897), 236–240. For a favorable descriptive editorial, see Editorial, "Union of the American and Southern Dental Association," *DHeadlight*, XVII (1896), 127–128. See also the plan as reported to the American Dental Association in *Trans.ADA* (1897), 14–15.

37. *Trans.ADA* (1897), 13–18; W. E. Walker, "Minutes of Convention Resulting in the Formation of the National Dental Association," *Trans.ADA* (1897), App., 1–2.

38. Editorial, "At Old Point Comfort," *DPractitioner and Advertiser*, XXVIII (Oct., 1897), 198–199. The official account of proceedings is W. E. Walker, "Minutes of the Convention Resulting in the Formation of the National Dental Association," *Trans.ADA* (1897), App., 1–2. Other sedate versions are "Union of the American and the Southern Dental Associations," *AmJDSc*, 3d ser., XXXI (Oct., 1897), 253–255; and Editorial, "A Subject of History," *DBrief*, II (Aug., 1897), 1–3.

CHAPTER XIII

1. For the diplomatic history of the United States at the turn of the century, see Samuel F. Bemis, *A Diplomatic History of the United States* (Rev. ed.; New York, Henry Holt & Co., 1950), chs. xxvi and xxvii; A. M. Griswold, *The Far Eastern Policy of the United States* (New York: Harcourt Brace & Co., 1938), chs. 11–14; George F. Kennan, *American Diplomacy 1900–1950* (Chicago: University of Chicago Press, 1951), chs. i–iii; Howard K. Beale, *Theodore Roosevelt and the Rise of America to World Power* (Baltimore: The Johns Hopkins University Press, 1956), *passim;* J. W. Pratt, *America's Colonial Experiment* (New York: Prentice Hall, 1950), *passim.*

2. There are a number of excellent studies of the changes in American economic life at the turn of the century, e.g., Harold U. Faulkner, *The Decline of Laissez Faire 1897–1917; The Economic History of the United States*, VIII, ed. by Henry David, *et al.* (New York: Rinehart & Co., Inc., 1951); Frederick C. Mills, *Economic Tendencies in the United States: Aspects of Pre-War and Post-War Changes* (New York: National

Bureau of Economic Research, 1932); George W. Edwards, *The Evolution of Finance Capitalism* (New York: Longmans, Green and Co., 1938). On fluctuations in the economy, see also Willard Thorp, *Business Annals* (New York: National Bureau of Economic Research, Inc., 1926), 138–143.

3. On social changes around 1900, see Harold U. Faulkner, *The Quest for Social Justice; A History of American Life,* XI, ed. by A. M. Schlesinger and D. R. Fox (New York: The Macmillan Co., 1928); Mark Sullivan, *Our Times, I, The Turn of the Century* (New York: Charles Scribner's Sons, 1946).

4. Reforms in the State Department are treated in Graham Stuart, *The Department of State* (New York: The Macmillan Co., 1949), 205–207; Philip Jessup, *Elihu Root* (New York: Dodd, Mead and Co., 1938), II, 100–112; Donald M. Dozer, "Secretary of State Elihu Root and Consular Reorganization," *Mississippi Valley Historical Review,* XXIX (Dec., 1942), 335–350.

5. The extensive reform of the War Department is recounted in Walter Millis, *Arms and Men* (New York: G. P. Putnam's Sons, 1956), 174–181; P. Jessup, *Elihu Root,* I, 225–227, 240–264.

6. P. M. Ashburn, *A History of the Medical Department of the United States Army* (Boston: Houghton Mifflin Co., 1929), 209. A summary of these developments may be found in "Report of the Committee on Army and Navy Dental Legislation," *Trans.ADA* (1906), 19–30.

7. "Report of the Committee on Army and Navy Legislation," *Trans.ADA* (1904–1905), 5; *ibid.* (1911), 28; P. M. Ashburn, *History of the Medical Department of the Army,* 211.

8. In addition to the sources cited above, ns 2 and 3, see Arthur Link, *American Epoch* (New York: A. A. Knopf, 1955), 108, 111–114; B. P. De Witt, *The Progressive Movement* (New York: Macmillan, 1915), Chs. x–xvi; Comer Vann Woodward, *The Origins of the New South 1877–1913* (*A History of the South,* Vol. IX) ed. by W. H. Stephenson and E. M. Coulter (Baton Rouge: Louisiana State University Press, 1951), Ch. xiv; Paul S. Reinsch, *American Legislatures and Legislative Methods* (New York: Century Co., 1913).

9. A. Hunter Dupree, *Science in the Federal Government* (Cambridge, Mass.: Belknap Press of Harvard University Press, 1957), 268–269, 271–279.

10. Richard H. Shryock, *American Medical Research, Past and Present* (New York: Commonwealth Fund, 1947), 91–99; Frederic L. Paxson, *Recent History of the United States* (Boston: Houghton Mifflin Co., 1922), 320–321; Merle Curti, *The Growth of American Thought* (New York: Harper and Brothers, 1943), 586.

11. "Minutes of the Meeting," *Trans.ADA* (1902), 248; "Report of the Committee on the Carnegie Institute," *ibid.* (1903), 222–224.

12. R. H. Shryock, *American Medical Research,* 108–109.

13. See, e.g., "Minutes of the Meeting," *Trans.ADA* (1903), 214–215; "Minutes of the Executive Council," *ibid.* (1908), 17.

14. A. H. Dupree, *Science in the Federal Government;* 263–267.

15. "Report of the Committee on National Museum," *Trans.ADA* (1898), 47–49. In 1906, the President of the National Dental Association recommended that the Association support a chair of research in the Museum while the campaign for government aid continued. See M. F. Finley, "Annual Address," *Trans.ADA* (1906), 46–47.

16. Editorial, "The A.D.A. and Reorganization," *International DJ,* XVIII (July, 1897), 468–469; Editorial, W. C. Barrett, an ex-president of the American Dental Association, "At Old Point Comfort," *DPractitioner and Advertiser,* XXVIII (Oct., 1897), 198.

17. James Truman, "Annual Address," *Trans.ADA* (1897), 46; E. H. Allen, Opinions of Illinois Dentists Regarding Dental Societies," *Trans.Ill.St.D Soc.* (1897), 56–57; Editorial, "Society Organizations of the Dental Profession," *DDigest*, V (Apr., 1899), 284–286; Editorial, "The National Dental Association—What Shall Be Its Character?" *ibid.* (Jan., 1899), 66–67.

18. E. H. Allen, "Opinions of Illinois Dentists Regarding Dental Societies," *Trans.Ill.St.D Soc.* (1897), 54–57, and *passim;* James Truman, "Annual Address," *Trans.ADA* (1897), 46.

19. Thomas N. Bonner, *Medicine in Chicago* (Madison, Wis.: American History Research Center, 1957), 66–68, 75–83, 84–102.

20. Editorial, "A New Movement in Illinois," *DReview*, XI (Feb., 1897), 134.

21. A. D. Black, *et al.*, "Reorganization of the Illinois State Dental Society, Presented by the Committee Appointed by the Odontographic Society of Chicago," *Trans.Ill.St.DA* (1904), 35–45.

22. "Minutes of the Meeting," *Trans.Ill.St.DA* (1904), 175, 176.

23. A. D. Black, *et al.*, "Reorganization . . . ," (discussion) *ibid.*, 58; "Minutes of the Meeting," *ibid.*, 177, 181–182.

24. "Constitution and By-Laws, as Amended 1904," *ibid.*, Appendix, 202; Proposed Revised Constitution and By-Laws," *ibid.*, Appendix, 215, 218–219.

25. A. D. Black, *et al.*, "Reorganization . . . ," *ibid.*, 37, 43; "Minutes of the Executive Council," *ibid.*, 191; "Minutes of the Meeting," *ibid.*, 180.

26. A. D. Black, *et al.*, "Report of the Reorganization Committee," *Trans.Ill.St.DA* (1905), 103–106, 114–121. See also C. N. Johnson, "President's Annual Address," *ibid.*, 17; and discussion by C. P. Pruyn of Chicago, *ibid.*, 20.

CHAPTER XIV

1. Richard Hofstadter, *Social Darwinism in American Thought* (Boston: Beacon Press, Inc., 1955), 105–110, 143–169; Henry Steel Commager, *The American Mind* (New Haven: Yale University Press, 1950), 168–177; Aaron I. Abell, "The Reception of Leo XIII's Labor Encyclical in America, 1891–1919," *Review of Politics*, VII (October, 1945), 464–495; Harold Underwood Faulkner, *The Quest for Social Justice, 1898–1911: A History of American Life*, XI, ed. by A. M. Schlesinger and D. R. Fox (New York: Macmillan Company, 1931), 157–162, 178–187, 218–228.

2. "A Plea for Dr. Dwinelle," *Trans.ADA* (1892), 112–115.

3. "The Chicago Fire," *DCosmos*, XIII (Nov., 1871), 590; Editorial "Aid to Chicago Dentists," *ibid.* (Dec., 1871), 650.

4. L. G. Noel, "Annual Address," *Trans.NDA* (1903), 17–18; Waldo E. Boardman, "Annual Address," *ibid.* (1904–1905), 41; "Report of the Committee on President's Address," in "Minutes of the Meeting," *ibid.*, 13.

5. "Minutes of the Executive Council," *Trans.NDA* (1901), 215; "Minutes of the Fifth Annual Meeting," *ibid.*, 197. The National Dental Association's contribution was one hundred dollars.

6. Mark A. Finley, "Annual Address," *Trans.NDA* (1906), 43–44; "Minutes of the Executive Council," *ibid.* (1907), 21–22; "Eleventh Annual Meeting," *ibid.*, 17–19; "Report of San Francisco Dental Relief Committee," *ibid.*, 21–22.

7. "Report of Committee on President's Address," in "Minutes of the Meeting," *Trans.NDA* (1909), 4; "Minutes of Executive Council," *ibid.*, 7; "Report of Committee on President's Address," in "Minutes of the Meeting," *Trans.NDA* (1911), 7–8.

8. "Minutes of the Executive Council," *Trans.NDA* (1911), 22; Arthur R. Melendy, "President's Address," *ibid.* (1912), 46–47; "Minutes of the Executive Council," *ibid.*, 19; "Report of Committee on President's Address," in "Sixteenth Annual Meeting," *ibid.*, 13; "Report of Committee on President's Address," in "Seventeenth Annual Meeting," *ibid.* (1913), 5.

9. In 1901 the Committee on Oral Hygiene suggested that "temperance educational laws" in the states had been the basis for introducing instruction in physiology into the schools. See *Trans.NDA* (1901), 224–225. On the prohibitionist movement see John Allen Krout, *The Origins of Prohibition* (New York: Alfred A. Knopf, 1925), *passim*. On the voluntary health groups, see Richard H. Shryock, *American Medical Research Past and Present* (New York: Commonwealth Fund, 1947), 111–112; "Minutes of the Executive Council," *Trans.NDA* (1908), 22; "Minutes of the Twelfth Annual Meeting," *ibid.*, 10.

10. "Report of the Oral Hygiene Committee," *Trans.NDA* (1901), 224–225; "Minutes of the Meeting," *ibid.* (1903), 203. On the general movement to introduce hygiene and physiology into the school curricula, see Ruth E. Grout, *Health Teaching in Schools* (Philadelphia and London: W. B. Saunders Co., 1958), 9ff.

11. "Minutes of the Fourth Annual Meeting," *Trans.NDA* (1900), 187, 191; "Minutes of the Executive Council," *ibid.*, 212; "Report of the Committee on Oral Hygiene," *ibid.*, (1901), 225–226; "Report of the Committee on Oral Hygiene," *ibid.*, (1902), 263–271.

12. See, e.g., the reports of the Committee in *Trans.NDA* (1903), 203–209; *ibid.* (1904–1905), 21–23; *ibid.* (1906), 15–17.

13. *Trans.NDA* (1908), 2–3. On the Massachusetts program, see also the remarks of Herbert L. Wheeler following L. C. Taylor, "Dentistry, Past and Present," *Trans.NDA* (1909), 215–216. On the pamphlet for distribution to the public, see "Report of the Committee on Oral Hygiene," *Trans.NDA* (1903), 209; "Report of the Oral Hygiene Committee," *ibid.* (1906), 15; "Report of the Special Committee on Revision of the Oral Hygiene Report," *ibid.* (1908), 17–19; discussion by J. D. Patterson of Kansas City following L. C. Taylor, "Dentistry, Past and Present," *ibid.* (1909), 212–213.

14. Discussion following L. C. Taylor, "Dentistry, Past and Present," *Trans.NDA* (1909), 214; discussion following J. G. Sharp, "Obstacles to our Educational Progress, and their Correction," *ibid.* (1910), 200.

15. "Minutes of the Executive Council," *Trans.NDA* (1904–1905), 24. On the Darwinian and neo-Darwinian controversies, see above, Ch. xi; Richard Hofstadter, *Social Darwinism in America* (Boston: Beacon Press, Inc., 1955) *passim*. On the historical development of the dental doctrine adumbrated here, see L. C. Taylor, "Dentistry, Past and Present, as Seen by a Modern Hygienist," *Trans.NDA* (1909), 206.

16. N. S. Hoff, discussion following L. C. Taylor, "Dentistry, Past and Present," *Trans.NDA* (1909), 210.

17. Discussion by Horace Warren following H. C. Brown, "Diseases Affecting the Buccal Mucous Membrane," *Trans.NDA* (1910), 285.

18. W. G. Ebersole, "Work of the N.D.A. Oral Hygiene Committee," *Trans.NDA* (1910), 266.

19. "Report of the Oral Hygiene Committee," *Trans.NDA* (1904–1905), 21–22; Safford G. Perry, "The Evolution of Dentistry," *ibid.* (1911), 39; See also "Minutes of the Meeting," *ibid.* (1903), 203–204: "The medical profession counts as its greatest triumph the discovery that disease may be prevented as well as cured."

20. Discussion by Herbert L. Wheeler following L. C. Taylor, "Dentistry, Past and Present," *Trans.NDA* (1909), 215; discussion by Truman W. Brophy following

J. G. Sharp, "Obstacles to our Educational Progress, and their Correction," *ibid.* (1910), 200; W. A. Evans, "The Teeth and Health in their Public Relations," *ibid.*, 258.

21. *Trans.NDA* (1910), 267: "The success of the past year's work is due to the fact that the policy of your committee has been changed from a philanthropic one to an educational or economic one."

22. "Report of Committee on Oral Hygiene," in "Minutes of Executive Council," *Trans.NDA* (1910), 18; Homer C. Brown, Columbus, to Charles S. Butler, Buffalo, Nov. 3, 1910, and C. S. B. to H. C. B., Nov. 5, 1910, Brown MSS. in custody of Brig. Gen. Neal A. Harper, USA (DC) (Ret.), of Columbus, Ohio. On the possibilities of a rival society, see H. C. Brown, to C. S. Butler, Aug. 10, 1910, Brown MSS.; Rodrigues Ottolengui, New York, to H. C. B., Mar. 1, 1911; H. C. B. to R. O., Mar. 3, 1911; Harvey J. Burkhart, Batavia, N. Y., to H. C. B., Apr. 30, 1911; H. C. B. to R. O., May 11, 1911; and H. J. B. to H. C. B., May 25, 1911, Brown MSS.

23. "Minutes of the Executive Council," *Trans.NDA* (1900), 230; M. D. K. Bremner, *The Story of Dentistry* (3d ed.; Brooklyn: Dental Items of Interest Publishing Co., 1954), 232–233. See also "Minutes," *Trans.NDA* (1900), 202; "Minutes of the Meeting," *ibid.* (1903), 199–200, 227; *ibid.* (1904–1905), 280.

24. Floyd L. Vaughan, *The United States Patent System: Legal and Economic Conflicts in American Patent History* (Norman: University of Oklahoma Press, 1956); R. H. Shryock, *American Medical Research*, 141–142; *Trans.NDA* (1898), 44–45; "Proceedings of the National Dental Association, Southern Branch," *ibid.*, 212, 213, 214; "Minutes of the Executive Council," *ibid.* (1902), 232; discussion by Emory A. Bryant following R. Ottolengui, "Dental Ethics and Dental Patents," *ibid.* (1911), 59.

25. M. D. K. Bremner, *Story of Dentistry*, 263–267.

26. M. D. K. Bremner, *Story of Dentistry*, 234–236; William Hunter, "Role of Sepsis and Antisepsis in Medicine," *Lancet* (London: Jan. 14, 1911), 79; Editorial [R. Ottolengui (?)], "Dr. Hunter's Address on Oral Sepsis," *Items of Interest*, XXXIII (Nov., 1911), 869–876; discussion by N. S. Hoff following L. C. Taylor, "Dentistry, Past and Present," *Trans.NDA* (1909), 210. See also the paper itself, especially p. 206.

27. M. D. K. Bremner, *Story of Dentistry*, 271–277.

28. Discussion by J. N. Crouse following R. Ottolengui, "Dental Ethics and Dental Patents," *Trans.NDA* (1911), 57; discussion by Richard Summa, *ibid.*, 57–58; M. D. K. Bremner, *Story of Dentistry*, 271–277, especially 272.

29. Discussion by R. Summa following R. Ottolengui, "Dental Ethics and Dental Patents," *Trans.NDA* (1911), 57; discussion by Emory A. Bryant, *ibid.*, 59.

30. "Minutes of the Executive Council," *Trans.NDA* (1911), 24; "Minutes of the Executive Council," *ibid.* (1912), 23; "Sixteenth Annual Meeting," *ibid.*, 12; discussion by Richard Summa following R. Ottolengui, "Dental Ethics and Dental Patents," *ibid.* (1911), 57.

31. R. Ottolengui, "Dental Ethics and Dental Patents," *Trans.NDA* (1911), 45–52.

32. See, e.g., discussion by R. Summa following R. Ottolengui, "Dental Ethics and Dental Patents," *Trans.NDA* (1911), 57–58; discussion by M. L. Rhein, *ibid.*, 58; discussion by J. P. Buckley, *ibid.*, 60.

33. Discussion by W. H. Taggart following R. Ottolengui, "Dental Ethics and Dental Patents," *Trans.NDA* (1911), 62.

34. "Minutes of the Meeting," *Trans.NDA* (1903), 213. See also the "Report of the Committee on the President's Address" recommending Examiners' responsibility for reciprocity, *ibid.* (1904–1905), 13; William H. Carr, "Annual Address," *ibid.* (1908), 29.

35. "Report of the Committee on State Interchange of License," in "Minutes of the Executive Council," *Trans.NDA* (1900), 215–216; "Report of the Committee on the President's Address," in "Minutes of the Meeting," *ibid.* (1904–1905), 13; Burton Lee Thorpe, "President's Address," *ibid.* (1910), 25; "Report of the Committee on the President's Address," in "Minutes of the Meeting," *ibid.*, 9.

36. "Minutes of the Executive Council," *Trans.NDA* (1903), 215–216; William H. Carr, "Annual Address," *ibid.* (1908), 29; "Report of the Committee on President's Address" in "Minutes of the Fourth Annual Meeting," *ibid.* (1900), 192; James McManus, "A Sidelight on Professional Interest," *ibid.* (1909), 45.

37. "Minutes of Transactions," *Trans.NDA* (1899), 26; "Minutes of the Executive Council," *ibid.* (1900), 216–218.

38. "Minutes of the Fifth Annual Meeting," *Trans.NDA* (1901), 186–193, 195, 202, 206; "Minutes of Eighth Annual Meeting," *ibid.* (1904–1905), 11, 2, 28; "Minutes of Eleventh Annual Meeting," *ibid.* (1907), 23.

39. S. D. Ruggles, "Phases of Improvement in Nomenclature," *Trans.NDA* (1909), 122.

40. R. H. Shryock, *American Medical Research*, 121; Thomas N. Bonner, *Medicine in Chicago, 1850–1950* (Madison, Wis.: American History Research Center, 1957), 119.

41. "Dental Faculties Association of American Universities," *DCosmos*, LI (July, 1909), 884–887.

42. Editorial, "An Educational Advance," *DCosmos*, LI (July, 1909), 888–891.

43. J. G. Sharp, "Obstacles to Educational Progress," *Trans.NDA* (1910), 187–188.

44. Report of Educational Council in "Minutes of Executive Council," *Trans.NDA* (1911), 16–17; Burton Lee Thorpe, "President's Address," *Trans.NDA* (1910), 27–28.

45. Henry Banzhaf, "Second Annual Report of the Secretary of the Dental Educational Council of America," in "Minutes of Executive Council," *Trans.NDA* (1912), 26, 29.

46. J. G. Sharp, "Obstacles to Educational Progress, and Their Correction," *Trans.NDA* (1910), 184, 189.

47. Discussion by B. Holly Smith, *et al.*, following J. G. Sharp, "Obstacles to Educational Progress," *Trans.NDA* (1910), 189–203.

CHAPTER XV

1. Editorial, "The National Dental Association—What Shall Be Its Character?" *DDigest*, V (Jan. 1899), 65–67; James Truman, "Annual Address," *Trans.ADA* (1897), 46, where he expresses the hope that the amalgamated society will establish a fund to aid research.

2. "Constitution . . . of the National Dental Association (Adopted Aug., 1897)," *Trans.ADA* (1897), App., 13–16. See, e.g., Editorial, "The National Dental Association—What Shall Be Its Character?" *DDigest*, V (Jan., 1899), 65–67.

3. "Constitution . . . of the National Dental Association (Adopted Aug., 1897)," *Trans.ADA* (1897), App., 10.

4. Editorial, "The A.D.A. and Reorganization," *International DJ*, XVIII (July, 1897), 468–469; Thomas Fillebrown, "Union of the American and Southern Dental Association," *DCosmos*, XXXIX (Apr., 1897), 317; Editorial, "Union of the American and Southern Dental Association," *DHeadlight*, XVII (1896), 127–128; B. Holly Smith, "Need of a National Dental Organization," *DCosmos*, XXXIX (Aug., 1897),

616. The Fillebrown article may also be found in *DDigest*, III (Mar., 1897), 138–142; and *International DJ*, XVIII (Apr., 1897), 236–240; "Constitution . . . of the National Dental Association (Adopted Aug., 1897)," *Trans.ADA* (1897), App., 11.

5. "Constitution . . . of the National Dental Association (Adopted Aug., 1897)," *Trans.ADA* (1897), App. 10.

6. *Trans.ADA* (1897), 29; J. A. Libbey, "Annual Address," *Trans.NDA* (1902), 10–11; L. G. Noel, "Presidential Address," *Trans.NDA* (1903), 11–14; W. E. Boardman, "Annual Address," *Trans.NDA*, (1904–1905), 37.

7. "Minutes of Transactions," *Trans.NDA* (1899), 21.

8. "Minutes of Transactions," *Trans.NDA* (1899), 20; "Minutes of Fourth Annual Meeting," *ibid.* (1900), 197, 199, 202.

9. "Minutes of the Transactions," *Trans.NDA* (1901), 183.

10. G. V. Black, "Annual Address," *Trans.NDA*, (1901), 9–21.

11. "Minutes of the Transactions," *Trans.NDA* (1901), 202, 211.

12. "Minutes of the Meeting," *Trans.NDA* (1902), 233, 237, 238; "Minutes of the Executive Council," *ibid.*, 272.

13. "Minutes of the Meeting," *Trans.NDA* (1903), 211; "Constitution of the National Dental Association," *ibid.* (1903), 266ff.

14. "Minutes of the Meeting," *Trans.NDA* (1904–1905), 12; "Minutes," *ibid.* (1906), 13; "Minutes," *ibid.* (1909), 2.

15. "Minutes of the Executive Council," *Trans.NDA* (1901), 214; L. G. Noel, "Annual Address," *ibid.* (1903), 10; "Minutes of Transactions," *ibid.* (1901), 183.

16. J. A. Libbey, "Annual Address," *Trans.NDA* (1902), 10.

17. L. G. Noel, "Annual Address," *Trans.NDA* (1903), 9, 10, 11–18. The Committee on President's Address opposed formation of more branches as leading to a dissipation of strength. "Minutes of Executive Council," *Trans.NDA* (1903), 212.

18. "Minutes of the Executive Council," *Trans.NDA* (1901), 239; "Minutes of the Executive Council," *ibid.* (1903), 212, 227.

19. "Eighth Annual Meeting, . . . St. Louis," *Trans.NDA* (1904–1905), 1, 3; H. J. Burkhart, Chairman of the Executive Council, proposed that the session in 1904 be confined to the election of officers and that the scientific portion of the meeting be merged with that of the International Dental Congress. "Minutes of the Meeting," *Trans.NDA* (1903), 211.

20. Waldo E. Boardman, "Annual Address," *Trans.NDA* (1904–1905), 37; "Minutes of the Meeting, Buffalo," *ibid.* (1904–1905), 9, 10, 13, 15.

21. Waldo E. Boardman, "Annual Address," *Trans.NDA* (1904–1905), 40–41; "Minutes of the Executive Council," *ibid.* (1904–1905), 23.

22. "Minutes of the Executive Council," *Trans.NDA* (1904–1905), 16–17.

23. "Minutes of the Executive Council," *Trans.NDA* (1904–1905), 13, 17–18, 28.

24. Mark F. Finley, "Annual Address," *Trans.NDA* (1906), 49; "Minutes of the Executive Council," *ibid.* (1905), 37.

25. A. H. Peck, "Annual Address," *Trans.NDA* (1907), 33–35.

26. "Eleventh Annual Meeting, Minneapolis," *Trans.NDA* (1907), 12–13.

27. George O. Orr, "The Functions of the State Dental Society," *Trans.NDA* (1907), 104–109. The quotation is from p. 107.

28. Discussion by C. P. Pruyn following George O. Orr, "The Functions of the State Dental Society," *Trans.NDA* (1907), 109–110. The remarks of the other participants continue through 113.

29. "Eleventh Annual Meeting," *Trans.NDA* (1907), 11–12.

30. William Carr, "Annual Address," *Trans.NDA* (1908), 28–35.

31. "Minutes of Executive Council," *Trans.NDA* (1908), 13–14.

32. R. Ottolengui, "Constitution of the N.D.A. Proposed at Boston," *Items of Interest*, XXX (Sept., 1908), 711–724.

33. "Minutes of Executive Council," *Trans.NDA* (1908), 13–14.

34. "Twelfth Annual Meeting, Boston," *Trans.NDA* (1908), 8.

35. R. Ottolengui, Editorial, "Reorganization Proposed for N.D.A.," *Items of Interest*, XXX (Sept., 1908), 709–711.

36. G. V. Black to the Editor, "Problem of Reorganizing the N.D.A.," *Items of Interest*, XXX (Nov., 1908), 875.

37. William C. King to the Editor, "Problem of Reorganizing," *Items of Interest*, XXX (Dec., 1908), 965. See also William A. Lovett to the Editor, "Problem of Reorganizing," *Items of Interest*, XXX (Nov., 1908), 876; Frederick Crosby Brush to the Editor, "Proposed Reorganization," *ibid.*, XXXI (Jan., 1909), 74.

38. Arthur D. Black to the Editor, "Problem of Reorganizing," *Items of Interest*, XXX (Dec., 1908), 958–961.

39. Harvey J. Burkhart to the Editor, "Proposed Reorganization," *Items of Interest*, XXXI (Mar., 1909), 214–216.

40. Arthur D. Black to the Editor, "Problem of Reorganizing," *Items of Interest*, XXX (Dec., 1908), 958–961. See also G. V. Black to the Editor, "Problem of Reorganizing," *Items of Interest*, XXX (Nov., 1908), 875; R. Ottolengui, Editorial, "Reorganization Proposed for N.D.A.," *ibid.*, XXX (Sept., 1908), 710.

41. R. Ottolengui, Editorial, "Proposed Reorganization of N.D.A.," *Items of Interest*, XXXI (Jan., 1909), 60–61. Ottolengui mentioned the figures in an editorial, "Proposed Reorganization of N.D.A.," *Items of Interest*, XXXI (Oct., 1909), 781–782.

42. R. Ottolengui, Editorial, "Reorganization Proposed for N.D.A.," *Items of Interest*, XXX (Sept., 1908), 710.

CHAPTER XVI

1. Editorial, "Reorganization," *DCosmos*, L (Oct., 1908), 1136–1138.

2. V. E. Turner, "President's Address," *Trans.NDA* (1909), 15–16.

3. "Minutes," *Trans.NDA* (1909), 3–4; "Minutes of Executive Council," *ibid.*, 13; "Minutes of Executive Council," *ibid.* (1910), 22; "List of Members," *ibid.*, App., 330–340.

4. "Minutes of Executive Council," *Trans.NDA* (1909), 5–6.

5. Discussion by B. Holly Smith, following James McManus, "A Sidelight on Professional Interest," *Trans.NDA* (1909), 56–57; "National Dental Association," *DCosmos*, LI (July, 1909), 859–860.

6. Discussion by Emory A. Bryant, following James McManus, "A Sidelight on Professional Interest," *Trans.NDA* (1909), 57–59.

7. S. D. Ruggles, "Phases of Improvement in Nomenclature," *Trans.NDA* (1909), 122; discussion by Emory A. Bryant, following E. C. Kirk, "The Dental Relationships of Arthritism," *ibid.*, 34; James McManus, "A Sidelight on Professional Interest," *ibid.*, 42–43, 45, 50–51.

8. Notice signed H. C. Brown, "National Dental Association," *Items of Interest*, XXXI (May, 1909), 389–390; "Minutes of Executive Council," *Trans.NDA* (1909),

9; Editorial, "Proposed Revision of the National Dental Association," *Items of Interest,* XXXI (Oct., 1909), 782–789; Editorial, "Proposed Amendments to the Constitution of the National Dental Association," *ibid.* (Sept., 1909), 716.

9. Editorial, "Proposed Reorganization of the National Dental Association," *Items of Interest,* XXXII (Jan., 1910), 71–73; "Minutes of Executive Council," *Trans.NDA* (1909), 9; Notice signed H. C. Brown, Corr. Sec., "National Dental Association," *Items of Interest,* XXXI (May, 1909), 389.

10. Editorial, "The Proposed Amendments to the Constitution of the National Dental Association," *Items of Interest,* XXXI (Sept., 1909), 715–716.

11. Editorial, "Proposed Revision of the National Dental Association," *Items of Interest,* XXXI (Oct., 1909) 782–789; L. L. Barber, Toledo, Ohio, to Homer C. Brown, Columbus, Ohio, Apr. 7, 1909, Homer C. Brown MSS. in the possession of Brig. Gen. Neal S. Harper, Columbus, Ohio; H. A. Kelley to the Editor, *Items of Interest,* XXXII (Jan., 1910), 71–73.

12. J. P. Root to the Editor, *Items of Interest,* XXXI (Nov., 1909), 883; "Minutes of the Meeting," *Trans.NDA* (1909), 3–4; Charles S. Butler, Recording Secretary, Buffalo, N. Y., to Homer C. Brown, Apr. 10, 1909; H.C.B., circular letter to The State Dental Societies (copy directed to New York State Dental Society), May 7, 1909; H. J. Burkhart, Batavia, N. Y., to H.C.B., May 18, 1909; B. Holly Smith, Baltimore, Md., to H.C.B., June 23, 1909; H.C.B. to B.H.S., June 21, 1909; C.S.B. to H.C.B., April 10, 1909, Brown MSS.

13. Homer C. Brown to B. Holly Smith, June 21, 1909; H.C.B., to Edward S. Barber, President, National Dental Guide, Chicago, Apr. 19, 1909; H.C.B. to Charles S. Butler, Albany, N. Y., May 7 and 17, 1909, Brown MSS.

14. Homer C. Brown to Charles S. Butler, May 7, 1909; C.S.B. to H.C.B., May 9, 1909, Brown MSS.

15. Homer C. Brown to Charles S. Butler, June 8, 1909; H.C.B. to Burton Lee Thorpe, St. Louis, May 28, 1910, Brown MSS.

16. "Fourteenth Annual Meeting," *Trans.NDA* (1910), 5.

17. "Fourteenth Annual Meeting," *Trans.NDA* (1910), 11; "Minutes of the Executive Council," *ibid.,* 22; "List of Members," *ibid.,* App., 330–340.

18. Burton Lee Thorpe, "President's Address," *Trans.NDA* (1910), 28.

19. "Fourteenth Annual Meeting," *Trans.NDA* (1910), 10.

20. "Minutes of Executive Council," *Trans.NDA* (1910), 14.

21. Rodrigues Ottolengui, New York, to Homer C. Brown, Dec. 17, 1910, and Mar. 27, 1911, Brown MSS.

22. Rodrigues Ottolengui to Homer C. Brown, Mar. 1, 1911, Brown MSS. See also Harvey J. Burkhart to H.C.B., Feb. 13, 1911, *ibid.*

23. Homer C. Brown to Members of the Revision and State and Local Societies Committees, Mar. 3, 1911, Brown MSS.

24. Homer C. Brown, "Reorganization of the National Dental Association," in "Proceedings of the Southern Branch," *Trans.NDA* (1911), 522–526.

25. Discussion by B. Holly Smith, following H. C. Brown, "Reorganization," in "Proceedings of the Southern Branch," *Trans.NDA* (1911), 527.

26. Homer C. Brown to Burton Lee Thorpe, Apr. 10, 1911, Brown MSS. See also H.C.B. to Harvey J. Burkhart, Apr. 20, 1911, *ibid.*

27. Discussion by J. D. Patterson and M. F. Finley following H. C. Brown, "Reorganization," in "Proceedings of the Southern Branch," *Trans.NDA* (1911), 527–528.

28. Homer C. Brown to Rodrigues Ottolengui, Apr. 27, 1911; R.O. to H.C.B., Apr. 29, 1911, Brown MSS.

29. Homer C. Brown to Otto U. King, Huntington, Ind., May 10, 1911; Rodrigues Ottolengui to H.C.B., May 11, 1911; H.C.B. to Charles S. Butler, June 23, 1911; C.S.B. to H.C.B., July 10, 1911, Brown MSS.

30. Editorial, "The National Dental Association Votes to Reorganize Along the Lines of the American Medical Association," *Items of Interest*, XXXIII (Sept., 1911), 712; Homer C. Brown to Rodrigues Ottolengui, Brant Lake, Horicon, N. Y., Aug. 8, 1911, Brown MSS.

31. Edward S. Gaylord, "President's Address," *Trans.NDA* (1911), 31.

32. "Minutes of the Executive Council," *Trans.NDA* (1911), 27; Editorial, "The National Dental Association Votes to Reorganize Along the Lines of the American Medical Association," *Items of Interest*, XXXIII (Sept., 1911), 711–715.

33. "Minutes of the Executive Council," *Trans.NDA* (1911), 27; "Fourteenth General Session," *ibid.*, 8–9.

34. "Ohio State Dental Society Meeting," *DSummary*, XXXII (Jan., 1912), 61–62.

35. Rodrigues Ottolengui to Homer C. Brown, Dec. 14, 1911, Brown MSS.

36. Homer C. Brown to Emory A. Bryant, Washington, Jan. 9, 1911 [1912]; E.A.B. to H.C.B., Jan. 11, 17, 26, Feb. 2, 22, Mar. 12, 1912; H.C.B. to E.A.B., Mar. 18 [not sent], 23, Apr. 16, 1912, Brown MSS.

37. Rodrigues Ottolengui to Homer C. Brown, Apr. 6, 1912, Brown MSS.

38. H. H. Wilson, Phoenix, to Homer C. Brown, Jan. 25, 1912; Emory A. Bryant, Washington, to H.C.B., Feb. 22, 1912; H. Janney Nichols, Secretary, Washington, to H.C.B., Mar. 19, 1912; Albert L. Midgley, Providence, to H.C.B., Apr. 4, 1912; H.C.B. to Charles S. Butler, Apr. 16, 1918, Brown MSS.

39. Homer C. Brown to Rodrigues Ottolengui, Apr. 27, 1912, R.O. to H.C.B., Apr. 16, 1912, Brown MSS.

40. Rodrigues Ottolengui to Homer C. Brown, Apr. 16, 1912; H.C.B. to R.O. and E. Gaylord, May 11, 1912, Brown MSS.

41. Arthur D. Black for the committee, Chicago, to W. M. Randall, May 20, 1912, Black MSS. in the possession of Dr. George B. Denton; Editorial, "The Peculiar Attitude of the Illinois State Dental Association towards the Reorganization of the National," *Items of Interest*, XXXIV (June, 1912), 471–472, quoting a similar letter to Otto U. King of the Indiana State Dental Society; S. C. A. Rubey, Secretary, Clinton, Mo., to Homer C. Brown, June 7, 1912, Brown MSS.

42. Editorial, "Reorganization of the National Dental Association Seems Assured," *Items of Interest*, XXXIV (May, 1912), 388–389.

43. Rodrigues Ottolengui to Homer C. Brown, May 2, 1912; R.O. and E. Gaylord, New York, to H.C.B., night letter telegram, May 10, 1912; A. P. Burkhart, Secretary, Auburn, N. Y., to H.C.B., May 29, 1912; Harvey J. Burkhart to H.C.B., May 16, 1912, Brown MSS.

44. Charles W. Rodgers, Secretary, Dorchester, Mass., to Rodrigues Ottolengui, night letter telegram, May 4, 1912 (copy); Homer C. Brown to R.O. and E. Gaylord, May 11, 1912; Arthur V. Prentis, New London, Conn., to H.C.B., May 14, 1912; George O. Mitchell, St. Albens, Vt., to H.C.B., May 18, 1912; R.O. to H.C.B., May 20, 1912, Brown MSS.

45. Resolutions regarding Reorganization of the National Dental Association Passed by the Illinois State Dental Society, May 1912, copy in Black MSS.; J.F.F.

Waltz, Decatur, Ill., to Homer C. Brown, May 21, 1912; Rodrigues Ottolengui to H.C.B., May 25, 1912, Brown MSS.; Editorial, "The Peculiar Attitude of the Illinois State Dental Society towards the Reorganization of the National," *Items of Interest,* XXXIV (June, 1912), 469–472.

46. Homer C. Brown to Rodrigues Ottolengui, May 27, 1912; H.C.B. to R.O. and E. Gaylord, May 23, 1912, Brown MSS. The phrase concerning the hat was Theodore Roosevelt's expression when he announced his candidacy for the Republican presidential nomination in 1912.

47. Homer C. Brown to R. Ottolengui and E. Gaylord, May 23, 1912; H.C.B. to Otto U. King, May 25, 1912; Rodrigues Ottolengui to H.C.B., June 5, 1912, Brown MSS.

48. Rodrigues Ottolengui to Arthur D. Black, May 28, 1912; A.D.B. to R.O. June 8, 1912; R.O. to A.D.B., June 10, 1912, Black MSS.

49. Homer C. Brown to Rodrigues Ottolengui, May 31, 1912; George T. Williams, Seattle, Wash., to H.C.B., June 5, 1912; J. D. Donahoe, Sioux Falls, S. D., to H.C.B., June 10, 1912; "Old Shot" [Frank O. Hetrick], Ottawa, Kans., to H.C.B., May 18, 1912; C. H. Kennedy, Secretary and Superintendent of District Societies, Des Moines, Ia., to H.C.B., June 11, 1912; E. N. Hegge, Hatton, N. D., to H.C.B., June 15, 1912; J. Eby, Atlanta, Ga., to H.C.B., June 17, 1912; M. M. Forbes, Atlanta, to H.C.B., June 28, 1912, Brown MSS.

50. Rodrigues Ottolengui to Arthur D. Black, June 12, 1912, Black MSS.

51. "Statement . . . Relative to the Attitude Taken by Certain Members of the Reorganization Committee" [Written on or before July 5, 1912]; Homer C. Brown to Reorganization Committee, July 9, 1912, Black MSS.

52. The "official" account of this meeting relates only the most superficial and circumstantial account of the episode. See "Meeting Relative to Reorganization of the National" [July 5, 1912], Black MSS. The tenor of the discussion can be pieced together fairly reliably from the following: Homer C. Brown to C. R. Converse, President, Ohio State Dental Society, Springfield, O., July 9, 1912 (copy); "Call for a Meeting of Representatives . . .", July 16, 1912, Black MSS.; H.C.B. to Reorganization Committee, July 9, 1912, Brown MSS.

53. Homer C. Brown to C. R. Converse, President, Ohio State Dental Society, Springfield, July 9, 1912 (copy); H.C.B. to W. D. DeLong, Otto U. King, W. M. Randall, and S.C.A. Rubey, July 11, 1912, (copy) Black MSS.

54. Rodrigues Ottolengui, Brant Lake, to Homer C. Brown, July 13, 1912, Brown MSS.

55. Arthur D. Black to S. A. Long, President, Oklahoma State Dental Society, McAllister, July 9, 1912; A.D.B. to Homer C. Brown, July 16, 1912; "Call for a Meeting of Representatives . . .", July 16, 1912, Black MSS.

56. Homer C. Brown to Arthur D. Black, July 19, 1912, Black MSS.

57. This summary is based on the information in "Report of the Meeting of Representatives . . . July 20, 1912," Black MSS. Arthur D. Black to Rodrigues Ottolengui, Brant Lake, July 22, 1912, *ibid.,* says there were thirteen men present. If so, the last man was probably a representative of Illinois.

58. Arthur D. Black to Homer C. Brown, July 22, 1912; A.D.B. to Rodrigues Ottolengui, Brant Lake, July 22, 1912, Black MSS.; Editorial, "The Present Status of Reorganization of the National Dental Association," *Items of Interest,* XXXIV (Aug., 1912), 637–638.

59. Homer C. Brown to Harvey J. Burkhart, Aug. 8, 1912; Frank L. Wright, Secretary, Wheeling, W. Va., to H.C.B., Sept. 3, 1912; W. G. Dalrymple, Ogden, Utah, to H.C.B., July 18, 1912, Brown MSS.

60. Arthur R. Melendy, "President's Address," *Trans.NDA* (1912), 47–48; "Sixteenth Annual Meeting," *ibid.*, 9–10; "The National Dental Association Reorganizes," *Western DJ*, XXIV (Nov., 1912), 32, 34, 36 (from *Items of Interest*); Alonzo M. Nodine, "The National Dental Association Meeting, Washington, D. C., Sept., 1912," *DDigest*, XVIII (Nov., 1912), 628; "Constitution and By-Laws," *Trans.NDA* (1912), App., 355.

61. "Constitution and By-Laws," *Trans.NDA* (1912), App., 355; Homer C. Brown to Harvey J. Burkhart, Oct. 1912, Brown MSS.; Rodrigues Ottolengui, Brant Lake, to Arthur D. Black, Aug. 9, 1912, Black MSS.

62. "Minutes of Executive Council," *Trans.NDA* (1912), 35, 37–39; "Sixteenth Annual Meeting," *Trans.NDA* (1912), 14, 15, 16.

63. "Constitution and By-Laws," *Trans.NDA* (1912), 354.

64. "Constitution of the National Dental Association," *Trans.NDA* (1910), App., 344.

65. "Constitution and By-Laws," *Trans.NDA* (1912), App., 354, 355.

66. "Constitution and By-Laws," *Trans.NDA* (1912), App., 355.

67. "Constitution and By-Laws," *Trans.NDA* (1912), App., 354.

68. Editorial, "The Washington Meeting," *DCosmos*, LIV (Oct., 1912) 1171–1172; Editorial, "The Revised Constitution and By-Laws of the National Dental Association," *DBrief*, XVII (Nov., 1912), 837 (The document itself is printed *ibid.*, pp. 850–866); Editorial, "The Washington Meeting," *DCosmos*, LIV (Nov., 1912), 1171–1173; "Reorganization of the National Association," *Monthly Bulletin of the Illinois State Dental Society*, VIII (Oct., 1912), 2–4.

69. Arthur D. Black, to Rodrigues Ottolengui, Dec. 14, 1912, Black MSS.; "Reorganization of the National Association," *Monthly Bulletin of the Illinois State Dental Society*, VIII (Oct., 1912), 2–4; "Reorganization of the National Association," *ibid.*, (Nov. 1912), 1; "What Illinois Should Do," and "Reorganization of the National Association," *ibid.*, (Dec., 1912), 2–3, 3–4. At the annual meeting, Arthur D. Black reported that "every Society Component to the State Society had voted upon the proposition, and every society had voted in favor of joining [the National Dental Association] in a body." "The Peoria Meeting," *Monthly Bulletin of the Illinois State Dental Society*, IX (May, 1913), 2.

CHAPTER XVII

1. Homer C. Brown, Columbus, to Harvey J. Burkhart, Batavia, Nov. 5, 1912, Brown MSS.

2. Homer C. Brown to Dr. and Mrs. Burton L. Thorpe, St. Louis, Nov. 11, 1912, Brown MSS.

3. Homer C. Brown to Arthur D. Black, Chicago, Oct. 22, 1912, Black MSS.; H.C.B. to Dr. and Mrs. Burton L. Thorpe, Nov. 11, 1912, Brown MSS.; MS. note headed "File under Weston A. Price," undated [Sept. 13, 1912] (on The New Willard Hotel stationary); Weston A. Price, Cleveland, to Homer C. Brown, Nov. 6, 1912; W.A.P. to H.C.B., Nov. 22, 1912; and H.C.B. to W.A.P., Dec. 10, 1912, Brown MSS.

4. Homer C. Brown to Arthur D. Black, Oct. 22, 1912, Black MSS.; H.C.B. to Harvey J. Burkhart, Oct. 23, 1912, Brown MSS.

5. Homer C. Brown to Arthur D. Black, Oct. 22, 1912, Black MSS.; H.C.B. to Rodrigues Ottolengui, New York, Oct. 22, 1912; H.C.B. to Harvey J. Burkhart, Oct. 23, 1912, Brown MSS.

6. Homer C. Brown to Rodrigues Ottolengui, Oct. 22, 1912; R.O. to H.C.B., Oct. 25, 1912; Harvey J. Burkhart to H.C.B., Oct. 22, 1912, Brown MSS.

7. Homer C. Brown to Rodrigues Ottolengui, Oct. 31, 1912; R.O. to H.C.B., Nov. 11, 1912, Brown MSS.

8. Arthur D. Black to Homer C. Brown, Dec. 17, 1912, Black MSS.

9. Homer C. Brown to Arthur D. Black, Dec. 9, 1912, Brown MSS.

10. Arthur D. Black to Homer C. Brown, Dec. 17, 1912, Black MSS.

11. Homer C. Brown to Burton L. Thorpe, Jan. 7, 1913, Brown MSS.

12. Homer C. Brown to Frank O. Hetrick, Ottawa, Kans., Jan. 24, 1912, Brown MSS.

13. "The Reorganization of the National Dental Association," enclosed in Homer C. Brown to Reorganization Committee, Jan. 23, 1913, Brown MSS.

14. Homer C. Brown to Arthur D. Black, Jan. 24, 1913, Black MSS.

15. Arthur D. Black to Homer C. Brown, Jan. 28, 1913, Black MSS.

16. "Statement Relative to the Transition Period," [Ca. Jan. 30, 1913], Black MSS.

17. "To the Representatives . . . at the Chicago Conference in July, 1912," [Ca. Feb. 1, 1913], Black MSS.

18. Homer C. Brown to Frank O. Hetrick, Feb. 5, 1913, Brown MSS.

19. Homer C. Brown to Arthur D. Black and others at the Chicago Conference, Feb. 5, 1913, Black MSS.

20. Rodrigues Ottolengui to Arthur D. Black, Feb. 6, 1913, Black MSS.

21. Otto U. King, Huntington, Ind., to Arthur D. Black, Feb. 6, 1913, Black MSS. See also Homer C. Brown to O.U.K., Feb. 7, 1913, Brown MSS.

22. S.C.A. Rubey, Warrenboro, Mo., to Arthur D. Black, Feb. 6, 1913, Black MSS.; Roscoe H. Volland, Iowa City, to A.D.B., Feb. 7, 1913, Black MSS.

23. F. J. Yerke, Minneapolis, to Arthur D. Black, Feb. 20, 1913, Black MSS.

24. Homer C. Brown to Arthur D. Black, Mar. 6, 1913, Black MSS.

25. Marcus L. Ward, Ann Arbor, to Arthur D. Black, Feb. 8, 1913, Black MSS.; George C. Bowles, Detroit, to A.D.B., Feb. 10, 1913, Black MSS.

26. Arthur D. Black to Marcus L. Ward, Feb. 17, 1913; M.L.W. to A.D.B., Feb. 24, Mar. 5, 1913; G. C. Bowles to A.D.B., Feb. 26, 1913, Black MSS.

27. Homer C. Brown to Reorganization Committee, Feb. 6, 1913; H.C.B. to "My dear Doctors," Feb. 15, 1913, Brown MSS.; "List of Questions Submitted to the National Dental Association Officers, Executive Committee, Executive Council, and Reorganization Committee," [Ca. Feb. 6, 1913]; Homer C. Brown to _____, Feb. 13, 1913, Black MSS. There is a tabulation of the responses to the former series of questions in the Brown MSS.

28. Homer C. Brown to Arthur D. Black, Feb. 14, 1913, Black MSS.

29. Arthur D. Black to Homer C. Brown, Feb. 15, 1913, Brown MSS.

30. Homer C. Brown to Frank O. Hetrick, Feb. 7, 1913; F.O.H. to H.C.B., Feb. 13, 1913, Brown MSS. For an example of Hetrick's peacemaking efforts, see F.O.H. to Arthur D. Black, Feb. 6, 1913, Black MSS.

31. Mark F. Finley, Washington, to Homer C. Brown, Feb. 18, 1913; H.C.B. to M.F.F., Feb. 19, 1913, Brown MSS.

32. Mark F. Finley to Homer C. Brown, Mar. 11, 1913; H.C.B. to Cameron A. Hawley, Washington, Mar. 12, 1913, Brown MSS.

33. Harvey J. Burkhart to Homer C. Brown, Feb. 15, 16, 1913; B. Holly Smith, Baltimore, to H.C.B., Feb. 18, 1913, Brown MSS.

34. Frank O. Hetrick to Homer C. Brown, Mar. 4, 1913; H.C.B. to F.O.H., Mar. 7, 1913; F.O.H. to H.C.B., Mar. 13, 1913, Brown MSS.

35. Harvey J. Burkhart to Homer C. Brown, Mar. 12, Apr. 14, 1913; Frank O. Hetrick to H.C.B., Apr. 14, 1913, Brown MSS.

36. Arthur D. Black to Homer C. Brown, Apr. 18, 1913; H.C.B. to Harvey J. Burkhart, Apr. 26, 1913, Brown MSS.

37. Harvey J. Burkhart to Homer C. Brown, Apr. 27, 1913; Frank O. Hetrick to H.C.B., May 12, 1913; Arthur D. Black to H.C.B., undated; H.C.B. to Rodrigues Ottolengui, May 15, 1913; R.O. to H.C.B., May 17, 1913; H.C.B. to R.O., May 19, 1913, Brown MSS.

38. "The Peoria Meeting," *Monthly Bulletin of the Illinois State Dental Society,* IX (May, 1913), 2; "National Dental Association," *ibid.* (Sept., 1913), 3–4; Homer C. Brown to Burton L. Thorpe, May 23, 1913; B.L.T. to H.C.B., June 2, 1913, Brown MSS.

39. Homer C. Brown to Burton L. Thorpe, June 3, 1913; B.L.T. to H.C.B., June 6, 1913; H.C.B. to B.L.T., June 10, 1913; B.L.T. to H.C.B., June 16, 1913; H.C.B. to B.L.T., June 25, 1913; Harvey J. Burkhart to H.C.B., May 27, 1913, Brown MSS.

40. "Seventeenth Annual Meeting," *Trans.NDA* (1913), 4–5.

41. Frank O. Hetrick, "President's Address," *Trans.NDA* (1913), 41–42; "Report of Committee on President's Address" in "Seventeenth Annual Meeting," *Trans.NDA* (1913), 5.

42. Weston A. Price, "Report of Committee on Scientific Foundation Fund," in "Seventeenth Annual Meeting," *Trans.NDA* (1913), 6–10.

43. "Executive Council," *Trans.NDA* (1913), 19–27.

44. "House of Delegates," *Trans.NDA* (1913), 31, 32.

45. Homer C. Brown to Weston A. Price, Cleveland, July 19, 1913; A. P. Burkhart, Auburn, N.Y., to H.C.B., July 26, 1913; H.C.B. to A.P.B., July 30, 1913; H.C.B. to Rodrigues Ottolengui, July 16, 1913, Brown MSS.

46. "House of Delegates," *Trans.NDA* (1913), 37.

47. "House of Delegates," *Trans.NDA* (1913), 33–35, 36, 37–38; Otto U. King to Homer C. Brown, Aug. 7, 1913, Brown MSS.

48. "Board of Trustees," *Trans.NDA* (1913), 40.

49. Editorial, "The National Dental Association, 1913 Meeting," *DBrief,* XVIII (Aug., 1913), 568–571; Editorial, "Reorganization of the National Dental Association," *Items of Interest,* XXXV (Aug., 1913), 627–629; "National Dental Association," *Monthly Bulletin of the Illinois State Dental Society,* IX (Sept., 1913), 3–4.

50. Otto U. King to Homer C. Brown, Sept. 15, 27, 1913, (two letters of the same date), Oct. 2, 18, 21, Nov. 23, 1913, Jan. 24, 1914, Brown MSS.

51. Edward S. Gaylord, New Haven, to Homer C. Brown, Nov. 7, 27, 1913; H.C.B. to E.S.G., Dec. 20, 1913, Brown MSS.; Editorial, "National Dental Association Relief Fund," *Items of Interest,* XXXV (Dec., 1913), 946–947; "An Appeal for the National Relief Fund," *Official Bull. of the National Dental Association,* I (Nov., 1913), 13–14; "Proceedings of the House of Delegates," *Trans.NDA* (1914), 33–34.

52. Weston A. Price to Homer C. Brown, Oct. 9, 1913; The Scientific Foundation and Research Commission Report of Progress, Oct., 18, 1913; W.A.P. to H.C.B., Oct. 24, 1913; W.A.P. to Members of the Commission, Dec. 17, 1913, Brown MSS.; "The Scientific Foundation and Research Commission," *Official Bull. of the National Dental Association,* I (Nov., 1913), 15–18; "The Scientific Foundation and Research Commission Report," *ibid.* (June, 1914), 30–33; "General Session," *Trans.NDA* (1914), 7–9.

53. Homer C. Brown, "President's Address," *Official Bull. of the National Dental Association,* I (Oct., 1914), 3–13.

54. "Report of Committee on President's Address," in "Proceedings of the House of Delegates," *Trans.NDA* (1914), 18–20.

55. "Proceedings of the House of Delegates," *Trans.NDA* (1914), 17, 28, 29, 30.

CHAPTER XVIII

1. Membership information abounds in the *Transactions*. The following citations contain figures covering periods up to five years. "Report of the General Secretary," "House of Delegates," *Trans.NDA* (1920), 41–42; "Report of the General Secretary, Schedule O," in "House of Delegates," *Trans.ADA* (1925), 72; "Treasurer's Report, Schedule 31," *ibid.* (1930), 144; "Secretary's Report," in "House of Delegates," *ibid.* (1935), 136. There are discrepancies among the various sources as to the total membership in any given year. This difficulty arises from the use of different base dates and from the inclusion of different categories of membership. Dr. George B. Denton, a research associate of the American Dental Association, has compiled an authoritative table based on information in the files of the Council on Membership.

2. "Board of Trustees," *Trans.ADA* (1926), 142.

3. See Henry L. Banzhaf, "President's Address to the House of Delegates," and "Report of the Committee on Officers' Reports," in "House of Delegates," *Trans.ADA* (1927), 45, 172.

4. For change of the Association's name cf. p. 351.

5. "House of Delegates," *Trans.ADA* (1931), 130–131, 237.

6. Martin Dewey, "President's Address," and "President's Report to the House of Delegates," *Trans.ADA* (1932), 8–9, 177–178.

7. "House of Delegates," *Trans.ADA* (1932), 329–333, 351–354, 357.

8. "Report of the Committee on Organization and Membership," in "House of Delegates," *Trans.ADA* (1933), 284–287; G. Walter Dittmar, "The Indiana Plan," *Illinois Dental Journal,* II (Nov. 1932), 105–108. (The same article may be found in a number of other dental periodicals of similar date); "Board of Trustees Meeting, Feb. 5, 1933," *Trans.ADA* (1933), 63–64.

9. "Board of Trustees Meeting, Aug., 1933," *Trans.ADA* (1933), 118–119.

10. "Board of Trustees Meeting, Aug., 1933," *Trans.ADA* (1933), 134–135.

11. "House of Delegates," *Trans.ADA* (1933), 344–345, 370–371, 375–377; "Report of the Committee on Organization and Membership," *ibid.,* 287.

12. Homer C. Brown, "President's Address," *Official Bulletin of The National Dental Association,* I (Oct., 1914), 3–4.

13. "Board of Trustees, Aug., 1933," *Trans.ADA* (1933), 139; "House of Delegates," *ibid.,* 371.

14. Based on the statistics compiled by Dr. George B. Denton, and corrected and verified from the files of the Council on Membership.

15. "Proceedings of the House of Delegates," *Trans.ADA* (1922), 37–39, 41.

16. "President's Annual Report," in "House of Delegates," *Trans.ADA* (1935), 125. The House adopted the recommendations, *ibid.,* 274.

17. "President's Annual Report," in "House of Delegates," *Trans.ADA* (1935), 117.

18. "Report of Committee on Survey," in "Board of Trustees," *Trans.ADA* (1935), 95–96.

19. "Report of Committee on Rules and Regulations of the Board," in "Board of Trustees," *Trans.ADA* (1935), 106–107; "Board of Trustees," *ibid.* (1936), 97–98.

20. "House of Delegates," *Trans.ADA* (1942), 307–310.

21. For the draft constitution and discussion stemming from its submission, see "Board of Trustees," *Trans.ADA* (1946), 336–339; "Supplemental Report of the Committee on Constitutional and Administrative ByLaws," in "House of Delegates," *ibid.*, 325; "Statement of the Board of Trustees," *JADA*, XXXIV (Jan., 1947), 39; "Report of the Committee on Constitutional and Administrative By-Laws," *Trans.ADA* (1947), 35–37, 68–69; "Report of Board of Trustees," *ibid.*, 185.

22. "Resolution on Changes in Procedure and Size of the House of Delegates," in "House of Delegates," *Trans.ADA* (1946), 287; "Board of Trustees," *ibid.* (1947), 286; Constitution of the American Dental Association, Art. V, sec. 10 and Bylaws, Ch. VII, Sec. 80D; Percy T. Phillips of New York in "Report of Committee on Constitution and Bylaws," "House of Delegates," *ibid.* (1948), 232, reminded the House of the existence of the standing resolution. References on the long history of the idea of a speakership of the House may be found in *Digest of Official Actions* (1922–1946), 58.

23. Bylaws, Ch. V, sec. 140; Ch. IX. Changes in the various standing committees, or councils, may be readily traced in *Digest of Official Actions* (1922–1946) and *ibid.* (1946–1953).

24. Constitution, Art. IV, sec. 20; Bylaws, Ch. VI.

25. "House of Delegates," *Trans.ADA* (1927), 147, 166; "House of Delegates," *ibid.* (1926), 93.

26. "Board of Trustees," *Trans.ADA* (1925), 220, 223.

27. "House of Delegates," *Trans.ADA* (1927), 183.

28. "House of Delegates," *Trans.ADA* (1946), 312–314; Bylaws, Ch. VIII, sec. 40A.

29. "Board of Trustees," *Trans.ADA* (1946), 352; Bylaws, Ch. VIII, sec. 40A.

30. Bylaws, Ch. VIII, sec. 40B, sec. 40C.

31. Gardner P. H. Foley and Marion W. McCrea, "Periodical Literature," *JADA*, XL (June, 1950), 772, 773.

32. Henry L. Banzhaf, "President's Address to the House of Delegates," *Trans.ADA* (1927), 48; "House of Delegates," *ibid.*, 173, 191.

33. "Board of Trustees," *Trans.ADA* (1942), 33; "Board of Trustees," *ibid.* (1947), 263; "House of Delegates," *ibid.*, 242; "Board of Trustees," *ibid.* (1948), 290–291, 322. For earlier moves toward a semi-monthly schedule for *JADA* see *Digest of Official Actions* (1922–1946), 287–288.

34. G. P. H. Foley and M. W. McCrea, "Periodical Literature," *JADA*, XL (June, 1950), 782.

35. For the rudiments of the American Dental Association abstracting service, see the reviews of current literature in *JADA* beginning in 1945; Harold Hillenbrand, "Editor's Report," in "Board of Trustees," *Trans.ADA* (1945), 118.

36. In addition to the publications issuing from the office of the Editor, the Association publishes a number of periodicals relating to special fields of interest: The Bureau of Public Information's *News Letter,* the Council on Dental Health's quarterly *Highlights,* the Council on Legislation's monthly *Bulletin,* and the Bureau of Membership Records' annual *American Dental Directory.*

37. See above, Ch. xiii, p. 234 for the background of the period.

38. A. Hunter Dupree, *Science in the Federal Government* (Cambridge, Mass.: Belknap Press of Harvard University Press, 1957), 178–180.

39. A. H. Dupree, *Science in the Federal Government,* 271–277.

40. See, e.g., "House of Delegates," *Trans.ADA* (1932), 347–348. The Bureau of Standards program is treated below, Ch. xix, p. 397.

41. "House of Delegates," *Trans.ADA* (1922), 87–88, 123; "House of Delegates," *ibid.* (1925), 57–58, 99–105, 143, 146.

42. The laboratory was originally operated under a cooperative arrangement with the American Medical Association. See "House of Delegates," *Trans.ADA* (1926), 62–65; Henry L. Banzhaf, "President's Address," *ibid.* (1927), 17–18; "House of Delegates," *ibid.,* 50, 171, 176–177; Roscoe H. Volland, "President's Address," *ibid.* (1928), 47; H. B. Pinney, "Report of the Secretary," in "House of Delegates," *ibid.,* 57. In 1931, the laboratory was brought under the American Dental Association roof. See *Trans.ADA* (1931), 140. A special committee began supervision of the work in January, 1930. See "House of Delegates," *Trans.ADA* (1929), 148, 174–175, 252, 264, and the committee report in "Board of Trustees," *ibid.* (1930), 34–37. The present Council on Dental Therapeutics dates from a constitutional amendment adopted in 1933. See "House of Delegates," *ibid.* (1933), 49, 132, 139, 346, 366.

43. Occasionally, the Board of Trustees used its authority over the contents of the Journal to exercise censorship on the reports of the Council. See "Board of Trustees," *Trans.ADA* (1929), 217; "House of Delegates," *ibid.* (1931), 101, 116, 174–175; "Board of Trustees," *ibid.* (1934), 147–148. For Dewey's remarks, see "President's Report," *ibid.* (1932), 183–184. Claridge's comment is in "Board of Trustees," *ibid.;* 43.

44. For action supporting the laboratory and the Council, see the resolution adopted by the Section on Histology, Physiology, Pathology, Bacteriology and Chemistry (Research), in *Trans.ADA* (1930), 24; the House resolution in "House of Delegates," *ibid.,* 259. Two moves rejecting suspension of the work are "Board of Trustees," *ibid.* (1932), 112; "House of Delegates," *ibid.* (1933), 318, 319, 349. One example of demands for publication of the Council's reports is the resolution of the American Association of Dental Schools in "Report of the Council on Dental Therapeutics," *ibid.* (1932), 415. See also "House of Delegates," *ibid.* (1946), 294.

45. A committee composed of Arthur Black, Chairman, J. N. Crouse, E. M. Robbins, C. R. E. Koch, and J. W. Cormany prepared the *Historical Booklet of the Illinois Dental Society . . . 1865–1914, With Classified Index of all Papers, Discussions and Clinics, and Personal Index of Administration, Papers, Discussions, and Clinics as Published in the Transactions of the Society* (Chicago, 1914).

46. Cf. Preface, *Index to Dental Literature,* 1939–41 (A.D.A., 1943), 5.

47. "Secretary's Report," in "House of Delegates," *Trans.ADA* (1927), 82–84.

48. "Annual Report of the Treasurer," in "Board of Trustees," *Trans.NDA* (1920), 102–106; "Report of General Secretary," in "House of Delegates," *Trans.ADA* (1925), 63–72; "Treasurer's Report," *ibid.* (1930), 117–144; "Report of Audit," *ibid.* (1940), 139–180; "Relief Fund Audit," *ibid.* (1950), 327–340.

49. "Report of Council on Relief," *Trans.ADA* (1956), 95; *ibid.* (1925), 91; *ibid.* (1926), 150; *ibid.* (1937), 128–130; Louis M. Cruttenden, "A.D.A. Relief Fund: A Voice in the Wilderness?", a Mimeographed paper read before the annual meeting of the California State Dental Association, 1958. Dr. Cruttenden is Assistant Secretary of the American Dental Association.

50. Louis M. Cruttenden, "A.D.A. Relief Fund: A Voice in the Wilderness?", a Mimeographed paper read before the annual meeting of the California State Dental Association, 1958.

51. "House of Delegates," *Trans.ADA* (1929), 92, 222, 248; "House of Delegates," *ibid.* (1935), 83, 252, 290–291: "Board of Trustees," *ibid.* (1952), 200, 210.

52. "Report of Committee on Legislation," *Trans.ADA* (1948), 86, 87, 88–89.

53. "Supplemental Report of Council on Legislation," *Trans.ADA* (1949), 97.

54. "House of Delegates," *Trans.ADA* (1949), 265–266.

55. "Board of Trustees," *Trans.ADA* (1951), 210.

56. Both Hawaii's and Massachusett's delegations urged adherence to the original policy. "House of Delegates," *Trans.ADA* (1951), 186–187; *ibid.* (1952), 179. The Massachusetts Dental Society asked that the American Dental Association establish no policy until the membership had been polled, "House of Delegates," *ibid.*, 179–180; "House of Delegates," *ibid.* (1953), 223–224.

57. Lon W. Morrey, "Inclusion of Dentists in OASI up to the Senate," *JADA*, XLIX (July, 1954), 84, quoting from Council on Legislation, "Association Testifies on OASI," *ibid.* (May, 1954), 565.

58. "Reference Committee on Insurance," in "House of Delegates," *Trans.ADA* (1955), 205–207.

59. "House of Delegates," *Trans.ADA* (1926), 68–69; "Report of the Committee on Legislation," in "House of Delegates," *ibid.* (1927), 98.

60. "House of Delegates," *Trans.ADA* (1931), 190–191, 233; "House of Delegates," *ibid.* (1930), 57.

61. "House of Delegates," *Trans.ADA* (1935), 320–325. For earlier discussion and changes in the Committee's composition and function, see "Report of the President," in "House of Delegates," *Trans.ADA* (1932), 180–182; *ibid.*, 349–351; "House of Delegates," *ibid.* (1934), 305–308, 338–339, 340–341.

62. "House of Delegates," *Trans.ADA* (1935), 283–287; the address by Judge Lawrence T. Harris in "General Meeting," *ibid.* (1936), 20–28; George B. Winter, "President's Annual Report to the House of Delegates," *ibid.*, 142–143. The Supreme Court opinion in the Semler case, which was written by Chief Justice Charles Evans Hughes, contained the latter's famous definition of professional ethics: "What is generally called the 'ethics' of the profession is but the consensus of expert opinion as to the necessity of such standards." (Harry Semler, Appellant *vs.* Oregon State Board of Dental Examiners, L. A. Rosenthal, Leonard R. Andrews, *et al.* 294 U.S. 608 [1935].)

63. Homer C. Brown, "A Resume of Fifteen Years of Federal Legislative Activity," in "House of Delegates," *Trans.ADA* (1939), 87; H. C. Brown, "Legislation as a Factor in Professional Advancement," *JADA*, XXI (July, 1934), 1192–1193.

64. "Report of the Committee on Legislation and Correlation" in "House of Delegates," *Trans.ADA* (1934), 220–221; Francis J. Garvey, "Dentistry and the Legislative Process," *JADA*, XL (June, 1950), 747–748. On the tariff, see, e.g., "House of Delegates," *Trans.ADA* (1922), 68–69, 86–87; *ibid.* (1923), 123; *ibid.* (1925), 88–89; *ibid.* (1929), 87–88.

65. In addition to the dental corps of the armed services, the Public Health Service, the Veterans Administration, the Indian Bureau, and the Civilian Conservation Corps all employed dentists.

66. George F. Jeffcott, *A History of the United States Army Dental Service in World War II,* (Washington: Government Printing Office, 1955), 6. The Navy has no official history for dentistry.

67. Jeffcott, *Army Dental Service,* 3, 22.

68. "House of Delegates," *Trans.ADA* (1931), 266–267; "Report of the Committee on Legislation," in "House of Delegates," *ibid.* (1932), 238, 246; "Report of Commit-

tee on Legislation and Correlation," in *ibid.* (1933), 242. On Fairbank's appointment, see "Board of Trustees," *ibid.* (1938), 129. As early as 1926, Congress provided that officers of the Dental Corps of the Navy might attain the rank of captain, but not until 1936 did anyone receive that rank. In 1942, the grade of rear admiral was established. The first appointment to that rank went to A. G. Lyle in 1943. See "Dentistry in the Navy," *DItems of Interest*, LXVI (Oct., 1944), 980ff; "Dental Care in the Navy," *JADA*, XXXII (Mar. 1, 1945), 346; "Present Status of Dentistry in the Armed Forces: A Report from the Committee on Legislation," *ibid.* XXXI (Feb. 1, 1944), 270–277; "Improvement in the Administrative Status of the Navy Dental Corps," *ibid.*, XXXIV (Mar. 1, 1947), 365.

69. See, e.g., "Report of the Committee on Dental Legislation," in "House of Delegates," *Trans.ADA* (1931), 189; *ibid.* (1932), 243; "Report of the Committee on Legislation and Correlation," in *ibid.* (1934), 222–223, 224.

70. "Board of Trustees," *Trans.ADA* (1938), 75.

71. "Board of Trustees," *Trans.ADA* (1940), 38–43; "President's Page," *JADA*, XXVIII (June, 1941), 982; G. F. Jeffcott, *Dental Service in World War II*, 83–84.

72. Initially known as the Committee on National Defense, it was soon termed the Committee on Dental Preparedness. In 1942, its name was changed to the War Service Committee and in 1944 it was renamed the War Service and Post War Planning Committee; Report of Military Affairs Committee in "Board of Trustees," *Trans.ADA* (1940), 87–89; Report of the Special Committee in *ibid.*, 108–110; Report of the Committee on National Defense in "House of Delegates," *ibid.*, 235–264; Report of Reference Committee ǒn National Defense in *ibid.*, 317–318; "Committee on Dental Preparedness," *JADA*, XXVII (Oct., 1940), 1658; G. F. Jeffcott, *Dental Service in World War II*, 78, 84.

73. "Committee on Dental Preparedness," *JADA*, XXVII (Dec., 1940), 1970–1977; "Questionnaire Information," *ibid.*, XXVIII (Feb., 1941), 331–332; "Report of Committee on Dental Preparedness" in "House of Delegates," *Trans.ADA* (1941), 268–297; G. F. Jeffcott, *Dental Service in World War II*, 70.

74. Report of Committee on Dental Preparedness in "House of Delegates," *Trans.ADA* (1941), 268–297; G. F. Jeffcott, *Dental Service in World War II*, 51–53.

75. "Board of Trustees," *Trans.ADA* (1941), 65; *ibid.* (1942), 46–47; G. F. Jeffcott, *Dental Service in World War II*, 53.

76. "Procurement and Assignment Agency," *JADA*, XXVIII (Dec. 1941), 2026–2030; G. F. Jeffcott, *Dental Service in World War II*, 78.

77. G. F. Jeffcott, *Dental Service in World War II*, 78, 85, 95.

78. G. F. Jeffcott, *Dental Service in World War II*, 6–7 and sources there cited.

79. The controversy is reviewed in Harold Hillenbrand, Editorial, "The Right to 'Gripe': The Fifth Freedom," *JADA*, XXXIII (Jan. 1, 1946), 118–122; Editorial, "Dental Officers Pay Again," *ibid.* (June, 1, 1946), 755–757; G. F. Jeffcott, *Dental Service in World War II*, 74, 339–341. Jeffcott insists that while the December, 1945, ratio was indeed 2.23 dentists per thousand men, if those dentists separated in January, 1946, had left during the preceding month, the ratio would have been 1.7 per thousand—less than actual need.

80. See, e.g., "Council on Federal Government Dental Services," *Trans.ADA* (1950), 74–77; "Board of Trustees," *ibid.*, 219, 242; "House of Delegates," *ibid.* (1951), 186.

81. See Leigh C. Fairbank, "Prosthetic Dental Service for the Army in Peace and War," *JADA*, XXVIII (May, 1941), 798–802; "Committee on Dental Preparedness," *ibid.* (Apr., 1941), 636–638; "Report of the National Health Program Committee" in "Board of Trustees," *Trans.ADA* (1941), 71–75; G. F. Jeffcott, *Dental Service in World War II*, 199–216, 225–229.

CHAPTER XIX

1. See above, Ch. xiv, pp. 262–266.

2. William J. Gies, *Dental Education in the United States and Canada; Bulletin 19* of the Carnegie Foundation for the Advancement of Teaching (New York: The Foundation, 1926), 54–55.

3. Harlan H. Horner, *Dental Education Today* (Chicago: University of Chicago Press, 1947), 5–8.

4. "House of Delegates," *Trans.ADA* (1922), 100; W. J. Gies, *Dental Education in the U.S. and Canada*, 53–54; and H. H. Horner, *Dental Education Today*, 8.

5. W. J. Gies, *Dental Education in the U.S. and Canada*, 53–54; and H. H. Horner, *Dental Education Today*, 8.

6. The January actions at Omaha were confirmed at a meeting in Cleveland in September, 1923. See W. J. Gies, *Dental Education in the U.S. and Canada*, 52–53.

7. "House of Delegates," *Trans.ADA* (1926), 67; H. H. Horner, *Dental Education Today*, 8–9.

8. For bibliographical data on Gies's report, see above, n 2.

9. W. J. Gies, *Dental Education in the U.S. and Canada*, 239–240.

10. See, e.g., Henry L. Banzhaf, "President's Address," *Trans.ADA* (1927), 11–23, *passim*, and especially 15–16 and 18–20; "House of Delegates," *ibid.*, 43–44, 168, 172; Martin Dewey, "President's Address," *ibid.* (1932), 6.

11. W. J. Gies, *Dental Education in the U.S. and Canada*, 239–240.

12. H. H. Horner, *Dental Education Today*, 54.

13. H. H. Horner, *Dental Education Today*, 54, quoting Gies's remarks before the National Association of Dental Faculties, January, 1923.

14. H. H. Horner, *Dental Education Today*, 5–8.

15. W. J. Gies, *Dental Education in the United States and Canada*, 111–113.

16. "House of Delegates," *Trans.ADA* (1925), 162.

17. "House of Delegates," *Trans.ADA* (1931), 118–119, 252–253; H. H. Horner, *Dental Education Today*, 9.

18. Martin Dewey, "President's Address," *Trans.ADA* (1932), 5–9.

19. Martin Dewey, "President's Report," *Trans.ADA* (1932) 182–183.

20. "Board of Trustees," *Trans.ADA* (1932), 160–162, 163, 169. See also, H. H. Horner, *Dental Education Today*, 9.

21. "Board of Trustees," *Trans.ADA* (1932), 45–46, 173, 366, 403–404.

22. H. H. Horner, *Dental Education Today*, 10.

23. "House of Delegates," *Trans.ADA* (1933), 146–147, 335, 375; *ibid.* (1934), 106–107, 136–137, 254–255, 309–310; H. H. Horner, *Dental Education Today*, 10–11.

24. "House of Delegates," *Trans.ADA* (1935), 287, 308–309; "Board of Trustees," *ibid.* (1936), 48; H. H. Horner, *Dental Education Today*, 10–11.

25. "House of Delegates," *Trans.ADA* (1936), 235–240, 268–275, 282–283.

26. H. H. Horner, *Dental Education Today*, 11.

27. "House of Delegates," *Trans.ADA* (1936), 251–252, 258.

28. Arthur R. McDowell, "President's Address," *Proceedings . . . of The American Association of Dental Schools* (1936), 22; *ibid.*, 214; Marcus L. Ward, "Report of The Retiring Member of The Dental Educational Council," *ibid.*, 216–221; *ibid.* (1937), 207–238, 404–415.

29. "House of Delegates," *Trans.ADA* (1937), 293, 302–304, 338–343; *ibid.* (1938), 354, 355, 356, 376, 379.

30. "House of Delegates," *Trans.ADA* (1937), 293, 302–304, 338–343; *ibid.* (1943), 366–367, 433, 467. The revised bylaws of 1948 provided for nominations by the various societies, but election by the House of Delegates. (Ch. ix, sec. 20B.) On the duties of the Council, see Bylaws, ch. ix, sec. 100C.

31. H. H. Horner, *Dental Education Today,* 15.

32. "Board of Trustees," *Trans.ADA* (1941), 62, 71, 73; H. H. Horner, *Dental Education Today,* 15.

33. "Board of Trustees," *Trans.ADA* (1945), 75, 87, 88–89.

34. The problem is discussed in W. J. Gies, *Dental Education in the U.S. and Canada,* 64–65.

35. "Proceedings of National Association of Dental Examiners," *DCosmos,* XXV (Sept., 1883), 455; H. H. Horner, *Dental Education Today,* 33–36; W. J. Gies, *Dental Education in the U.S. and Canada,* 35, 69–70, for short sketches of the history of the N.A.D.E. For examples of discussion of reciprocity and uniform licensing at the sessions of the A.D.A., see above, Ch. xii, p. 216; Ch. xiv, pp. 259–260.

36. W. J. Gies, *Dental Education in the U.S. and Canada,* 69–70.

37. "Board of Trustees," *Trans.ADA* (1924), 165, 170–171; *ibid.* (1925), 172; "House of Delegates," *ibid.,* 140; Henry L. Banzhaf, "President's Address," *ibid.* (1927), 11–23; H. L. Banzhaf, "President's Address to House of Delegates," *ibid.,* 55. For the action of the House, see "House of Delegates," *ibid.,* 57, 165, 168–169, 172.

38. Roscoe H. Volland, "President's Address," in "House of Delegates," *Trans.ADA* (1928), 50–52; "House of Delegates," *ibid.,* 145–146, 153–154.

39. "House of Delegates," *Trans.ADA* (1928), 145–146; *ibid.* (1929), 158–166; "Board of Trustees," *ibid.,* 261–262, 265; "House of Delegates," *ibid.* (1930), 245, 248, 292–293.

40. "Report of the National Board of Dental Examiners," *Proceedings of the National Association of Dental Examiners* (1935), 82.

41. *Proceedings of the National Association of Dental Examiners* (1934), 95–106. See also the resolutions of the N.A.D.E. printed in "House of Delegates," *Trans.ADA* (1936), 123.

42. "Report of Committee on Advisability of Remaining a Member of the National Board of Dental Examiners," *Proceedings of the National Association of Dental Examiners* (1935), 57–71.

43. "Minority Report by Morton H. Jones of Ohio," *Proceedings of the National Association of Dental Examiners* (1935), 72–76.

44. "Fifty-third Annual Meeting," *Proceedings of the National Association of Dental Examiners* (1935), 119–129; "Report of National Board of Dental Examiners," *ibid.,* 82; "House of Delegates," *Trans.ADA* (1936), 123.

45. "Report of National Board of Dental Examiners," in "House of Delegates," *Trans.ADA* (1935), 216–218; *ibid.,* 269.

46. The demands of the N.A.D.E. are reprinted in "Board of Trustees," *Trans.ADA* (1937), 137–138.

47. "House of Delegates," *Trans.ADA* (1937), 291–293, 337–338.

48. See reports of the Committee on National Board of Dental Examiners, "House of Delegates," *Trans.ADA* (1938), 264–265; *ibid.* (1939), 228; *ibid.* (1940), 203.

49. "Report of the Committee on National Board of Dental Examiners," in "House of Delegates," *Trans.ADA* (1941), 203.

50. Bylaws (1948), ch. ix, sec. 20C and sec. 100–0. The Board of Trustees directed the President to appoint a special committee to study the administration of the National Board in 1949. See "Board of Trustees," *Trans.ADA* (1949), 362. The special committee reported no recommendations. See "Report of Special Committee to Survey Program of National Board of Dental Examiners," in "Board of Trustees," *ibid.* (1950), 247. See reports of the Council on National Board of Dental Examiners, *ibid.*, 111; *ibid.* (1955), 108; *ibid.* (1957), 171; *ibid.* (1958), 174–176.

51. See above, Ch. xiv, p. 256. See also M. D. K. Bremner, *"The Story of Dentistry"* (Brooklyn, N.Y., Dental Items of Interest Pub. Co., 1946), 278–283; N. C. Hudson, "Process Patent Litigation" *JADA*, LVIII (June, 1959), 162.

52. N. C. Hudson, "Process Patent Litigation," *JADA*, LVIII (June, 1959), 162; and M. D. K. Bremner, *Story of Dentistry*, 284–290.

53. "Board of Trustees," *Trans.ADA* (1932), 39; M. D. K. Bremner, "A Statement of the Gift to the A.D.A. Made by the Dentists' Mutual Protective Alliance," *JADA*, XIX (June, 1932), 1035–1039; M. D. K. Bremner, *Story of Dentistry*, 292.

54. "House of Delegates," *Trans.ADA* (1943), 74–75, 149–150, 204, 367–368, 434, 467; *ibid.* (1944), 303–304, 366; By-laws (1948), ch. ix, sec. 100-M.

55. See above, Ch. vi, pp. 116–119; Ch. xi, pp. 208–211; Ch. xii, pp. 236–237.

56. See above, Ch. xvii, pp. 336, 337, 341.

57. "House of Delegates," *Trans.NDA* (1915), 396; C. T. Messner, "Aims and Accomplishments of the Research Commission," *JADA*, XXI (Sept., 1934), 1558; Homer C. Brown, "Historical Review of the Research Activities of Organized Dentistry," *ibid.*, XXII (July, 1935), 1174–1175.

58. "House of Delegates," *Trans.NDA* (1917), 70.

59. "House of Delegates," *Trans.NDA* (1920), 58; "Report of Research Commission," in "House of Delegates," *Trans.ADA* (1922), 63–66; C. T. Messner, "Aims and Accomplishments," *JADA*, XXI (Sept., 1934), 1558–1559; H. C. Brown, "Historical Review," *ibid.*, XXII (July, 1935), 1176.

60. "House of Delegates," *Trans.ADA* (1923), 83.

61. This statement is based on the summary in C. T. Messner, "Aims and Accomplishments," *JADA*, XXI (Sept., 1934), 1559. The figures seem well supported in the reports of the Research Commission. See, e.g., "Report of the Research Commission," in "House of Delegates," *Trans.ADA* (1925), 131; Roscoe H. Volland, "Report of the Secretary-Treasurer of the Research Commission," *ibid.* (1930), 172–188.

62. H. C. Brown, "Historical Review," *JADA* XXII (July, 1935), 1176, 1178; Weston A. Price, representative of the A.D.A. on the N.R.C., "Report," in "House of Delegates," *Trans.ADA* (1925), 110; A. Hunter Dupree, *Science in the Federal Government* (Cambridge: Belknap Press of Harvard University Press, 1957), 239.

63. H. C. Brown, "Historical Review," *JADA* XXII (July, 1935), 1176, contrasted achievements of dental research, supported by dentistry, with medical research, aided by philanthropists and "some of the well-known foundations." See also F. O. Hetrick's comments in "Report of Research Commission," in "House of Delegates," *Trans.ADA* (1922), 63–66.

64. F. O. Hetrick, "Report of Scientific Foundation and Research Commission," in "House of Delegates," *Trans.ADA* (1925), 115–117; Henry L. Banzhaf, "President's Address," *ibid.* (1927), 17; C. T. Messner, "Aims and Accomplishments," *JADA*, XXI (Sept., 1934), 1561; H. C. Brown, "Historical Review," *ibid.*, XXII (July, 1935), 1182–1183; Executive Board, Research Commission, "Past, Present, and Future Plans

of the Research Commission," *ibid.*, XXXV (Sept. 15, 1947), 401–402. The last citation contains the best description of the research associate arrangements at the Bureau.

65. "Report of the Research Commission," in "House of Delegates," *Trans.ADA* (1922), 63; C. T. Messner, "Aims and Accomplishments of the Research Commission," *JADA*, XXI (Sept., 1934), 1554–1555; H. C. Brown, "Historical Review," *ibid.*, XXII (July, 1935), 1177. Messner, *op. cit.*, 1559, lays particular stress on the achievements of T. B. Hartzell, A. T. Henrici, and H. J. Leonard in the study of the effects of mouth infections. He says their findings "upset the ideas of dentistry as to the further conservation of badly infected teeth."

66. Martin Dewey, "President's Address," *Trans.ADA* (1932), 5; Frank O. Hetrick, "Report of Scientific Foundation and Research Commission," in "House of Delegates," *ibid.* (1925), 115–117; Henry L. Banzhaf, "President's Address," *ibid.* (1927), 16–17; Martin Dewey, "President's Report," *ibid.* (1932), 180–181; H. C. Brown, "Historical Review," *JADA*, XXII (July, 1935), 1176.

67. "Board of Trustees," *Trans.ADA* (1935), 58–59; "House of Delegates," *ibid.*, 205–216; "Report of Research Commission," *ibid.*, 147; C. T. Messner, "Aims and Accomplishments," *JADA*, XXI (Sept., 1934), 1556, 1559; C. T. Messner, "The Research Commission," *ibid.*, XXIII (Apr., 1936), 657; P. C. Lowery, "Policies of the Research Commission," *ibid.*, XXIV (Apr., 1937), 643.

68. "Report of Research Commission," in "House of Delegates," *Trans.ADA* (1935), 205–216; H. C. Brown, "Historical Review," *JADA*, XXII (July, 1935), 1177; C. T. Messner, "The Research Commission," *ibid.*, XXIII (Apr., 1936), 657. See also C. T. Messner, "Aims and Accomplishments," *ibid.*, XXI (Sept., 1934), 1560.

69. The quotation is from "Report of Research Commission," *Trans.ADA* (1932), 138. On the early history of the National Institutes of Health, the Dental Division of the Public Health Service, and the relations of the A.D.A. with the agency, see Henry L. Banzhaf, "President's Address," *Trans.ADA* (1927), 17–18; "Report of Research Committee," *ibid.* (1932), 137–138; Executive Board, Research Commission, "Past, Present, and Future Plans," *JADA*, XXXV (Sept., 15, 1947), 414; A. H. Dupree, *Science in the Federal Government*, 365.

70. C. T. Messner, "The Research Commission," *JADA*, XXIII (Apr., 1936), 656–657; P. C. Lowery, "Policies of the Research Commission," *JADA and DCosmos*, XXIV (Apr., 1937), 643; C. T. Messner, "Aims and Accomplishments," *JADA*, XXI (Sept., 1934), 1560.

71. P. C. Lowery, "Policies of the Research Commission," *JADA and DCosmos*, XXIV (Apr., 1937), 643; "Report of Research Commission," *ibid.* (Oct., 1937), 1703; Report of Research Commission," *JADA*, XXVIII (Apr., 1941), 657, 661; "Report of Research Commission," *ibid.*, XXVIII (Nov., 1941), 1889–1891; M. D. Huff and D. F. Lynch, "Report of Research Commission," *ibid.*, XXXI (Jan., 1944), 126. The quotations are from the report in *JADA*, XXVIII (Nov., 1941), 1889–1890.

72. "Report of Research Commission," *JADA*, XXVIII (Apr., 1941), 662; *ibid.* (Nov., 1941), 1886; Executive Board, Research Commission, "Past, Present, and Future Plans," *ibid.*, XXXV (Sept. 15, 1947), 412–419.

73. See, e.g., "Report of Research Commission," *JADA*, XXIX (Oct., 1942), 1891–1896; *ibid.*, XXXI (Jan., 1944), 123–126; "Report of Audit," *Trans.ADA* (1945), 257, 270, 282; *ibid.* (1946), 64, 87; Executive Board, Research Commission, "Past, Present, and Future Plans," *JADA*, XXXV (Sept., 15, 1947), 399–419; ADA, *Report of Audit* (1957), 16–17, 24, 30; Editorial, *JADA*, LVII (Sept., 1958), 445; News item, *ibid.*, 451.

74. "House of Delegates," *Trans.ADA* (1949), 255; "Report of Council on Dental Research," *ibid.* (1952), 41; ADA, *Report of Audit* (1957), 16–17, 24, 30.

CHAPTER XX

1. See above, Ch. xiv, p. 249.

2. See the annual reports of the Committee in the *Transactions*. See also the resolutions of the Section on Mouth Hygiene and Preventive Dentistry in *Trans.ADA* (1925), 46–47; "Board of Trustees," *ibid.* (1927), 347–348, 365, 371, 378; "Board of Trustees," *ibid.* (1928), 210–211, 293; "House of Delegates," *ibid.*, 146; Raymond G. Bishop, "Dental Health Education of the Laity," *Pennsylvania DJ*, XII (May, 1945), 280; Lon W. Morrey, "New Resources for Dental Health Education," *JADA Midmonthly*, XXXII (July 15, 1945), 932.

3. "Board of Trustees," *Trans.ADA* (1922), 111, 114–123; "House of Delegates," *ibid.* (1933), 178, 317, 349; "Board of Trustees," *ibid.* (1936), 49; "Board of Trustees," *ibid.* (1938), 136, 155; "House of Delegates," *ibid.*, 300–303, 334, 335, 349–350; "House of Delegates," *ibid.* (1939), 298–310; L. W. Morrey, "New Resources," *JADA Midmonthly*, XXXII (July 15, 1945), 931.

4. The foundations were the Carnegie Corporation, the Milbank Memorial Fund, the Russell Sage Foundation, the Twentieth Century Fund, and, later, the Josiah Macy, Jr., Foundation, the Julius Rosenwald Fund, and the Rockefeller Foundation. On American Dental Association participation in these investigations, see "Board of Trustees," *Trans.ADA* (1928), 151, 163, 288, 200; "House of Delegates," *ibid.* (1930), 282–287. For appraisals of the results, see "House of Delegates," *ibid.* (1932), 135; "Report of Secretary," in "House of Delegates," *ibid.* (1933), 183; Homer C. Brown, "Report of Committee on Legislation," in "House of Delegates," *ibid.* (1934), 223–224. See also Michael M. Davis, "Status of Dentistry in our Economic System," *JADA*, XVII (May, 1930), 843–844; H. E. Phillips, "Bureau of Dental Health Education," *ibid.* (Nov., 1930), 2133–2134; Dixon Wecter, *The Age of the Great Depression, 1929–1941* (New York: Macmillan Co., 1948), 273.

5. Michael M. Davis, "Status of Dentistry in our Economic System," *JADA*, XVII (May, 1930), 843–848, and discussion, 848–850; H. E. Phillips, "Bureau of Dental Health Education," *ibid.* (Nov. 1930), 2132–2139; H. E. Phillips, "Committee on the Study of Dental Practice," *ibid.*, XVIII (Feb., 1931), 326–329; Robert T. Oliver, "President's Address," *Trans.ADA* (1931), 128–129; Dorothy F. Beck, "A Preliminary Summary of the Facts," *JADA*, XIX (Feb., 1932), 230–251; "House of Delegates," *Trans.ADA* (1933), 372–373; Homer C. Brown, "Report of Committee on Legislation," *ibid.* (1934), 223–224; "Results of a Survey. . . ." *JADA*, XVIII (Oct., 1931), 1990–1996; Editorial, "New Light on Panel Dentistry in America," *ibid.*, 1997–1999. See also, for further evidence of the importance of this new role for the Bureau of Public Relations, Frank M. Casto, "President's Report," *Trans.ADA* (1935), 115–116; "House of Delegates," *ibid.*, 273–274.

6. "Report of the Bureau of Public Relations," in "Board of Trustees," *Trans.ADA* (1938), 69–70; "House of Delegates," *ibid.*, 104; Vern D. Irwin and Netta W. Wilson, *An Evaluation of Dental Health Literature* (St. Paul: Bruce Publishing Co., 1942); Raymond G. Bishop, "Dental Health Education of the Laity," *Pennsylvania DJ*, XII (May, 1945), 281; L. W. Morrey, "New Resources for Dental Health Education," *JADA Midmonthly*, XXXII (July 15, 1945), 934–939.

7. In anticipation of the adoption of the Social Security Act of 1935, the Committee on Dental Economics enunciated a series of principles which were adopted with modifications by the House of Delegates, "House of Delegates," *Trans.ADA* (1934), 345; *ibid.* (1935), *passim;* "Board of Trustees," *ibid.* (1936), 122, 201, 286; *ibid.* (1937), 238, 344. For subsequent reaffirmations of dental health education as a device in the social program of the American Dental Association, see the eight principles of the Association's National Health Program Committee in *Trans.ADA* (1938), 326–333; "House of Delegates," *ibid.* (1944), 376–380; *ibid.* (1949), 264; *ibid.* (1956), 203; "Council on Dental Health," *ibid.* (1957), 96.

8. The figures from the American Institute of Public Opinion (Gallup) survey are quoted in American Dental Association, Bureau of Economic Research and Statistics, *Survey of Needs for Dental Care* (Chicago: The Association, 1952), 7. The AIPO release was dated June 21, 1950. See also Clayton K. Gross, "A Survey Study of Public Opinion and Education concerning Dentistry," *Oregon St. DJ*, XXV (Sept., 1955), 2–9; "Bureau of Economic Research and Statistics," Family Dental Survey: II. Frequency of Visits," *JADA*, XLVIII (Jan., 1954), table 9, p. 75.

9. Bureau of Economic Research and Statistics, "A Motivational Study of Dental Care," *JADA*, LVI (Mar., 1958), 442; Vern D. Irwin and Netta W. Wilson, "What Does the Layman Know about Dental Health," *ibid.* XXX (July, 1943), 1091.

10. V. D. Irwin and N. W. Wilson, "What Does the Layman Know," *JADA*, XXX (July, 1943), 1088–1091; Bureau of Economic Research and Statistics, "Family Dental Survey: I. Dental Health Concepts," *ibid.*, XLVII (Nov., 1953), table 6, p. 578.

11. Bureau of Economic Research and Statistics, "Family Dental Survey: II. Frequency of Visits," *JADA*, XLVIII (Jan., 1954), 74.

12. V. D. Irwin and N. W. Wilson, "What Does the Layman Know," *JADA*, XXX (July, 1943), 1088–1091; Bureau of Economic Research and Statistics, "Family Dental Survey: I. Dental Health Concepts," *ibid.*, XLVII (Nov., 1953), table 8, p. 579.

13. On the Gies report, see above, Ch. xix, pp. 378–379. The best-known of the governmental study groups were the Committee on Recent Economic Changes, and the Committee on Recent Social Trends. Among private studies perhaps the best-known was by Robert S. and H. M. Lynd, *Middletown: A Study in Contemporary American Culture* (New York: Harcourt, Brace and Co., 1929). Many features of the twenties challenged American ideals in a less formal way. The debunking biographies of George Washington and other American heroes by Woodward and others, and the irascibilities of Henry L. Mencken may serve as examples of this disturbing tendency.

14. H. E. Phillips, "Bureau of Dental Health Education," *JADA*, XVII (Nov., 1930), 2134; C. N. Johnson, editorial, "The Committee on the Costs of Medical Care," *ibid.*, (Jan., 1930), 146; H. E. Phillips, "Committee on the Study of Dental Practice," *ibid.*, XVIII (Feb., 1931), 328; M. M. Davis, "Status of Dentistry in our Economic System," *ibid.*, XVII (May, 1930), 843–848.

15. These developments may be traced in detail through the following citations: "Board of Trustees," *Trans.ADA* (1928), 151, 163, 288; Report of Committee in "Board of Trustees," *ibid.* (1929), 253–256; "Board of Trustees," *ibid.* (1930), 86–88; "House of Delegates," *ibid.*, 109–110, 259–260, 282–288; "Board of Trustees," *ibid.* (1931), 73–74, 112–113; "House of Delegates," *ibid.*, 236, 249; "Board of Trustees," *ibid.* (1933), 98–99, 144; "House of Delegates," *ibid.*, 366–367, 372–373; *ibid.* (1934), 133, 144, 323, 324, 343–344; C. N. Johnson, editorial, "The Committee on the Costs of Medical Care," *JADA*, XVII (Jan., 1930), 144–147; Francis J. Garvey, "Dentistry and the Legislative Process," *JADA*, XL (June, 1950), 748.

16. H. E. Phillips, "The Bureau of Dental Health Education," *JADA*, XVII (Nov., 1930), 2132–2139; Dorothy F. Beck, "A Preliminary Summary of the Facts," *ibid.*, XIX (Feb., 1932), 230–251; H. E. Phillips, "Final Report of the Committee," *DDigest*, XXXVIII (Dec., 1932), 424–429.

17. "Results of a Survey Conducted . . . for Ritter Dental Manufacturing Co., Inc.," *JADA*, XVIII (Oct., 1931), 1990–1996; "New Light on Panel Dentistry in America," *ibid.*, 1997–1999; G. Walter Dittmar, "The Indiana Plan," *Ill. DJ*, II (Nov., 1932), 105–108; Harold J. Noyes, "Dentistry Recognizes its Responsibilities to the Public," *JADA*, XL (June, 1950), 761.

18. "House of Delegates," *Trans.ADA* (1932), 400; Martin Dewey, "President's Address," *ibid.*, 7–8; Robert T. Oliver, "President's Report," *ibid.* (1931), 128–129;

504 *A History of the American Dental Association*

and "Results of a Survey," *JADA*, XVIII (Oct., 1931), 1990–1996. On the recommendation of the Reference Committee on Legislation, adopted by the House, a special committee was named to survey existing dental programs in state and municipal health organizations and recommend an appropriate policy for the Association. "House of Delegates," *Trans.ADA* (1932), 346.

19. Robert T. Oliver, "President's Report," *Trans.ADA* (1931), 128–129; Martin Dewey, "President's Address," *ibid.* (1932), 7–8; Report of Committee on Legislation in "House of Delegates," *ibid,* (1933), 252; Report of Committee on Legislation by Homer C. Brown in "House of Delegates," *ibid.* (1934), 223–224; "Results of a Survey," *JADA*, XVIII (Oct., 1931), 1990–1996; Harold J. Noyes, "Dentistry Recognizes its Responsibilities," *ibid.*, XL (June, 1950), 761.

20. "House of Delegates," *Trans.ADA* (1933), 67–77, 343–344, 371; H. J. Noyes, "Dentistry Recognizes its Responsibilities," *JADA*, XL (June, 1950), 763.

21. "House of Delegates," *Trans.ADA* (1934), 303, 304, 345, 347; *ibid.* (1935), 62–63, 65, 67, 226–244, 309–311; M. W. Carr, *Dentistry*, 181–185; Richard H. Shryock, *American Medical Research Past and Present* (New York: The Commonwealth Fund, 1947), 271.

22. "Board of Trustees," *Trans.ADA* (1935), 35, 51–52; Frank M. Casto, "President's Report," in "House of Delegates," *ibid.*, 115–116; "House of Delegates," *ibid.*, 226–244, 273–274, 309–311.

23. "House of Delegates," *Trans.ADA* (1935), 62–63, 65, 67, 226–244, 309–311; M. W. Carr, *Dentistry*, 181–185.

24. "House of Delegates," *Trans.ADA* (1938), 326–333. The Board of Trustees directed the Committee on Legislation to oppose placing U. S. Public Health Service "under the jurisdiction of the Social Welfare Department." The Board favored cabinet rank for a Secretary of Health, but held that at the very least the "health profession [should] direct its own service." "Board of Trustees," *ibid.*, 76; H. J. Noyes, "Dentistry Recognizes its Responsibilities," *JADA*, XL (June, 1950), 760–761.

25. "House of Delegates," *Trans.ADA* (1939), 281–286, 236, 330.

26. On developments in survey techniques and analysis in the late thirties, see Norman F. Gerrie, "Dental Public Health," *JADA*, XL (June, 1950), 754. Gerrie cites the epoch-making studies themselves. On problems of dentistry and war-time manpower, see above, Ch. xviii, 370–371. On the shortage of dentists, see "Board of Trustees," *Trans.ADA* (1941), 62, 65–66; M. L. Dollar, "Dental Needs and Dental Costs," *Ill. DJ*, XIV (May, 1945), 195.

27. "Board of Trustees," *Trans.ADA* (1942), 39–44; "House of Delegates," *ibid.*, 280–282; "House of Delegates," *ibid.* (1943), 475; "Board of Trustees," *ibid.* (1944), 154; "House of Delegates," *ibid.*, 376–380; "Board of Trustees," *ibid.* (1945), 51–53; H. J. Noyes, "Dentistry Recognizes its Responsibilities," *JADA*, XL (June, 1950), 760–761.

28. See the reports of the Council on Dental Health, *Trans.ADA* (1943), 327; *ibid.* (1944), 253.

29. Lon W. Morrey, "Dental Personnel," *JADA*, XXXII (Feb., 1945), 135; M. L. Dollar, "Dental Needs and Dental Costs," *Illinois DJ*, XIV (May, 1945), 185–199; P. E. Blackerby, Jr., "Help Wanted: Dentists," *DHealth*, VI (May 19, 1946), 3–4.

30. M. L. Dollar, "Dental Needs and Dental Costs," *Illinois DJ*, XIV (May, 1945), 185–199.

31. See, e.g., C. Raymond Wells, "President's Report," *Trans.ADA* (1944), 175–176; L. W. Morrey, "Dental Personnel," *JADA*, XXXII (Feb., 1945), 131–144; P. E. Blackerby, Jr., "Help Wanted: Dentists," *DHealth*, VI (May 19, 1946), 4; H. J. Noyes, "Dentistry Recognizes its Responsibilities," *JADA*, XL (June, 1950) 766.

32. C. Raymond Wells, "President's Report," *Trans.ADA* (1944), 175–176; "Board of Trustees," *ibid.* (1945), 54, 56–58, 168–169; Paul H. Belding, editor, "Oh Hum! The Shape of Things to Come?" *DItems of Interest,* LXVI (Aug., 1944), 794–799.

33. "Council on Dental Health," *Trans.ADA* (1957), 96; "House of Delegates," *ibid.* (1956), 203; F. J. Garvey, "Dentistry and the Legislative Process," *JADA,* XL (June 1950), 749; Norman F. Gerrie, "Dental Public Health," *ibid.,* 752; H. J. Noyes, "Dentistry Recognizes its Responsibilities," *ibid.,* 767.

34. "House of Delegates," *Trans.ADA* (1956), 203; "Council on Dental Health," *ibid.* (1957), 96; N. F. Gerrie, "Dental Public Health," *JADA,* XL (June, 1950), 751–752; H. J. Noyes, "Dentistry Recognizes its Responsibilities," *ibid.,* 765.

35. "House of Delegates," *Trans.ADA* (1922), 66–68, 185; "Board of Trustees," *ibid.,* 124; H. L. Banzhaf, "President's Address," *ibid.* (1927), 20; R. Boyd Bogle, "President's Report," *ibid.* (1930), 110; "House of Delegates," *ibid.,* 288; "Report of the Committee to Study Dental Education," *ibid.* (1935), 254–255; *ibid.* (1936), 239–240; "Council on Dental Education," *ibid.* (1944), 242–246; "House of Delegates," *ibid.* (1949), 252–253, 257–258; *ibid.* (1950), 210–211, 204; *ibid.* (1952), 169–170.

36. "Council on Dental Economics," *Trans.ADA* (1940), 299–301; "House of Delegates," *ibid.,* 333; "Council on Dental Economics," *ibid.* (1941), 101–103; "House of Delegates," *ibid.,* 354; Oren A. Oliver, "President's Report," *ibid.* (1942), 142; "House of Delegates," *ibid.* (1952), 215, 245.

37. C. R. Wells, "President's Report," *Trans.ADA* (1944), 175–176; ADA Bureau of Economic Research and Statistics, *The 1953 Survey of Dental Practice* (Chicago: The Association, 1954), 9, 14 (Reprinted from *JADA,* vols. XLVII–XLIX.); Abram Cohen, "Dental Health Education in Private and Institutional Practice," *New York J of Dentistry,* XXVII (Mar., 1957), 97.

38. H. J. Noyes, "Dentistry Recognizes its Responsibilities," *JADA,* XL (June, 1950), 764–767; "House of Delegates," *Trans.ADA* (1956), 203; "Council on Dental Health," *ibid.* (1957), 92–95.

39. Editorial, "The Program of the American Dental Association: An Immediate Plan of Action," *JADA,* XXXVIII (Apr., 1949), 513; F. J. Garvey, "Dentistry and the Legislative Process," *ibid.,* XL (June, 1950), 749; N. F. Gerrie, "Dental Public Health," *ibid.,* 755; H. J. Noyes, "Dentistry Recognizes its Responsibilities," *ibid.,* 766–767.

40. ADA Bureau of Economic Research and Statistics, *The 1956 Survey of Dental Practice* (Chicago: The Association, 1957), 51 (Reprinted from *JADA,* vols. LIII–LV).

41. Henry Klein, "Civilian Dentistry in War Time," *JADA,* XXXI (May, 1944), 648; L. W. Morrey, "Dental Personnel," *ibid.,* XXXII (Feb., 1945), 138–140; P. E. Blackerby, "Help Wanted: Dentists," *DHealth,* VI (May 19, 1946), 3–4; B. Duane Moen, "Nineteen-Fifty Survey of the Dental Profession: VII: Summary," *JADA,* XLII (Apr., 1951), 444–447; L. W. Morrey, editor, "Dentistry Demonstrates its Ability to Meet a Major Portion of the Increasing Demand for its Services," *ibid.* (Mar., 1951), 323–324.

42. J. Ben Robinson, "Auxiliary Dental Personnel," *JADA,* XL (June, 1950), 704; B. D. Moen, "Nineteen-Fifty Survey," *ibid.,* XLII (Apr., 1951), 444–447; "Council on Dental Education," *Trans.ADA* (1951), 21; *ibid.* (1952), 17; *ibid.* (1955), 21–22; *ibid.* (1956), 25; *ibid.* (1957), 67–69; *ibid.* (1958), 82–84.

43. B. D. Moen, "Nineteen-Fifty Survey," *JADA,* XLII (Apr., 1951), 445; ADA Bureau of Economic Research and Statistics, *The 1956 Survey,* 22.

44. "Board of Trustees," *Trans.ADA* (1922), 111–112; "House of Delegates," *ibid.* (1925), 139–140; "Board of Trustees," *ibid.* (1928), 211; "House of Delegates," *ibid.*

(1944), 172, 369; "House of Delegates," *ibid.* (1947), 254; "House of Delegates," *ibid.* (1949), 245, 263–264; "House of Delegates," *ibid.* (1950), 228–229; "Board of Trustees," *ibid.*, 240-T; H. Klein, "Civilian Dentistry in War Time," *JADA*, XXXI (May, 1944), 648; L. W. Morrey, "Dental Personnel," *ibid.*, XXXII (Feb., 1945), 140–141; J. B. Robinson, "Auxiliary Dental Personnel," *ibid.*, XL (June, 1950), 705–709; B. D. Moen, "Nineteen-Fifty Survey," *ibid.*, XLII, (Apr., 1951), 445–446; H. H. Horner, *Dental Education Today* (Chicago: University of Chicago Press, 1947), 49, 268–275, 400–401; ADA Bureau of Economic Research and Statistics, *The 1956 Survey*, 21–22; U.S. Department of Health, Education and Welfare, *Health Manpower Service Book* (Washington, 1957), sec. 8. The House has declared that it opposes any laws authorizing non-dentists "to render intra-oral operative, surgical or prosthetic dental services . . . in the interest of the dental health of children and the long range protection of the health of the public." "House of Delegates," *Trans.ADA* (1950), 227–228.

45. L. W. Morrey, "Dental Personnel," *JADA*, XXXII (Feb., 1945), 142; B. D. Moen, "Nineteen-Fifty Survey," *ibid.*, XLII (Apr., 1951), 445–446; ADA *Information Bulletin* (July, 1952), 1; ADA Bureau of Economic Research and Statistics, *The 1956 Survey*, 18, 22.

46. "House of Delegates," *Trans.ADA* (1924), 93, 117–118; "Board of Trustees," *ibid.* (1925), 228–229; H. L. Banzhaf, "President's Address," *ibid.* (1927), 58; "House of Delegates," *ibid.*, 171, 174; "House of Delegates," *ibid.* (1933), 371–372; "House of Delegates," *ibid.* (1939) 124, 318, 323; "House of Delegates," *ibid.* (1941), 305, 330.

47. "House of Delegates," *Trans.ADA* (1942), 294, 316; *ibid.* (1944), 172, 369; *ibid.* (1946), 114, 187; F. J. Garvey, "Dentistry and the Legislative Process," *JADA*, XL (June, 1950), 749.

48. "Board of Trustees," *Trans.ADA* (1945), 99–107, 110–112; "House of Delegates," *ibid.* (1946), 309.

49. "House of Delegates," *Trans.ADA* (1947), 236, 244, 245; J. B. Robinson, "Auxiliary Dental Personnel," *JADA*, XL (June, 1950), 704–705.

50. "House of Delegates," *Trans.ADA* (1947), 244, 245, 247; *ibid.* (1948), 249, 260; *ibid.* (1949), 255–256; *ibid.* (1950), 201–202; J. B. Robinson, "Auxiliary Dental Personnel," *JADA*, XL (June, 1950), 708–709.

51. J. B. Robinson, "Auxiliary Dental Personnel," *JADA*, XL (June, 1950), 704–705.

52. "Board of Trustees," *Trans.ADA* (1952), 193–194, 213; ADA *Information Bulletin* (July, 1952), p. 2; Federal Trade Commission, *Trade Practice Rules for the Commercial Dental Laboratory Industry, Promulgated Nov. 4, 1955;* Federal Trade Commission, *Amendment of "Definition" and of Rules 1, 2, and 12 of the Trade Practice Rules Promulgated Nov. 4, 1955, for the Commercial Dental Laboratory Industry, Promulgated June 14, 1957.*

53. "House of Delegates," *Trans.ADA* (1956), 187; "House of Delegates," *ibid.* (1957), 123; Council on Dental Education, "Educational Requirements and a Program of Certification for Dental Laboratory Technicians," *JADA*, LVI (Jan., 1958), 100–102; Shailer Peterson, "The Education and Certification of the Dental Laboratory Technician," Mimeo., prepared for presentation at the Minneapolis Dental Society meeting, Feb. 20, 1958, p. 4. The author is Secretary of the Council on Dental Education.

54. ADA *Information Bulletin* (July, 1952 and Dec., 1957); ADA Council on Dental Trade and Laboratory Relations, *Program for Maintaining Proper and Effective Relations Between the Dental Profession and the Dental Trade and Laboratory Groups.*

55. *ADA Information Bulletin* (July, 1952); ADA Bureau of Economic Research and Statistics, *The 1956 Survey*, 18, 22.

56. L. W. Morrey, "Dental Personnel," *JADA*, XXXII (Feb., 1945), 143.

57. Donald R. McNeil, *The Fight for Fluoridation* (New York: Oxford University Press, 1957), 1–13.

58. "House of Delegates," *Trans.ADA* (1925), 110; D. R. McNeil, *Fight for Fluoridation*, 13–22.

59. "House of Delegates," *Trans.ADA* (1933), 367–368; Executive Board, Research Commission, "Past, Present, and Future Plans," *JADA Midmonthly*, (Sept. 15, 1947), 414; D. R. McNeil, *Fight for Fluoridation*, 22–35.

60. D. R. McNeil, *Fight for Fluoridation*, 35–43.

61. "Board of Trustees," *Trans.ADA* (1945), 40; D. R. McNeil, *Fight for Fluoridation*, 71, 74, 75, 76.

62. "Council on Dental Therapeutics," *Trans.ADA* (1946), 131; D. R. McNeil, *Fight for Fluoridation*, 64–69, 70.

63. "Board of Trustees," *Trans.ADA* (1949), 316; "House of Delegates," *ibid.* (1950), 224–225; D. R. McNeil, *Fight for Fluoridation*, 76–81.

64. "Board of Trustees," *Trans.ADA* (1951), 215; *ibid.* (1952), 204, 205.

INDEX

Accepted Dental Remedies
history of, 361
Advertising
A.D.A. effects on, 190, 363
Crawcours use in N.Y. in 1834, 22
early dental health education tracts, 52
Aid to distressed dentists
after San Francisco earthquake, 246
after Galveston flood, 246
A.D.A. program, 365
Am. Soc. plans, 37
Nat. D.A. activities, 247, 342
President Noel proposes fund, 273
Allen, J.
charged with unethical advertising, 58
controversy with Am.Soc., 55
Allport, W.W.
on amendment on college education, 164
on dental-medical education, 171, 189
Amalgam
campaign for, revived, 204
objections to use of, 22
use of, by Crawcours, 22
use of denounced by S. Brown, 23
war, 67–87
American Academy of Dental Science
founded to elevate dentistry through education, 170, 185
purpose and activities, 186
American Association of Dental Schools
advise dental Army training, 375
educational policy, 384
elects members on National Board of Examiners, 391
established, 379
American Dental Association
activities on behalf of government and military dentists, 370
Advisory Committee on Dental Caries, 402
appointive offices, history of, 359
Army Medical Museum and Library offered to, 210
Board of Trustees' function, 358
Bureau of Public Relations, 406
business manager, office, 358

Committee on Costs of Dental Care established in 1928, 411
Committee on Dental Economics, 412
Committee on Dental Health Survey, 414
Committee on Education reorganized, 383
Committee on National Defense, 372
Committee on Organization and Membership established in 1932, 351
Committee on Prize Essays established, 138
Committee on Process Patents, 396, 397
Committee to Study Education report, 383
condemns advertising, 190
constitution and bylaws of 1948, 354
constitution proposed, 126
constitution, two major revisions since 1913, 353
consultants survey work of, 354
cooperates on training program for technicians, 432
Council on Dental Education, 384, 385
Council on Dental Education interest in training of assistants, 426
Council on Dental research, duties, 403, 404
Council on Dental Therapeutics, 363
Council on Dental Trade and Laboratory Relations, 430
Council on Hospital Dental Service, 423
Council on Legislation, history of, 368, 397
Council on Mouth Hygiene and Public Instruction work in dental health, 406
councils' and committees' functions, 355
Division of Chemistry's history, 363
efforts to establish National Board of Examiners, 389
encourages local and state societies, 184
ethnological study of dentistry, authorized by, 200
Family Dental Survey of 1953, 410
fluoridation study, 436
formed, 125
functions of, controversy over, 215

508

government as it now exists, 354
health program, policy, 414, 416
House of Delegates' function, 354
how it achieved and failed as national
society, 267
indigent care policy, 414, 419
influence on dental education, 155–176
Journal, history, 360
legislation problem, 173, 216
mediator between profession and public, 405
meeting during Civil War, 144
merger with South.D.A. and Am. Convention proposed, 181
merges with Southern Association to
form Nat. D.A., 222, 229, 253
Methods of Payment Committee report,
419
membership from 1914 to present, 349
membership, modern plan begins 1932,
350
membership not representative of profession, 217
membership qualifications, 242
membership restrictions for Am.Con-
vention and other societies' delegates,
179
membership, student, origin of, 352
name restored in 1922, 353
Preparedness Committee activities in
1940–1941, 372
professional services decentralized and
service activities centralized, 354
publication of *Transactions* controversy,
195
publications, history of, 359, 360, 361
relation with Am. Convention, 177
Relief Fund inaugurated, 366
Relief Fund incorporated, 366
Research Commission activities, 397
research subsidizing, 211, 397
restatement of social program, 414
secretaryship history, 358
Social Security for dentists, policy, 367
Speaker of House authorized in 1930,
355
sponsorship of society of colleges proposed, 174
sponsors group insurance plan, 366
Standing Committee on Constitutional
and Administrative By-Laws established in 1942, 354
system of organization adopted, 212
Traynor bill on mail-order laboratories,
endorsed by, 429

treasurer, history of office, 359
welfare program, 365
American Dental Convention
Am.Soc. dissolves during, 98
beginnings and history, 103–121
Civil War meetings, 142, 144
expired in 1883, 177, 183, 187
membership policy controversy, 109,
129
propose consolidation with South.A. and
A.D.A., 181, 187
American Dental Protective Union, court
fight over vulcanized rubber fees, 166
American Dental Society of Europe
Americans participate in, 219
American Dental Trade Association
founded, 193
American Journal of Dental Science
founded, early history, 25, 26, 27, 51
publication abandoned to C. Harris, 90
American Medical Association
organizational pattern proposed for
dentistry, 132, 135, 137, 168, 212,
236, 283, 297
American Society of Dental Surgeons
amalgam question, 68–87, 89, 90
approves Baltimore College, 36
charitable activities, 37
constitution described, 35
founded, history, 23–98
membership requirements, 36, 60–66
supports and adopts *Am.J.D.Sc.*, 26, 27
supports dental education, 36, 50
Angle, Edward H., early patent holder,
258
Anesthesia, local, interest in, 203
Anthony, L. Pierce, editor 1938–1944, 359
Armed Forces, history of dentistry in, 231,
233, 370–376
Army
dentists in, during Civil War, 143
Medical Museum and Library opened to
dentistry, 210
Assistants, dental, use of, 425–433
Association of Colleges of Dentistry
early history, 29, 159–162
Atkinson, William H.
efforts in nomenclature, 220
influence on professionalism, 184, 198
on dental education, 154, 164
tries to make peace between A.D.A. and
Am. Convention, 177, 181
Austin, Professor
encourages dental organization, 190
encourages education, 170

Awards
    Committee on Prize Essays established, 138
    means of rewarding inventors, 207

Bacon, Josiah, murdered over patent fees, 166
Bacteriology
    dentistry applies new discoveries, 202
Baker, Elisha
    co-founder of Am.Soc., 34
    expelled from Am. Soc., 81
    helps found *Am.J.D.Sc.*, 25
Baltimore College of Dental Surgery
    alumni organize, 50
    beginnings, 29, 30, 31
Banzhaf, Henry L.
    proposes increased membership, 350
    suggests registration of laboratories, 429
    urges National Board of Examiners, 390
Barnum, S. C.
    prize for rubber dam invention, 207
Barrett, W. C.
    quoted on reporting dental progress, 211
    quoted on science in dentistry, 199
Black, Arthur D.
    devises index of dental literature, 363
    in Nat.D.A. reorganization, 241, 243, 282, 283, 302–311, 320–345
Black, Greene Vardiman
    advocates Nat.D.A. reform, 270, 281
    bacterial origin of caries studies, 202
    methods of treating caries, 203, 206
    translates Herbst's gold method, 219
    "Boston Dental Parlors" condemned, 238
Bremner, M.D.K., in patent fight, 256, 396
British Dental Association
    as model for membership, 275
Brophy, Truman W.
    early patent holder, 258
    quoted on education, 167, 169
    quoted on legislation, 173
    reports Chicago children's dental needs, 249
Brown, Homer C.
    appointed to Ohio Board of Health, 335, 337
    chosen president of Nat.D.A., 339, 342
    in Nat.D.A. reorganization, 290–313, 319–335
    quoted on indigent care, 408
    suggests policy on official bulletin, 340
Brown, Solyman
    co-founder of *Am.J.D.Sc.*, 25
    co-founder of Am. Soc., 34

in amalgam controversy, 23, 67, 76
    quoted on admission to professions, 21, 33
    quoted on Am.Soc. membership, 61, 62
    quoted on dental health education, 51
    quoted on importance of education, 49
    quoted on supply of dentists in New York, 20
Bryant, Emory A.
    in Legislative Committee controversy, 340
    in patent reform campaign, 256
    on Nat.D.A. reorganization, 288, 300
"Buckeye," "random thoughts" on Convention, 111
Buckley, J. P., speaks on patent issue, 258
Burkhart, Harvey J.
    in Nat.D.A. reorganization, 272, 274, 281–283, 291, 304, 313, 320, 321, 331–335, 338–340
Butler, Charles S.
    on Nat.D.A. reform, 291, 297

Camalier, C. Willard
    recommends military preparedness, 372
Care, Dental
    A.D.A. works to expand, 423
    children's needs in Cleveland and Chicago, 249
    civilians and military needs, 1940, 372
    needs of country, 406, 409
Caries
    A.D.A. offers prize for paper on, 208
    bacterial origin theories appear, 202
    Control Program of A.D.A., 417
    endemic character and cause, 151
    environmental theory of causation, 250
    fluoridation inhibits, 403, 434
    renewed interest in, 402
    research proposed, 116
Carnegie Institution
    funds for dental research, 236
Casto, Frank M.
    aids in advertising litigation, 369
    on compulsory health insurance, 415
    proposes A.D.A. absorb Educational Council, 383
    proposes A.D.A. revision in 1935, 354
Celluloid, substitute for vulcanized rubber in dentures, 166
Central States Dental Association
    educational requirements, 156
Chalfont, Samuel P.
    murdered Bacon over patent fees, 167
Chicago conference on 1912 constitutional difficulties, 324–326

Cincinnati A. D. Surgeons
propose new national society, 124
Civil War
effect on dental profession, 141–154
Clark, F. Y.
argues over Am.Convention program, 183
secedes from Am. Convention, 142
served Sherman's forces, 147
Committee on Costs of Medical Care
surveys dental health education, 407, 410
Cone, C. O.
on disseminating information, 53–55
on local societies, 94
quoted on ethics, 58
quoted on importance of education, 50, 93
Copper amalgam vogue, 206
Crawcour brothers
methods, influence of, 22, 23, 67
Crawford, J. Y.
urges union of A.D.A. and South.A., 228
Crouse, J. N.
Chicago dentist, 239
defends trade publishing dental journal, 195
in Dental Protective Association, 168, 253, 395
in fight over patent rights, 255–256

Darwinian theory divides dentists, 149, 199
Davis, N. S.
physician speaks on specialization, 169
Dean, H. Trendley
proposes fluoridation, 403, 434
Dental Abstracts, history of, 361
Dental Art
by C. A. Harris, published in 1839, 30
Dental Association of Western New York
endorses *Am.J.D.Sc.*, 26
Dental Cosmos combines with *Journal*, 359, 360
Dental Digest, established, 253
Dental Educational Council of America
A.D.A. relation to, 377, 381
closes in 1936, 383
organization, 264
Dental Faculties Association of American Universities founded, 262
Dental Institute of America
dental health education program, 405
Dental News Letter begins publication, 27
Dental Protective Association, 168
in patent controversy, 253, 255, 394

Dental Register of the West
founded, 27, 39, 94
succumbed in 1923, 360
Dental Welfare Foundation
dental health education program, 407
Dentistry
aspects of, analyzed, 54
community relationships, 132
conditions in 1830's, 20
corporate practice charge against university-related colleges, 382
early western, 39, 43
in 1840's characterized, 68
medicine, relation to, 48, 168, 201
national society, relation to, 128, 130
operative and mechanical, problems of, 57, 165
organized, A.D.A. inaugurates new phase, 139
panel system, poll on, 412
practical emphasis, 45, 53
practice, admission to, 21, 32, 36
practice in government service, 370
practice, statutory regulation, 173
practice, uniform standards sought, 387
preventive, challenge, 52, 251, 436
standards and quality, societies' effects on, 130, 131, 181
Dentists
Americans participate in International Medical Congress in London, 168
civilian, problems during Civil War, 146
dissatisfied with Am. Convention, 123
foreign, relations with, 218
in Armed Forces: See Armed Forces
in Public Health Service and Veterans Administration, duties of, 376
Mutual Protective Alliance fights patent claims, 395, 396
number and distribution, 412
number in New York and Cincinnati around 1830, 20, 21, 40
qualifications of, in 1830's, 21
shortage of, 424
social recognition sought by, 190
Southern, lot after Civil War, 147
supply, question revived, 419
support *Am.J.D.Sc.*, 26
Dewey, Martin
attacks Educational Council, 382
quoted on dental research, 400
speaks on dental economics, 413
urges membership drive, 350
Dittmar, G. Walter
promotes membership drive, 351

Dollar, Melvin L.
  quoted on dental needs and supply of
    dentists, 419
Donnally, Williams
  role in legislative controversy, 340
  reports Army Medical Museum open to
    dentistry, 210
Draper, John William, scientist, 150
Dues: See Economics, Dental
Dunning, E. J., on advertising, 59
Dwinelle, William H.
  on patent abuses, 116
  unfortunate plight of, 246

Eastman, George
  endowed children's dental clinic, 406
Ebersole, W. G.
  quoted on oral hygiene program, 252
  reports on dental needs of Cleveland's
    children, 249
Economics, Dental
  A.D.A. Committee on Costs of Dental
    Care established, 411
  A.D.A. Committee on Dental Economics
    established, 412
  A.D.A. deferred payment plan, 416
  A.D.A. investigates low-income and in-
    surance schemes, 419
  A.D.A. on behalf of military pay, 371
  A.D.A. sought revenue code changes,
    370
  competition amongst manufacturers,
    suppliers and dentists, 193
  costs of dental care, 428
  dentists' opinions on Ritter survey, 413
  dues assessment, 320
  dues question in Nat.D.A. reorganiza-
    tion, 297
  fees discussed, 111, 146
  financial considerations of journal, 276
  motives and A.D.A., 192
  preceptorial system supplements in-
    come, 163
  research subsidizing, 116, 211, 236
  responsibility to indigent, 407
Education, Dental
  Am.A. Dental Schools founded, 379, 384
  A.D.A. influence on, 155–176
  A.D.A.'s role since 1913, 377–387
  A.D.A. sponsorship of society of col-
    leges proposed, 174
  Am. Soc. membership requirements, 36
  Association of Colleges of Dentistry
    organized, 29, 159
  battle to stamp out fraudulent schools,
    188

Bureau of Library and Indexing Service
    promotes, 364
  clinics supported as best mode of, 154
  degree requisite for society member-
    ship, 93, 275
  Dental Faculties Association of Ameri-
    can Universities founded, 262
  early methods of, 28
  early proponents, 27, 49
  early schools, 30, 31
  first list of approved schools, 386
  international problem of diploma mills,
    260
  legislation's effect on, 173
  licensure problems, 216
  Nat.A.Dental Examiners role in improv-
    ing standards, 389
  preceptorial training problem, 163
  proprietary schools, drive against, 262,
    380
  *Requirements for Approval of Dental
    Schools* issued, 385
  role of, in profession, 24
  schools classified by Educational Coun-
    cil, 378
  should not be done in medical schools,
    171
  societies concerned with, 155
  standards attacked by Thompson, 198
  standards of admission to schools, 266
  standards, problem thrust on A.D.A.,
    162
  standards, uniformity sought, 259
  Taft's influence on, 185
  training assistants, 426, 430
Education, Dental Health
  A.D.A. campaign for school instruction,
    209, 248, 406
  A.D.A. program, 406–410, 418
  Am.Soc. supports, 51
  hygienists role in, 426
  journalism aids, 24
  oral hygiene question in Nat.D.A., 252,
    298
Electricity, applications in dentistry, 204
Ethics, Dental
  Am. Soc. pioneer in, 57
  dentistry vs. trade, 193
  patents and unprofessional conduct, 257

Fairbank, Leigh Cole
  first dentist to become brigadier gen-
    eral, 371
Federal Dental Health Work Relief Proj-
    ect
  for children proposed, 416

Fellowships: See National Bureau of Standards; National Institutes of Health
Fillebrown, Thomas
  proposes union of A.D.A. and South.A., 228
Filling materials
  gold vs. amalgam, 22, 73
  "Royal Mineral Succedaneum," 22
  Taggart's casting process introduced, 254
Finley, Mark F.
  advocates generous membership policy, 276
  on patent reform, 256, 395
  stand on Nat.D.A. reorganization, 296, 331
Flagg, J. Foster
  amalgam campaign, 204
  sponsors support for national society, 106, 124
Flexner, Abraham, medical education, 262
Fluoridation as preventive measure, A.D.A.
  stand on, 433–436
Forsyth brothers
  endowed children's dental clinic, 406
Foster, Joseph H.
  co-founder of Am.Soc., 34
  quoted on Am.Soc.'s purposes, 60, 62, 63
  quoted on importance of education, 50
  quoted on membership policy, 64, 90
Franklin, B. W., on Civil War, 143

Gallie, Don M., patent controversy, 395
Gardette, E. B.
  relations with Am. Soc., 61
Gaylord, Edward S.
  quoted on Nat.D.A. reform, 297
  supports relief fund, 247, 365
Gies, William J.
  surveys dental education, 380, 381, 410, 411
  conceives national examination system, 389
Gold
  crowns, controversy over patents, 167
  excise tax regulations, 370
  filling, new casting method, 1907, 254
  new preparation from Paris, 114
Goodyear Dental Vulcanite Company
  monopoly, 166, 194
Grady, Richard
  proposes school dental hygiene education, 249

Graham, Sylvester, on coarse flour, 152

Harris, Chapin A.
  amalgam policy, 75, 79
  biographical data, 29
  co-founder of Am.Soc., 34
  defends James Taylor, 85
  early editor of *Am.J.D.Sc.*, 30
  offers *Am.J.D.Sc.* to Am.Soc., 27
  on dental organization, 33, 48, 93
  quarrels over printing bill, 54
  quoted on dental legislation, 31, 32
  quoted on supply of dentists, 42
  supports Baltimore College of Dental Surgery, 30
  supports dental education, 27, 36, 50, 93, 168
Hartzell, Thomas B.
  recommends Illinois charter and original A.D.A. title, 351
Hayden, Horace H.
  advocates dental education, 28
  biographical data, 28
  co-founder of Am.Soc., 34
  quoted on membership policy, 64
Health, Dental
  A.D.A. on national and state programs, 416, 422, 423
Hetrick, Frank O.
  in Nat.D.A. transition debate, 331–338
  quoted on dental research, 399
  supporter of T. Roosevelt, 319
Hillenbrand, Harold
  editor 1944–1946, 359
  secretary since 1946, 358
History, Dental
  A.D.A. activities in, 383, 384
History of Dental and Oral Science
  published by Am. Acad. D. Sc., 186
Holmes, Oliver Wendell
  quoted on contemporary medicine, 71
Horner, Harlan H.
  challenge on preventive dentistry, 436
  Council on Education's function, 385
Hospitals, dental service in
  A.D.A. efforts to provide, 423
Hullihen, S.P.
  appointed to prepare public address, 52
  involved in patent controversy, 57
  on revising program of Am. Soc., 90
Hunt, George E.
  quoted on Indiana's membership in Nat. D.A., 302
Hunter, William, attacks prosthetics, 254
Hygienists
  training and licensing of, 426–428

Illinois
 center of progressive dentistry, 238
 Dental Society in Nat. D.A. reform,
  291, 304–310, 318, 320
 Dental Society reforms constitution on
  membership, 240
 society plan introduced to Nat. D.A.,
  277
Index to Dental Literature, history, 363
Indiana Plan on membership adopted, 351
Indigent
 providing dental needs, 407, 414, 416,
  417, 421
Industry
 dental programs recognized by A.D.A.
  423
Inlays: see Taggart, William F.
Insurance
 compulsory, warning against, 420
 credit and deferred payment plans,
  A.D.A., policy on, 415
 group plan for A.D.A. members, 366
International
 Association for Dental Research aids
  in journal publication, 400
 Dental Congress, plans for, fail, 219
 International Dental Journal, offered to
  Nat. D.A., 276, 287
 Medical Congress, American dentists
  participate in, 168, 219
 Medical Congress, theories on origin of
  caries presented, 202
 recognition and cooperation sought, 218
 Tooth Crown Co., 167, 253

Johnson Brothers
 merges with S.S. White's company, 193
Johnson, C. N.
 Chicago dentist, 239
 Dental Protective Association, 393
 editor 1925–1938, 359
 on Illinois society membership, 243
 on medicine-dentistry analogy, 408
Johnston, J. F.
 polled Indiana on national society pro-
  posal, suggests organizing panel, 125
Jones, White and Company
 publishes *Dental News Letter*, 27
Journalism, Dental
 A.D.A. editor, history of office, 359
 A.D.A. *Journal*, history of, 360
 A.D.A. members, free journal sub-
  scription proposed, 220
 Am. J.D. Sc. abandoned to C. Harris, 90
 Am. J.D. Sc. founded, 25
 Am. Soc. supports, 51

Dental Cosmos combines with *Journal*
 in 1936, 359
Dental Digest established, 253
Dental Register of West inaugurated,
 94
 early periodicals founded, 27
 history of *Dental News, Midmonthly,
  Journal of Oral Surgery,* and *Dental
  Abstracts,* 360
Index to Dental Literature, 363
 included in medical journals, 25
Internat. D.J. offered to Nat.D.A., 276
Items of Interest opened to Nat. D.A.
  reorganization debate, 281
 means to protect material against patent
  claims, 257
 Nat. D.A. journal proposed, 274, 275,
  279, 280, 287, 336, 340, 341, 343
 Nat. D.A. *Transactions,* problems of
  publishing, 274
 1940 survey, dental health literature,
  408
 on policy of Am. Soc., 91, 98
 reports on new A.D.A., 127
 role in Amalgam War, 76, 82
 success of *J.A.M.A.* cited, 279
 supports second convention, 104, 108
 value of Convention proceedings, 119
Judd, Homer
 on medical education for dentists, 169
 requests Missouri College be member
  in A. of Colleges of Dentistry, 159
Junius, pseudonym: See McQuillen, J. H.
Jurisprudence, Dental
 intimidation and legal action over gold
  crown patents, 167
 litigation on advertising in Oregon, 367
 litigation, Taggart's patents, 255, 393
 patent litigation, 116
 vulcanized rubber fees fought, 166

King, Otto U.
 aid for reorganization plan sought, 297
 A.D.A. editor until 1925, 359
 A.D.A. secretary and *Journal* editor,
  339, 341, 358
 Indiana's stand on Nat. D.A. reform,
  326
 Legislative Committee controversy, 340
Kirk, E. C.
 emphasized need for Nat. D.A. reform,
  286
Koch, C. R. E.
 reports problems of raising school admission standards, 266

Law, bar association organized, 189
Lawrence, Ambrose, amalgam experiments, 205
Lawrence, Amos, on refined flour, 152
Leber, T.
  on bacterial origin of caries, 202
Legislation, Dental
  A.D.A. active in state problems, 368
  A.D.A. and tariff legislation, 370
  A.D.A. Council on Legislation, 368
  A.D.A. opposes Wagner-Murray-Dingell Health Bill, 418
  A.D.A. policy on Social Security for dentists, 367
  A.D.A. sponsors bill for aid to research, 418
  commission for dental officers won, 231
  Committee on Uniform Legislation formed, 264
  early discussion of, 31, 32
  model state dental law drafted, 366
  Massachusetts requires dental examination for children, 249
  necessary for high standards, 173
  patent law reform movement, 254, 257
  role of, in profession, 24
  societies' efforts in, 387
  Traynor mail-order laboratory bill, 429
  uniform, problem for A.D.A., 216
Lewis, John R.
  reports on Civil War army rejections, 145
Licensure, Dental
  A.D.A. action in promoting uniform standards, 387, 388
  Colorado legislation proposed on, 368
  functions of examining boards, 216
  National Board of Examiners, 389
  uniform procedures conceived, 259
Literature, Dental: See Journalism, Dental
Litigation: See Jurisprudence, Dental
Logan, W.H.G., Chicago dentist, 239
Lowery, P.C., on dental research, 401

McCabe, John C.
  quoted on achievements in dentistry, 68
  quoted on objects of organization, 59
McKay, Frederick S.
  encouraged research on mottled teeth, 434
McKellops, H. J.
  pleads for society unification, 181, 224
  urges army dental corps, 120
McQuillen, J. H.
  as "Junius," writes on membership policies, 123, 127, 129, 135

attacks preceptor educational system, 164
  exponent of dental science, 148
  heads constitution organizing panel of A.D.A., 126, 133
  investigates A.D.A. Credentials Committee report, 179
  membership ideas, 99, 109, 128, 132
  on influence of national society, 130
  pioneer dental researcher, 202
  quoted on A.D.A.'s position on educational requirements, 157
  quoted on Darwin and Bible, 150
  quoted on mid-19th century America, 46
Maryland Medical and Surgical Journal
  praises *Am. J.D. Sc.*, urges dental colleges 27
Massachusetts State Dental Society
  recommends Nat. D.A. reforms, 279
Medicine
  cults applied to dentistry, 152
  dentistry, relation to, 48, 69, 71, 168
  developments in mid-19th century, 46
  federal relations with, 209
  societies reflected specialization, 188
Melendy, Arthur R.
  Nat. D.A. president 1911–1912, treasurer 1914–1928, 359
  quoted on Nat. D.A. revision, 312
Mercury, in amalgam, 22, 71
Merritt, Arthur H.
  brought tuberculosis crusade before Nat. D.A., 248
Messner, C. T., on dental research, 401
Michigan Dental Association
  educational requirements, 156
Midgley, Albert L.
  defends Educational Council, 382
Miller, Willoughby D.
  international memorial to, 247
  writes on caries, 203, 208
Milles, W. T., on septic theory of caries, 202
Miner, Leroy M. S.
  quoted on compulsory health insurance, 421
Mississippi Valley Association of Dental Surgeons
  debility threatens existence, 183
  delegates consider new national society, 125
  establishes journal, 27
  founded, 40, 94
  opposes amalgam, 41

Morgan, W. H.
  on dentists in Confederate Army, 144
  quoted on society and college relation-
    ships to profession, 172
Morrey, Lon W.
  editor since 1947, 359
  emphasizes dental health publicity, 408
  proposed use of assistants, 426, 433
  quoted on supply of dentists, 419
Museums, A.D.A. committee created on,
  384

National Association of Dental Examiners
  cooperates with A.D.A. membership
    plan, 352
  efforts to improve licensing, 389
  for uniform educational standards, 259
  vs. National Board, 391
National Association of Dental Faculties
  formed, 176
  for uniform educational standards, 259
National Association of Dental Labora-
    tories
  training program for technicians, 432
National Association of Oral Hygiene
  possibility of organization, 295
National Association of State Boards of
    Examiners
  establishes educational standards, 175
National Board of Dental Examiners
  established, 389, 391, 394
  role in educational policy, 384
National Bureau of Standards
  dental program, 362
  dental fellowship program, 399
National Council on Rehabilitation
  A.D.A. cooperates with, 418
National Dental Academy, Museum and
  Library, proposed, 210
National Dental Association
  beginnings, 187, 229
  Board of Trustees proposed, 280
  committee and president-elect systems
    recommended, 344
  Committee on Dentists in Army and
    Navy appointed, 231
  Committee on Revision of Constitution
    and By-Laws named, 281
  Committee on Scientific Research estab-
    lished, 236
  constituent societies, means of accepting
    new ones, 316, 345
  constitution and by-laws revised in
    1912, 312-318
  constitution, Old Point Comfort and
    1912 compared, 314

  constitutional changes in 1897, 268
  constitutional difficulties, 322, 324
  dental health education in schools cam-
    paigned for, 248
  district branch provisions of 1912 con-
    stitution, 316
  dues assessment controversy, 321-336
  early relief activities, 245
  Executive Council established, 269
  first *Bulletin* in 1913, 341
  House of Delegates, confusion over first
    meeting, 322-326
  House of Delegates, first slate, 338
  House of Delegates proposed, 280, 289
  Illinois charter recommended, 353
  membership from 1914 to present, 349
  membership in 1903 and 1905, 275
  membership in 1910, 286
  membership provisions and problems,
    267-275, 278-284, 286, 288, 298,
    301-312, 315
  nomenclature problem, 261
  original A.D.A. name adopted, 1922,
    353
  object, means of accomplishing aim, 313
  patent debate, 256, 259
  reform campaign, 237-243
  reorganization accomplished, transition
    problems, 319-344
  reorganization begun, 267-284
  Research Institute history, 395
  state societies on reorganization, 310
  State Society Officers' Section, 338
National Institute of Dental Research
  founded in 1948, 401
National Institutes of Health
  fellowship program, 401
National Mouth Hygiene Association
  Nat. D.A. relation to, 343
National Pharmacopeial Convention
  A.D.A. represented in, 362
National Physical Fitness Program
  A.D.A. cooperates with, 418
National Relief Fund, established, 247
National Research Council
  funds for dental research, 398
National Tuberculosis Association
  Nat. D.A. endorses fund crusade, 248
New York College of Dentistry
  Parmly, professor and first president, 29
New York Dental Recorder
  begins publication, 27, 82
New York Dental Society
  outlines amendment to patent laws, 254
  Nat.D.A. reform involves, 299, 300, 303

New York Odontological Society
promotes professional improvement, 186

New York Protective Union
vulcanized rubber fees fight, 166

New York Society of Dental Surgeons
formation over amalgam controversy, 94

Noel, L. G.
discusses membership, 273
supports welfare program, 365

Nomenclature
A.D.A. program, 383, 384
international problems, 220
Nat. D.A. involved in problem, 261
uniform, need for, 115

North Carolina Dental Association
approves research fund, 119

Noyes, Enoch, endorses *Am.J.D.Sc.*, 26

Noyes, Harold J.
quoted on shortage of dentists, 424

Ohio
College of Dental Surgery founded, 31, 40, 94
Dental College Association, delegates consider new national society, 125
Dental Society, affiliates with Nat. D.A., 299, 320

Old Age and Survivors' Insurance: See Social Security

Oliver, Robert T.
Army colonel becomes A.D.A. president, 371
proposes reducing Educational Council's status, 381
quoted on dental economics, 413
urges membership drive, 350

Ottolengui, Rodrigues
action in planning Nat. D.A. reorganization, 280–284, 289–290, 293–311
advocates patent reforms, 254
correspondence on Illinois question, 320
defends Taggart's patent cause, 257, 395
in transition period controversy, 320–322, 326, 327, 334
on dues in Nat. D.A., 297, 298, 321
revises constitution for Nat. D.A., 280, 286–294

Parmly, Eleazar
advocates dental education, 28
anti-amalgam leader, 76, 83
co-founder of *Am.J.D. Sc.*, 25
early New York leader, 29

on dental legislation, 32
operative and mechanical dentistry, distinguished by, 57
quoted on dental organization, 34
warns Am. Soc. on membership policy, 63
proposes preventive measures, 52

Patents
abuses, importance of opposing, 116
A.D.A. Committee on Process Patents established, 394
Am. Soc. policies on, 55
denture material fight, 166
reform of laws movement, 254
Taggart's process causes crisis, 255, 395

Patterson, J. D.
in planning Nat. D.A. reform, 294, 296, 298, 313

Pennsylvania
Association of Dental Surgeons, in support of national society, 124, 136
College of Dental Surgeons, withdraws from college association, 160
Society of Dental Surgeons formed, 94

Perkins opposes emphasis on dental theory, 148

Philanthropy, impulse toward, 235, 245

Philbrook, B. F.
claims inlay process prior to Taggart, 395

Phillips, Herbert E.
reports on compulsory health insurance in foreign countries, 411

Physicians: See also American Medical Association; Medicine
conservatism and skepticism delays progress, 201
cooperates in preventive dentistry, 251
Dr. Brown criticizes amalgam policy, 92
Dr. Davis speaks on medical education for dentists, 169
fund drive for special problems, 248
invited to dental meetings, 168
membership on boards of dental examiners opposed, 32
oppose calomel, 22
praise early dental colleges, 31
quoted on quackery, 100
urged to support journalism, 40

Pinney, H. B., secretary for 19 years, 358

Politics
Brown-Bryant correspondence on, 300
in dental societies, 279
Nat. D.A. charged with, 238, 282
reform in A.D.A. excluding, advised, 214

Price, Weston A.
  proposes study of mottled enamel, 432
  Scientific Foundation Fund drive, 337,
    338
Prostheses
  problems of vulcanized rubber, 166
  section of A.D.A. well received, 168
  substitutes for gold, 166
  Taggart's casting method makes remov-
    able type possible, 255

Quackery
  acceptance of, 44
  amalgam associated with, 67, 83
  Am. Soc. fight against, 97
  Crawcours in New York in 1834, 22
  dental health education to suppress, 51
  in 1830's, 23, 24
  legislation regulating dental practice,
    32
  medical and dental, 201
  physician quoted on, 100
  western dentists denounce, 41

Research: See Science, Dental
Rich, John B.
  anti-amalgam leader, 76
  chairman of A.D.A.-South. D. A.
    union convention, 229
  defends Am. Convention, 177
  resigns from Am. Soc., 87
Richardson, James
  on A.D.A. constitution organization
    panel, 126
  quoted on nomenclature, 115
Ritter Dental Manufacturing Co.
  poll on panel dentistry, 412
Robinson, J. Ben
  proposes changing water supply in
    endemic fluorosis areas, 434
  proposes re-establishment of office
    laboratory, 431
  writes on use of dental assistants, 426
Ross, A. R.
  introduces Indiana membership plan,
    351
Rottenstein, J. B.
  study on bacterial origin of caries, 202
Rubber, vulcanized, problems from use in
    dentures, 166
Rubey, S. C. A.
  stand on Nat. D.A. reorganization, 326

St. Louis Dental College
  delegate's credentials challenged, 158

San Francisco Dental Relief Committee
  funds after earthquake and fire, 246
Scherer, Walter H.
  warns profession against compulsory
    insurance, 421
Schools, Dental: See Education, Dental
Science, Dental
  advances through discoveries, 199
  Am. Convention action on research, 116
  A.D.A. and Nat. D.A. fail to foster
    scientific leadership, 267
  A.D.A. encourages local and state so-
    cieties, 184
  A.D.A. investigates state of, 137, 138
  A.D.A. research program regains prom-
    inence, 416
  Am. Soc. supports, 36, 53, 55
  journalism aids, 24
  meetings, advances should be reported
    at, 211
  meetings to devote more time to, 270,
    271
  methods of 1840's, 69
  National Bureau of Standards fellow-
    ship program, 397
  Nat. D.A.'s aims, 187
  Nat. D.A. Committee on Scientific Re-
    search established, 236
  Nat. D.A. seeks research funds, 235
  Nat. D.A. sponsorship of research
    proposed, 336
  National Institutes of Health fellowship
    established, 402
  national society's role in, 131
  New York Odontological Society sup-
    ported, 186
  prizes offered to encourage research,
    207
  research subsidizing, 395
  Scientific Foundation and Research
    Commission activities, 337, 338, 342
  standards after Civil War, 147
Semler, Harry
  advertising dentist challenges Oregon
    restrictions, 369
Sharp, J. G.
  gives objections to dental schools, 263
  solicits Nat. D.A. backing for
    universities' society, 265
Shepard, proposes Army dentistry, 146
Shryock, Richard H., on calomel, 71
Smith, B. Holly
  counterattacks Dean Sharp on dental
    education, 265
  on Nat.D.A. reorganization, 287, 291,
    292, 295

quoted on sectionalism and national society, 227
reports on Carnegie Institution, 236
writes on transition controversy, 332
Smith, H. A.
persuades Nat. D.A. to offer prize for paper on caries, 208
speaks on society-college relationships, 172
urges joint meeting of A.D.A. and South. D.A., 225
Social Security, A.D.A. policy on including dentists, 365
Societies, Dental
advocated, 33
A.D.A. sponsorship of college society proposed, 174
Association of Colleges of Dentistry formed, 29, 159
Canadians request seats at A.D.A. meeting, 179
constituent societies: See Nat.D.A.
effect of Civil War on, 141
founding of pro-amalgam society opposed, 84
local and state, functions questioned, 216
local, control of practice by, 42
local, cooperation between, 42
local, elevate professional standards, 130
local, formation urged by Am. Convention, 110
local, important in national society, 106
membership, diploma requirement for, 165
propose means of recognizing accomplishment, 206
relation to legislation and public welfare, 388
sectionalism in, problems created by, 38, 43, 91, 134, 222, 227, 316
state and local, growth of, 93, 134
state delegates plan A.D.A., 125
state, delegates to national body, 268
state, support for Nat. D.A., reorganization, 285, 290, 301, 308
state, two-thirds membership clause in Nat. D.A. reform, 297, 303
states not supporting Nat. D.A. reform plan, 304, 307
Society of Surgeon Dentists of New York organized, 23, 29, 84
Southern Dental Association
educational requirements, 156

history of union with A.D.A., 181, 187, 222, 229, 253
status in Nat. D.A. reorganization plan, 295
temporarily changes name to Nat. D.A., 224
Spalding, Christopher W.
advocates uniform nomenclature, 115
differentiates dental and medical education, 169
Spooner, Shearjashub
on elevating profession, 24
quoted on dental legislation, 32
Starr, A., presented Am. Convention credentials at A.D.A. meeting, 178
Stockton's Dental Intelligencer
begins publication, 27

Taft Jonathan
exponent of research, 116
influence on establishment of societies, 185
on influence of national society, 127, 130
on raising educational standards, 162
opposes revival of amalgam, 204
quoted on Am. Convention's effects on dental standards, 182
quoted on colleges and associations, 155
reports on Army dentists during Civil War, 144
Taggart, William F.
inlay process, patent problems, 254, 394
Taylor, C. R., quoted on increasing state society membership, 241
Taylor, Edward
quoted on Amalgam War, 83
Taylor, James
amalgam position, 79, 82, 85
on influence of national society, 130
quoted on Convention membership, 113
quoted on dental curriculum, 169
quoted on dentistry and medicine, 69
quoted on early western dentistry, 39, 40
quoted on quackery, 40
proposes same status for Army medicine and dentistry, 145
Technicians, Dental
growth of, 428–433
"Requirements for Accreditation of School for Training," 431
Therapeutics
Council on Dental Therapeutics established, 363

history of *Accepted Dental Remedies*, 361

Thompson, A. H.
attacks dental education, 198
delivers paper on "Dentition of Felidae," 199

Thorpe, Burton Lee
claims credit in educational matters for Nat. D.A., 260
proposes deferring action on Nat. D.A. reorganization, 293
report of Southern meeting refused by *Dental Brief*, 296

Toland, John
surgeon in Civil War, 143

Townsend, Elisha
amalgam position, 85
on Convention membership, 113
on reorganization of Am. Soc., 98, 103, 105
on role of Am. Soc., 60, 90, 95
quoted on specialization, 48
quoted on western dentistry, 43
remarks on professional fees, 111

Trenor, John
relations with Am. Soc., 61

Truman, James
attacked permanent membership, 269
quoted on proposed union of A.D.A. and South. D.A., 229
urges Nat. D.A. reform, 237

Tucker, E. G., cofounder of Am.Soc., 34

Turner, V. E.
address on Nat. D.A. reorganization, 286

Underwood, Arthur S.
septic theory of caries, 202

United States
as world power, 231
Dental Supply Co., organized, 253
Dental Union of Boston, court fight over vulcanized rubber fees, 166
government aid for dental research sought, 237
government, early relations with dentistry, 209
government service, interest of dentists in, 370
Public Health Service, A.D.A. cooperation in survey of children's dental needs, 414
Public Health Service, dentists in, 376
Public Health Service endorses fluoridation, 436

Public Health Service establishes dental service, 401
Public Health Service studies fluorosis, 434

University of Maryland
dental department in medical school, 171

Veterans Administration, dentists in, 376

Virchow, Rudolph
cellular studies in dentistry, 151

Virginia Society of Surgeon Dentists
founded in 1842, 94

Volland, Roscoe H.
quoted on proposed National Board of Examiners, 390
stand on Nat. D.A. reorganization, 327
treasurer 1928–1948, 359

Ward, Marcus L.
stand on transition controversy, 328

Washburn, H. B.
treasurer since 1948, 359

Weiber
introduces gold filling from Paris, 114

Weinstein, Louis J.
provides dental fellowship program, 399

Wells, C. Raymond
predicts number of salaried dentists, 424
quoted on supplying dental care to indigent, 421
recommends committee to work with laboratory industry, 430

Westcott, Amos
amalgam policy, 76, 78, 83, 86
opposes advertising, 59
proposes code of ethics, 58
quoted on local societies, 42, 94
reply on national society purpose, 100

Western Dental Society, leads fight for Army dental corps, 120

White, Samuel S.
aid to victims of Chicago Fire, 246
company merges with Johnson Brothers, 193
interviews President Lincoln on dentists' status in Army, 144
on art and science of dentistry, 109
quoted on Am. Convention, 120

World War II, dentists' experiences, 372

Yerke, F. J.
urges Nat. D.A. reorganization, 328

DATE DUE